ARCTIC CIRCLE
TRENCH
North Pacific Basin
Mendocino Fracture Zone
Murray Fracture Zone
TROPIC OF CANCER
Clarion Fracture Zone
MEXICAN TRENCH
GUATEMALA TRENCH
Clipperton Fracture Zone
Albatross Plateau
COCOS RIDGE
EQUATOR
MAS ISLAND RIDGE
South-Eastern Pacific Basin
PERU-CHILE TRENCH
TUAMOTU RIDGE
TROPIC OF CAPRICORN
AUSTRAL RIDGE
SAN FELIX-JUAN FERNANDEZ RIDGE
thwestern Pacific Basin
PACIFIC ANTARCTIC RIDGE
Pacific-Antarctic Basin
ANTARCTIC CIRCLE

Physical Geology

HARVARD UNIVERSITY **L. DON LEET**

PRINCETON UNIVERSITY **SHELDON JUDSON**

ILLUSTRATOR **EDWARD A. SCHMITZ**

THIRD EDITION

PHYSICAL GEOLOGY

PRENTICE-HALL, INC., ENGLEWOOD CLIFFS, NEW JERSEY

PHYSICAL GEOLOGY, *Third Edition*
L. Don Leet *and* **Sheldon Judson**

Library of Congress Catalog Card No. 65-10094

PRENTICE-HALL INTERNATIONAL, INC., *London*
PRENTICE-HALL OF AUSTRALIA, PTY., LTD., *Sydney*
PRENTICE-HALL OF CANADA, LTD., *Toronto*
PRENTICE-HALL OF INDIA (PRIVATE) LTD., *New Delhi*
PRENTICE-HALL OF JAPAN, INC., *Tokyo*

Preface

For those who will use PHYSICAL GEOLOGY in their initial, and perhaps only, course in the subject, and for those who will go on to professional study, the third edition is the authors' attempt to provide a suitable, stimulating introduction.

The general sequence of topics follows that of the earlier editions; the approach and emphasis have also been preserved. Concepts of chemistry and physics have been incorporated when appropriate, but in such a way that the geologic story remains our primary goal. Technical terms are explained when first introduced and are defined again in a revised glossary for handy reference.

In the process of bringing the material up to date—both text and illustrations—three new chapters have been added:

3. The earth's place in space
16. Deformation of the earth's crust
21. Earth magnetism and continental drift

The chapters on mountains and mountain-building (Chapter 17) and metamorphism and metamorphic rocks (Chapter 18) were extensively rewritten.

The drawings, old and new, in this edition are from the pen of Edward A. Schmitz, who also collaborated with us on each of the previous editions. His death, just as this book goes to press, is a personal and professional loss to us both. It is comforting to know, however, that his art has not died with him, a fact happily testified to by the end papers of this book, drawn by his daughter, Mrs. Anna Nash.

In the preparation of this edition, we acknowledge with pleasure the skillful assistance of Maurine Lewis of Special Projects and James M. Guiher, Jr., Geology Editor, Prentice-Hall, Inc.

Leet was assisted in his part of the revision by his wife, Florence J. Leet, to an extent that could be fully acknowledged only by joint authorship. Judson acknowledges with pleasure the editorial assistance of Guenever Pendray Knapp.

We are indebted to colleagues who have given of their time and abilities in reading and criticising sections within their particular fields. For the first two editions, these colleagues included Sturges Bailey, Marland Billings, Frances Birch, Bart Bok, Perry Byerley, Erling Dorf, William Drescher, Alfred G. Fischer, Clifford Frondel, C. S. Hurlbut, Jr., George Kennedy, Paul MacClintock, Eugene Robertson, Franklyn B. Van-Houten, the late Henry Stetson, the late Frederik Thwaites, and the late Stanley Tyler. Many of their suggestions have been carried over into this edition. In connection with the third edition, we are further indebted to Robert Hargraves and Ulrich Peterson, and again to Marland Billings.

We also greatly appreciated the help in this and the previous edition of Keith P. Young, Sidney E. White, Donald Eschman, Stanley N. Davis, Richard Jahns, Richard B. Mattox, John R. Moseley, Fred M. Bullard, Marvin E. Kauffman, William Muehlberger, and Willard H. Parsons, who read and commented on all or parts of the manuscript.

We acknowledge our deep indebtedness to all who have aided us, but of course reserve to ourselves alone responsibility for any errors in fact or judgment.

L.D.L.
S.J.

Contents

Physical Geology

The nature and scope of physical geology

1

Geology is the science of the earth, an organized body of knowledge about the globe on which we live—about the mountains, plains, and ocean deeps, about the history of life from slime-born amoeba to man, and about the succession of physical events that accompanied this orderly development of life.

Geology helps us to unlock the mysteries of our environment. Geologists explore the earth from the ocean floor to the mountain peaks to discover the origins of our continents and the encircling seas. They try to explain a land surface so varied that in than less than an hour a traveler can fly over the Grand Canyon of the Colorado River, over man-made Lake Mead, over Death Valley, the lowest point in the United States, and over Mt. Whitney, the highest point. They probe the action of glaciers that crawled over the land and then melted away a half-billion years ago, and of some that even today cling to the high valleys and cover most of Greenland and Antarctica, remnants of a recent but receding ice age.

Geologists search for the record of life from the earliest one-celled organisms of ancient seas to the complex plants and animals of the present. This story, from the simple algae to the seed-bearing trees, from the primitive protozoa to the highly organized mammals, is told against the ever-changing physical environment of the earth.

For the earth has not always been as we see it today, and it is changing (though slowly) before our eyes. The highest mountains are built of material that once lay beneath the oceans. Fossil remains of animals that swarmed the seas half a billion years ago are now dug from lofty crags. Every continent is partially covered with sediments that were once laid down on the ocean floor, evidence of an intermittent rising and settling of the earth's surface.

PHYSICAL AND HISTORICAL GEOLOGY

We usually divide the study of geology into physical and historical geology. *Physical geology,* the subject of this book, covers the nature and properties of the materials composing

FIG. 1-1
A dirty, ash-laden cloud of hot gases billows skyward during an eruption of Kilauea Volcano, Hawaii. The island of Hawaii, like the other islands of the Hawaiian chain, has been built upward from the sea floor as molten material has been periodically extruded through the earth's crust. Photo by Tai Sing Loo.

the earth, the distribution of materials throughout the globe, the processes by which they are formed, altered, transported, and distorted, and the nature and development of the landscape.

Historical geology is a record of life on the earth from the earliest stirrings two billion years ago to the flora and fauna of the present, and to man himself. It is also a record of changes in the earth itself through four or five billion years—of advancing and retreating seas, of deposition and of erosion, of rocks fashioned into mountain ranges—the whole chronological story of how the processes of physical geology have operated.

THE PRESENT IS THE KEY TO THE PAST

We have all seen the forces of nature changing in a small way the face of our earth. Perhaps we have watched sea waves beating against a rocky headland, or gentler waves sloshing the pebbles back and forth on the slope of a sandy beach. Perhaps we have felt the sting of swiftly moving sand grains against our ankles as we waded across a mountain stream, or observed mud-charged rivulets flowing from a new-plowed field. And some of us have seen dust swirled from the parched plains. In these and countless other ways the earth's surface is being changed. Wind, water, and glacier ice erode the earth's surface and carry material to lower levels. Volcanoes erupt through unstable portions of the earth's surface, and earthquakes shake the foundations of our continents. These processes are going on today.

Modern geology was born in 1785 when James Hutton (1726–1797), a Scottish medical man, gentleman farmer, and geologist, formulated the principle that the same processes operating in the present also operated in the past. The principle is known to geologists as the *doctrine of uniformitarianism,* which simply means that the processes now operating to modify the earth's surface have also operated in the geologic past, that there is a uniformity of processes past and present.

Here is an example. We know from observations that modern glaciers deposit a distinctive type of debris made up of rock fragments that range in size from submicroscopic particles to boulders weighing several tons. This debris is jumbled, and many of the large fragments are scratched and broken. We know of no other agent but glacier ice that produces such a deposit. Now suppose we find in the New England hills, or across the plains of Ohio, or in the deep valleys of the Rocky Mountains, deposits that in every way resemble glacial debris. But we can find no glaciers in the area. We can

FIG. 1-2
This specimen from Fossil, Wyoming, records an episode in earth history that occurred about 60 million years ago. Involved in this "ancient error" are a predatory perch (Mioplosus) *and its intended victim, a herring* (Knightia). *They lived in ancient Lake Gosiute, a large, shallow, fresh-water body that occupied the region of present Green River Basin in southwestern Wyoming and adjacent areas. The story of life as recorded in rocks is a part of historical geology. Specimen #14,705, Princeton University Museum of Natural History. Photo by Fred Anderegg.*

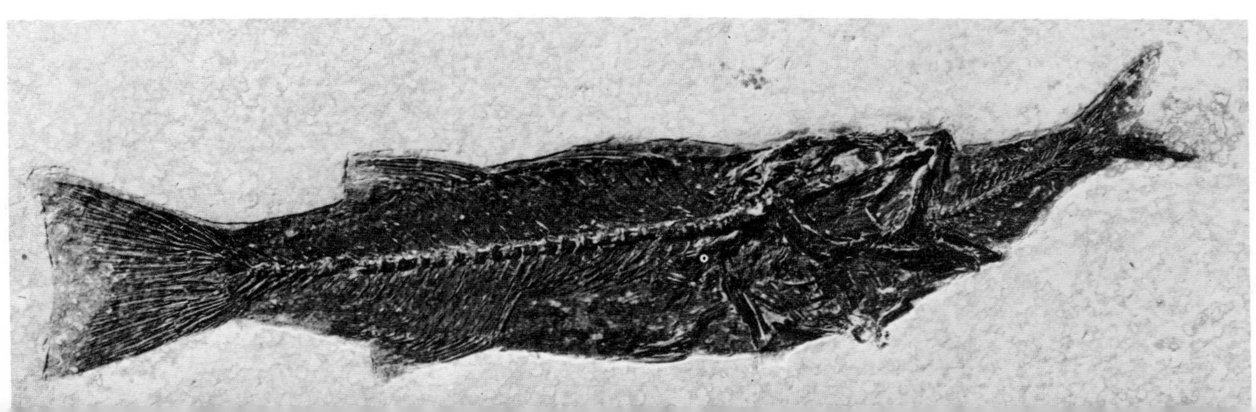

still assume that the debris was deposited by now-vanished glaciers. On the basis of evidence like this, geologists have worked out the concept of the Great Ice Age (see Chapter 13).

This example can be multiplied many times. Today, the great majority of earth features and of the rocks exposed at the earth's surface are explained as the result of past processes similar to those of the present. We shall find that many of the conclusions of physical geology are based on the conviction that modern processes also operated in the past.

TIME

Armed with Hutton's concept of uniformitarianism, geologists were able to explain earth features on a logical basis. But the very logic of the explanation raised a new concept for students of the earth. Past processes presumably operated at the same slow pace as those of today. Consequently, very long periods of time must have been available for the processes to accomplish their tasks. It was apparent that a great deal of time was needed for a river to cut its valley, or for hundreds or thousands of feet of mud and sand to be deposited on an ocean bottom, hardened into rock, and raised above the level of the sea.

The concept of almost unlimited time in earth history is a necessary outgrowth of the application of the principle that "the present is the key to the past." For example, geologists know that mountains as high as the modern Rockies once towered over what are now the low uplands of northern Wisconsin, Michigan, and Minnesota. But only the roots of these mountains are left. The great peaks have long since disappeared. Geologists explain that the ancient mountains were destroyed by rain and running water, wind and creeping glaciers, landslides and slowly moving rubble, and that these processes acted essentially as they do now in our present-day world.

Now think of what this explanation means. We know from firsthand observation that streams, glaciers, and winds have some effect on the surface of the earth. But can such feeble forces level whole mountain ranges? Instinct and common sense tell us that they cannot. But this is where the factor of time comes into the picture. True, the small, almost immeasurable amount of erosion that takes place in a human lifetime has little effect. But when the erosion during one lifetime is multiplied by thousands and millions of lifetimes, it becomes clear that mountains can be destroyed. Time makes possible what seems impossible.

The distinguished American geologist, Adolph Knopf, has written:

> If I were asked as a geologist what is the single greatest contribution of the science of geology to modern civilized thought, the answer would be the realization of the immense length of time. So vast is the span of time recorded in the history of the earth that it is generally distinguished from the more modest kinds of time by being called "geologic time." [1]

[1] Adolph Knopf, *Time and Its Mysteries,* Series III (New York: N. Y. Univ. Press, 1949).

FIG. 1-3
Many concepts of present-day geology stem directly from observations of the Scotsman James Hutton (1726-1797). (See also Fig. 1-10.) From F.D. Adams, Birth and Development of the Geological Sciences. Reprinted by permission of Dover Publications, Inc., New York.

FIG. 1-4
Running water does more work than any other surface agent in fashioning the face of the earth. Clear Creek Falls, near Creede, Colorado, chews its way into the solid rock. Photo by Tozier.

CHANGE

The great extent of time included in the geologic calendar, and the ceaseless operation of earth processes force us to admit that "as everlasting as the hills" refers to a permanency only in terms of human lifetimes. In the vastness of geologic time, everything changes, nothing is permanent.

We usually think of change through time in relation to living things, as in evolution. But inorganic things change and evolve as well as living things. Thus solid rock is changed by weathering at, and near, the earth's surface, and the original minerals of the rock are converted to new minerals within a soil that rests on still unaltered bedrock. Then water, wind, and ice conspire to move the soil minerals, to sort them, and to deposit them in a new environment as vast sheets of debris. These layers, in time, may be converted into rock quite different from the rocks from which they came.

This constant change comes about as an adjustment to new conditions, to changing environments. In a sense, it is an attempt to establish an equilibrium. But nature is complex, and a shift toward equilibrium under one set of conditions sets up a new situation that demands still other changes.

Remember, then, that even the inanimate subjects of physical geology have been derived from some pre-existing state and that they will change to a new form at some future time. The hard rock you hold in your hand may have flowed as lava from a now-extinct volcano millions of years ago, and may form part of a fertile soil in some unknown future. The crag on a nearby hill may have formed an ancient shoreline

FIG. 1-5
In the Grand Canyon of the Colorado River the erosion of alternating resistant and nonresistant sedimentary rocks has produced temple-like forms. The Colorado River flows in a steeep-walled inner gorge cut in igneous and metamorphic rocks. Photo by U.S. Army Air Corps.

and, in some future existence, an as-yet-unborn stream may carry its fragments back to the ocean.

ENERGY

All change is an expression of energy, which is a common factor in all earth processes, both organic and inorganic. Thus different forms of matter result from differences in the energy that holds atoms together. Energy keeps materials molten so that they may break forth as a volcanic flow. Energy causes water to move and rock masses to slide in response to gravity. Solar energy supports life, produces changes in the weather, and helps keep the oceans in motion. All geology—and all existence—is a manifestation of energy.

GATHERING AND USING GEOLOGIC DATA

As the geologist traces the changing record of the earth, he gathers his facts in the out-of-doors—from the hills, the plains, and the glaciers, along the shore, and in the depths of the oceans. In short, the facts are not easy to come by, and gathering them often costs a great deal of time, manpower, and money. Moreover, there are many important facts that we cannot study in the laboratory. We cannot conjure up a volcanic eruption. We must wait for nature to provide one and hope that we can get to it when it occurs.

To make matters more difficult, the geologic record is often incomplete. This is true not only because it is difficult to gather the data, but also because time may obscure the geologic record. And just as with the written record, so it is with the rock record: the further back we go in time, the scantier our information becomes. Some of our geologic data may be obscured by burial, some may have been destroyed, and perhaps some were never recorded. In any event, much of the record is simply not available to us.

The very fact that the record is incomplete means that it is extremely important to use effectively all the data we do have. It means that our reasoning from the facts must be even more rigorous than if we had more complete data.

The geologist, then, must be prepared to produce a decision on the basis of very incomplete data. So he is anxious to make his information just as precise as he can, and the story of geology is in part the story of increasingly precise measurements and observations. Over the last 180 years, the science of geology has changed from an essentially qualitative science to a more quantitative one. In the past, the geologist was content with a superficial description of a rock layer. But now he he uses refined techniques to determine the nature of the minerals that make up the rock. A century ago the only way a geologist could judge the violence of an earthquake, and even its approximate position, was to depend on subjective reports from widely scattered and untrained observers. Today, sensitive instruments manned by trained scientists enable us to measure an earthquake's intensity and to locate from afar its position on the earth's surface and the depth of the disturbance within the earth's crust.

Although geologists have learned a great deal about this earth in a few generations, there is still much more to be

FIG. 1-6
Many of the basic data used in geologic studies must be gathered in the field. Here a geologist uses his compass to determine the angle of dip of a steeply inclined bed of sandstone in the Wind River Range, Wyoming. Photo by Standard Oil Co. (N.J.).

FIG. 1-7
The New River, West Virginia, has carved its valley deep into the flat-lying rocks of the Appalachian Plateau. Sediments carried by this river eventually reach the Gulf of Mexico, where they are deposited in layers, perhaps to become rocks of some future time. Photo by U.S. Geol. Survey.

FIG. 1-8
These rocks were once horizontal sedimentary rocks deeply buried beneath the surface. They were then tilted and folded by earth forces. Subsequent erosion has exposed the layers to view. Photo by Geol. Survey of Canada.

learned. We have some fairly definite answers to a number of questions, but many problems exist for which we have but tentative answers. We need more facts and more precise data. Many questions remain completely unsolved, and there are undoubtedly many questions yet to be posed.

THE THREE ROCK FAMILIES

Geology is based on the study of rocks. We seek to know their composition, their distribution, how they are formed and how destroyed, why they are lifted up into continental masses and depressed into ocean basins.

Rock is the most common of all the materials on earth. It is familiar to us all. We may recognize it as the gravel in a driveway, the boulders in a stream, the cliffs along a ridge. And it is common knowledge that firm bedrock is exposed at the earth's surface or lies beneath a thin cover of soil or loose debris. Were we to examine rock material from locality to locality, we would begin to note the differences and the similarities of the various rock exposures. On the basis of our observations, we could begin to classify rocks into different groups.

Observations have led geologists to divide the earth's rocks into three main groups, based on mode of origin. These three types are *igneous, sedimentary,* and *metamorphic.* Later on, we shall discuss each type in detail, but here is a short explanation of all three.

Igneous rocks, the ancestors of all other rocks, take their name from the Latin, *ignis,* "fire." These "fire-formed" rocks were once a hot, molten, liquid-like mass known as a *magma,* which subsequently cooled into firm, hard rock. Thus the lava flowing across the earth's surface from an erupting volcano soon cools and hardens into an igneous rock. But there are other igneous rocks now exposed at the surface that actually cooled some distance beneath the surface. We see such rocks today only because erosion has stripped away the rocks that covered them during their formation.

Most sedimentary rocks (from the Latin, *sedimentum,* "settling") are made up of particles derived from the breakdown of pre-existing rocks. Usually these particles are transported by water, wind, or ice to new locations where they are deposited in new arrangements. For example, waves beating against a rocky shore may provide the sand grains and pebbles for a nearby beach. If these beach deposits were to be hardened, we would have sedimentary rock. One of the most characteristic features of sedimentary rocks is the layering of the deposits that make them up.

Metamorphic rocks compose the third large family of rocks. Metamorphic, meaning "changed form," refers to the fact that the original rock has been changed from its primary form to a new form. Earth pressures, heat, and chemically active fluids beneath the surface may all be involved in changing an originally sedimentary rock into a new metamorphic rock.

The rock cycle

We have suggested that there are definite relationships among sedimentary, igneous, and metamorphic rocks. With time and changing conditions, any one of these rock types may be changed into some other form. These relationships form a cycle, as shown in Fig. 1-9. This is simply a way of tracing out the various paths that earth materials follow. The outer circle represents the complete cycle; the arrows within the circle represent short cuts in the system that can be, and often are, taken. Notice that the igneous rocks are shown as having formed from a magma, and as providing one link in a continuous chain. From these parent rocks, through a variety of processes, all other rocks can be derived.

First, weathering attacks the solid rock, which either has been formed by the cooling of a lava flow at the surface, or is an igneous rock that was formed deep beneath the earth's surface and then was exposed by erosion. The products of weathering are the materials that will eventually go into the creation of new rocks—sedimentary, metamorphic, and even igneous. Landslides, wind, running water, and glacier ice all help to move the materials from one place to another. In the ideal cycle, this material seeks the ocean floors, where layers of soft mud, sand, and gravel are consolidated into sedimentary rocks. If the cycle continues without interruption, these new rocks may in turn be deeply buried and subjected to heat, to pressures caused by overlying rocks, and to forces developed by earth movements. The sedimentary rocks may then change in response to these new conditions and become metamorphic rocks. If these metamorphic rocks undergo continued and increased heat and pressure, they may eventually lose their identity and melt into a magma. When this magma cools, we have an igneous rock again, and we have come full cycle.

But notice, too, that the complete rock cycle may be interrupted. An igneous rock, for example, may never be exposed at the surface and hence may never be converted to sediments by weathering. Instead, it may be subjected to pressure and heat and converted directly into a metamorphic rock without passing through the intermediate sedimentary stage. Other interruptions may take place if sediments, or sedimentary rock, or metamorphic rock are attacked by weathering before they continue to the next stage in the outer, complete cycle.

This concept of the rock cycle was probably first stated in the late eighteenth century by James Hutton, of whom we have already spoken:

> We are thus led to see a circulation in the matter of this globe, and a system of beautiful economy in the works of nature. This earth, like the body of an animal, is wasted at the same time that it is repaired. It has a state of growth and augmentation; it has another state, which is that of diminution and decay. This world is thus destroyed in one part, but it is renewed in another; and the operations by which this world is thus constantly renewed are as evident to the scientific eye, as are those in which it is necessarily destroyed.[2]

[2] James Hutton, *Theory of the Earth* (Edinburgh, 1795), II, 562. Hutton's theory of the earth was first presented as a series of lectures before the Royal Society of Edinburgh in 1785. These lectures were published in book form in 1795. Seven years later, Hutton's concepts were given new impetus through a more readable treatment called *Illustrations of the Huttonian Theory* by John Playfair.

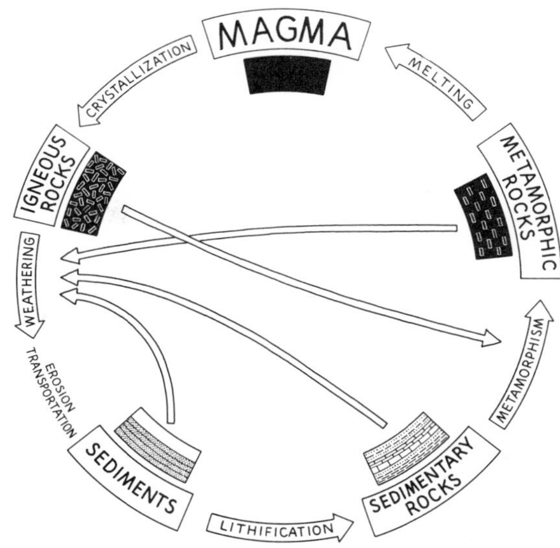

FIG. 1-9
The rock cycle, shown diagrammatically. If uninterrupted, the cycle will continue completely around the outer margin of the diagram from magma through igneous rocks, sediments, sedimentary rocks, metamorphic rocks, and back again to magma. The cycle may be interrupted, however, at various points along its course and follow the path of one of the arrows crossing through the interior of the diagram.

FIG. 1-10
Title page of the book that brought Hutton's concepts of geology to the attention of the scientific world. Reproduced from a facsimile published by U. of Ill. Press, 1956.

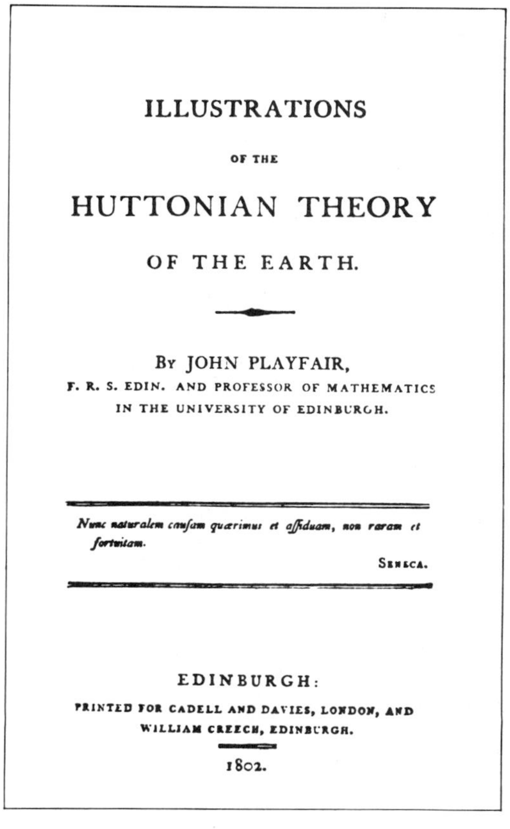

ILLUSTRATIONS

OF THE

HUTTONIAN THEORY

OF THE EARTH.

By JOHN PLAYFAIR,

F. R. S. EDIN. AND PROFESSOR OF MATHEMATICS IN THE UNIVERSITY OF EDINBURGH.

Nunc naturalem causam quærimus et assiduam, non raram et fortuitam.

SENECA.

EDINBURGH:

PRINTED FOR CADELL AND DAVIES, LONDON, AND WILLIAM CREECH, EDINBURGH.

1802.

We can consider the rock cycle to be an outline of physical geology, as a comparison of Fig. 1-9 with the table of contents of this book will show. Each step has its place; each is a part of the whole picture. But we must remember that in a more fundamental sense the rock cycle represents a response of earth materials to various forms of energy. We must realize that matter and energy are inseparable, that earth materials change and features of the earth's face are altered in response to changes in energy.

SELECTED REFERENCES

Albritton, C. C., Jr., ed., *The Fabric of Geology*. Reading, Mass.: Addison-Wesley Publishing Co., Inc., 1963.

Hutton, James, *Theory of the Earth, with proofs and illustrations* (2 vols.). Edinburgh, 1795. Facsimile reprint, New York: Hafner Publishing Co., Inc., 1959.

Mather, K. F. and S. L. Mason, *A Source Book in Geology*. New York: McGraw-Hill Book Company, 1939.

Playfair, John, *Illustrations of the Huttonian Theory of the Earth*. Edinburgh: Cadell and Davies and William Creech, 1802. Facsimile reprint, Urbana, Ill.: U. of Ill. Press, 1956.

Matter and energy

2

MATTER

The physical universe is composed of what we call matter, yet one of the most elusive problems in science is to define matter precisely. It has long been customary to refer to states of matter as solid, liquid, or gas. And we say that matter has physical properties, such as color or hardness, as well as chemical properties, which govern its ability to change or to react with other bits of matter. But all this simply tells us *about* matter, not what matter is.

Centuries ago, Greek philosophers speculated on this problem, arguing at length over whether the smallest pieces into which anything could be divided were just miniatures of the original—microscopic drops of water, extremely small grains of sand, infinitesimal pieces of salt—or whether at some point down the line certain particles would be found that were joined together in different ways to form water, sand, salt, and all the other substances of the material world.

Today, we know that the second explanation is the true one. These particles are called *atoms*. So if we are to understand matter, we must first learn about the atoms and the ways in which they combine. This information will give us a basic understanding of what rocks actually are, why they differ, and how they can be changed.

Electric charge

All matter appears to be essentially electrical in nature. Some of the earliest ideas about what we now call electricity sprang from a very simple experiment—the rubbing together of a piece of amber and a piece of fur. After they were rubbed together, both the fur and the amber were found to be capable of picking up light pieces of other materials, such as feathers or wool. But the interesting thing was that materials *attracted* by the amber were *repelled* by the fur. So scientists decided that there must be two kinds of electricity. One we now call positive, and the other negative. This fact was first discovered by the Greeks about 600 B.C. Then, late in the sixteenth century, William Gilbert, personal physician to

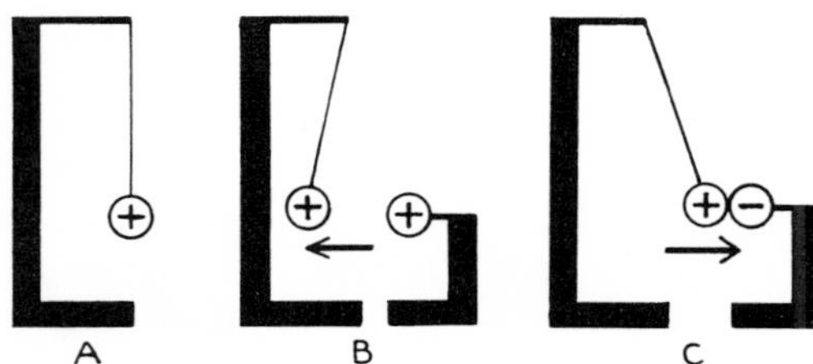

FIG. 2-1
Like charges of electricity repel each other; unlike charges attract each other.
A: *A small, positively charged sphere.*
B: *This sphere is repelled by the approach of another positive charge.*
C: *The positive charge is attracted by a negative charge.*

TABLE 2-1
Fundamental particles

	ELECTRIC CHARGE	MASS
Electron	−1	0.00055
Proton	+1	1.00760
Neutron	0	1.00890

Queen Elizabeth I, proposed that the power responsible for this phenomenon be called electricity, from the Greek word *elektron,* meaning "amber."

In technical terms, we say that *like electric charges repel each other and unlike charges attract each other* (see Fig. 2-1). You may have seen this principle active in the poles of magnets, where the so-called north poles repel each other but are attracted by the south poles, and vice versa.

Atoms

Just what happens when amber is rubbed with fur? Particles pass from the fur to the amber, and the amber becomes negatively charged. So we reason that the particles that bring about this condition must be negatively charged. These negatively charged particles are called *electrons,* and they are fundamental particles of atoms.

Atoms cannot be assembled from electrons alone, however, for all electrons have negative electric charges and would not stick together by themselves. So scientists reasoned that there had to be some other particle with a *positive* charge. At last this particle was found and was called a *proton.* But in addition to having a positive charge, the proton differs from the electron in another respect: it acts like a much heavier unit of matter. Since any quantity of matter is arbitrarily described by a number called its *mass,* the proton is said to have greater mass than the electron. In fact, *we define the fundamental particles of atoms in terms of mass and electric charge* (see Table 2-1).

Scientists continued to chip away at atoms until finally they turned up a third particle, with a mass about equal to that of the proton, but with no electric charge. This electrically neutral particle they called the *neutron.*

Protons, neutrons, and electrons are the fundamental particles that combine to form atoms. All matter is composed of atoms.

Nobody has yet come forward with an explanation of exactly what these particles are, but we do know that *energy* is intimately involved in their makeup.

ATOMIC STRUCTURE. Some of the most important information we have about the structure of atoms has been established by indirect observation of the behavior of things we cannot see. Physicists using doubly charged positive particles called *alpha particles*[1] to bombard atoms have made some interesting discoveries. For example, if these particles are shot at a target, such as a piece of metal made up of billions of atoms, no more than one alpha particle in 10,000 hits anything inside the target. It has been concluded, therefore, that the materials of the target must be largely open space.

Repeated tests have shown that *atoms contain a nucleus of protons and neutrons surrounded by a cloud of electrons. They have also revealed that a normal atom has as many electrons as it has protons.* The neutrons contribute to the mass of the atom, but they do not affect its electrical charge. The number of protons plus the number of neutrons in an

[1] Two protons and two neutrons bound together.

atom constitute the atom's *mass number.* The negative electrons spin very rapidly around the nucleus, like planets around the sun (in order to keep from being pulled in by the attraction of the positive protons). In fact, they complete several thousand million million round trips a second, at a speed of hundreds of miles per second. Again like the planets revolving about the sun, electrons revolve around the nucleus at different distances.

ATOMIC SIZE. The electrons form a protective shield around the nucleus and give *size* to the atom. Atomic dimensions are too small to have any real meaning as absolute numbers, but they yield some interesting comparisons in terms of relative size. In describing atomic dimensions, we use a special unit of length, the *angstrom,* which is one hundred-millionth of a centimeter, .00000001 cm., usually written 1×10^{-8} cm.[2]

Atomic nuclei have diameters that range from a ten-thousandth to a hundred-thousandth of an angstrom—that is, from 10^{-4} to 10^{-5}A. Atoms of the most common elements have diameters of about 2A, which is roughly 20,000 to 200,000 times the diameter of the nucleus. Again we see that matter consists mostly of open space. If the sun were truly the nucleus of our atomic model, the diameter of the atom would be greater than the diameter of the entire solar system.

ATOMIC MASS. Although the nucleus occupies only about a thousandth of a billionth of the volume of an atom, it contains 99.95 per cent of the atom's mass. In fact, if it were possible to pack a cubic centimeter with nothing but protons, this small cube would weigh more than 100 million tons at the earth's surface.

IONS. *An ion is an electrically unbalanced form of an atom or group of atoms.* An atom is electrically neutral. But if it loses an electron from its outermost shell, the portion that remains behind has an extra unmatched positive charge. This unit is known as a positively charged ion. If the outermost shell gains an electron, the ion has an extra negative charge and is known as a negatively charged ion. As we shall see later, more than one electron may be lost or gained, leading to the formation of ions with two or more units of electrical charge.

Almost all matter as we know it owes its existence to ions and is held together by electrical attractions.

Elements

An atom is the smallest unit of an element. Ninety-two elements have been found in nature, others have been made in the laboratory. *Each element is a special combination of protons, neutrons, and electrons.* The distinguishing feature of each element is the number of protons in its nucleus. An element has an atomic number corresponding to the number of protons in its nucleus, and it is given a name and a symbol.

Element No. 1 is a combination of one proton and one electron (see Fig. 2-2). Long before its atomic structure was known, this element was named hydrogen, or "water-former,"

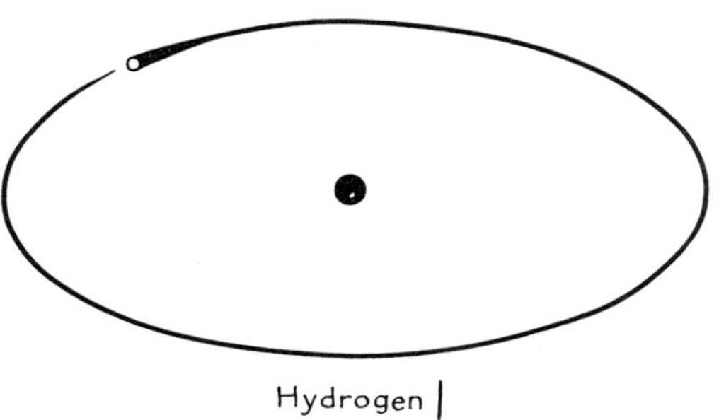

FIG. 2-2
Schematic sketch of hydrogen atom, which consists of 1 proton and 1 electron. This is the simplest atom.

[2] In dealing with very small or very large numbers, it is convenient to express them in *powers of ten,* as described in Appendix B.

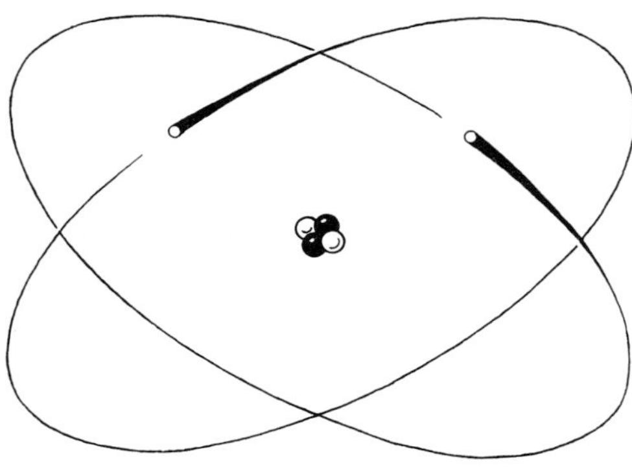

FIG. 2-3
Diagrammatic representation of an atom of helium. The nucleus consists of 2 protons and 2 neutrons, and accordingly has a mass number of 4. There are 2 electrons (negative charges) to balance the positive charges on the 2 protons. Since there are 2 protons in the nucleus, this atom is number 2 in the table of elements. The symbol $_2He^4$ indicates number 2 in the table of elements, He for the name helium, and a mass number of 4. The nucleus of helium (2 protons + 2 neutrons) without any accompanying electrons is sometimes called an alpha particle.

from Greek roots meaning "water" and "to be born"—*hydro* and *gen*—because water is formed when hydrogen burns in air. The symbol of hydrogen is H. Because it has a nucleus with one proton, hydrogen assumes place No. 1 in the table of elements.

Element No. 2 consists of two protons (plus two neutrons in the most common form) and two electrons (see Fig. 2-3). It was named helium, with the symbol He, from the Greek *helios,* "the sun," because it was identified in the solar spectrum before being isolated on the earth. Because of the two protons in its nucleus, helium takes No. 2 place in the table of elements.

Each addition of a proton, with a matching electron to maintain electrical balance, produces another element. Neutrons seem to be included more or less indiscriminately, though there are about as many neutrons as protons in the common form of many of the elements. The list of elements appears in Appendix A.

ISOTOPES. Every element has forms which, though essentially identical chemically and physically, have different masses. Such forms are called *isotopes* (pronounced eye′-so-tope), from the Greek *iso,* "equal" or "the same," and *topos,* "place," since each form having the same number of protons in the nucleus as other forms, assumes the same position in the table of elements. Isotopes show differences in mass as a result of differences in the number of neutrons in their nuclei. For example, hydrogen with 1 proton and no neutrons in its nucleus has a mass number of 1. When a neutron is present, however, the atom is an isotope of hydrogen with a mass number of 2, called *deuterium* (see Fig. 2-4). All elements have isotopes (see Appendix A).

Compounds

Each electron follows a definite path of travel, called its energy-level orbit, around the nucleus. These orbits are arranged systematically at different distances from the nucleus (see Fig. 2-5), and a specific amount of energy is required to maintain an electron at a given distance from its nucleus. For convenient reference, these distances are sometimes referred to as *energy-level shells.*

If you examine the list of elements in Appendix A, you will see that as electrons are added to match the increasing numbers of protons in going to higher and higher numbers, they follow a simple pattern for the first 18 elements. After that, the system changes somewhat, but in the entire list there is *no element with more than 8 electrons in its outermost shell.* The elements that have that maximum number are inert gases: neon, argon, krypton, xenon, and radon, which rarely combine with other elements. The number of electrons in the outer shell of an atom of an element determines the manner and ease with which the atom can join with other atoms to form compounds.

Compounds are combinations of atoms of elements, mostly through the joining of ions. Those formed by life processes are *organic compounds.* Others are *inorganic compounds.*

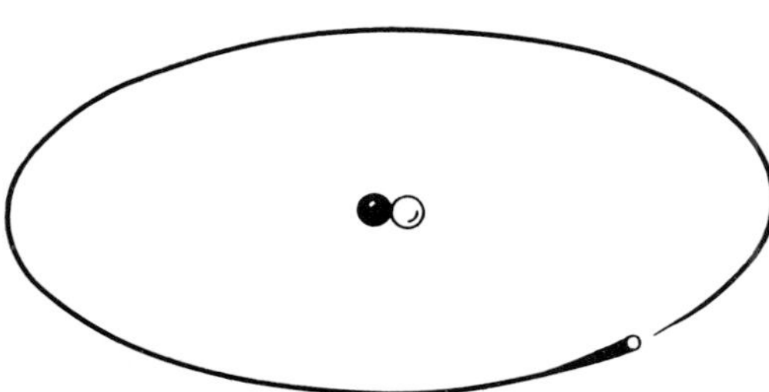

FIG. 2-4
Schematic sketch of deuterium, an isotope of hydrogen formed by the addition of a neutron to the nucleus. It has a mass number of 2.

FIG. 2-5
Electron shells around a nucleus. In true scale, diameter of the shells is 20,000 to 200,000 times the diameter of the nucleus. If the sun were the nucleus, the electron shells would embrace more space than the entire solar system. Yet, the nucleus contains 99.95 per cent of the mass of the entire atom.

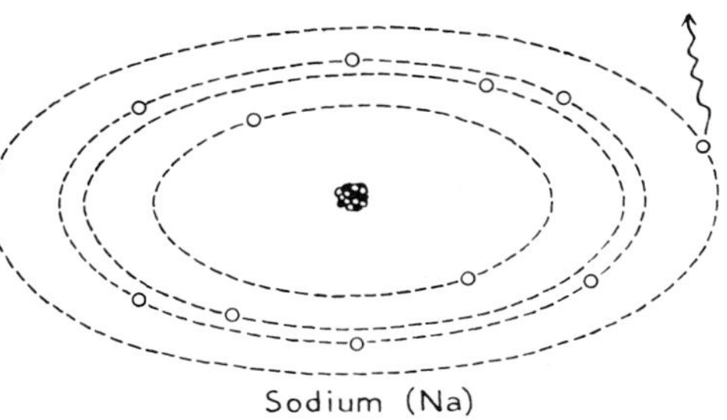

FIG. 2-6
Formation of the sodium ion Na^{+} results when the sodium atom loses the only electron in its outermost shell.

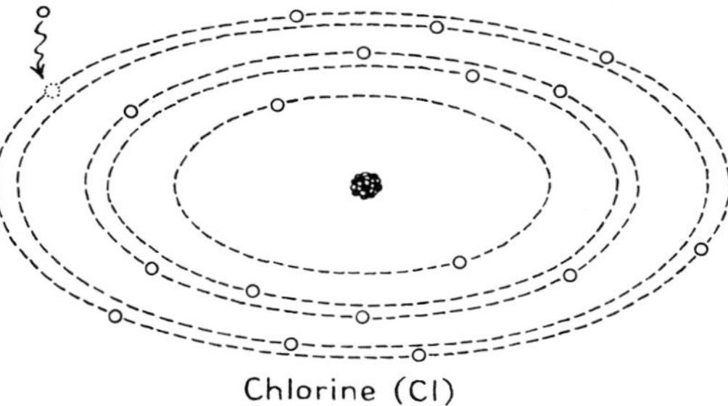

FIG. 2-7
Formation of the chlorine ion Cl^{-} results when a chlorine atom gains an electron in its outermost shell, to make the total 8.

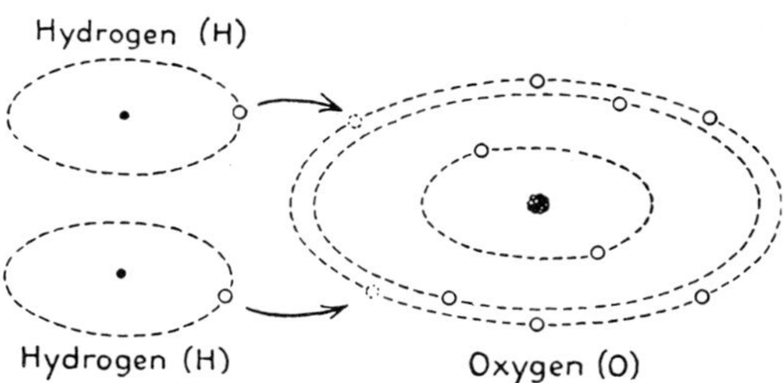

FIG. 2-8
Two hydrogen atoms and 1 oxygen atom join to form water, H_2O, by a covalent bond. In this bond, the hydrogen electrons do double duty in a sense, filling the two empty places in the outer shell of oxygen, yet remaining at their normal distance from their hydrogen nuclei. The result is the formation of a molecule of water, the smallest unit that displays the properties of that compound.

As we have just seen, elements with 8 electrons in their outermost shell do not combine readily with other elements. On the other hand, elements that have fewer than 8 electrons in their outermost shell readily shed or pick up electrons in an effort to achieve that magic number.

For example, an atom of sodium has only 1 electron in its outer shell, but 8 in the next shell (see Appendix A). By losing that outside electron, it becomes a positively charged ion (represented by the symbol Na^{+}), with 8 electrons in its outer shell (see Fig. 2-6). Chlorine, on the other hand, has 7 electrons in its outer shell. By picking up one more, it becomes a negatively charged ion (represented by the symbol Cl^{-}), with 8 electrons in its outer shell (see Fig. 2-7).

If a positive sodium ion and a negative chlorine ion approach each other, the electrical attraction of their opposite charges brings them firmly together with what is called an *ionic bond,* to form a new product with properties unlike those of either sodium or chlorine. This product is the compound halite (hay′-light), or common table salt, one of the world's most abundant substances. The chemical designation for this compound is simply a combination of the symbols for the elements that compose it, NaCl.

The atoms of elements can combine in other ways to form compounds, as, for example, in the formation of a water molecule. Oxygen has 6 electrons in its outer shell (see Appendix A) and therefore needs 2 more to achieve 8. If 2 hydrogen atoms, each of which has only a single electron, approach an oxygen atom, the hydrogen electrons in effect slip into the vacant slots in the outer shell of the oxygen atom, but do not separate from their own protons. So the hydrogen nuclei are really *sharing* their electrons with the oxygen nucleus (see Fig. 2-8). When this happens, the atoms are said to be *covalently bonded.* Again, the result is a compound that

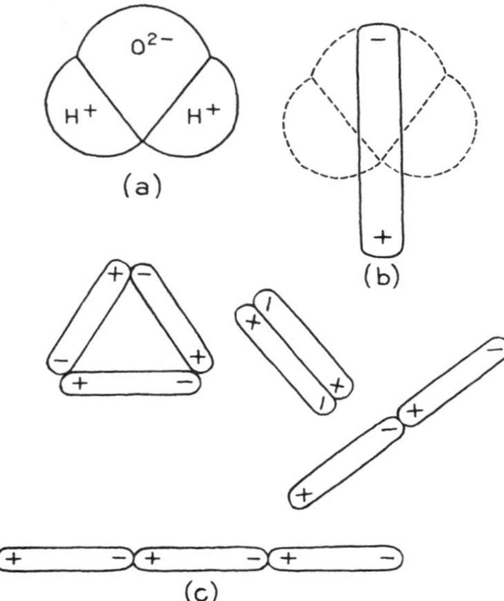

FIG. 2-9
The dipolar character of water. The oxygen has, in effect, gained 2 electrons, hence a double negative charge, whereas the hydrogen atoms have each lost the effective service of an electron and represent positive charges. Accordingly, the water molecule acts like a small rod with a positive charge on one end and a negative charge on the other, as suggested in B. *Combinations of water molecules are suggested in* C.

FIG. 2-10
Mechanism by which water dissolves salt. Water dipoles attach themselves to the ions that compose the salt and overcome the ionic attractions that hold the salt together as a solid. Each Na^+ *and* Cl^- *ion is then convoyed by a number of water dipoles into the body of the liquid.*

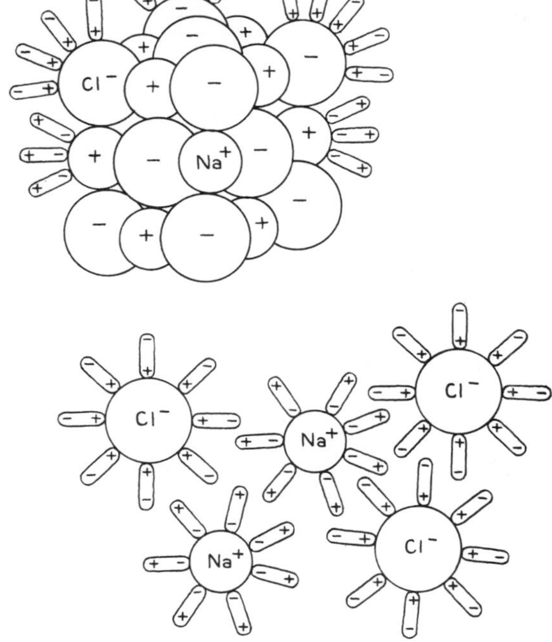

is different in every way from the elements themselves. This compound is water, whose symbol H_2O represents the elements that make it up and the proportions in which they are present. The combination of two atoms of hydrogen and one atom of oxygen forms the smallest unit that possesses the properties of water. This unit is called a *molecule* of water. *A molecule is the smallest unit of a compound which displays the properties of that compound.*

Since the oxygen atom has in effect gained 2 electrons, it takes on a negative charge. And each hydrogen atom, acting as though it had lost its electron, takes on a positive charge. As a result, a molecule of water acts like a small rod, with a positive charge on one end and a negative charge on the other (see Fig. 2-9). These ends are referred to as a positive pole and a negative pole, because of the molecule's similarity to a bar magnet. The molecule, then, is a *dipole* ("two-pole"), and water is known as a *dipolar compound.* This fact gives water special properties that make it an extremely important agent in geological processes. The mechanism by which water dissolves salt (see Fig. 2-10) is an illustration of the ease with which water dissolves various substances and participiates in weathering and other geological activities.

Organization of matter

We have seen that matter is composed of atoms. Atoms are combinations of the fundamental particles: protons, neutrons, and electrons (except for hydrogen which is a combination of one proton and one electron). Ninety-two different kinds of these particles have been found in nature. Eleven additional atoms have been made by man. Each combination is a different element. Atoms also have other forms, such as isotopes and ions. Atoms of elements combine to form compounds. These relationships are outlined in Table 2-2.

ENERGY

Energy is a word that sounds familiar enough. We speak of energy-producing foods, of the energy needed to climb stairs, of energy radiated to us from the sun. But what is energy? Scientists have attempted to define it by saying that *energy is the capacity for producing motion,* and have found that no form of matter is entirely devoid of motion. The motion may be in things we see, such as an automobile speeding down the highway, or in things we cannot see, such as atoms and parts of atoms. All motion is produced by energy in one form or another. And since everything in the universe possesses motion, everything is said to possess energy.

In fact, we can think of the entire universe as a great bundle of energy. Heat and light from the sun represent energy in one form; the revolution of the earth around the sun represents energy in another form; and the chemical transformation of food into heat and body activity represents energy in yet another form.

In geological processes, through the motion of running water, energy sculptures the land, through the deformation of rocks it builds mountains, and through the rupture of

TABLE 2-2 *The Organization of Matter*

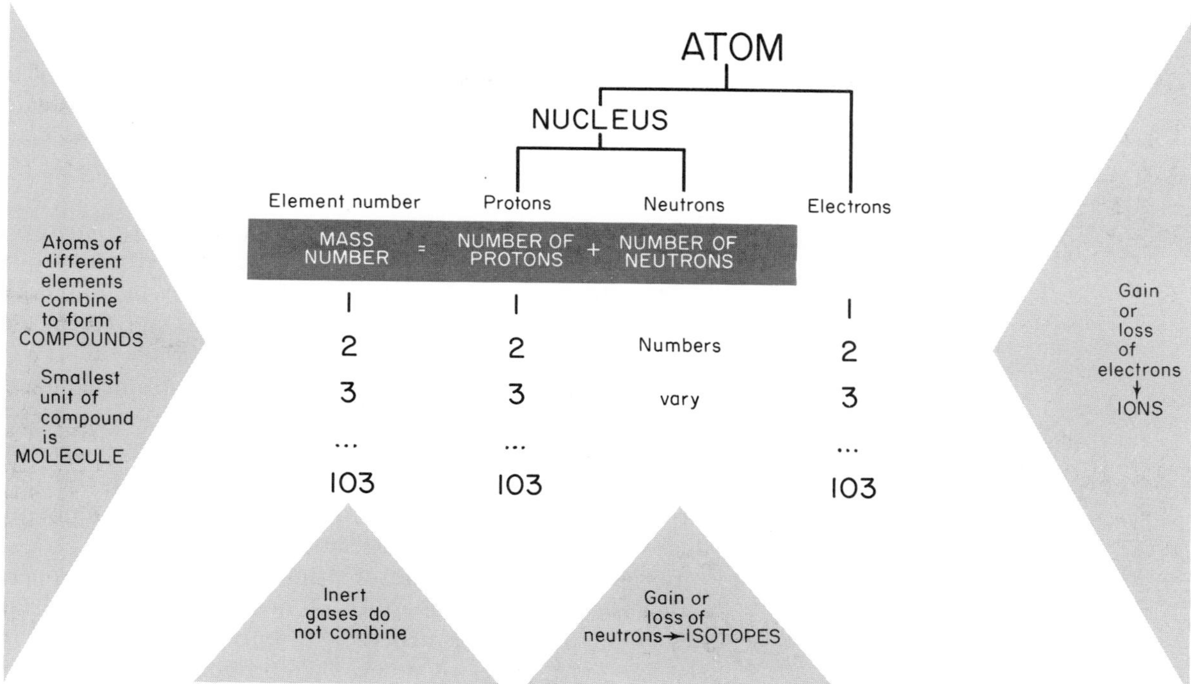

(Note: This table is continued in Table 4-3, p. 41.)

rocks it produces earthquakes. In fact, energy is the driving force behind every geological process.

Energy manifests itself in different forms that have descriptive given names: *potential, kinetic, heat, chemical, electrical,* and *atomic.*

Potential energy

Potential energy is stored energy that is waiting to be used. Uranium, petroleum, coal, and natural gas are eagerly sought after because the potential energy they contain can be effectively released and put to work. Water in the clouds, or in lakes and reservoirs at high altitudes, has potential energy that is released when the water falls or runs downhill. A boulder poised on a hilltop has potential energy. Less obvious, but just as real, is the potential energy stored in the nucleus of every atom and in the molecules of every compound.

Kinetic energy

The potential energy of a 10-ton boulder resting on a hillside is transformed into the energy of movement when the boulder is dislodged and rolls downhill (see Fig. 2-11). This energy of movement is called *kinetic energy. Every moving object possesses kinetic energy.*

The amount of kinetic energy possessed by an object depends on the mass of the object and on the speed with which it moves. For instance, a 10-ton boulder rolling down a hill has more energy at the bottom of the slope than a pebble that has rolled down the same slope at the same speed. On the other hand, this same 10-ton boulder moving a few feet per

FIG. 2-11 *The potential energy of a 10-ton boulder resting on a hillside is transformed into kinetic energy, the energy of movement, when the boulder is dislodged and rolls downhill.*

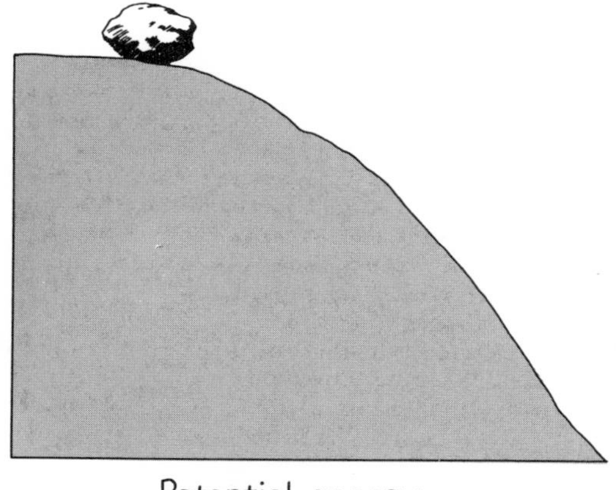

Potential energy

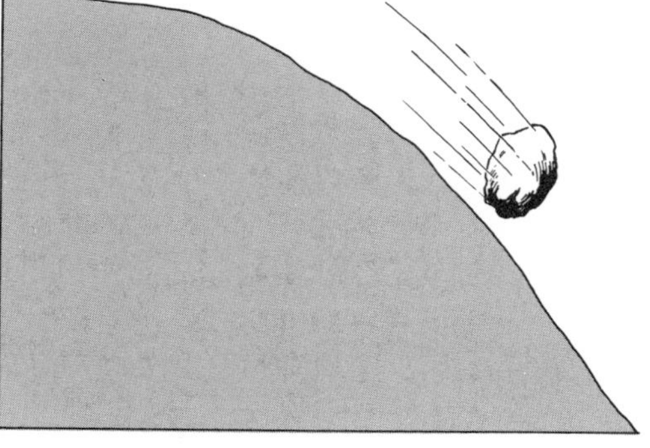

Kinetic energy

hour would have less energy than if it were hurtling along at 30 miles per hour.

The kinetic energy of running water produces much of its effectiveness as a geological agent. Waves beating on a shore and glaciers creeping down a mountain slope do geological work by means of kinetic energy.

Heat energy

Heat energy is a special manifestation of kinetic energy in atoms. All atoms are moving constantly. They vibrate around fixed positions in solids and move about freely in liquids and gases. But all are in motion. And it is this movement that produces the effect we call heat.

Everybody is familiar with ice, water, and steam. These are the compound H_2O in three different states: solid, liquid, and gas. What we call *temperature* is actually an arbitrary number that represents the activity of atoms. Since the atoms are less active in ice, we say that ice has a lower temperature than water, in which they are moving more rapidly.

In addition to temperature, heat has another property, called *quantity*. The quantity of heat is measured in calories.[3] Quantity of heat depends not only on temperature, but also on the number of atoms that produce the temperature by their activity. We feel intuitively, for example, that a cup of boiling water and a bucket of boiling water represent different total quantities of heat, even though they are at the same temperature. Evidence of this difference would be provided by the volume of ice melted by each. The filament of an incandescent light bulb is at a very high temperature because its atoms are extremely agitated, but the quantity of heat it produces would do a poor job of heating a home.

Heat energy is the avenue through which most forms of energy are applied to the needs of man. And heat has supplied much of the energy involved in the formation of earth materials and the processes by which these materials have been altered throughout their history. An understanding of the nature of heat is fundamental to a full appreciation of the formation of igneous and metamorphic rocks, igneous activity, and, probably, the formation of mountains.

Chemical energy

An atom is the smallest unit of an element, and a molecule is the smallest unit of a compound. When the atoms of elements combine to form compounds, or when compounds combine to form other compounds, the process is called a chemical process, and the energy that is released or absorbed by the process is called chemical energy.

Chemical energy is the energy that binds atoms together into molecules. For example, the sodium and chlorine that make up salt (see "Compounds," this chapter) start out as electrically neutral atoms with as many electrons as protons. So long as they remain electrically neutral, they have no chemical energy and do not enter into the formation of com-

[3] A calorie is the quantity of heat required to raise by 1 degree Centigrade the temperature of 1 gram of water.

pounds. Only when they become ions as the result of changes in their electron population do they have the energy to form compounds. Thus, *chemical energy is the energy necessary to form compounds,* and it becomes available when atoms have lost or gained electrons.

Electrical energy

All around us are electrons that are "loose"—in the sense that they are not firmly bound to any particular nucleus. Scientists have discovered that electrons of this sort move readily through metals, and they have found methods of concentrating them and causing them to move under controlled conditions. This flow of electrons, called electric current, supplies us with the electrical energy that we use in countless ways.

Atomic energy

Atomic energy is the energy that holds the nucleus of an atom together. At present, we are using the atomic energy of only a few heavy elements, such as uranium, which are so unstable that they break down spontaneously (see Fig. 2-12). The potential atomic energy of 2.2 pounds of coal has been computed as 25 billion kilowatt hours, but we are now able to recover only the *chemical* energy of this material, which is 8.5 kilowatt hours.

The sun's energy is believed to originate from atomic reactions in which nuclei of helium are built up from nuclei of hydrogen. It has been found that the mass of an atomic nucleus is less than the total mass of the separate particles that make it up. The reason is that when a nucleus forms, part of the mass of the component particles is changed into energy, which is then radiated away (see Appendix A). The quantity of energy released in reactions of this kind is almost inconceivably greater than the quantity released by any other type of reaction involving similar quantities of material. Every second, the sun sends into space a million times as much energy as is stored in all our coal, petroleum, and natural gas fields. If we could duplicate the method by which this energy is released, we could revolutionize the world. And the possibility of doing just this is no more fantastic today than the concept of an atomic bomb was in 1900. The time may come when the hydrogen from a cubic mile of sea water will provide enough energy to satisfy our needs at the 1960 rate for 300 centuries.

Energy transformations

Energy can be transformed from one form to another. In fact, the entire universe owes its continued existence to energy transformations. Without these, there would be nothingness. But no matter how energy is transformed, the total amount of energy *after* the transformation is the same as it was *before* the transformation. Energy can be neither created nor destroyed. This basic principle is known as the law of the conservation of energy.

In geology, energy transformations occur when a liquid

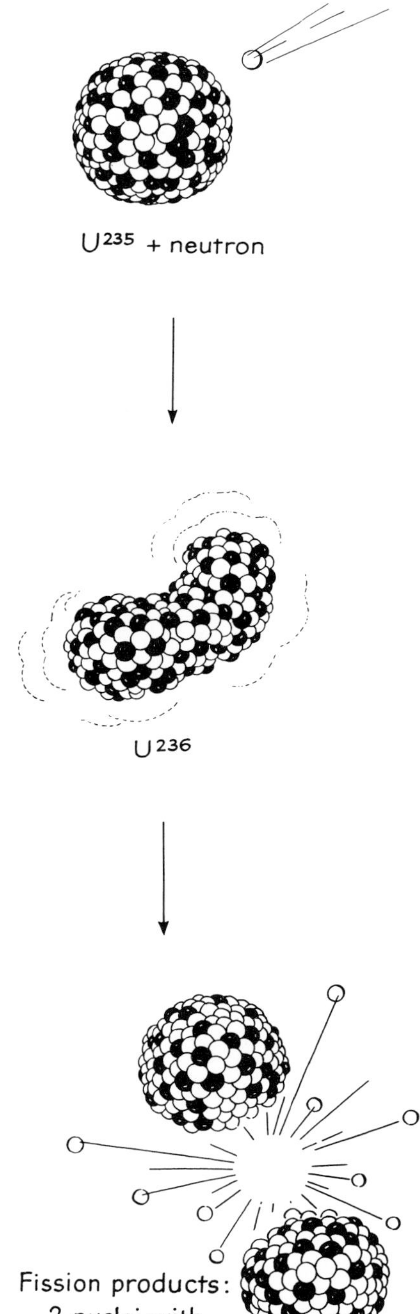

FIG. 2-12
Energy released by the splitting of U^{236}, an unstable isotope of uranium. When U^{235} captures a neutron, it becomes U^{236}, which immediately splits into two lighter elements. These have no place in their nuclei for several of the neutrons. If such free neutrons are liberated in the presence of more U^{235}, a chain reaction results, and tremendous quantities of energy are released.

hardens into a solid rock, and when one kind of rock is changed into another. Energy transformations also occur during the formation of coal, petroleum, and gas. All geological processes consist of energy transformations.

SUMMARY OUTLINE

Matter
Composed of atoms

Atoms
Combinations of protons, neutrons, and electrons
Smallest unit of an element
Mass and electric charge

Ions
Electrically unbalanced forms of atoms or groups of atoms
Produced by gain or loss of electrons

Elements
92 special kinds of atoms in nature
Combine to make compounds

Isotopes
Alternate forms of elements
Produced by gain or loss of neutrons

Compounds
Combination of atoms of elements

Molecule
Smallest unit of a compound

Energy
Capacity for producing motion

Potential energy
Stored energy

Kinetic energy
Energy of motion

Heat energy
Movement of atoms and molecules

Chemical energy
Depends on electrons

Electrical energy
Flow of electrons

Atomic energy
Depends on protons and neutrons

SELECTED REFERENCES

Frey, Paul R., *College Chemistry* (3rd ed.). Englewood Cliffs, N.J.: Prentice-Hall, Inc., 1965.

Pauling, Linus, *General Chemistry* (2nd ed.). San Francisco: W. H. Freeman & Co., 1953.

Shortley, G. and D. Williams, *Elements of Physics* (3rd ed.). Englewood Cliffs, N.J.: Prentice-Hall, Inc., 1962.

The earth's place in space

Space extends in all directions and is unbounded. It is that in which all physical things are ordered and related. It is the nothing that provides a place for everything.

Looking out into space at night from the earth, we see countless points of light. Most of these are *stars* that stay in the same positions relative to each other. But among them are a few that wander about from night to night. These are *planets*. And scattered about the sky are hazy patches of light that a telescope does not resolve as sharp points as it does the stars. These are *nebulae*. The complete assemblage of all we can see and imagine out there is called the *universe*.

All the stars we can see constitute the Milky Way and belong to a family of about 100 billion. This is our *galaxy*. It has been named the Milky Way Galaxy. The nebulae are other galaxies. It has been estimated that there are millions of these distributed through space.

In our galaxy, some stars appear to be grouped together. These are called *constellations*. About 90 constellations exist; they were named centuries ago after mythical personages, animals, or inanimate objects they were fancied to resemble. They are still used today as convenient means of describing the locations of portions of the sky.

This chapter discusses the earth's place in space, and some of the ideas that have been put forward to explain it.

OUR SOLAR SYSTEM

We are able to exist physically because of heat and light from our personal star, the sun. As we observe it from the earth, the sun rises in the east to bring daytime and sets in the west to bring night. This phenomenon led to the assumption that the sun moves around a stationary earth. Likewise, the stars appear to rise in the east and set in the west. So for a long segment of human history, the earth was believed to be the center of the universe, about which everything else revolved. This belief, supported by even noted Greek scientists who were dominated by the teachings of Aristotle, was widely held until about three centuries ago. One Greek, Aristarchus, had the temerity in the third century B.C. to suggest that the planets, including the earth, circle about the sun, and that the earth rotates on its axis, giving us night and day. But he failed to convince most of the people of his time, and his explanation for the movements of the planets around the sun was not to be firmly established until 1543, by another man—Copernicus. Still another century passed, however, before there was universal acceptance of Aristarchus' idea.

We now know that the sun is the center of our physical existence. Everything within the sun's gravitative control constitutes what we call our *solar system*. This includes 9 planets, 31 satellites or "moons," thousands of asteroids, scores of comets, and uncounted millions of meteors. All these revolve about the sun.

The sun

The sun is a star. Like all other stars, it is a self-luminous globe of gas. Located 93 million miles from the earth, it has a diameter of about 864,000 miles and a mass 332,000 times that of the earth.

The most abundant elements of the earth's crust are all present in the sun's atmosphere, but they are in highly heated and excited atomic states and do not resemble their forms on earth. The bulk of the sun, however, is composed of two elements: its volume is 81.76 per cent hydrogen and 18.17 per cent helium. All other elements total only .07 per cent.

When the sun is at the zenith on a clear day, its light has a luminosity at the earth's surface of 10,000 foot-candles. In other words, it is 10,000 times as luminous as a candle at a distance of one foot. But at the sun itself, every square inch shines with the intensity of 300,000 candles. The sun's light represents radiant energy, upon which terrestrial life depends for existence.

The sun's radiant energy is believed to be generated by atomic reactions that form helium nuclei from hydrogen nuclei, in a process called *the carbon cycle*. On the sun, when the nucleus of hydrogen ${}_1H^1$ collides with the nucleus of carbon ${}_6C^{12}$ and joins it to form the nucleus of nitrogen ${}_7N^{13}$, radiant energy is emitted. After five more steps, the process terminates with the ${}_6C^{12}$ back in its original state but accompanied by a newly assembled helium nucleus that was formed along the way, and by the energy converted from mass during the synthesis of helium (see Appendix A). The carbon has acted simply as a *catalyst;* it takes part in the reaction but emerges unchanged, so it is used over and over again. The hydrogen has been converted to helium. In effect, the sun is "burning" 4 million tons of hydrogen per second, producing an "ash" of helium. Even at this rate, the sun can keep on for 30 billion years.

These atomic reactions take place at temperatures of several million degrees and are automatically controlled. If the temperature increases, the process operates too rapidly and expands the gas of the sun. This expansion causes cooling, which lowers the rate of energy production.

Planets and satellites

The name *planet* was given to certain celestial bodies that appear to wander about the sky, in contrast to the seemingly fixed stars. It came from the Greek, *planetes,* meaning "wandering." Our earth is a planet, one of nine that circle the sun.

There is a systematic uniformity in the motion of the planets. All travel around the sun from west to east in nearly the same plane, the *ecliptic.* And they revolve on their respective axes (with the exception of Uranus) in a "forward" sense, or from west to east.

In order of distance from the sun, the first four planets are Mercury, Venus, Earth, and Mars. These planets are about the same size and fairly dense, as though they were made of iron and stone. They are called the *terrestrial planets* because of their similarity to the earth. Next in order of distance from the sun are Jupiter, Saturn, Uranus, Neptune, and Pluto. The first four of these are of relatively large size and low density. Little is known about Pluto, whose discovery was announced on March 12, 1930, but it is more like the terrestrial planets than the others. A uniform pattern of spacing outward from the sun is broken between Mars and Jupiter. In the "gap" are the thousands of asteroids ranging in size from a mile to about 480 miles in diameter. Some 1,500 have been catalogued to date. The asteroids occupy an orbit believed to have been either that of a planet that exploded, or of matter that never completed the planet-forming process.

THE EARTH. Our planet is a sphere 8,000 miles in diameter. Once a day it completely rotates on an axis inclined 23.5° to the ecliptic; once a year it completes one revolution around the sun, in the plane of the ecliptic. The annual revolution about the sun, combined with the inclination of its axis of rotation, produces the seasons. When the Northern Hemisphere is inclined toward the sun, that zone of the earth gets more heat and has summer. On the opposite side of the orbit, the Northern Hemisphere "leans" away from the sun and has winter.

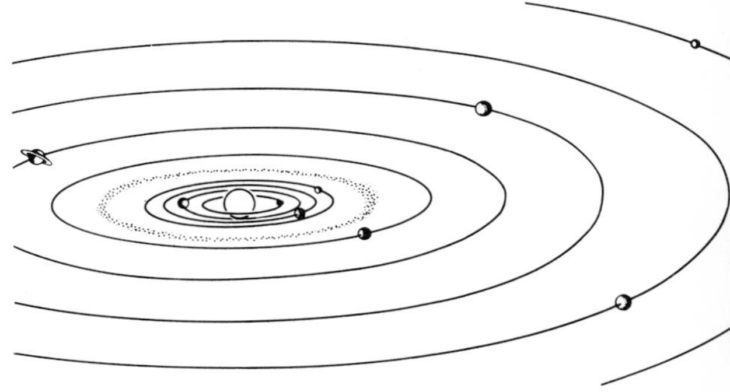

FIG. 3-1
Schematic arrangement of the planets in our solar system. Closest to the sun are the four inner planets: Mercury, Venus, Earth, and Mars. Then there are the asteroids and the outer planets: Jupiter, Saturn, Uranus, Neptune, and Pluto. The planets are not shown to scale. (See Fig. 3-3.)

The earth is not actually a perfect sphere. Because of centrifugal forces created by rotation, the diameter at the equator is about 27 miles greater than from pole to pole. And measurements by artificial satellites have revealed two 100-foot dimples in the Northern Hemisphere, giving the earth a slightly pear-shaped appearance.

The sun provides the earth with a heat range sufficient to maintain its life forms. An important factor here is the earth's blanketing atmosphere, which protects its surface from lethal doses of ultraviolet radiation. If no ultraviolet were filtered out by our atmosphere, it is doubtful that life in any form could exist. The atmosphere also protects the earth's surface from millions of meteors each day, traveling at speeds up to 45 miles per second when they hit our atmosphere. Most burn up in it. Occasionally, large meteors have bulled their way through to the earth's surface. The Great Siberian Meteor of 1908, on reaching the earth, exploded so violently that trees were laid flat out to 30 miles from the area of impact. On the average, only one person is killed by a meteor every 100 years; but if a large one like that of 1908 should hit a modern city, it would be more destructive than an atomic bomb blast.

Early man-made satellites took measurements that led to the discovery of the Van Allen belts. These belts are contained within the earth's atmosphere. They consist mostly of very energetic ionized nuclei of hydrogen atoms and electrons trapped by the earth's magnetic field. The Van Allen belts are so dangerous to living organisms, that space travelers need to be shielded by the equivalent of half an inch of lead.

The density of our atmosphere decreases with height. Half our air is contained in the first 3.5 miles, half the remainder in the next 3.5, and so on. At almost 60 miles above the earth, density is one-millionth of the surface value. At this height, short-wave radio signals are reflected.

Details of composition, structure, and other physical features of the earth have been discussed in earlier chapters.

THE MOON. Our nearest neighbor in space, and our natural satellite, the moon is a spectacular sight when viewed through a telescope of almost any size. Galileo, the first man to view it thus and to record what he saw, named some of its prominent features. The great dark areas looked like seas to him, so he called them *maria* (plural of the Latin *mare,* for "sea"). But now we know that there are no bodies of water on the moon. On its surface, mountains tower to 5 miles, and great areas are pocked by craters. The largest crater, Clavius, stretches to a diameter of 146 miles. The moon presents the same face to us at all times because it rotates once on its axis in the same time it takes to revolve once around the earth. But with the aid of Russian science, the world now has a picture of its other side. This was obtained on October 4, 1959, when the U.S.S.R. shot a rocket past the previously unseen face, and it sent back television pictures that revealed a surprising feature: the other side of the moon has relatively few maria.

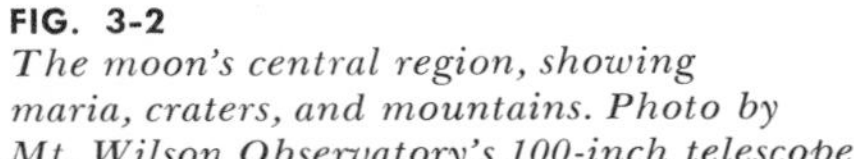

FIG. 3-2
The moon's central region, showing maria, craters, and mountains. Photo by Mt. Wilson Observatory's 100-inch telescope.

The moon has been studied intensively for centuries. Today, the largest telescopes show its image with about the same degree of focus as that of a naked eye looking at a landscape 200 miles distant. This is close enough to permit distinguishing objects 1,000 feet apart. From telescopic observations, it is now known that the moon has no atmosphere and that no permanent surface changes have taken place in centuries. From the way in which the moon's surface reflects light to the telescopes, it has been determined that the top surface material must be extremely porous, made up of small interwoven needles of rock or dust grains stacked together, with the open spaces comprising 90 per cent of the volume. Such material would be crunchy to walk on. Computations based on the moon's distance, size, and speed in its orbit indicate that it has an average specific gravity of 3.3, compared to the earth's 5.5, and that gravity at the moon's surface is about one-sixth that of the earth at its surface.

The origin of the moon's craters has long been debated. It was suggested that the craters were once parts of volcanoes. But many craters have a feature that raises doubts about this theory. The volume of material piled around some of them is about equal to the volume of the crater, and there seems to have been no addition of material from below. This fact has led astronomers to suggest formation by some other means. Craters have been made in the earth's crust by meteor impact (see Fig. 3-2), so this has been proposed as a cause of some of the moon's craters.

The maria are believed to be formed by a combination of meteor impact and lava flooding. In fact, the markings of about half the visible moon surface have been linked to impact of one gigantic meteor in the center of Mare Imbrium. The impact is believed to have started the formation of the mare. It tore huge quantities of material from the moon's crust, throwing it in all directions and forming a huge crater. This impact occurred at a time when the moon's crust overlay partially molten material. The mass of material thrown out overloaded a section of the crust. This section and its load settled into the partially molten material. Cracks then opened and lava welled out from the moon's interior to spread over the Mare Imbrium and level out the irregularities that were produced by the settling and cracking.

Conditions permitting the formation of craters and maria could have resulted from the moon growing in size by accumulating matter from space. Its surface would therefore be cool. The interior could have become heated by short-lived radioactive elements. Outer layers would provide good insulation, holding the generating heat until some melting took place. At this stage, the bottoms of many craters and cracks, as well as the maria, could have filled with lava. Rapid loss of internal heat through outpouring of the lava would quickly cool the liquid rock below the surface and result in solidification.

On November 3, 1958, N.A. Kozyref, at the Kharkov Observatory in the U.S.S.R. happened to have his spectrograph aimed at the central peak of Crater Alphonsus. He recorded gas effusion from the crater that lasted about two hours, showing that the old orb isn't completely dead yet.

VENUS. About the same as the earth in diameter, Venus is only eight-tenths of the earth's mass. Its year is 225 days in length, compared to our 365. Our best observations indicate that its day is as long as its year, because Venus seems to revolve on its axis in the same time it takes to travel once around the sun.

On December 14, 1962, the U.S. spaceship Mariner II approached to within 21,600 miles of Venus and radioed scientific information 37 million miles back to earth. From this information, scientists were able to confirm their earlier conclusions that the surface of Venus must be dry and far too hot for the existence of any organic life. Its surface temperature is probably about 600° F. Its atmosphere is much thicker than the earth's and may be extremely dusty below the lower cloud layers, the nature of which remains unknown. The upper cloud layers are probably composed of ice. A great unsolved mystery is how it is possible for Venus and earth, so nearly the same in size and mass, to have such different surfaces and atmospheres.

MARS. If earthlike plant or animal life is to be found any-

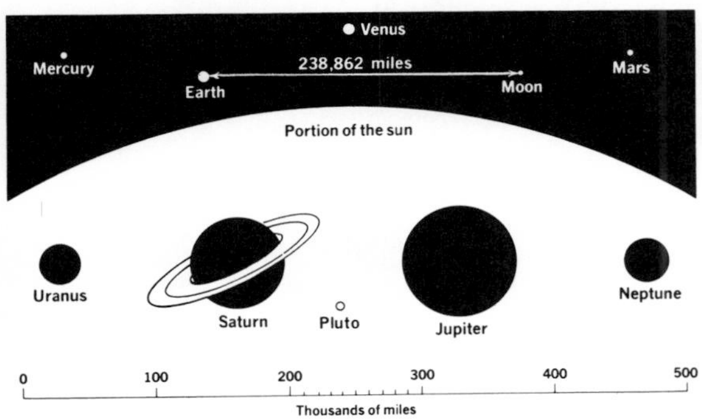

FIG. 3-3
The size of the planets compared with a portion of the sun.

where in our solar system, it now seems that Mars will have to be the place. The possibilities are based to an important degree on the amount and kind of atmosphere as well as the presence and quantity of water on Mars.

The most conspicuous markings on Mars are its "polar ice caps," which form in winter and disappear in summer. These imply the presence of water, but for all we can tell they may be no more than a few inches thick. As the "ice caps" disappear, there is a spread of dark coloration that advances toward the equator at about 2 miles per hour. Are these dark areas vegetation? In 1959, an infrared spectrum of the dark areas of mars did indicate organic material.

Mars's atmosphere would not be poisonous to plant life, but it would be suffocating to earth's animals: it contains 14 times as much carbon dioxide as ours, and most of the rest is nitrogen. Surface pressure would be an added obstacle, being about equal to that in our atmosphere at 50,000 feet. At such low pressure, the ready evaporation of water prevents pools from forming and probably accounts for the fact that we cannot see any body of water large enough to reflect the sun's image. Temperatures range from about 70° F at noon near the point directly under the sun, to a sunrise minimum well below −100° F.

It has been suggested that some of the many pronounced markings on Mars's surface were sculptured by running water, now dry. At the turn of the century, man-made canals were thought to exist, but astronomers now generally reject this interpretation. Despite the lack of water, however, clouds frequently form; and in 1956, E. C. Slipher observed an apparent physical reaction related to the clouds: a darkening of the soil when the clouds left an area. Since the planet's dry atmosphere prevents rainfall, rain as we know it could not have caused this change, but some kind of moisture transfer from cloud to soil is regarded as possible.

Extensive and persistent dust storms occur on Mars. There is evidence that its surface materials are composed of iron oxides, such as limonite and goethite. Below a light dry dust of these rust materials, the ground is probably solid and permanently frozen.

The range of uncertainty in much of our information about Mars has left room for speculation. It may be, for example, that there is plant life resembling desert vegetation on earth—probably mostly mosses and lichens. Also, though little oxygen and water remain on the planet, they may have been abundant in the distant past. One theory hypothesizes that much of the oxygen was used up by combining with iron in the rocks. And great quantities of water may be held in chemical combination with rocks, as well as in the form of permafrost. In any event, it seems clear that the Mars we see today is a dying world.

JUPITER, SATURN, URANUS, AND NEPTUNE. These giant, rapidly rotating planets—very much alike—have thick atmospheres of methane and probably ammonia, with considerable amounts of helium and hydrogen concentrated toward their centers. They offer no possible abode for life of any kind now known. They differ so greatly from the terrestrial planets Mercury, Venus, Earth, Mars, and Pluto that they hardly seem to belong in the same system.

Jupiter has 12 satellites. It just missed being large enough to collapse into a radiating star like the sun. With a mass 300 times that of the earth, its diameter is 10 times as large, and its volume is 1,000 times as great. All of this enormity rotates at a tremendous speed to complete the day in 9 hours and 55 minutes. The vari-colored clouds that band this colossal planet may be aligned by powerful trade winds. An unusual feature, first observed in 1878, is the Great Red Spot, 30,000 miles in length or nearly 4 times the earth's diameter. It drifts around as though it were not fixed to a solid surface, and it has not been explained.

Saturn is the most picturesque of the planets. Its faint bandings are similar to Jupiter's, though more regular. Girdling it above its equator is a set of rings unique among the planets. These rings are composed of individual fragments of matter, each fragment moving in its own orbit about the planet. The fragments could be pieces of rock coated with ice; the rings may be no more than a few inches thick. The planet itself has an average specific gravity of 0.7. Saturn has 9 satellites.

Uranus and Neptune are similar giants in the cold outer reaches of the solar system. Their specific gravities are 1.53 and 2.41. Each is about 4 times the earth's diameter. For Uranus and its 5 satellites, the plane of rotation is tipped 98° to the plane of revolution about the sun, so that their motions are retrograde in relation to all the other planets.

Pluto, quite different from the four outer giants, may be a large, slightly misplaced asteroid. Indications are that it is more like the inner planets.

OUR GALAXY

All the stars visible without the aid of a telescope and most of those visible *with* a telescope are in our Milky Way Galaxy. This group of at least 100 billion stars seems to be distributed about a center in the vicinity of the constellation Sagittarius, the Archer, which is visible from northern latitudes as it hangs low in the southeastern sky in summer. Our galaxy

FIG. 3-4
The planet Saturn. Photo by Mt. Wilson Observatory's 100-inch telescope.

FIG. 3-5
A distant galaxy showing a discus shape similar to our galaxy viewed edgeways. Photo by Mt. Wilson Observatory.

is shaped like a discus of truly Olympian proportions: about 20,000 light-years thick at the center, thinner at the edges, and 100,000 light-years in diameter. Our solar system is located in the principal plane of the galaxy, about 30,000 light-years from the center, a position that makes it difficult for us to work out the details of star distribution. It seems probable, however, that from a distance of 1,500,000 light-years the galaxy looks not unlike one of the nearest of our neighboring galaxies (see Fig. 3-5). Such external galaxies are sometimes called *nebulae* because of their filmy, nebulous appearance in the telescopes through which they were first seen. Those known to have the spiral structure of Fig. 3-6 are called *spiral nebulae.* Our Milky Way Galaxy is a spiral nebula.

Distributed fairly uniformly around the edge of our galaxy are about 100 globular clusters of stars (see Fig. 3-7). Each cluster contains from 50,000 to 100,000 stars within a diameter of about 100 light-years. Since stars are about one light-year apart, they are more closely crowded together than in any other region.

All the stars in our galaxy move around a galactic center. Our solar system travels at a speed of about 150 miles per second and requires 200 million years to complete a circuit.

Our sun is a very ordinary star compared to others in our galaxy. Some stars are so large that they would encompass the orbit of sun and earth. They are 5 times as hot as the sun, 10,000 times as bright, 400 times its mass. Others are diminutive in comparison, having only a fifth of the sun's

FIG. 3-6
The Great Nebula in Andromeda. It is a spiral nebula similar in shape to our galaxy.

mass, one ten-thousandth of its brilliance, one-third of its heat.

Matter in interstellar space

Distributed irregularly in interstellar space throughout the universe are myriads of tiny pieces of dust and gas. The dust and gas in the neighborhood of the sun, it has been estimated, account for half the total matter of our entire solar system. These pieces of matter are larger than molecules and atoms, but so small that they could not be seen without the aid of the most powerful microscopes. They appear to be dusty grains of silica, or even frozen gases, or some other common substances converted to an unknown form by the low temperature, close to absolute zero, that prevails in interstellar space.[1]

Light that has passed through this interstellar matter in certain directions becomes polarized—that is, it ends up vibrating in only one plane, in contrast to the random pattern of vibration common to most light. This polarizing effect is interpreted as evidence that the pieces are not spherical, but are rather elongated bodies aligned either by a gigantic magnetic field or by "winds" from moving gas.

The presence of interstellar matter is strikingly demonstrated in areas like the Horsehead Nebula in Orion, where some parts of the sky are blacked out by the material, while other areas glow with light that it reflects.

It is now believed that most of the common elements found on earth can be found in interstellar space. The density of this material is very low—about what we would get by pulverizing an ordinary marble and then spreading the dust uniformly throughout the volume of a sphere 1,000 miles in diameter. Yet its presence is significant. There is too much of it to have been blown out of occasional exploding stars or to have escaped from others. Theorists believe this matter to be left over from the creation of the universe—pieces of the very stuff from which the stars and planets were compounded.

FIG. 3-7
A globular cluster. At 22,000 light-years, this is one of the clusters nearest to us. Photo by Harvard University's Boyden Station, Bloemfontein, South Africa.

ORIGIN OF OUR SOLAR SYSTEM

Many ideas have been put forth on the origin of the planets. Some two centuries ago, the Comte de Buffon proposed that the planets were formed when a large mass collided with the sun, and caused blobs of matter to be thrown out. These blobs became the planets. To figure out when this event took place, Buffon performed timed experiments on balls of metals and of rock. After heating these to white heat, he measured the rate at which they cooled. Then he computed how long it would have taken a ball as large as the earth to cool. His answer: 74,832 years. But Buffon overlooked some important factors: his samples were not fair representatives of the complex earth, and he neglected the fact that size governs rate of cooling.

A later idea on the origin of our solar system combined suggestions from three of science's great men—Kant, Laplace, and Helmholtz. The story begins with a very large, nebulous star, not very hot, because its matter was so spread out that

FIG. 3-8
Horsehead Nebula in Orion, where some parts of the sky are blacked out while other areas glow with light reflected by interstellar matter. Photographed in red light by 200-inch telescope. Mt. Wilson and Palomar Observatories.

[1] Leo Goldberg and Lawrence H. Aller, *Atoms, Stars, and Nebulae* (Philadelphia: The Blakiston Co., 1943), pp. 203, 213.

it filled all the space included in the orbits of the planets then known. This original "sun" was assigned a diameter of 2 billion miles. It was rotating. As it lost energy by radiating heat into space, it shrank; and as it shrank, it rotated faster and faster, as required by the law of conservation of angular momentum. As speed at its equator increased, centrifugal force there mounted. Finally this force became greater than the counterbalancing gravitative force, and some of the sun's matter was thrown off. This caused a minor collapse to make up for the lost matter. The ejected matter contracted into a sphere, forming a planet. The sun became stable until, losing heat through radiation, it began to shrink again and speed up, which led to throwing off more matter—another planet. This cycle continued until all the planets were formed. The remaining matter then collapsed into the present sun, which has not, up to now, lost enough heat to make it rotate fast enough to throw off any more planets.

Part of this theory was sound, because a star can develop its heat by collapsing, or contracting. It happens that our sun does not. A sequence of events like these might produce a solar system, but it did not produce ours. By this theory, the planets should all rotate in the plane of the sun's equator. They miss by about 6 degrees. This isn't much, but it is important. Also, this theory would leave the sun with 98 per cent of the solar system's energy of motion, called angular momentum.[2] It actually has about 2 per cent.

Failure of this theory to explain some features of our solar system threw speculation back toward the Buffon idea. Instead of a massive body having collided with the sun, these later theories proposed that such a body passed close by. The Chamberlain-Moulton Planetesimal Theory blamed an invading star for tearing some matter from the sun. It proposed that our planets were built up from this separated matter. They started small in size and grew to present dimensions by sweeping up the detached matter as they circled the sun. In the Jeans-Jeffries Tidal Theory, the planets condensed from gaseous filaments torn from both the sun and a passing star. These two theories had to be modified before long, after it was shown that matter torn from the sun and the passing star would fall back into the parent bodies because it would not receive sufficient angular momentum from the pull to go into orbit. It was then postulated that the passing star was in fact a double star, therefore three masses were involved. One of these was destroyed because of the pull of the other two stars on it. The debris from this destroyed star supplied the matter for the planets. Later calculations showed that stellar matter could be supplied under such conditions and could go into orbit around the sun, but it would not coagulate into planets. Science was making progress toward proving that our solar system could not be formed.

Early generations limited their speculation to origins of the planets. The origin of the sun itself was left to unexplained processes that occurred at an earlier date.

By the middle of the present century, theories that come

[2] The product of *mass* times *radius of orbit* times *velocity*.

under a general heading of *dust-cloud hypotheses* were sprouting and dying in close succession. Many included explanation of the origin of the sun as well as the planets. One begins with interstellar matter widely distributed throughout space. Light pressure from the stars is supposed to have caused this matter to pack together to form a cloud about 6,000 billion miles in diameter. At about that size, the cloud began to collapse, very slowly at first, under the force of its own gravity. But having reached a diameter of about 3,700 million miles, it swiftly completed the collapse in a few hundred years. The increased pressure in the contracting cloud greatly pushed up the temperature, and in the last white-hot phase of its collapse, the sun began to radiate as a star. The planets and satellites were derived from minor dust streams in the original cloud before there had been much contraction.

Two important features of our solar system remained unexplained by dust-cloud hypotheses. They do not explain the spacing of the planets from the sun, and they do not explain the high angular momentum of the planets.

Dust-cloud hypotheses have been modified by using the properties of electric currents and magnetic fields to explain the angular momentum of the sun and planets. The physical laws governing behavior of the hot gases involved are thereby changed. Ordinarily, gases respond directly to the pull of gravity, rotation, and pressure. But in a magnetic field maintained by electric current—that is, a *magnetohydrodynamic field*—the ionized gas has a wiry strength that resists these forces. In 1960, Fred Hoyle proposed that magnetohydrodynamics governed the behavior of the original matter in the dust clouds, composed of rapidly rotating ionized gases. Through these gases ran lines of magnetohydrodynamic force similar in some respects to long, elastic threads tied to the gases. The gas in the outer portions of the cloud was revolving more slowly than the center, so the threads tended to wind around and around and stretch. This increased the angular momentum of the outer portion, which became the planets and slowed down the center, which became the sun. The amounts of slowing down of the sun and speeding up of the planets necessary to this theory, however, are still not sufficient to explain the actual distribution of angular momentum in our solar system.

In the mid-twentieth century, as radioactive dating methods (see Chapter 9) were applied to more and more of the earth's rocks, evidence accumulated that some of the oldest were formed over 3 billion years ago. Estimates of the age of the earth itself rose to around 5 or 6 billion years. At the same time, astronomers were considering theories that the entire "known" universe is expanding from a volume of limited extent, from which it evolved 4 to 5 billion years ago. And the elements composing all this embryonic universe were formed within 5 minutes from a primordial plasma of photons, that is, light.

Whatever the processes that have resulted in the formation of the universe, they seem to have produced an overwhelming preponderance of double stars, which are dynamically unlikely to be able to hold families of planets. Possibly one star in a hundred is a single star, like our sun, and thus capable of having planets. And in our galaxy of 10^{11} stars, one in a million, or possibly even one in a thousand may have a planet like the earth under similar conditions of heat supply. This statistical fact means that in our galaxy alone there may be one million to one billion planets on which "human" beings might exist. And there are millions of galaxies in the universe.

SUMMARY OUTLINE

Space
- Unbounded nothingness occupied by everything

The universe
- Composed of all matter we can see or imagine; estimated to include millions of galaxies

Stars
- Self-luminous masses of gas

Groups of stars
- Constellations
- Galaxies
- Clusters

Our solar system
- Composed of the sun, 9 planets, 39 satellites, thousands of asteroids, scores of comets, and uncounted millions of meteors

The sun
- An average star
- Composed primarily of hydrogen and helium

The planets
- Revolve around the sun
- Four inner planets:
  - Mercury, Venus, Earth, and Mars—all about the same size, fairly dense, terrestrial planets
- Outer planets:
  - Jupiter, Saturn, Uranus, Neptune—giant planets very much alike
  - Pluto, possibly a slightly misplaced asteroid

Satellites
- Revolve around planets
- Moon, the earth's satellite

Our galaxy
- Called the *Milky Way Galaxy*
- Composed of at least 100 billion stars distributed in a spiral nebula 100,000 light-years in diameter

Matter in interstellar space
- Tiny pieces of dust and frozen gases representing most of the common elements found on earth

Theories on origin of our solar system
- Derived from matter thrown out of the sun
  - *a*) when the sun collided with another star
  - *b*) when the sun passed close to another star
  - *c*) as the sun shrank from former great size and cast off rings of matter
- Derived from the condensation of matter in great dust clouds
- None accounts for the fact that the sun has only about 2 per cent of the system's angular momentum

SELECTED REFERENCES

Shapley, Harlow, *Galaxies* (rev. ed.). Cambridge: Harvard Univ. Press, 1963.

Goldberg, Leo and Lawrence H. Aller, *Atoms, Stars and Nebulae*. Cambridge: Harvard Univ. Press, 1963.

Whipple, Fred L., *Earth, Moon, and Planets*. Cambridge: Harvard Univ. Press, 1963.

4

Minerals

MINERAL COMPOSITION

MINERAL STRUCTURE

IDENTIFICATION OF MINERALS

ROCK-FORMING MINERALS

ORGANIZATION OF MINERALS

Scientists now believe that the earth was formed at the same time as the sun and the other planets, some four to five billion years ago, from great turbulent clouds of dust-sized pieces of matter. Within these clouds, concentrations of matter began to develop. Once started, each concentration attracted to itself more pieces and gradually grew in size. The earth is the end product of one of these collections of matter.

MINERALS

During the process of concentration, the pieces became so active that they were transformed into a molten state. All the elements known today were present in this original molten matter. Very slowly, as these molten elements cooled, some of the iron and nickel—the heavier elements—sank to the center, while the lighter ones escaped. Eventually, some elements accumulated to form the earth's atmosphere or else, when surface temperatures permitted, combined to form our oceans' water. In the end, the mass of matter became our planet, a sphere 8,000 miles in diameter composed largely of compounds of elements. It is surrounded by gaseous elements —the atmosphere—and covered over much of its surface area with water.

We are most familiar with the surface of the earth, the part on which we live. It is composed of minerals—solid elements and compounds of relatively few elements (see Table 4-1). Minerals are everywhere about us. Almost any small plot of ground will offer numerous samples. They may occur in several forms, such as rocky outcrops, the soil of plowed fields, or the sands of a river bottom. Even some of the most common types are valuable enough to make mining them commercially worthwhile, and the rarer minerals such as gold and silver have provided the basis of wealth and power since the dawn of civilization.

The word "mineral" has many different meanings in everyday usage. Some people use it to refer to anything that is neither animal nor vegetable, according to the old classification of all matter as animal, vegetable, or mineral. To prospec-

TABLE 4-1
Most abundant elements in the earth's crust *

ELEMENT NUMBER	NAME AND SYMBOL	VOLUME PER CENT
8	Oxygen (O)	93.77
19	Potassium (K)	1.83
11	Sodium (Na)	1.32
20	Calcium (Ca)	1.03
14	Silicon (Si)	.86
13	Aluminum (Al)	.47
26	Iron (Fe)	.43
12	Magnesium (Mg)	.29

* Based on Brian Mason, *Principles of Geochemistry,* 2nd ed. (New York: John Wiley & Sons, Inc., 1960), p. 46.

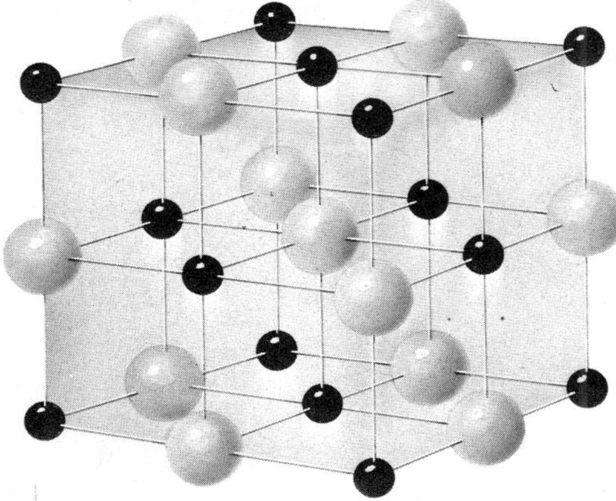

FIG. 4-1
Schematic arrangement of sodium ions with positive electrical charge, Na^+, and chlorine ions with negative electrical charge, Cl^-, to form the ionic compound NaCl, common salt. The ions are held together by their unlike electrical charges. They are actually thought of as spheres (Na^+ with a radius of .98A, and Cl^- with a radius of 1.8A) packed together as closely as possible. Here, the structure has been opened up to show the arrangement of ions in three dimensions.

tors and miners, mineral is an ore. And advertisers of pharmaceutical products associate the term with vitamins. But in our discussion "mineral" will be used to refer to a *solid element or compound that has been formed by inorganic processes.* Later on, we shall expand this definition, to make it more comprehensive.

Mineral composition

More than 2,000 minerals are known. Some are relatively simple compounds of elements in the solid state, others are complex. The diamond is composed of only one element—carbon. Common table salt, really the mineral halite, is composed of two elements, sodium and chlorine, in equal amounts. The chemical symbol for salt, NaCl, indicates that every sodium ion present is accompanied by one chlorine ion. The mineral pyrite (pie′-right), sometimes known as "fool's gold," is also composed of two elements, iron and sulfur. But in this mineral there are two ions of sulfur for each ion of iron, a relationship expressed by the chemical symbol for pyrite, FeS_2. *Every mineral has a constant composition of elements in definite proportion.* Later on, we shall see that a mineral's composition can vary slightly with an occasional substitution of other elements; but not enough substitutions take place to create a new mineral.

Mineral structure

Relatively simple changes took place as the earth cooled from a molten mass. When we say that the molten earth "cooled," we mean that the ions comprising it became less active. This decrease in activity permitted many of the ions to respond to their electrical attractions. Some grouped together to form molecules of gases that became the atmosphere; others joined in compounds but retained fluid mobility in the waters of the ocean. Others joined together in the fixed positions of solids.

The formation of a solid can be illustrated in the laboratory by preparing a white-hot liquid composed of sodium and chlorine. So long as the temperature of the liquid is kept at a high enough level, the activity of the ions is great enough to overcome their electrical attraction for one another. Even though they come into contact from time to time, the high temperature keeps them moving about freely. Then, as the temperature is reduced, they begin to lose their freedom of movement, and join together to form the compound sodium-chlorine. With further cooling, larger and larger clusters develop until finally all the ions are united in fixed positions. Now the sodium and chlorine appear as solid sodium chloride, the mineral halite.

The composition of the resulting solid is the same as that of the white-hot liquid; but in the solid state, the ions of sodium and chlorine are joined together in a definite pattern (see Fig. 4-1). The pattern that the atoms of elements assume in a mineral is called its *crystalline structure,* the orderly arrangement of its atoms. In halite, the ions of sodium alternate with ions of chlorine.

FIG. 4-2
Different arrangements of atoms of carbon. The crystalline structure of diamond.

Each mineral has a unique crystalline structure that will

distinguish it from another mineral even if the two are composed of the same element or elements. Consider the minerals diamond and graphite, for example. Each is composed of one element, carbon (see Fig. 4-2). In diamond, each atom of carbon is bonded to four neighboring carbon atoms. This complete joining of all its atoms produces a very strong bond and is the reason why diamond is so hard. In graphite, each atom of carbon is bonded in a plane to three neighboring atoms. This bonding forms sheets or layers of carbon piled one on another, but the sheets can be separated easily. Thus graphite is a soft substance.

Pyrite and marcasite are two other minerals with identical composition, FeS_2, but with different crystalline structures. In pyrite, ions of iron are equally spaced in all directions. In marcasite, they are not equally spaced. The difference in spacing accounts for their being two different minerals, although their composition is the same (see Fig. 4-3).

Other minerals may have more complicated crystalline structure: they may contain more elements and have these joined together in more complex patterns. The color, shape, and size of any given mineral may vary from one sample to another, but the *internal atomic arrangement of its component elements is identical in all specimens of a particular mineral.*

After taking all these factors into account, we find it necessary to include in our definition of a mineral not only the fact that it is an inorganic solid element or compound with a diagnostic chemical composition but also that it has a *unique orderly internal atomic arrangement of its elements.*

IDENTIFICATION OF MINERALS

All the properties of minerals are determined by the composition and internal atomic arrangement of their elements. So far, we have been talking about chemical properties—the factors that account for the existence of so many different minerals from such a limited number of elements. We can identify minerals on the basis of their chemical properties, but their physical properties are the ones most often used. Physical properties include such things as crystal form, hardness, specific gravity, cleavage, color, streak, and striations.

Crystal form

When any mineral grows without interference, it develops a characteristic *crystal form* that will be evident as soon as the mineral is large enough. If its development is constricted or impeded in any way, the characteristic form becomes distorted or modified.

The mineral quartz, for example, occurs in many rocks as irregular grains because its growth was constricted. Yet even in these irregular grains, the ions are arranged according to their typical crystalline structure. In some parts of the world, however, where conditions permitted the mineral to develop freely, crystals of quartz can be readily identified: they are always six-sided prisms. Whether an individual crystal of quartz is a quarter of an inch long or ten inches long, the

(cont.) **FIG. 4-2** *Graphite. Photos by Navias.*

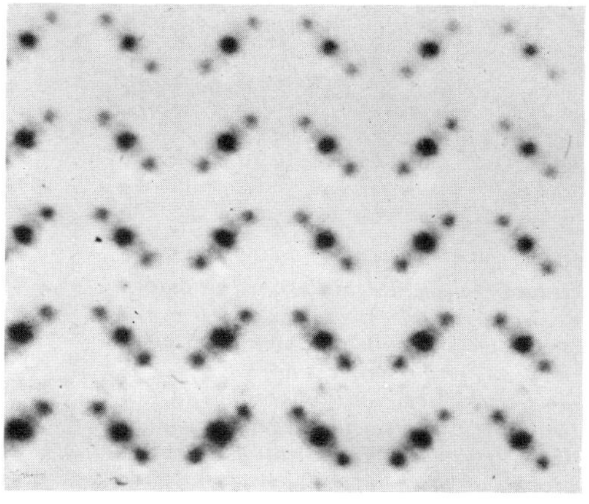

FIG. 4-3 *X-ray photographs of atoms.* TOP: *Pyrite shows orderly arrangement characteristic of crystalline structure. The mineral is composed of iron and sulfur, FeS_2. Large spots are atoms of iron; small ones are atoms of sulfur. Each atom of iron is bonded to 2 atoms of sulfur, and spacing of iron atoms is the same in both directions of the plane of the photograph. Magnification approximately 2.2 million diameters.* BOTTOM: *Marcasite, FeS_2. Note difference between horizontal and vertical spacing of iron atoms. Compare with pyrite. Magnification about 2.8 million diameters. Photos by Martin J. Buerger.*

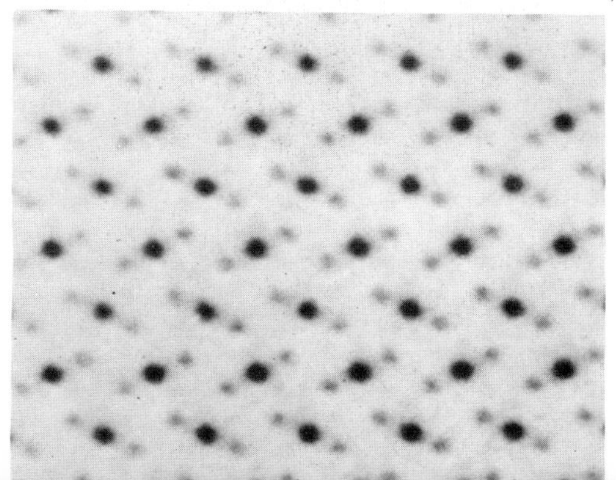

FIG. 4-4
Quartz crystals. Regardless of the shape or size of crystals, the angles between true crystal faces remain the same. Transverse striations on prism faces are most clearly seen on the faces of the two large crystals, which also carry blotches of foreign matter, but striations are present on faces of the other crystals, too. Reference grid of 2-inch squares in this picture and other pictures in chapter supplies scale. The large, stubby crystal came from Dauphine, France; the others from Brazil. Harvard Mineralogical Collection. Photo by Walter R. Fleischer.

sides of the prism always come together at the same angle, and the basic crystal form is always the same (see Fig. 4-4).

The crystal form of diamond is an eight-sided figure called an octahedron (see Fig. 4-5); the crystal form of graphite is a flat crystal with six sides. Both minerals are composed of carbon. The difference in their crystal forms comes from the arrangement of carbon atoms—one pattern in diamond, another in graphite.

The crystal form of the mineral pyrite is a cube; that of marcasite is a flattened or tubular shape. Here, again, the reason for the difference in crystal form lies in the internal arrangement of their atoms.

Every mineral has a characteristic crystal form, which is the external shape produced by its crystalline structure.

Hardness

Hardness is another property governed by the internal atomic arrangement of the elements of minerals. Again, graphite and diamond come to mind because they represent different arrangements of atoms of carbon and because graphite is one of the softest minerals known while diamond is the hardest. Their difference results from the ways in which the atoms of carbon are joined.

Hardness is a measure of the resistance that a smooth surface of a mineral offers to being scratched. It might be called the mineral's "scratchability." For example, if you pick up a piece of granite and try to scratch one of its light-colored grains with a steel knife blade, the granite simply refuses to be scratched. But if you drag one of its light-colored grains across a piece of glass, a scratch is easily made. Clearly, then, these particular mineral grains in granite are harder than either steel or glass. But if you have a piece of topaz handy, you can reveal the vulnerability of these light-colored mineral grains. For although they are harder than either steel or glass, they are not as hard as topaz.

Minerals differ widely in hardness (see Appendix C). Some are so soft that they can be scratched with a fingernail. Some are so hard that a steel knife is required to scratch them. But diamond, which is the hardest mineral known, cannot be scratched by any other substance.

Specific gravity

Every mineral has a definite weight per cubic inch. This characteristic weight is usually described by comparing it with the weight of the same volume of water. The number that represents this comparison is called the *specific gravity* of the mineral.

The specific gravity of a mineral increases with the mass numbers of its constituent elements and with the closeness with which these elements are packed together in their crystalline structure.

Most rock-forming minerals have a specific gravity of around 2.7, although the average specific gravity of metallic minerals is about 5. Pure gold has the highest specific gravity, 19.3.

It is not difficult to acquire a sense of relative weight by which to compare specific gravities. We learn to tell the difference between two bags of equal size, one filled with feathers and one filled with lead, and experience in hefting stones has given most of us a sense of the "normal" weight of rocks.

Cleavage

Cleavage is the tendency of a mineral to break in certain preferred directions along smooth plane surfaces. Cleavage planes are governed by the internal arrangement of the atoms. They represent the directions in which the atomic bonds are relatively weak.

Cleavage is a *direction* of weakness, and a mineral sample tends to break along planes parallel to this direction.

Color

Although color is not a very reliable property in identifying most minerals, it is useful in making certain general distinctions. For example, minerals containing iron are usually "dark-colored." In geologic usage, "dark" includes dark gray, dark green, and black. Minerals that contain aluminum as a predominate element are usually "light-colored," a term that includes purples, deep red, and some browns.

Streak

The *streak* of a mineral is the color it displays in finely powdered form. The streak may be quite different from the color of a hand specimen. For example, specimens of the mineral hematite may be brown, green, or black in color, but they always have a distinctive red-brown streak. One of

FIG. 4-5
A large, perfect crystal of diamond (uncut), which is the external expression of the orderly internal arrangement of atoms of carbon. Weight 84 carats. From Kimberley, South Africa. Harvard Mineralogical Collection. Photo by Harry Groom.

FIG. 4-6
Cubic crystals of pyrite. Striations are clear on the large specimen. Note that those in adjacent faces are perpendicular to each other. The small specimen consists of three cubes intergrown. Harvard Mineralogical Collection. Photo by Walter R. Fleischer.

FIG. 4-7
The silicon-oxygen tetrahedron $(SiO_4)^{4-}$. The upper view is from above and the lower from the side. This is the most important complex ion in geology, since it is the central building unit of nearly 90 per cent of the minerals of the earth's crust.

the simplest ways of determining the streak of a mineral is to rub a specimen across a piece of unglazed porcelain known as a *streak plate*. The color of the powder left behind on the streak plate helps to identify the mineral.

Striations

A few common minerals have parallel, threadlike lines or narrow bands called *striations* running across their surfaces. These can be seen clearly on crystals of quartz and pyrite, for example (see Figs. 4-4 and 4-6). Once again, this property is a reflection of the internal arrangement of the atoms of the crystals.

ROCK-FORMING MINERALS

Though there are more than 2,000 minerals known, only a few of these are *rock-forming minerals*, the minerals that comprise most of the rocks of the earth's crust.

Silicates

More than 90 per cent of the rock-forming minerals are silicates, compounds containing silicon and oxygen and one or more metals. Each silicate mineral has as its basic compound a complex ion called the *silicon-oxygen tetrahedron* (see Fig. 4-7), one of the first compounds to form as the molten earth cooled. It is a combination of one "small" silicon ion with a radius .42A surrounded as closely as geometrically possible by four "large" oxygen ions with radius 1.32A (forming a tetrahedron). The oxygen ions contribute an electric charge of -8 to the tetrahedron, and the silicon ion contributes $+4$. So the tetrahedron is a complex ion with a net charge of −4. Its symbol is $(SiO_4)^{4-}$.

The basic unit of silicate structure is the silicon-oxygen tetrahedron. Some silicates consist of single tetrahedra alternating with positive metal ions. In others, tetrahedra are joined together into chains, sheets, or three-dimensional structures. The most common of the silicate minerals are olivine, augite, hornblende, biotite, muscovite, feldspars, and quartz. Each one of these common rock-forming silicate minerals has a skeleton of silicon-oxygen tetrahedra.

FERROMAGNESIANS. In the first four of these rock-forming silicates—olivine, augite, hornblende, and biotite—the silicon-oxygen tetrahedra are joined by ions of iron and magnesium. Iron is interchangeable with magnesium in the crystalline structure of these silicates, because the ions of both elements are approximately the same size and have the same negative electric charge. These silicate minerals are known as ferromagnesians, from the joining of the Latin *ferum*, "iron," with magnesium. All four ferromagnesians are very dark or black in color and have a higher specific gravity than the other rock-forming silicate minerals.

Olivine. Silicon-oxygen tetrahedra joined with positive ions of iron or magnesium or both form olivine; thus, its formula is best written $(Mg,Fe)_2\ SiO_4$. Its specific gravity ranges from 3.27 to 3.37, increasing with the amount of iron present. This mineral, named for its characteristic olive color, usually occurs in grains or granular masses, without well-developed cleavage.

Augite. The crystalline structure of *augite* is based on single chains of tetrahedra,[1] as shown in Fig. 4-8, joined together by ions of iron and magnesium. Its color is very dark green to black; its streak is colorless; its specific gravity ranges from 3.2 to 3.4, and its cleavage is along two planes almost at *right* angles to each other. This cleavage angle is important in distinguishing augite from hornblende. A good way to remember it is to recall that augite rhymes with "right."

Hornblende. The crystalline structure of the mineral *hornblende* is based on double chains of tetrahedra, as shown in Fig. 4-9, joined together by the iron and magnesium ions common to all ferromagnesians, and also by ions of calcium, sodium, and aluminum. Hornblende's color is dark green to black, like that of augite; its streak is colorless; its specific gravity is 3.2. Two directions of cleavage meet at angles of approximately 56° and 124°, which helps distinguish hornblende from augite (see Fig. 4-10).

Biotite. Named in honor of the French physicist J.B. Biot, biotite (buy′-oh-tight) is a mica (my′-ka, from the Latin *micare*, "to shine"). Like all the other micas, it is constructed of tetrahedra in sheets, as shown in Fig. 4-11. Each silicon ion shares three oxygen ions with adjacent silicon ions to form a pattern like wire netting. The fourth, unshared oxygen ion of each tetrahedron stands above the plane of all the

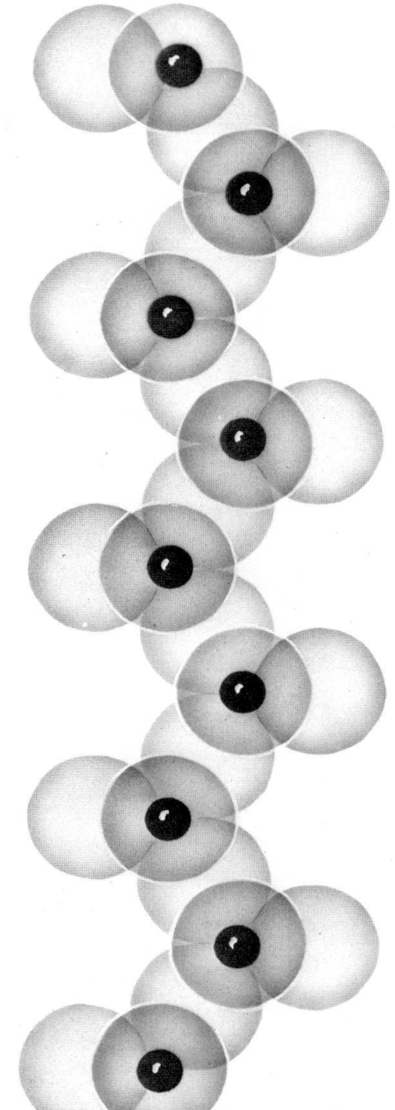

FIG. 4-8
TOP: *Single chain of tetrahedra viewed from above.*
BOTTOM: *Viewed from an end. Each silicon ion (small black sphere) has 2 of the 4 oxygen ions of its tetrahedron bonded exclusively to itself, and it shares the other 2 with neighboring tetrahedra fore and aft. The resulting individual chains are in turn bonded to one another by positive metallic ions. Since these bonds are weaker than the silicon-oxygen bonds that form each chain, cleavage develops parallel to the chains.*

1 The term "tetrahedra" will be used throughout this chapter to refer to silicon-oxygen tetrahedra.

others. The basic structural unit of mica consists of two of these sheets of tetrahedra, with their flat surfaces facing outward and their inner surfaces held together by positive ions. In biotite, the ions are iron and magnesium. These basic double sheets of mica, in turn, are loosely joined together by positive ions of potassium.

Layers of biotite, or any of the other micas, can be peeled off easily (see Fig. 4-12), because there is perfect cleavage along the surfaces of these weak potassium bonds. In thick blocks, biotite is usually dark green, brown, to black. Its specific gravity is 2.8 to 3.2.

NONFERROMAGNESIANS. The other common rock-forming silicate minerals are known as the *nonferromagnesians,* simply because they do *not* contain iron or magnesium. These minerals are muscovite, feldspars, and quartz. They are all marked by their light colors and relatively low specific gravities ranging from 2.6 to 3.0.

Muscovite. This white mica was so named because it was once used as a substitute for glass in old Russia (Muscovy). It has the same basic crystalline structure as biotite, but in muscovite each pair of tetrahedra sheets is tightly cemented together by ions of aluminum. As in biotite, however, the double sheets are held together loosely by potassium ions, along which cleavage readily takes place. In thick blocks, the color of muscovite is light yellow, brown, green, or red. Its specific gravity ranges from 2.8 to 3.1.

Feldspars. The most abundant rock-forming silicates are the feldspars. The name comes from the German *feld,* "field," and *spar,* a term used by miners for various nonmetallic minerals. Its name reflects the abundance of these minerals by calling them "field minerals," or minerals found in any field. Feldspars make up nearly 54 per cent of the minerals in the earth's crust.

In the feldspars, all the oxygen ions in the tetrahedra are shared by adjoining oxygen ions in a three-dimensional network. However, in one-quarter to one-half of the tetrahedra, aluminum ions with a radius of .51A and electric charge of

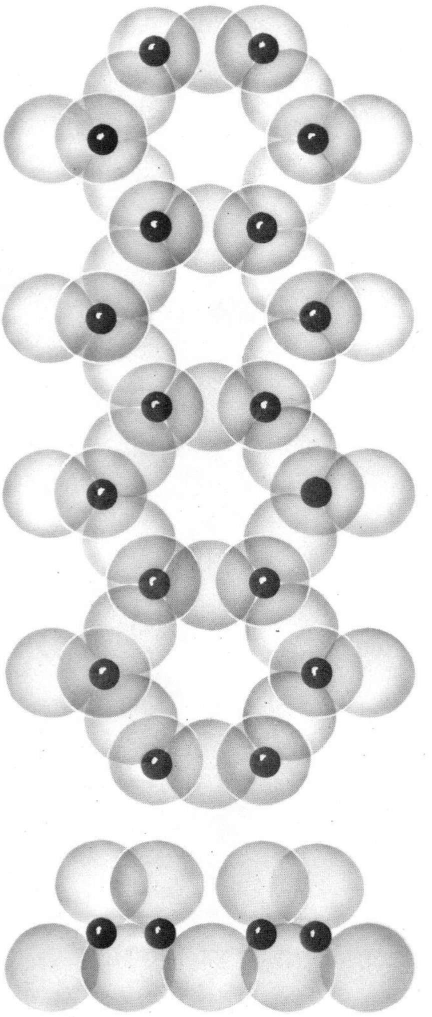

FIG. 4-9
TOP: *Double chain of tetrahedra viewed from above.*
BOTTOM: *Viewed from an end. The doubling of the augite chain is accomplished by the sharing of oxygen atoms by adjacent chains.*

FIG. 4-10
Cleavage of hornblende (left) compared with that of augite (right). The top "roof" of the hornblende specimen and the top and perpendicular left-hand faces of the augite are cleavage surfaces. Throughout each specimen, easiest breaking is parallel to these surfaces. On the front face of the augite are some "steps" outlined by cleavage planes. Such steps are the most common manifestation of cleavage, which seldom produces pieces as large as those shown here. Harvard Mineralogical Collection. Photo by Walter R. Fleischer.

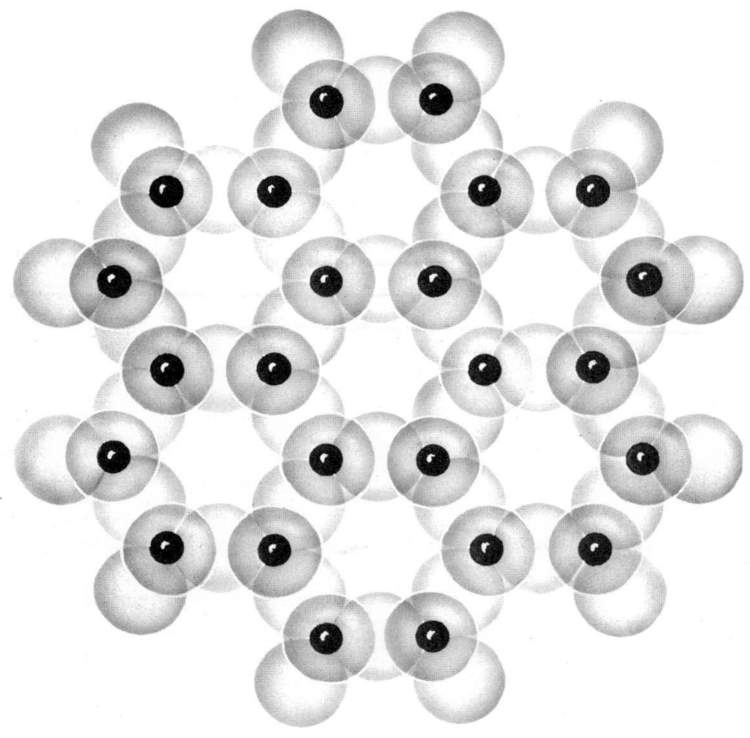

FIG. 4-11
Tetrahedral sheets. Each tetrahedron is surrounded by 3 others, and each silicon ion has 1 of the 4 oxygen ions to itself, while sharing the other 3 with its neighbors.

+3 have replaced silicon (with its radius of .42A and electric charge of +4) in the centers of the tetrahedra. The negative electric charge resulting from such substitution in the tetrahedra is corrected bv the entry into the crystalline structures of K^{+1}, Na^{+1}, or Ca^{+2}. The proportions of K, Na, and Ca that enter the structure are determined by temperature at the time of crystallization. Since the feldspars contain these elements in different proportions, they grade continuously into one another.

The mineral names given the feldspars are *orthoclase* and *plagioclase*. Plagioclase is in turn subdivided into the two minerals: albite and anorthite. Each one is classified in terms of the "end members" of the sequence. *Orthoclase* is the one

FIG. 4-12
Mica cleavage. The large block (or "book") is bounded on the sides by crystal faces. Cleavage fragments lying in front of the large block are of different thicknesses, as indicated by their degrees of transparency. Photo by Walter R. Fleischer.

FIG. 4-13
Feldspar cleavage in specimens of orthoclase. The large block on the right and the small fragment on the black box show the cleavage planes at nearly 90°, a characteristic of feldspars. Photo by Walter R. Fleischer.

with potassium; *albite* has sodium; *anorthite* has calcium. The feldspars are listed in Table 4-2.

TABLE 4-2 *Feldspars (aluminosilicates)*

DIAGNOSTIC POSITIVE ION	NAME	SYMBOL	DESCRIPTIVE NAME		FORMULA *
K^+	Orthoclase	Or	Potassic feldspar		$K(AlSi_3O_8)$
Na^+	Albite	Ab	Sodic feldspar	plagioclase feldspars	$Na(AlSi_3O_8)$
Ca^{+2}	Anorthite	An	Calcic feldspar		$Ca(Al_2Si_2O_8)$

* In these formulas, the symbols *inside* the parentheses indicate the tetrahedra. The symbols *outside* the parentheses indicate the diagnostic ions—that is, the ions that are worked in among the tetrahedra.

In this table, the column headed "Diagnostic positive ion" (from the Greek *diagnostikos,* "able to distinguish") indicates the ion that corrects the electrical unbalance caused by substitution of aluminum for silicon.

Orthoclase is named from the Greek *orthos,* "straight," and *klasis,* "a breaking," because the two dominant cleavages intersect at a right angle when a piece of orthoclase is broken (see Fig. 4-13). Aluminum replaces silicon in every fourth tetrahedron, and positive ions of potassium correct the electrical unbalance. The streak of orthoclase is white; its color is white, gray, or pinkish, and its specific gravity is 2.57.

Plagioclase ("oblique-breaking") feldspars are so named because they have cleavage planes that intersect at about 86°. One of the cleavage planes is marked by striations. The two plagioclase feldspars are albite and anorthite.

In albite, aluminum replaces silicon in every fourth tetrahedron, and positive ions of sodium correct the electrical unbalance. The specific gravity of albite is 2.62.

In anorthite, aluminum replaces silicon in every second tetrahedron, and positive ions of calcium correct the electrical unbalance. The specific gravity of anorthite is 2.76.

Both plagioclase feldspars may be colorless, white, or gray, although some samples show a striking play of colors called opalescence.

Quartz. Sometimes called *silica, quartz* is the only rock-forming silicate mineral that is composed exclusively of silicon-oxygen tetrahedra. Every oxygen ion is shared by adjacent silicon ions, which means that there are two ions of oxygen for every ion of silicon. This relationship is represented by the formula SiO_2. The specific gravity of quartz is 2.65.

Quartz usually appears smoky to clear in color, but many less common varieties include purple or violet *amethyst,* massive rose-red or pink *rose quartz,* smoky yellow to brown *smoky quartz,* and *milky quartz.* These color differences are caused by other elements being present as impurities. They are not caused by, and do not affect, the crystalline structure of the quartz.

Oxide minerals

Oxide minerals are formed by the direct union of an element with oxygen. These are relatively simple minerals compared to the complicated silicates. The oxide minerals are usually harder than any other class of minerals except the silicates, and they are heavier than others except the sulfides. Within the oxide class are the chief ores of iron, chromium, manganese, tin, and aluminum.

Some common oxide minerals are ice (H_2O), corundum (Al_2O_3), hematite (Fe_2O_3), magnetite (Fe_3O_4), and cassiterite (SnO_2).

Sulfide minerals

Sulfide minerals are formed by the direct union of an element with sulfur. The elements that occur most commonly in com-

TABLE 4-3
The organization of common minerals (continuation of Table 2-2)

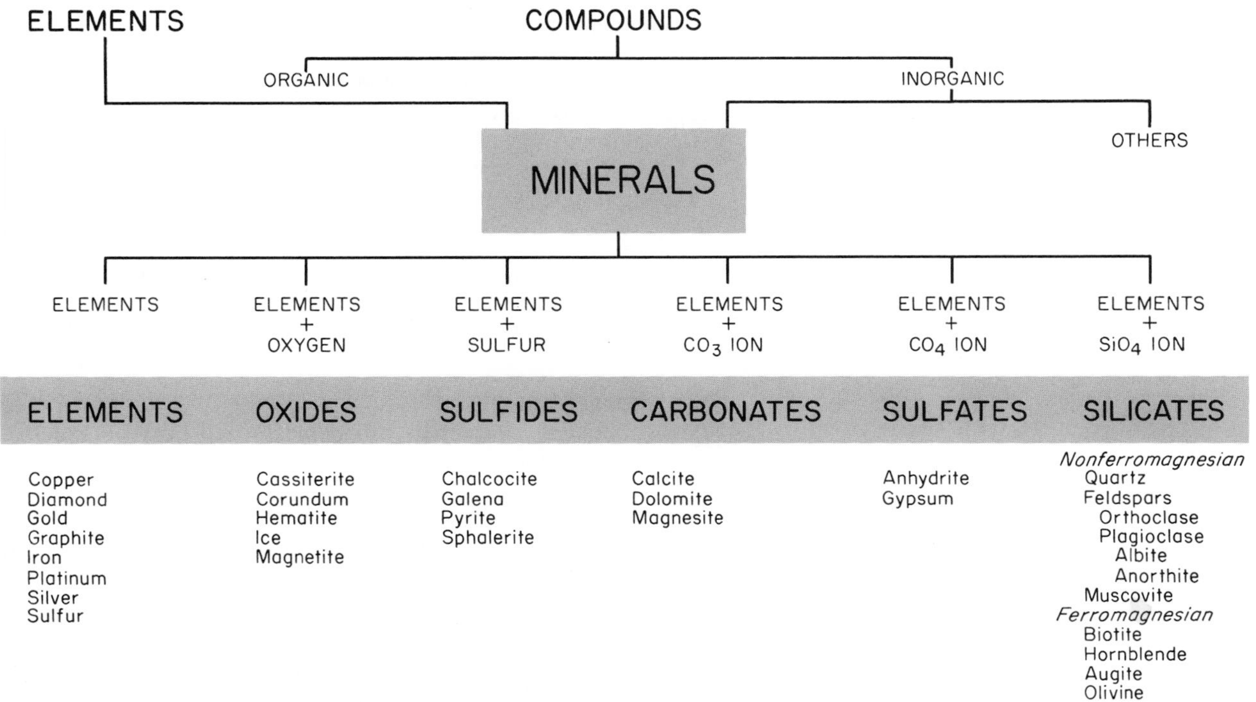

bination with sulfur are iron, silver, copper, lead, zinc, and mercury. Some of these sulfide minerals occur as commercially valuable ores, such as pyrite (FeS_2), chalcocite (Cu_2S), galena (PbS), and sphalerite (ZnS).

Carbonate and sulfate minerals

In discussing silicates, we found them to be built around the complex ion $(SiO_4)^{4-}$, that is, the silicon-oxygen tetrahedron. But two other complex ions also are of great importance in geology. One of these consists of a single carbon ion with three oxygen ions packed around it—the complex ion $(CO_3)^{2-}$. Compounds in which this complex ion appears are called carbonates. For example, the combination of a calcium ion with a carbon-oxygen ion produces calcium carbonate, $CaCO_3$, known in its mineral form as *calcite*. This mineral is the principal component of the common sedimentary rock, limestone. The other complex ion is $(SO_4)^{2-}$, a combination of one sulfur ion and four oxygen ions. This complex ion combines with other ions to form sulfates; for example, it joins with a calcium ion to form calcium sulfate, $CaSO_4$, the mineral anhydrite.

ORGANIZATION OF MINERALS

We know that minerals are special combinations of elements or compounds in the solid state, and now we can complete our definition of a mineral: (1) it is a naturally occurring element or inorganic compound in the solid state;[2] (2) it has a diagnostic composition; (3) it has a unique crystalline structure; and (4) it exhibits certain physical properties as a result of its composition and crystalline structure.

SUMMARY OUTLINE

Mineral
- Solid element or compound formed by inorganic processes

Mineral composition
- Component elements; constant or limited range

Mineral structure
- Pattern of arrangement of component elements

Properties of minerals
- Crystal form
  - External shape determined by crystalline structure
- Hardness, specific gravity, cleavage, color, streak, striations

Rock-forming minerals
- Silicates
  - Ferromagnesian: olivine, augite, hornblende, biotite
  - Nonferromagnesian: muscovite, feldspars, quartz
- Oxide, sulfide, carbonate, and sulfate minerals

SELECTED REFERENCES

Hurlbut, Cornelius, Jr., *Dana's Manual of Mineralogy* (17th ed.). New York: John Wiley & Sons, Inc., 1961.

Mason, Brian, *Principles of Geochemistry* (2nd ed.). New York: John Wiley & Sons, Inc., 1960.

Pough, Frederick H., *A Field Guide to Rocks and Minerals.* Boston: Houghton Mifflin Company, 1953.

[2] Some mineralogists do not restrict the definition to the solid state, but include such substances as water and liquid mercury.

5

Igneous activity

VOLCANOES

ERUPTIONS

VOLCANIC GASES

PYROCLASTIC DEBRIS

CLASSIFICATION OF VOLCANOES

CALDERAS

BASALT PLATEAUS

CAUSE OF IGNEOUS ACTIVITY

From time to time throughout geologic history, masses of rocks have melted within the earth's crust. Some of the melted rock, working its way to the surface through covering rock, poured out or was blown onto the ground, there again to solidify into rock. Igneous activity consists of movements of molten rock inside and outside the earth's crust. It also includes the variety of effects associated with these movements.

In some areas, molten rock extruded through extensive fissures in the earth's surface. This activity, called *fissure eruption*, built large plateaus. In other places, molten rock escaped from within the crust through vents, and around these vents the ejected material accumulated to build up landforms that we know as volcanoes.

VOLCANOES

A volcano, the surface pile of material that accumulates around a *vent* or vents during successive volcanic eruptions, may grow in size until it becomes a mountain (see Fig. 5-1). Normally cone-shaped, it has a pit at the summit, which may be either a crater or a caldera. A *crater* is a steep-walled depression out of which volcanic materials are ejected. Its floor is seldom over 1,000 feet in diameter; its depth may be as much as several hundred feet. A crater may be at the top of a volcano or on its flank. The much larger *caldera* is a basin-shaped depression, more or less circular, with a diameter many times greater than that of the included volcanic vent or vents. Most calderas, in fact, are more than a mile in diameter; some are several miles across and several thousand feet deep.

Between eruptions, the volcano's vent may become choked with rock congealed from the magma of a past eruption. Sometimes small jets of gas come out through cracks in this rock plug (see Fig. 5-2). A volcano is built by, and remains active because of, materials coming from a large deep-seated reservoir of molten rock. While in the ground, this molten rock is called *magma*. When extruded on the surface, it is called *lava*.

The world's largest volcano is Mauna Loa, on the island of

FIG. 5-1
Pavlof Volcano, Alaskan Peninsula. Official U.S. Navy Photograph.

FIG. 5-2
Jets of gas from cracks in congealed magma plugging vent. Kilauea Volcano, Hawaii. Photo by 11th Photo Section, U.S. Army Air Corps.

Hawaii. It is 400 miles around the base, and its summit towers nearly 6 miles above the surrounding ocean bottom. This and the rest of the island represent accumulations from eruptions that have gone on for more than a million years.

Volcanic eruptions

In its reservoir far below the earth's surface, magma is composed of rock-forming minerals in solution. Some of the components of magma and of the rocks that it penetrates are vaporized into gases by temperatures and pressures that prevail as magma approaches the surface. These volatile components play an extremely important role in igneous activity.

Water is the principal volatile component and the primary agent in producing a *volcanic eruption*. As the magma nears the surface, water tends to separate from the other components and migrates through them to the top of the moving mass. The water, by now steam, accumulates if the volcanic vent is blocked. Pressure builds up until it can no longer be confined—the steam pushes out. If its temperature is 1,800° F or more, this steam expands several thousandfold as it escapes, shattering the rock that blocks the vent, throwing it and magma into the air. After the explosion, the magma still in the ground is left poorer in water, but fluid enough to pour out (see Fig. 5-3). Magma virtually devoid of water, hence highly viscous, moves to the surface more and more slowly, and finally stops moving, blocking the vent again. But water continues to migrate toward the top of the magma until enough has accumulated to cause another explosion and eruption.

If an old volcano's entire reservoir of molten rock has lost most of its original supply of water, it will have very stiff magma. Steam that collects under the rock plugging its vent can build up to a violent explosion that will blow off the covering rock; but since there is not enough water left to supply fluidity, extensive outpourings of lava will not follow.

Minor explosions are sometimes caused when magma moves into a region of abundant ground water. The heat in the molten rock converts the ground water to steam, which explodes.

Volcanic eruptions vary from relatively quiet outpourings of lava to violent explosions accompanied by showers of volcanic debris. If magma reaching the surface above the reservoir does not find its avenue of escape blocked, it flows out quietly.

FIG. 5-3
Congealed lava. Photo by U.S. Geol. Survey.

Volcanic gases

As one might expect, taking an accurate sampling of volcanic gases is not an easy job. It is also difficult to decide whether the gases have come exclusively from the magma or partly from the surrounding rocks. We can, however, make a few generalizations from measurements at Kilauea in Hawaii.

Close to 70 per cent of the volume of gases collected directly from a molten lake of lava was steam. Next in abundance were carbon dioxide, nitrogen, and sulfur gases, with smaller amounts of carbon monoxide, hydrogen, and chlorine. Even when gases other than steam make up only a small percentage of the total volume, their absolute quantities may be large. For example, in 1919 during the cooling of material erupted in 1912 from Katmai in Alaska, the total amount of HCl released was estimated at 1,250,000 tons, and the total amount of HF was approximately 200,000 tons.

When any igneous rock is heated, it yields some quantity of gases. Again, water vapor predominates, and measurements indicate that it constitutes about 1 per cent of fresh—that is, unweathered—igneous rocks. Estimates of the average water content of actual magma range from about 1 to 8 per cent, with the weight of opinion centering around 2 per cent. A silicate melt will not hold more than about 11 per cent of volatiles under any circumstances.

Pyroclastic debris

Fragments blown out by explosive eruptions and subsequently deposited on the ground are called *pyroclastic debris* (pyroclastic means "broken by fire"). The finest pyroclastic debris is *dust,* which is made up of pieces on the order of one ten-thousandth of an inch in diameter. When volcanic dust is blown into the upper atmosphere, it can remain there for months, traveling great distances. The following fragments settle around or near the volcanic crater (see Fig. 5-4):

Ash: finer cinders.

Blocks: pieces of the cone or angular masses broken away from rock that blocks the vent.

Bombs: rounded masses that congeal from magma as it travels through the air.

Cinders: small, slaglike, solidified pieces of magma or broken pieces of the cone or plug, two-tenths to one inch across.

Pumice: pieces of magma up to several inches across that have trapped bubbles of steam or other gases as they were thrown out. After these solidify, they are honeycombed with gas-bubble holes that give them enough bouyancy to float on water (see Fig. 5-5).

FIG. 5-4
Pyroclastic debris that accumulated to depths of 4 feet at a distance of 3,500 feet from Kilauea Iki, an active vent of Kilauea, during an eruption in 1959. Photo by Hawaiian Volcano Observatory.

FIERY CLOUDS. During the Katmai eruption in 1912, a great avalanche of incandescent ash mixed with steam and other gases was extruded. Heavier than air, this highly heated mixture rolled down the mountain slope. Masses of such material are called *fiery clouds* (sometimes referred to by the French equivalent, *nuée ardente*). The volume of material extruded was so great that it covered a valley of 53 square miles, 100 feet thick. For the next ten years the steam and gases kept erupting from this extruded material through a great number of holes called *fumaroles,* and the area was given the name Valley of Ten Thousand Smokes.

In 1902, fiery clouds also erupted at Mt. Pelée on Martinique island in the West Indies. The magma left in the vent by a previous eruption had solidified into a plug of rock blocking the vent of the volcano. By the latter part of 1901, steam inside the volcano had built up enough pressure to push this plug upward until it protruded 1,500 feet above the rim of the crater. It became stuck at that height, looking like a gigantic blunted needle, and was named "The Spine of Pelée." But the pressures were still building up underneath it and could not be contained indefinitely. A few minutes before 8 o'clock on Thursday morning, May 8, 1902, a gigantic explosion occurred as steam pushed out through one side of the volcano. A fiery cloud at temperatures around 1,500° F swept down the mountainside and engulfed the city of St. Pierre, wiping out its 25,000 inhabitants and many refugees from other parts of the island who had gathered there during the preceding days, when the eruption was building up with minor explosions and earthquakes. Estimates of the death toll ran as high as 40,000.

WORLDWIDE EFFECTS. In 1783, Asama in Japan and Laki in Iceland had explosive volcanic eruptions. Large quantities of dust were blown into the upper atmosphere. Dry fogs in the stratosphere were recorded simultaneously at places as widely separated as northern Africa and Scandinavia. At one place, the density of the dry fog was so great that the sun was invisible until it had reached a position 17 degrees above the horizon. The sun's effectiveness in heating the earth's surface was so reduced that the winter of 1783–1784 was one of the severest on record. Benjamin Franklin was the first person to connect the unusual weather with the volcanic eruptions. He published his ideas in May, 1784.

During 1814 and 1815, the earth's temperature was reduced, following volcanic eruptions of Mayon on the Philippine Islands and Tambora on Sumbawa island, east of Java. The eruption of Tambora threw so much dust into the air that for three days there was absolute darkness for a distance of 300 miles. With this dust and the dust erupted from Mayon in the atmosphere, the amount of the sun's heat reaching the earth's surface was significantly reduced. The year 1815 became known as the "year without a summer," marked throughout the world by long twilights and spectacular sunsets caused by the dust in the stratosphere.

The remarkable ability of volcanic dust to travel around the world was observed again in 1912. In June of that year, an observer from the Smithsonian Institution was in Algeria mak-

FIG. 5-5
Pumice.

FIG. 5-6
A fiery cloud sweeping down the side of Mt. Pelée, Martinique, in 1902. Fresh lava flows form the shoreline in the foreground. Photo by Underwood and Underwood.

FIG. 5-7
Ruins of St. Pierre, Martinique, shortly after its destruction by a fiery cloud on the morning of May 8, 1902. Photo by Underwood and Underwood.

ing measurements of the quantity of heat reaching the earth from the sun. During observations on June 19, he noticed streaks of dust lying along the horizon. These were joined by others, and in a few days the sky appeared "mackereled," although no clouds were present. Finally, the sky became so obscured that observations had to be discontinued. By June 29, the whole sky was filled with the dust, which persisted for months. At first, it was assumed that the condition was local, but reports gathered from many regions eventually indicated that the phenomenon was actually worldwide, caused by an eruption of Mt. Katmai on the Alaskan Peninsula. This eruption caused a 20 per cent decrease in the amount of direct solar radiation reaching the earth's surface during the summer of 1912. The sun's rays, bouncing from dust in the upper atmosphere, caused an abnormal brightness of the sky. If the dust from Katmai had stayed in the atmosphere long enough, it would have been capable of so reducing the amount of heat received by the earth that the average world temperature would have dropped almost 13°F.

History of some volcanoes

A volcano is considered *active* if there is some record of its having erupted in historic time. If it has not done so, but shows notable lack of erosional alteration, pointing to eruption within quite recent geologic time, it is considered *dormant*, or merely "sleeping," and capable of renewed activity. If a volcano not only has not erupted within historic time, but also shows wearing away by erosion and no signs of activity (such as escaping steam or local earthquakes), it is considered *extinct*.

VESUVIUS. Vesuvius, on the shore of the Bay of Naples, has supplied us with a classic example of the reawakening of a dormant volcano (see Fig. 5-8). At the time of Christ, Vesuvius was a vine-clad mountain called Mt. Somma, a vacation spot in southwest Italy, favored by wealthy Romans. For centuries it had given no sign of its true nature. Then, in A.D. 63, a series of strong earthquakes shook the area, and around noon on

FIG. 5-8
Vesuvius in eruption, 1906. The snow-clad slopes mark the modern volcano. To the left of it and in the foreground is the jagged remnant of Mt. Somma. Photo by A. and C. Caggiano.

August 24, 79, Vesuvius started to erupt. The catastrophe of that August day lay silent and impenetrable for nearly 17 centuries. When the remains of Herculaneum and Pompeii were discovered—cities that had been buried by the eruption—a story evolved to grip the world's imagination. Roman sentries had been buried at their posts. Family groups, in the supposed safety of subterranean vaults, had been cast in molds of volcanic mud cemented to a rocklike hardness, along with their jewels, candelabra, and the food that they had hoped would sustain them through the emergency.

Mt. Somma is believed to have erupted first about 10,000 years ago as a submarine volcano in the Bay of Naples. It then emerged as an island and finally filled in so much of the bay around it that it became a part of the mainland. It is the youngest volcano in that vicinity.

There must have been an exceedingly long interval of quiet before the eruption of the year 79, because no earlier historical records of volcanic activity exist. Then, in 79, part of the old Mt. Somma cone was destroyed and the new cone, Vesuvius, started. During this eruption, Pompeii was buried by pyroclastic debris; people died from asphyxiation due to gases from the ash and suffocation from the dust. Herculaneum was overwhelmed by mudflows of water-soaked ash.

Eruptions of pyroclastic debris occurred at intervals after 79. The longest period of quiescence lasted 494 years and was followed by an eruption in 1631 that poured out the first lava in historic time. Since then, Vesuvius has erupted 14 times. Each eruption is the last of a series of events that repeat themselves in a cycle. Bullard [1] describes the cycle as follows:

> The eruptive cycles vary in length, but the two latest cycles ran thirty-four and thirty-eight years respectively. The cycle begins with a repose period, averaging about seven years, in which only gases issue from the crater. The renewal of explosive activity begins with the building of small cinder cones on the crater floor. Outpourings of lava may also occur in the crater until the crater is gradually filled. Sometimes the lava flows spill over the top or issue from fissures in the crater rim, but such flows are of small volume and cause little damage. This type of moderate activity may continue for years (perhaps twenty to thirty years). When the cinder cones and the lava flows have filled the crater, the stage is set for the culminating eruption of the cycle. The column of lava now stands high in the throat of the volcano, and it is under tremendous pressure and saturated with gases. Finally, when the pressure becomes too great to be contained by the surrounding material, the eruption begins. Accompanied by sharp earthquakes and strong explosions, which give rise to great ash clouds, the cone splits. From the fractures, which frequently extend from the crater rim to the base, floods of lava pour out and flow rapidly down the side of the cone. These actions constitute the paroxysmal eruption which marks the end of a cycle. Such eruptions usually last for two or three weeks and are followed by a repose period which is the beginning of a new cycle.

KRAKATOA. One of the world's greatest explosive eruptions took place in 1883 at Krakatoa, in Sunda Strait between Java and Sumatra. Krakatoa had once been a single island consisting entirely of a volcanic mountain built up from the sea bottom. Then, at a remote period in the past, it split apart during

[1] Fred M. Bullard, *Volcanoes in History, in Theory, in Eruption* (Austin: U. of Texas Press, 1962), p. 159.

an eruption. By 1883, after a long period of rebuilding, three cones had risen above sea level and had merged. These cones, named Rakata, Danan, and Perboewatan, and various unnamed shoals completed the outline of Krakatoa.

On the afternoon of Sunday, August 26, 1883, a series of explosions began. The next day, at 10:20 A.M., a gigantic explosion blew the two cones Danan and Perboewatan to bits. A part of the island that had formerly stood 2,600 feet high was left covered by 900 feet of water. The noise of the eruption was heard on Rodrigues Island, 3,000 miles across the Indian Ocean, and a wave of pressure in the air was recorded by barographs around the world. A great flood of water created by the activity drowned 36,500 persons in the low coastal villages of western Java and southern Sumatra.

Columns of ash and pumice soared miles into the air, and fine dust rose to such heights that it was distributed around the globe and took more than two years to fall. During that time, sunsets were abnormally colored all over the world. A reddish-brown circle known as Bishop's Ring, which was seen around the sun under favorable conditions, gave evidence not only of the continued presence of dust in the upper air, but of the approximate size of the pieces—just under two thousandths of a millimeter, or less than one ten-thousandth of an inch. Since 1883, Krakatoa has revealed from time to time that it is actively rebuilding (see Fig. 5-9).

DISAPPEARING ISLANDS. Submarine volcanoes like Krakatoa, which build themselves up above sea level, blow off their heads and then rebuild, producing the so-called disappearing islands of the Pacific. One day in 1913, for example, Falcon Island (20.4°S., 175.6°W.), in the South Pacific, suddenly disappeared after an explosive eruption. On Tuesday, October 4, 1927, accompanied by a series of violent explosions, it just as suddenly reappeared. The island of Bogosloff (about 56°N., 168°W.), in the Aleutians, was first reported in 1826 and has been playing hide-and-seek with mapmakers ever since.

PARICUTIN. About 200 miles west of Mexico City (19.50°N., 102.05°W.) Parícutin sprang into being on February 20, 1943. Nine years later, it had become quite inactive. But during its life it was studied more closely than any other newborn vent in history.

Many stories of the volcano's first hours have been told. According to the version now generally regarded as the most reliable, Parícutin began about noon as a thin wisp of smoke rising from a cornfield that was being plowed by Dionisio Pulido. By four o'clock, explosions were occurring every few seconds, dense clouds of ash were rising, and a cone had begun to build up. Within five days, the cone was 300 feet high, and after one year it had risen to 1,410 feet. Two days after the eruption began, the first lava flowed from a fissure in the field about 1,000 feet north of the center of the cone. At the end of seven weeks, this flow had advanced about a mile. Fifteen weeks after the first explosion, lava had also begun to flow from the flanks of the cone itself.

After nine years of activity, Parícutin abruptly stopped its eruptions and became just another of the many small "dead" cones in the neighborhood. The histories of these other cones,

FIG. 5-9
Krakatoa rebuilding through an eruption of Anak Krakatoa on January 12, 1960, as it appeared from a distance of about 1,000 feet. This vent is within the caldera. Photo by R. W. Decker.

FIG. 5-10
Schematic drawing of the five volcanoes that have been built up from the sea floor to merge and form the island of Hawaii.

FIG. 5-11
Creating a lake of lava on the crater floor, this 900-foot fountain of lava is erupting through the side of Kilauea Iki's crater, November 19, 1959. Photo by U.S. Geol. Survey.

parasites of Toncítaro or of neighboring major volcanoes, undoubtedly parallel the story of Parícutin.

Other new volcanoes that have developed during historic time are Jorullo (18.85°N., 101.82°W.) and Monte Nuovo (40.83°N., 14.10°E.). Jorullo broke out in the middle of a plantation about 45 miles southeast of Parícutin, in 1759. Monte Nuovo erupted in 1538, just west of Vesuvius.

HAWAII. The Hawaiian Islands are peaks of volcanoes projecting above the ocean and strung out along a line running 1,500 miles to the northwest. The Marquesas, Society, Tuamotu, Tubuai, Samoan, and other volcanic groups of the South Pacific Ocean form lines roughly parallel to the Hawaiian Islands.

At the northwestern end of the Hawaiian chain are the low Ocean and Midway islands. At the southeastern end is Hawaii, the largest of the group. Hawaii, 93 miles long and 76 miles wide, is the tallest deep-sea island in the world. The igneous activity that produced this group of islands apparently started at the northwestern end of the chain, where activity has now ceased, and worked southeastward to the present focus of most recent activity, on Hawaii itself.

The island of Hawaii is composed of five volcanoes—Kohala, Hualalai, Mauna Kea, Mauna Loa, and Kilauea (see Fig. 5-10). Each volcano has developed independently, and each has its own geologic history. Lava from Mauna Kea has buried the southern slope of Kohala, and lava from Mauna Loa has buried parts of Mauna Kea, Hualalai, and Kilauea. The dimensions of the volcanoes are listed in Table 5-1. They represent portions of the volcanoes above sea level at the present time and do not take into account buried slopes.

TABLE 5-1 *Volcanoes of the island of Hawaii*

NAME	AREA (SQ. MI)	PERCENTAGE OF ISLAND	SUMMIT ELEVATION (FT)
Mauna Loa	2,035	50.5	13,680
Mauna Kea	920	22.8	13,784
Kilauea	550	13.7	4,090
Hualalai	290	7.2	8,250
Kohala	235	5.8	5,505

From H. T. Stearns and G. A. Macdonald, "Geology and Ground-Water Resources of the Island of Hawaii," *Bulletin 9,* Hawaii Division of Hydrography (1946), p. 24.

Kohala has been extinct for many years, but Mauna Kea shows evidence of having been active in the recent geological past, though not within recorded history. Hualalai last erupted in 1801, and Mauna Loa was active about 6 per cent of the time from 1832 to 1945. During the same interval, Kilauea was active about 66 per cent of the time. Prior to that, extending back to A.D. 140, native legend tells of 40 to 50 eruptions of Kilauea.

Measurements made at the Hawaiian Volcano Observatory show that both Mauna Loa and Kilauea swell up during the period when magma is rising from below, just before an eruption. The mountains actually rise up higher above sea level and show a tendency to tilt. After the eruption, the mountains shrink back again.

When Kilauea is active, magma rises up into the mountain and floods out as lava into a pit in the floor of the caldera (see fig. 5-11). Occasionally, the lava flows out over the rim of the pit onto the caldera floor and gradually raises the level of the floor. Usually, however, the lava is confined to the pit, forming what is termed a *lava lake*. This lava lake may last for years, and then disappear completely for equally long periods. The level of the lake falls when lava flows from the flanks of the volcano, both above and below sea level. From time to time, the system is drained and the caldera floor collapses. Then the magma rises again, lava floods into the caldera, and the process is repeated.

Some observers have tried to show that this activity occurs in regular cycles. But the evidence so far has not been convincing. Apparently, the Hawaiian volcanoes behave in no regular, predictable manner.

FIG. 5-12
Profile of one of the world's most nearly perfect composite cones: Mayon, on Luzon, Philippine Islands. Photo from Gardner Collection, Harvard University.

Classification of volcanoes

Volcanoes are classified according to the materials that have accumulated around their vents. Thus we have *shield volcanoes, composite volcanoes,* and *cinder cones.*

When the extruded material consists almost exclusively of lava poured out in quiet eruptions from a central vent or from closely related fissures, a dome builds up that is much broader than it is high, with slopes seldom steeper than 10° at the summit and 2° at the base. A dome of this sort is called a *shield volcano*. The five volcanoes of the island of Hawaii are shield volcanoes.

Sometimes a cone is built up of a combination of pyroclastic material and lava flows around the vent. This form is called a *composite volcano* and is characterized by slopes of close to 30° at the summit, tapering off to 5° near the base. Mayon, on Luzon in the Philippines, is one of the finest examples of a composite cone (see Fig. 5-12).

A single volcano may develop as a shield volcano during part of its history and as a composite volcano later. Mt. Etna is an example of such a volcano (see Fig. 5-13).

FIG. 5-13
Mt. Etna viewed from the sea near Catania, Sicily. The flat slopes to the left are those of a shield volcano. When Etna changed its eruptive habit late in its history, the explosive ejection of fragmental material built a 1,000-foot pyroclastic cone on the summit of the broad shield of lava flows. These pyroclastics form the irregular and steepened slopes nearest the smoking vent. Photo by Vittorio Sella.

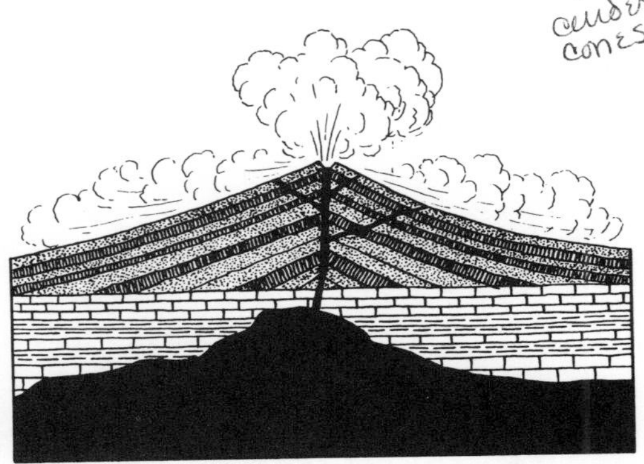

An eruption begins with fiery clouds and dust clouds distributing material on slopes and surrounding country.

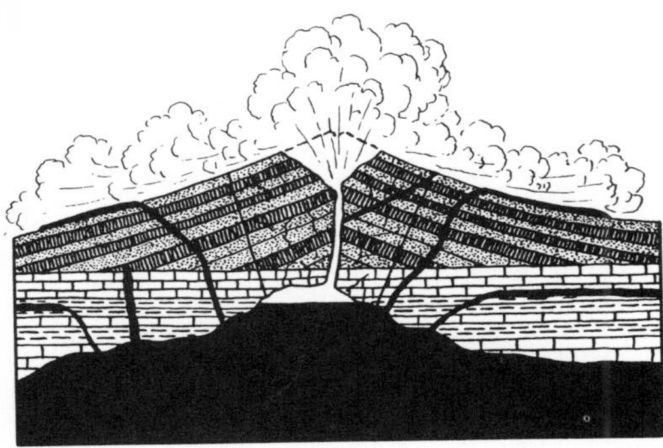

Eruption continues. Part of cone is blown away, and lava flows join in draining the magma reservoir.

Most of cone collapses into the reservoir; later activity forms cinder cone in caldera.

FIG. 5-14
Sequence of events proposed by one theory for the formation of a caldera.
After H. Williams, "Calderas and Their Origin."

cinder cones

Finally, small cones consisting mostly of pyroclastic material, particularly cinders, are called *cinder cones.* They achieve slopes of 30° to 40° and seldom exceed 1,500 feet in height. Parícutin, in Mexico, is an example of a cinder cone that has developed in modern times.

Distribution of active volcanoes

We find evidence of volcanic eruptions in rocks of all ages. Apparently, therefore, igneous activity has been going on throughout geologic time. Seemingly, no special geographic-environment has particularly fostered such activity, which has occurred on the bottom of the ocean, in the highest mountain ranges, and on open plains.

There are 454 active volcanoes,[2] situated mostly in distinct belts, in the world today. Two hundred and eighty-three border the Pacific Ocean, with a belt called its "girdle of fire." Other volcanoes exist in the main basin of the Pacific, arranged along lines that run toward the northwest. A second belt, the Alpine-Himalayan belt, has 98 volcanoes and extends from southeastern Europe through the Mediterranean and southern Asia into the East Indies Archipelago.

Modern volcanic activity in the Atlantic is limited largely to islands on the Mid-Atlantic Ridge. These include the Azores, the Canary Islands, Cape Verde Islands, Ascension, St. Helena, and Tristan da Cunha. There is also volcanic activity on islands of the Lesser Antilles.

In the Indian Ocean, active volcanoes exist on Malagasy, Réunion, Mauritius, Rodrigues, and Kerguelen.

Formation of calderas

Calderas may be formed by explosion, by collapse, or by a combination of both. It is often difficult to determine just which mechanism is responsible.

The caldera on Bandai (37.58°N., 140.05°E.), on the island of Honshu, Japan, is one example of a caldera formed by explosion. After a thousand years of dormancy, Bandai exploded on July 15, 1888, blowing off its summit and part of its northern slope. After the violent explosion had subsided a caldera was discovered, over a mile in diameter with walls 1,200 feet high.

The caldera on Kilauea was probably formed by the collapse of the summit, rather than by explosion. As great quantities of magma escaped from the reservoir beneath the volcano, support for the summit was withdrawn, and large blocks of it fell in, forming the caldera.

Crater Lake, in southern Oregon, lies in a basin that is an almost perfect example of the typical caldera shape. This caldera is circular, with a diameter of a little more than 5 miles and a maximum depth of 4,000 feet, and is surrounded by a cliff that rises 2,500 to 4,000 feet. Crater Lake itself is about 2,000 feet deep. The caldera was formed when the top of a symmetrical volcanic cone, called Mt. Mazama, vanished dur-

[2] Bullard, *op. cit.,* p. 367.

ing an eruption. Geologists have studied the deposits on the slopes and have tried to piece together its history.

First, a composite cone was slowly built up to a height of around 12,000 feet. Then glaciers formed, moving down from the crest and grooving the slopes as they traveled. Finally, an explosive eruption occurred, and the caldera was formed a few, possibly ten, thousand years ago. Later activity built up a small cone inside the caldera, which protrudes above the surface of Crater Lake as Wizard Island (see Fig. 5-14).

Not all observers agree on the origin of the Crater Lake caldera itself, however. The question is whether all or nearly all the missing material from the cone was actually blown out during an eruption, or whether the caldera was created when the summit collapsed. The answer to the mystery should be provided by an analysis of the unconsolidated material found in the vicinity: Does this material consist of pyroclastics formed during an eruption, or does it consist of the broken remnants of Mazama's blown-off summit? The problem is that the summit itself originally included pyroclastics and congealed lavas from earlier eruptions. It is hard to distinguish between the two. One investigator[3] has concluded that of the 17 cubic miles of Mazama that disappeared, only 2 cubic miles are represented in the materials now lying on the immediate slopes, and that the rest of it was dropped into the volcano when the roof of an underlying chamber collapsed. This chamber may have been partially emptied by the ejection of large volumes of material during an eruption. Williams finds evidence that ash spread over a radius of nearly 30 miles. And some of the magma may have worked its way beneath the surface into adjoining areas. But this explanation of the Crater Lake caldera has been challenged on the grounds that it is based on an invalid distinction between "old" and "new" pyroclastics in the debris that covers the area.

BASALT PLATEAUS

On Wednesday, June 11, 1783, after a series of violent earthquakes on Iceland near Mt. Skapta, an immense outpouring of lava began along a ten-mile line, the Laki Fissure. Erosion has cut away parts of the top of this plateau, but remnants protruding above sea level include Iceland, the Antrim Plateau of northeastern Ireland, the Inner Hebrides, the Faero Islands, and southern Greenland.

Of equal magnitude is the Columbia Plateau in Washington, Oregon, Idaho, and northeastern California (see Fig. 5-15). In some sections, more than 5,000 feet of rock have been built up by a series of fissure eruptions. Individual eruptions deposited layers ranging from 10 to 15 feet thick, with an occasional exception of greater thickness. In the canyon of the Snake River, Idaho, granite hills from 2,000 to 2,500 feet high are covered by 1,000 to 1,500 feet of basalt from these flows. The Columbia Plateau has been built up during the past 30

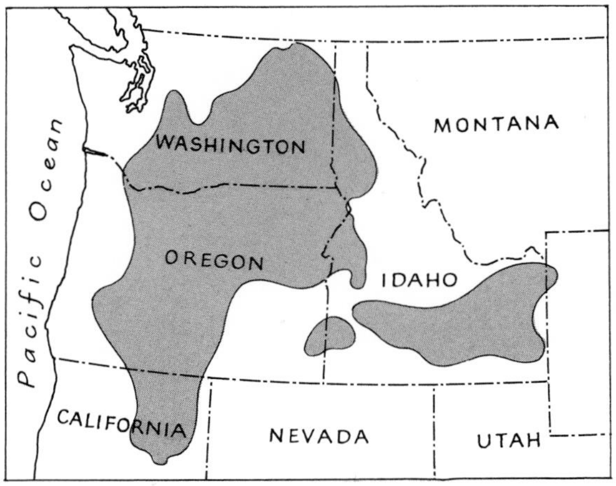

FIG. 5-15
Map of Columbia Plateau, showing areas built by fissure eruptions.

[3] H. Williams, "Calderas and Their Origin," *Bulletin,* U. of Calif., Dept. of Geological Sciences, XXV (1941).

million years. The principal activity took place about a million years ago in northeastern California and Idaho. But some of the flows in the Crater of the Moon National Monument in southern Idaho are believed to have occurred within the last 250 to 1,000 years and are probably the most recent fissure eruptions in the United States.

Other extensive areas built up by fissure eruptions include north-central Siberia; the Deccan Plateau of India; Ethiopia; around Victoria Falls on the Zambezi River, Africa; and parts of Australia.

FISSURE. A great flood of lava poured into the Skapta River, drying up the water and overflowing the stream's channel, which was 400 to 600 feet deep and 200 feet wide in places. Soon the Skapta's tributaries were dammed up, and many villages in adjoining areas were flooded. Another lava flow followed, a week later, and a third came on Sunday, August 3. So great was their volume—over 15 billion cubic yards—that the flows filled a former lake, as well as an abyss at the foot of a waterfall. They spread out in great tongues 12 to 15 miles wide and 100 feet deep. As the eruption diminished, the Laki Fissure began to choke up. Twenty-two small vents then formed along its length, through which final extrusion of matter was made.

Never before in history, and never again, has a fissure eruption occurred. There is strong evidence, however, of such gigantic eruptions in the geologic past. The landforms produced by these repeated fissure eruptions are known as *basalt plateaus*. The low viscosity that lava must have to flood freely over such great areas seems to be characteristic only of lavas with basaltic composition (see "Dark-colored igneous rocks" in Chapter 6).

Extensive lava floods have been going on for over 50 million years in the North Atlantic. These formed the great Brito-Arctic Plateau, and they blanket more than 200,000 square miles. They are believed to be at least 9,000 feet thick.

CAUSE OF IGNEOUS ACTIVITY

Igneous activity requires magma. Yet evidence indicates that there are no extensive zones of molten rock within 1,800 miles of the surface of the earth. Therefore, it becomes necessary to explain the formation of localized masses of magma.

We do not know the exact depth at which magma forms, but it is probably at depths no greater than 40 miles. Present-day volcanoes provide us with clues about the depth from which magma is coming. We know that liquid will rise to heights comparable to the pressure applied to it. This principle may be applied to the volcanoes we find today standing from 2,000 to 20,000 feet high. Thus the weight of a couple of miles of rock would supply enough pressure to lift magma to the top of a 2,000-foot cone; but 15 or 20 miles of rock would be needed to push the magma up to the top of a 20,000-foot volcano. We conclude, then, that the magma feeding modern volcanoes comes from different depths, none of which, however, probably exceeds 40 miles.

Rocks must be melted to form magma, and this requires a

large quantity of heat. The source of this heat is the big problem.

Because it must expand to melt, a greater quantity of heat is required to melt rock under pressure than to melt it at the surface. As a result, the temperature of melting becomes higher as pressure increases. This means that rocks buried under the pressure of several miles of other rocks melt at a higher range of temperature than similar rocks at the surface. The relationship between pressure and melting temperature can be expressed mathematically for relatively uncomplicated conditions. And, although these simple conditions are not precisely the same as actual conditions in the earth, they do serve as a useful guide to speculation.

It has been computed that a rock of basaltic composition that melts at 2,280°F (1,250°C) at the surface will melt only at about 2,600°F (1,400°C) at a depth of 20 miles. Since we know that rocks at this depth in most areas around the world are solid, we can assume that the temperature there does not exceed 2,600°F. But it might be *almost* that high, so far as we can tell from our evidence, and only a slight increase might be needed to reach the melting point. It may be that in areas where rock masses are being squeezed and broken during the formation of mountains (see Chapter 17) the extra heat to melt rocks locally is produced by friction.

Measurements have shown that temperature increases below the surface in tunnels, deep bore holes, and mines. The rate of this increase, which is called the *thermal gradient,* seems to be around 30°C per kilometer of depth, or 150°F per mile. If the thermal gradient increased at this constant rate, temperatures at certain depths would surpass the melting range of all known rocks. Since we know that the crust at these depths is in fact solid (except in limited areas of igneous activity), we must assume that the gradient does not increase at this constant rate. We must therefore look for another source of heat that, added to the high temperatures present, causes igneous activity.

One theory offered as an explanation for the local melting of rock involves certain elements that have an unusual property called *radioactivity* (see Chapter 10). These are natural isotopes (see Chapter 2) of potassium, actinium, thorium, and uranium, which exist in significant abundance in the earth's crust, even though they are unstable from the moment they are formed. The nuclei of these isotopes spontaneously emit particles that carry large amounts of energy, and this energy appears in the form of heat. It has been proposed that in certain zones of the crust, trapped beneath a thick cover of rock that prevents rapid escape of the heat, radioactive isotopes may generate enough heat to remelt the surrounding rock into magma. The increase in volume produced by melting would fracture the overlying rocks and provide avenues through which the magma could move toward the surface.

In summing up, then, we may say that a good part of the high temperature needed to melt rock comes from the temperature gradient; the rest probably comes from radioactivity. (For a diagrammatic representation of energy released by the splitting of U^{236}, see Fig. 2-12, repeated at right.)

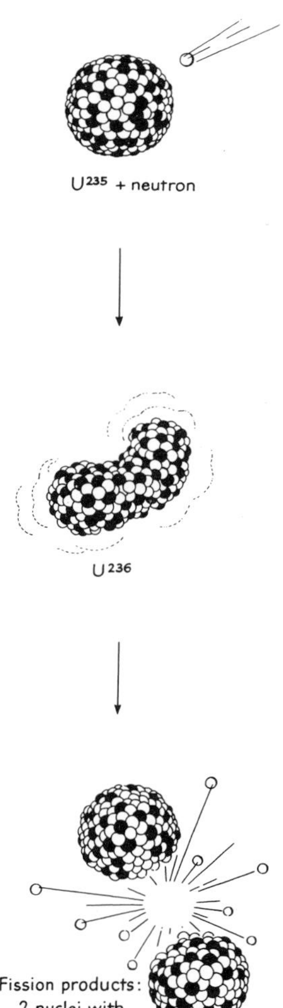

SUMMARY OUTLINE

Igneous activity
- Caused by movements of molten rock

Volcanoes
- Landforms built by volcanic eruptions

Volcanic eruptions
- Explosive eruptions
  - Pyroclastic debris and fiery clouds
- Quiet eruptions
  - Lava flows

Pyroclastic debris
- Blocks, bombs, pumice, ash, cinders, and dust
- Fiery clouds

Worldwide effects
- Produced by dust in the upper atmosphere

History of some volcanoes
- Vesuvius, Krakatoa, Parícutin, and Hawaii

Classification of volcanoes
- Shield volcanoes, composite volcanoes, and cinder cones

Distribution of volcanoes
- The active 454
- "Girdle of fire" around Pacific

Basalt plateaus
- Landforms built by fissure eruptions

Cause of igneous activity
- Magma formed within outer 40 miles of the earth's surface
- Theories on source of heat
  - Friction in mountain-building
  - Radioactivity

SELECTED REFERENCES

Bullard, Fred M., *Volcanoes in History, in Theory, in Eruption.* Austin: U. of Texas Press, 1962.

Cotton, C. A., *Volcanoes as Landscape Forms.* Wellington, N.J.: Whitecombe and Tombs, Ltd., 1944.

Daly, R. A., *Architecture of the Earth.* New York: Appleton-Century-Crofts, Inc., 1938.

6

Igneous rocks

Formed from the solidification of molten matter, igneous rocks comprised the earth's first crust. That first crust has long since been transformed, but all rocks have derived from the material of those first igneous rocks. Younger igneous rocks have been formed and are still being formed today. In fact, 95 per cent of the volume of the outermost 10 miles of the globe is composed of rocks of igneous origin.

Pockets of molten rock are generated within the earth's crust; from time to time this molten rock works its way out to the surface. There it may pour or blow forth from vents or fissures and solidify into rock. Or it may remain trapped within the crust, where it slowly cools and solidifies.

MASSES OF IGNEOUS ROCKS

During our discussion of igneous activity, we dealt primarily with the extrusion of lava and pyroclastic debris and with some of the landforms that result: basalt plateaus and volcanoes. These are surface masses of igneous rock.

When magma *within the crust* loses its mobility and ceases activity, it solidifies in place, forming igneous rock masses of varying shapes and sizes. Today, such rock masses can be seen at the surface on continents whose rocks have been worn away by erosion in certain areas.

The first internal part of a volcano to be exposed by erosion is the plug that formed when magma solidified in the vent. Revealed next are the channels through which the magma moved to the surface. Finally, in some regions of ancient activity, the crust has been so elevated and eroded that the huge reservoir that once supplied all the magma can now be seen as a solid rock mass at the surface.

As uplift (see Chapter 15) and erosion expose an extinct volcano's internal construction to view, other igneous rock masses can be seen. Solidified offshoots of magma from the reservoir, having intruded themselves into other rocks within the crust, are included in these masses, which were not necessarily connected with the eruption of a volcano.

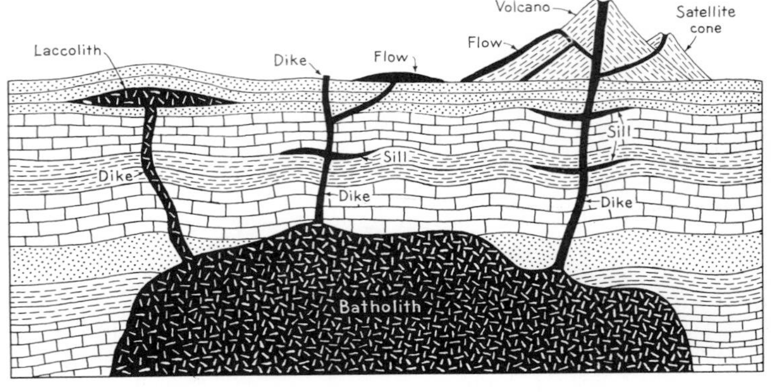

FIG. 6-1
Plutons and landforms associated with igneous activity.

Plutons

All igneous rock masses that were formed when magma solidified within the earth's crust are called *plutons*. When rocks have a definite layering, we may speak of the magma that invades them as *concordant* if its boundaries are parallel to the layering, or *discordant* if its boundaries cut across the layering.

Plutons are classified according to their size, shape, and relationship to surrounding rocks. They include sills, dikes, laccoliths, and batholiths (see Fig. 6-1).

TABULAR PLUTONS. A pluton with a thickness that is small relative to its other dimensions is called a *tabular* pluton.

Sills. A tabular concordant pluton is called a *sill* (see Fig. 6-2). It may be horizontal, inclined, or vertical, depending on the attitude of the rock structure with which it is concordant.

Sills range in size from sheets less than an inch in thickness to tabular masses hundreds of feet thick. A sill must not be confused with an ordinary lava flow that has been buried by other rocks later on. Since a sill is an intrusive form—that is, it has forced its way into already existing rocks—it is always younger than the rocks that surround it. There are fairly reliable ways of distinguishing between the two types: A buried lava flow usually has a rolling or wavy-shaped top pocked by the scars of vanished gas bubbles and showing evidence of erosion, whereas a sill has a more even and unweathered surface. Also, a sill may contain fragments of rock that were broken off when the magma forced its way into the surrounding structures.

The Palisades along the west bank of the Hudson River near New York are the remnants of a sill that was several hundred feet thick. Here the magma was originally intruded into flat-

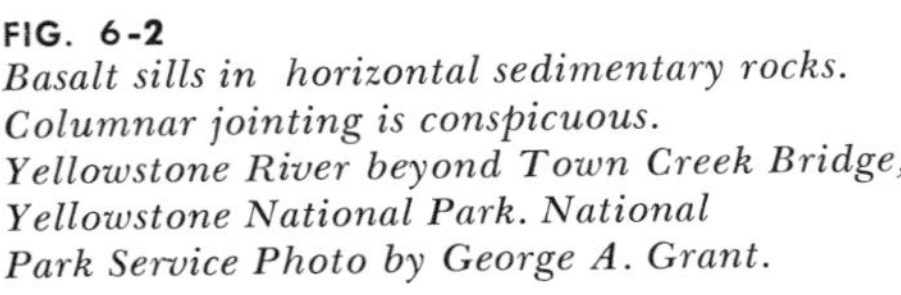

FIG. 6-2
Basalt sills in horizontal sedimentary rocks. Columnar jointing is conspicuous. Yellowstone River beyond Town Creek Bridge, Yellowstone National Park. National Park Service Photo by George A. Grant.

lying sediments. These are now inclined at a low angle toward the west.

Dikes. A tabular discordant pluton is called a *dike* (see Fig. 6-3). Dikes originated when magma forced its way through the fractures of adjacent rocks.

The width of individual dikes ranges from a few inches to many feet. The Medford dike near Boston, Massachusetts, is 500 feet wide in places, but this is an extreme case and rare. Just how far we can trace the course of a dike across the countryside depends in part on how much of it has been exposed by erosion. In Iceland, dikes 10 miles long are common and many can be traced for 30 miles; at least one is known to be 65 miles long.

As magma forces its way upward, it sometimes pushes out a cylindrical section of the crust. Today, as a result, we find exposed at the surface some roughly circular or elliptical masses of rock that outline the cylindrical sections of the crust. These solidified bodies of magma are called *ring dikes.* Large ring dikes may be many miles around, and hundreds or thousands of feet deep. Ring dikes have been mapped with widths of 1,600 to 4,000 feet and diameters ranging from 1 to 15 miles.

Some dikes occur in concentric sets. These originated in fractures that outline an inverted cone, with the apex pointing down into the former magma source. These dikes are called *cone sheets.* In Scotland, the dip of certain cone sheets suggests that their apex is approximately 3 miles below the present surface of the earth.

MASSIVE PLUTONS. Any pluton that is not tabular in shape is classified as a *massive* pluton.

Laccoliths. A massive concordant pluton that was created when magma pushed up the overlying rock structures into a dome is called a *laccolith* (from the Greek, *lakkos,* "a cistern," and *lithos,* "stone"). If the ratio of the lateral extent of a pluton to its thickness is less than 10, the pluton is arbitrarily classed as a laccolith; if this ratio is more than 10, the pluton is classed as a sill. Obviously, since it is extremely difficult to establish the lateral limits of a pluton, in many cases it is best to use the term "concordant pluton," supplemented by whatever dimensional details we can observe.

A classic development of laccoliths is found in the Henry, La Sal, and Abajo mountains of southeastern Utah, where their features are exposed on the Colorado Plateau, a famous geological showplace.

Batholiths. A large discordant pluton that increases in size as it extends downward, and that has no determinable floor, is called a *batholith* (from the Greek *bathos,* "deep," and *lithos,* "stone"). "Large" in this connection is generally taken to mean a surface exposure of more than 40 square miles. A pluton that has a smaller surface exposure, but that exhibits the other features of a batholith, is called a *stock.*

Batholiths are really the solidified reservoirs of magma that once, in the molten state, fed active volcanoes. Today, these great masses of solid igneous rock lie exposed thousands of feet above sea level, where they have been lifted by forces operating in the earth's crust. The miles-high layer of rock

FIG. 6-3
Basalt dike cutting through granite at Cohasset, Massachusetts. Photo by John A. Shimer.

that covered the batholiths when they were still reservoirs of magma have been stripped away by the erosion of millions of years. We can observe these remnants of the roots of vanished volcanoes in the White Mountains of New Hampshire and in the Sierra Nevada of California.

Although batholiths provide us with some valuable data, they also raise a host of unsolved problems. All these problems bear directly on our understanding of igneous processes and the complex events that accompany the folding, rupture, and eventual elevation of sediments to form mountains. (We shall discuss these mountain-forming processes in Chapter 17.)

We can summarize what we *do* know about batholiths as follows:

1. They are located in mountain ranges. Although in some mountain ranges we find no batholiths at all, we never find batholiths that are not associated with mountain ranges. In any given mountain range, the number and size of the batholiths are directly related to the intensity of the folding and crumpling that has taken place. This does *not* mean, however, that the batholiths *caused* the folding and crumpling. Actually, there is convincing evidence to the contrary, as we shall see in some of the following features.

2. Batholiths usually run parallel to the axes of the mountain ranges.

3. Batholiths have formed only *after* the folding of the mountains, although the folding may have continued after the batholiths were formed.

4. Batholiths have irregular dome-shaped roofs. This characteristic shape is related to *stoping,* one of the mechanisms by which magmas that solidify to form batholiths move upward into the crust, at least in the final stages. As the magma moves upward, blocks of rock are broken off from the structures into which the magma is intruding. At low levels, when the magma is still very hot, the stoped blocks may be melted and assimilated by the magma reservoir. Higher in the crust, as the magma approaches stability and its heat has nearly vanished, the stoped blocks are frozen in the intrusion as *xenoliths* (zee′-no-liths)—that is, "strange rocks."

5. Batholiths are usually composed of granite (a light-colored, igneous rock) or granodiorite (a combination of granite with another igneous rock, diorite). The composition is relatively homogeneous—at least as far down as we have been able to observe.

6. Batholiths give the impression of having *replaced* the rocks into which they have intruded, instead of having pushed them aside or upward. But if that is what really took place, what happened to the great volumes of rock that the batholiths appear to have replaced? Here we come up against the problem of the origins of batholiths—in fact, against the whole mystery of igneous activity. Some observers have been led to question even whether granitic batholiths were formed from true magmas at all. The suggestion has been made that the batholiths may have been formed through a process called *granitization,* in which solutions from magmas move into solid rocks, exchange ions with them, and convert them into

rocks that have the characteristics of granite but have never actually existed as magma. We shall return to this highly controversial proposal in Chapter 18.

7. Batholiths contain a great volume of rock. The Coast Range batholith of Alaska and British Columbia, for example, is roughly 1,100 miles by 80 to 120 miles; the Sierra Nevada batholith of California is 400 by 40 to 70 miles (see Fig. 6-4); and a partially exposed batholith in southern California and Baja California is probably about 1,000 by 70 miles.

FORMATION OF IGNEOUS ROCKS

Igneous rocks at the surface today were formed from magma that came from deep-seated reservoirs. As we pointed out in Chapter 5, molten rock in the ground is called magma. When magma is extruded on the surface, it is called lava. And when solidified pieces of magma are blown out they are pyroclastic debris.

Pyroclastic debris eventually becomes hardened into rock through the percolation of ground water. In one sense, rocks formed in this way could be classified as sedimentary; but because they consist of solidified pieces of magma, we shall include them in our discussion of igneous rocks. Volcanic ash that has hardened into rock is called *tuff*. If many relatively large angular blocks of congealed lava are imbedded in a mass of ash, then hardened to rock, the rock is called *volcanic breccia*. If such included pieces are mainly rounded fragments, the rock is called *volcanic conglomerate*.

FIG. 6-4
Weathering has exposed this portion of the Sierra Nevada batholith in Yosemite National Park, California. Photo by W. C. Bradley.

Magma, extruded as lava at the surface, cools and solidifies to form igneous rocks. The offshoots of magma that work their way into surrounding rock below the surface cool more slowly and solidify. Even the magma reservoir eventually cools and solidifies, but it takes much longer because it is a larger mass. *All igneous rocks were formed from the solidification of magma.*

Crystallization

Magma solidifies through the process of *crystallization*. At first, magma is a *melt*, a liquid solution of ions at high temperature. Once a decrease occurs in the heat that keeps the magma liquid, the melt starts to solidify. Bit by bit, mineral grains begin to grow. As this growth goes on, gases are released. Now we no longer have a complete liquid, but rather a liquid mixed with solid and gaseous materials.[1] As the temperature continues to fall, the mixture solidifies until igneous rock is formed.

Igneous rocks are aggregates of silicate minerals that were formed as magma cooled. Their great variety is a product of the diverse compositions of magmas and the conditions under which they have crystallized. Some magmas are rich in iron and magnesium; others are rich in silicon and aluminum. When ferromagnesian-rich magmas cool, the igneous rocks formed are composed of ferromagnesian minerals. Magmas rich

[1] To reflect this changing picture, we define a magma as any naturally occurring silicate melt, whether or not it contains suspended crystals or dissolved gases.

in silicon and aluminum yield rocks with large amounts of feldspars and quartz.

No two volcanoes erupt magma of the same composition, and the lava from a single volcano may vary from one eruption to another. The temperature of ferromagnesian lavas is approximately 2000°F (1100°C); lavas richer in silicon and aluminum, such as those that erupted from Mt. Etna in 1910, had temperatures of 1650°F to 1830°F (900°C to 1000°C). The minimum temperature of lavas is 1380°F (750°C). Approximately at this temperature, granite melts.

Igneous rocks may consist of interlocking grains of a single mineral, or a mixture of many or all of the nine silicate minerals: olivine, augite, hornblende, biotite, anorthite, albite, orthoclase, muscovite, and quartz.

BOWEN'S REACTION SERIES. N. L. Bowen[2] found that the silicates could be arranged in two series of crystallization. Each mineral in each of the two series is derived from the preceding mineral as the result of a chemical reaction with the remaining liquid of the magma. For this reason, these two series are called the *Bowen's reaction series.*

In the ferromagnesian series (see Chapter 4), olivine is the first to form. It consists of single tetrahedra held together by positive ions of iron and magnesium. Augite is built around single chains of tetrahedra; hornblende is built around double chains; and biotite, the most complex in this series, is built around sheets of tetrahedra. Since each new ferromagnesian to form has a different crystalline structure from the one that preceded it, Bowen called this a *discontinuous reaction series.*

The first feldspar to form is anorthite. This mineral crystallizes at about the same temperature as olivine. As it reacts with the remaining liquid of the magma, anorthite gradually assimilates greater and greater amounts of sodium. Finally, when all the calcium characteristic of anorthite has been replaced by sodium, the resulting mineral is albite. Because of this continuous replacement of calcium ions by sodium ions in the same silicate structure, Bowen referred to the crystallization of the plagioclase feldspars as a *continuous reaction series.*

This gradual, progressive change does not occur, however, between the formation of albite and the formation of orthoclase. There is no ion-by-ion replacement of sodium by potassium because the radius of the potassium ion is so much greater than that of the sodium ion (see Table 6-1).

TABLE 6-1
Ionic radii and electric charges for positive ions of the feldspars *

		ELECTRIC CHARGE	RADIUS (ANGSTROMS)
Calcium	Ca^{2+}	+2	0.99
Sodium	Na^{+}	+1	0.97
Potassium	K^{+}	+1	1.33

* After Brian Mason, *Principles of Geochemistry,* 2nd ed. (New York: John Wiley & Sons, Inc., 1960), pp. 287-88.

Order of crystallization. Even when a magma contains all the ions necessary to form the nine silicate minerals, these minerals do not all form at once. There is a definite temperature or temperature range at which each mineral crystallizes.

The complex ions of the silicon-oxygen tetrahedra develop first. And as the mixture continues to cool, the tetrahedra join in various ways and combine with other ions to form the silicate minerals. The ferromagnesians form, beginning with olivine and progressing in order through augite, hornblende, and

[2] N. L. Bowen, "The Reaction Principle in Petrogenesis," *Jour. Geol.,* XXX (1922), pp. 177-198.

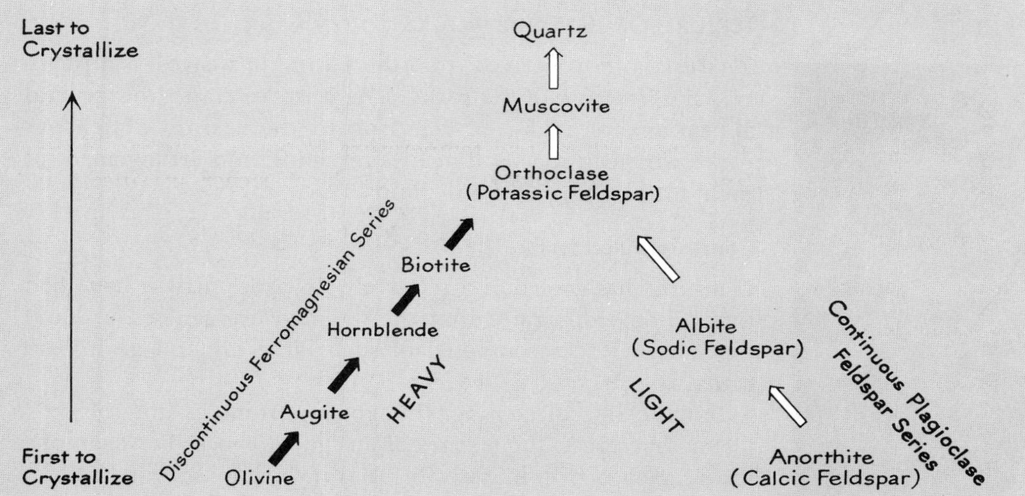

FIG. 6-5
Bowen's reaction series.

biotite. At the same time, the plagioclase feldspars form, starting with anorthite and progressing through albite. After these minerals have crystallized, orthoclase, muscovite, and then quartz are formed. This progression is illustrated by the diagram in Fig. 6-5.

Interruptions in crystallization. The reaction series show in what order the silicate minerals crystallize. All minerals in a magma would eventually become quartz if they were all able to run through the complete reaction series. But this seldom happens; in fact, perhaps it never happens. The reaction series is usually interrupted before it runs its full course, and these interruptions explain why there are igneous rocks of differing mineral composition.

Sometimes interruptions in crystallization occur when volatiles escape. In solution, volatiles give the magma the fluidity that allows minerals to move about freely and enter into chemical reactions. When volatiles escape, reaction is reduced and eventually stopped.

The settling out of early formed minerals is another source of interruption. This occurs in some low viscosity magmas and removes minerals from the remaining liquid, which would have reacted on them. Such a process is called *fractionation.*

Rate of crystallization. The rate at which a magma crystallizes influences the extent to which fractionation and reaction take place. When magma cools rapidly, there is no time for minerals to settle or to react with the remaining liquid. This occurs when a partially crystallized magma is extruded onto the surface or injected into thin dikes or sills. But when a large body of magma cools slowly, deep within the crust, a high degree of fractionation or chemical reaction may take place.

The rate of crystallization varies with depth. For example, a magma consisting largely of nonferromagnesians at 2,000°F (1,100°C), exposed to the air on top, and ranging in thickness from 3 to 30,000 feet, would solidify as shown at right.[3]

THICKNESS *(ft.)*	TIME REQUIRED
3	12 days
30	3 years
300	300 years
3,000	30,000 years
30,000	3,000,000 years

[3] R. A. Daly, *Igneous Rocks and the Depths of the Earth* (New York: McGraw-Hill Book Company, 1933), p. 63.

TEXTURE OF IGNEOUS ROCKS

Texture, a term derived from the Latin "to weave," is a physical characteristic of all rocks. The term refers to the general appearance of rocks. In referring to the texture of igneous rocks, we mean specifically the size, shape, and arrangement of their interlocking mineral grains.

FIG. 6-6
Enlarged photograph of a piece of coarse-grained igneous rock, taken through a slice that has been ground to translucent thinness (known as a thin section). The photo shows the rock to be compounded of interlocking crystals of different minerals.

Coarse-grained texture

If magma has cooled at a relatively slow rate, it will have had time to develop grains that the unaided eye can see in hand specimens. Rocks composed of such large mineral grains are called *coarse-grained* (see Fig. 6-6).

But the rate of cooling, though important, is not the only factor that affects the texture of an igneous rock. For example, if a magma is of low viscosity—that is, if it is thin and watery and flows readily—large, coarse grains may form even though the cooling is relatively rapid; for in a magma of this sort, the ions can move easily and quickly into their rock-forming mineral combinations.

Fine-grained texture

The rate at which a magma cools depends on the size and shape of the magma body, as well as on its depth below the surface. For example, a small body of magma with a large surface area—that is, a body that is much longer and broader than it is thick—surrounded by cool, solid rock, loses its heat more rapidly than would the same volume of magma in a spherical reservoir. And since rapid cooling usually prevents large grains from forming, the igneous rocks that result have *fine-grained textures.* Individual minerals are present, but so small that they cannot be identified without the aid of a microscope.

Glassy texture

If magma is suddenly ejected from a volcano or a fissure at the earth's surface, it may cool so rapidly that there is no time for minerals to form at all. The result is a *glass,* which by a rigid application of our definition (see Glossary) is not really a rock but generally treated as one. Glass is a special type of solid in which the ions are not arranged in an orderly manner. Instead, they are disorganized, like the ions in a liquid. And yet they are frozen in place by the quick change of temperature.

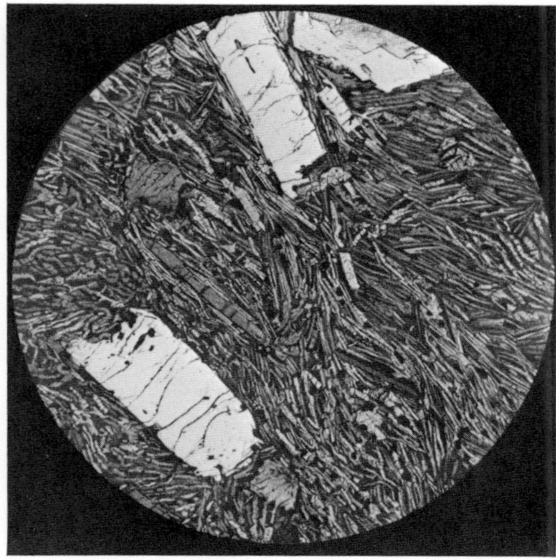

FIG. 6-7
Enlarged photograph of a thin section of porphyritic igneous rock.

Porphyritic texture

Occasionally, a magma cools at variable rates—slowly at first, then more rapidly. It may start to cool under conditions that permit large mineral grains to form in the early stages, and then it may move into a new environment where more rapid cooling freezes the large grains in a *groundmass* of finer-grained texture (see Fig. 6-7). The large minerals are then called *phenocrysts* (fee′-no-krists), from the Greek *phainein,* "to show." The resulting texture is said to be *porphyritic. Porphyry,* from the Greek word for "purple," was originally applied to rocks containing phenocrysts in a dark red or purple groundmass.

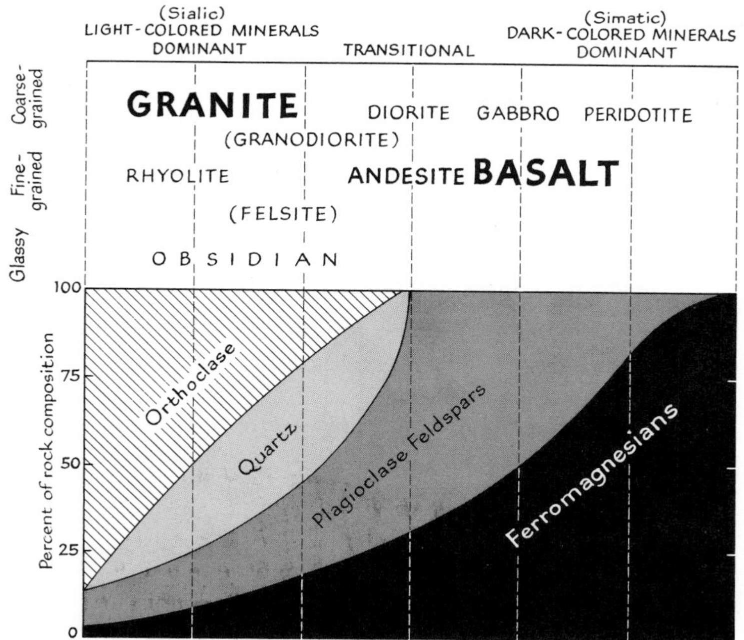

FIG. 6-8
General composition is indicated by a line from the name to the composition chart: granite and rhyolite consist of about 50 per cent orthoclase, 25 per cent quartz, and 25 per cent divided among plagioclase feldspars and ferromagnesian minerals. Relative importance is stressed by the size of the lettering for rock names: granite is the most important coarse-grained rock, basalt the most important fine-grained rock. Composition chart modified after Pirsson and Knopf, Rocks and Rock Minerals (New York: John Wiley & Sons, Inc., 1926), p. 144.

In rare cases, magma may suddenly be expelled at the surface after large mineral grains have already formed. Then the final cooling is so rapid that the phenocrysts become embedded in a glassy groundmass.

TYPES OF IGNEOUS ROCKS

Several systems have been proposed for the classification of igneous rocks. All are artificial in one detail or another, and all rely on certain characteristics that cannot be determined in the field or from hand specimens. For our present purposes, we shall emphasize texture and composition. Such a classification is entirely adequate for an introductory study of physical geology, and even for many advanced phases of geology.

This classification appears in tabular form in Fig. 6-8, together with a graph that shows the proportions of silicates in each type of igneous rock. The graph gives a better picture than the table of the *continuous progression from rock types in which light-colored minerals predominate to rock types in which dark-colored minerals predominate.* The names of rocks are arbitrarily assigned on the basis of average mineral composition and texture. Sometimes intermediate types are indicated by such names as *granodiorite,* a composition between that of granite and of diorite. Actually, there are many more igneous rocks than are shown in Fig. 6-8.

Light-colored igneous rocks

The igneous rocks on the "light" side of the classification chart are light both in color and specific gravity. They are sometimes referred to as *sialic rocks.* The term *sial* was coined from the chemical symbols for silicon and aluminum, and is generally used in speaking of the composite of rocks typical of continental areas of the earth. This composite is dominated by

FIG. 6-9
Granite. Photo by Navias.

FIG. 6-10
Obsidian, the glassy equivalent of granite. Photo by Navias.

FIG. 6-11
Columnar jointing, a special pattern sometimes found in basalt, consists of breaks that outline perfectly developed six-sided columns. Giant's Causeway, near Portrush, Antrim, Northern Island, is one of the world's best-known exposures of this feature. Here basalt poured out onto the surface in a series of flows, each 10 to 50 feet thick. Photo by David M. Owen.

granites and granodiorites and by their allies and derivatives. It has been estimated that granites and granodiorites together comprise 95 per cent of all rocks that have solidified from magma trapped within the outer 10 miles of the earth's surface. The origin and history of some granites are still under debate, but we shall use the term here only to indicate composition and texture, not origin.

Granite is a coarse-grained rock (see Fig. 6-9). Its mineral composition is as follows:

2 parts orthoclase feldspar + 1 part quartz + 1 part plagioclase feldspars + small amt. ferromagnesians = GRANITE

Rocks with the same mineral composition as granite, but with a fine-grained rather than a coarse-grained texture, are called *rhyolite.*

The glassy equivalent of granite is called *obsidian* (see Fig. 6-10). Although this rock is listed near the "light" side of the composition chart, it is usually pitch black in appearance. Actually, though, pieces of obsidian thin enough to be translucent turn out to be smoky white against a light background.

Dark-colored igneous rocks

The darker, heavier rocks are sometimes designated collectively as *sima*. This name was coined from *si* for silicon and *ma* for magnesium, and is generally used in speaking of the shell of dark, heavy rock that encircles the earth. The sima underlies the crust of the continents and is believed to be the outermost rock layer under deep, permanent ocean basins, such as that of the mid-Pacific.

Of the total volume of rock formed from magma that has poured out onto the earth's surface, it is estimated that 98 per cent are basalts and andesites.

A popular synonym for basalt is *trap rock,* from a Swedish word meaning "step." This name refers to the tendency of certain basalts to weather or break down into columns that look like stairways (see Fig. 6-11).

Basalt is a fine-grained igneous rock (see Fig. 6-12). Its mineral composition is as follows:

1 part plagioclase feldspars + 1 part ferromagnesians = BASALT

The coarse-grained equivalent of basalt is *gabbro.*

Peridotite, named from *peridot,* another word for olivine, is a coarse-grained igneous rock that is composed largely of the mineral olivine.

FIG. 6-12
Basalt. Photo by Navias.

Intermediate types—composition

Igneous rock compositions blend continuously from one to another as we go from the light to the dark side of the classification chart. *Andesite* is the name given to the fine-grained igneous rocks that are intermediate in composition between granite and basalt. These rocks were first identified in the Andes mountains of South America—hence the name andesite. Andesites are almost always found in areas around the Pacific Ocean where active mountain-making has taken place (see Chapter 17). The coarse-grained equivalent of andesite is *diorite.*

FIG. 6-13
Orthoclase phenocrysts in a granite porphyry. Photo by Navias.

Intermediate types—texture

Going from the top to the bottom of the chart in Fig. 6-8, we find that the rock textures grade continuously from coarse-grained to fine-grained, whereas the composition remains the same. For example, if we read down along the first vertical rule, we find that granite, rhyolite, and obsidian become progressively finer-grained, although all three have essentially the same composition. The same is true of gabbro and basalt.

In addition to these textures, any of the rocks may have porphyritic texture. Essentially, this means that a given rock has grains of two distinctly different sizes: conspicuously large phenocrysts embedded in a finer-grained groundmass. When the phenocrysts constitute less than 25 per cent of the total, the adjective *porphyritic* is used to modify the rock name, as in porphyritic granite or porphyritic andesite.

When the phenocrysts constitute more than 25 per cent, the rock is called a *porphyry* (see Fig. 6-13). The composition of a porphyry and the texture of its groundmass are indicated by using as modifiers such rock names as granite porphyry or andesite porphyry. These relationships are summarized for the most common rocks in Table 6-2.

TABLE 6-2
Porphyritic rock and rock porphyry

LESS THAN 25% PHENOCRYSTS	MORE THAN 25% PHENOCRYSTS
Porphyritic granite	Granite porphyry
Porphyritic rhyolite	Rhyolite porphyry
Porphyritic diorite	Diorite porphyry
Porphyritic andesite	Andesite porphyry

Pegmatite

The solutions that develop late in the cooling of a magma are called *hydrothermal solutions.* These crystallize into exceptionally coarse-grained igneous rock called *pegmatite,* which embodies the chief minerals to form from the hydrothermal solutions: potassic feldspar and quartz. So intimately intergrown are the grains of these minerals that they form what is essentially a single unit. The quartz is darker than the feldspar, and the over-all pattern suggests the wedge-shaped figures of the writing of ancient Assyria, Babylonia, and Persia. As a result, this has become known as *graphic structure* (from the Greek *graphein,* "to write"). The intimate association of the feldspar and quartz also led to the rock of which they are a part being named *pegmatite,* which is derived from the Greek *pegma,* "fastened together."

Pegmatite is found in dikes at the margins of batholiths and stocks. The dikes range in length from a few inches to a few hundred yards, and contain crystals of very large size. In fact, some of the largest crystals known have been found in pegmatite. Crystals of spodumene (a lithium mineral) that measure 40 feet in length have been found in the Black Hills of South Dakota; crystals of beryl (a silicate of beryllium and aluminum) that measure 18 by 4 feet have been discovered in Albany, Maine. Great masses of potassic feldspar weighing over 2,000 tons, yet showing the characteristics of a single crystal, have been mined from pegmatite in the Karelo-Finnish Soviet Socialist Republic.

Nearly 90 per cent of all pegmatite is *simple pegmatite* of quartz, orthoclase, and unimportant percentages of micas. It is more generally called *granite pegmatite,* because the composition is that of granite, the texture that of pegmatite. The remaining 10 per cent include extremely rare *ferromagnesian pegmatites,* and *complex pegmatites.* The major components of complex pegmatites are the same sialic minerals that we find in simple pegmatites, but in addition they contain a variety of rare minerals. These include lepidolite (a mica containing lithium); tourmaline (a complex silicate of boron and aluminum), best known as a semiprecious gem; topaz (a silicate of aluminum and fluorine), also a gem; tantalite (an oxide of

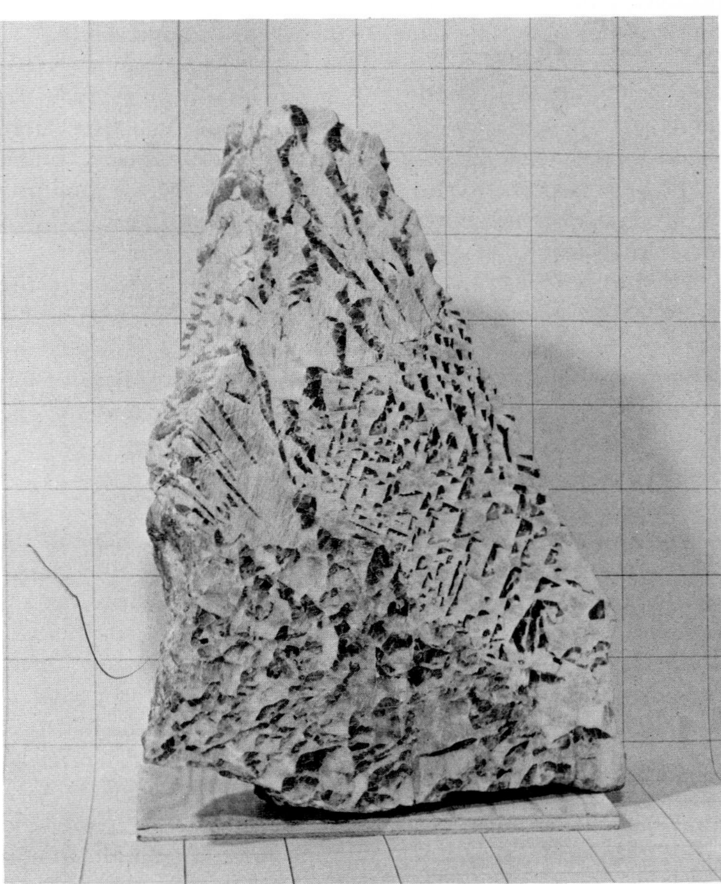

FIG. 6-14
Graphic granite. Photo by Walter R. Fleischer.

tantalum, iron, and manganese); uraninite, sometimes called pitchblende (a complex oxide of uranium with small amounts of lead and the rare elements radium, thorium, yttrium, and argon, as well as nitrogen and helium).

Simple pegmatites are common in some regions, complex in others. In southwestern New Zealand, for example, pegmatites are uniformly simple, but throughout the Appalachian regions of North America complex pegmatites are more abundant.

SUMMARY OUTLINE

Igneous rocks
- Solidified magma

Masses of igneous rocks
- Formed on the surface
  - Basalt plateaus
  - Volcanoes
- Formed within the crust
  - Plutons

Plutons
- Concordant
  - Tabular—sills
  - Massive—laccoliths
- Discordant
  - Tabular—dikes
  - Massive—batholiths, stocks

Formation of igneous rocks
- Crystallization of minerals

Composition of igneous rocks
- Interlocking silicate minerals
- Dependent on order and rate of crystallization

Order of crystallization
- Bowen's reaction series
- Interrupted by fractionation and loss of volatiles

Rate of crystallization
- Influences kinds of minerals developed and size of their grains

Texture of igneous rocks
- Coarse-grained, fine-grained, glassy, porphyritic

Types of igneous rocks
- Based on texture and composition
  - Light-colored (sialic): granite, rhyolite, obsidian
  - Dark-colored (simatic): basalt, gabbro, peridotite
  - Intermediate composition: andesite, diorite
  - Intermediate texture: rock porphyry, porphyritic rock
- Pegmatite

SELECTED REFERENCES

Daly, R. A., *Igneous Rocks and the Depths of the Earth.* New York: McGraw-Hill Book Company, 1933.

Mason, Brian, *Principles of Geochemistry* (2nd ed.). New York: John Wiley & Sons, Inc., 1960.

Williams, H., F. J. Turner, and C. M. Gilbert, *Petrography.* San Francisco: W. H. Freeman and Company, 1954.

7

Weathering and soils

TYPES OF WEATHERING

MECHANICAL WEATHERING

CHEMICAL WEATHERING

CHEMICAL WEATHERING OF IGNEOUS ROCKS

RATES OF WEATHERING

SOILS

SOIL CLASSIFICATION

SOME SOIL TYPES

The blurred inscription on a gravestone, the crumbling foundation of an ancient building, the broken rock exposed along a roadside—all tell us that rocks are subject to constant destruction. Marked changes of temperature, moisture soaking into the ground, the ceaseless activity of living things, all work to destroy rock material. This process of destruction we call *weathering,* and we define it as the changes that take place in minerals and rocks at or near the surface of the earth, in response to the atmosphere, to water, and to plant and animal life. Later on we will extend this definition slightly, but for the time being it will serve our purpose.

Weathering leaves its mark everywhere about us. The process is so common, in fact, that we tend to overlook the way in which it functions and the significance of its results. It plays a vital role in the rock cycle, for by attacking the exposed material of the earth's crust—both solid rock and unconsolidated deposits—it produces the raw materials for new rocks (see Chapter 1 and Fig. 1-9, repeated at right). The products of weathering are usually moved by water and by the influence of gravity, and less commonly by wind and glacier ice. They are then dropped, to settle down and accumulate in new places. The mud in a flooding river, for example, is really weathered material that is being moved from the land to some settling basin, usually the ocean. Sometimes, however, the products of weathering remain right where they are formed and are incorporated into the rock record. Certain ores, for example, such as those of aluminum, are actually old zones of weathering. (See Chapter 22.)

TYPES OF WEATHERING

There are two general types of weathering: *mechanical* and *chemical.* It is hard to separate these two types in nature, for they often go hand in hand, though in some environments one or the other predominates. Still, for our purposes here it is more convenient to discuss them separately.

Mechanical weathering

Mechanical weathering, which is also referred to as *disintegra-*

tion, is the process by which rock is broken down into smaller and smaller fragments as the result of energy developed by physical forces. For example, when water freezes in a fractured rock, enough energy may develop from pressure due to expansion of the frozen water to split off pieces of the rock. Or a boulder moved by gravity down a rocky slope may be shattered into smaller fragments.

EXPANSION AND CONTRACTION RESULTING FROM GAIN AND LOSS OF HEAT. Changes in temperature, if they are rapid enough and great enough, may bring about the mechanical weathering of rock. In areas where bare rock is exposed at the surface and is unprotected by a cloak of soil, forest or brush fires can generate enough heat to break up the rock. The rapid and violent heating of the exterior zone of the rock causes it to expand; and if the expansion is great enough, flakes and larger fragments of the rock are split off. Lightning often starts such forest fires and, in rare instances, may even shatter exposed rock by means of a direct strike.

FIG. 7-1
Differential weathering of horizontally bedded and vertically jointed sedimentary rock has helped to produce the towering turrets of the Giant's Castle in south-central Wisconsin. Both bedding and jointing planes provide zones where weathering can proceed more rapidly. Photo from Gardner Collection, Harvard University.

The debate continues, concerning whether variations in temperature from day to night, or from winter to summer, are great enough to cause mechanical weathering. Theoretically, such changes in temperature cause disintegration. For instance, we know that the different minerals forming a granite expand and contract at different rates as they react to rising and falling temperatures. We expect that even minor expansion and contraction of adjacent minerals would, over long periods of time, weaken the bonds between mineral grains, and that it would thus be possible for disintegration to occur along these boundaries. But laboratory evidence to support these speculations is inconclusive. In one laboratory experiment, coarse-grained granite was subjected to temperatures ranging from 58°F to 256°F every 15 minutes. This alternate heating and cooling was carried on long enough to simulate 244 years of daily heating and cooling. Yet the granite showed no signs of disintegration. Perhaps experiments extended over longer periods of time would produce observable effects. In any event, we are still uncertain of the mechanical effect of daily or seasonal temperature changes; if these fluctuations do bring about the disintegration of rock, they must do so very slowly.

FROST ACTION. Frost is much more effective than heat in producing mechanical weathering. When water trickles down into the cracks, crevices, and pores of a rock mass and then freezes, its volume increases about 9 per cent. This expansion of water as it passes from the liquid to the solid state sets up pressures that are directed outward from the inside of the rock. These pressures are great enough to dislodge fragments from the rock's surface. By the time the temperature has fallen to about −7.6°F, the resulting pressure may be as great as 30,000 pounds per square inch, equivalent to the pressure produced by a 15-ton granite block (on a base one square inch in cross section). This temperature is not unusually low and is experienced several times a year, even in temperate latitudes.

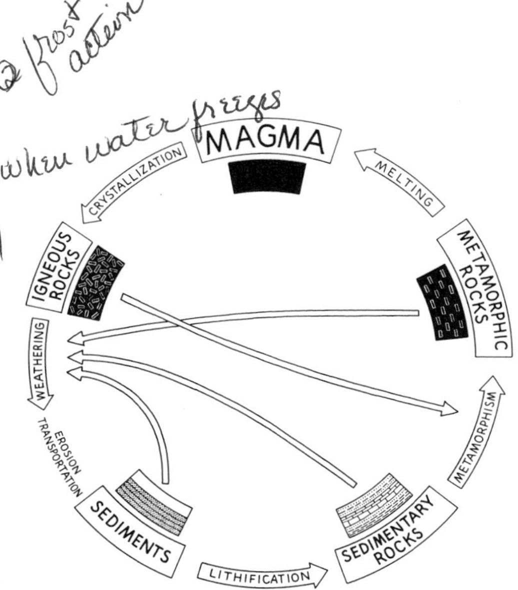

Under actual conditions, however, such great pressures are probably never produced by frost action, at least never close to the earth's surface. For an internal pressure of 30,000 pounds per square inch to build up, a rock crevice would have to be

FIG. 7-2
Strong frost action high in the Medicine Bow Range, Wyoming, has produced this field of angular boulders. Alternate freezing and thawing of water in the crevices of the bedrock has dislodged these large fragments from the solid rock beneath. Photo by E. N. Cameron.

completely filled with water and completely sealed off, and the containing rock would have to be strong enough to withstand pressures at least up to that point. But most crevices contain some air in addition to water, and are open to either the surface or other crevices. Furthermore, no rock can withstand a pressure of 30,000 pounds per square inch if the pressure is directed from within toward the outside.

And yet frost action is responsible for a great deal of mechanical weathering. Water that soaks into the crevices and pores of a rock usually starts to freeze at its upper surface, where it is in contact with the cooling air. The result is that, in time, the water below is confined by an ice plug. Then, as the freezing continues, the trapped water expands, and pressure is exerted outward. Rock may be subjected to this action several times a year. In high mountains, for example, the temperature may move back and forth across the freezing line almost daily.

Shape & size of fragments of mech. weathered rock

The dislodged fragments of mechanically weathered rock are angular in shape, and their size depends largely on the nature of the bedrock from which they have been displaced. Usually the fragments are only a few inches in maximum dimension, but in some places—along the cliffs bordering Devil's Lake, Wisconsin, for instance—they reach sizes of up to 10 feet.

A second type of mechanical weathering produced by freezing water is *frost heaving*. This action usually occurs in fine-grained, unconsolidated deposits, rather than in solid rock. Much of the water that falls as rain or snow soaks into the ground, where it freezes during the winter months. If conditions are right, more and more ice accumulates in the zone of freezing as water is added from the atmosphere above and drawn upward from the unfrozen ground below, much as a blotter soaks up moisture. In time, lens-shaped masses of ice are built up, and the soil above them is heaved upward. Frost heaving of this sort is common on poorly constructed roads, and lawns and gardens are often soft and spongy in the springtime as a result of the soil's heaving up during the winter.

Certain conditions must exist before either type of frost action can take place: (1) there must be an adequate supply of moisture; (2) the moisture must be able to enter the rock or soil; and (3) temperatures must move back and forth across the freezing line. As we might expect, frost action is most pronounced in high mountains and moist regions where temperatures fluctuate across the freezing line, either daily or seasonally.

EXFOLIATION. Exfoliation is a mechanical-weathering process in which curved plates of rock are stripped from a larger rock mass by the action of physical forces. This process produces two features that are fairly common in the landscape: large, dome-like hills, called *exfoliation domes,* and rounded boulders, usually referred to as *spheroidally weathered boulders.* It seems likely that the forces that produce these two forms originate in different ways.

Let us look first at the manner in which exfoliation domes develop. Fractures or parting planes, called *joints,* occur in many massive rocks. These joints are broadly curved and run more or less parallel to the rock surface. The distance between joints is only a few inches near the surface, but it increases to several feet as we move deeper in the rock (see Chapter 16). Under certain conditions, one after another of the curved slabs between the joints is spalled or sloughed off the rock mass. Finally, a broadly curved hill of bedrock develops, as shown in Fig. 7-3.

Just how these slabs of rock come into being in the first place is still a matter of dispute. Most observers believe that as erosion strips away the surface cover, the downward pressure on the underlying rock is reduced. Then, as the rock mass begins to expand upward, lines of fracture develop,

FIG. 7-3 *Stone Mountain, Georgia, is an example of an exfoliation dome. The massive granite in this dome has developed a series of partings or joints more or less parallel to the surface. Rock slabs spall off the hill, giving it a rounded aspect. The jointing probably originated as the granite expanded after the erosion of overlying material. Photo by U.S. Geol. Survey.*

FIG. 7-4
Granite boulders are beginning to develop by spheroidal weathering in King's Canyon, California. Weathering is proceeding most rapidly along the joint system. Photo by U.S. Geol. Survey.

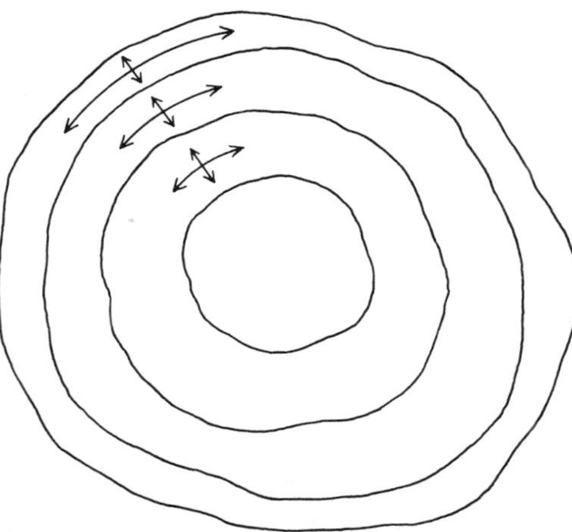

FIG. 7-5
This cross section through a spheroidally weathered boulder suggests the stresses set up within the rock. The stress is thought to develop as a result of the change in volume as feldspar is converted to clay. Note that the shells become thinner toward the surface. (See also Figs. 7-4 and 7-6.)

marking off the slabs that later fall away. Precise measurements made on granite blocks in New England quarries provide some support for this theory. Selected blocks were accurately measured and then removed from the quarry face, away from the confining pressures of the enclosing rock mass. When the free-standing blocks were measured again, it was found that they had increased in size by a small but measurable amount. Massive rock does expand, then, as confining pressures are reduced, and this slight degree of expansion may be enough to start the exfoliation process.

Among the better-known examples of exfoliation domes are Stone Mountain, Georgia; the domes of Yosemite Park, California; and Sugar Loaf, in the harbor of Rio de Janeiro, Brazil.

Now let us look at a smaller-scale example of exfoliation—spheroidally weathered boulders. These boulders have been rounded by the spalling off of a series of concentric shells of rock (Figs. 7-4, 7-5, 7-6). But here the shells develop as a result of pressures set up within the rock by chemical weathering, rather than by the lessening of pressure from above by erosion. We shall see later on that when certain minerals are chemically weathered, the resulting products occupy a greater volume than the original material. And it is this increase in volume that creates the pressures responsible for spheroidal weathering. Since most chemical weathering takes place in the portions of the rock most exposed to air and moisture, it is there that we find the most expansion and hence the greatest number of shells.

Spheroidally weathered boulders are sometimes produced by the crumbling off of concentric shells. If the cohesive strength of the rock is low, individual grains are partially weathered and dissociated, and the rock simply crumbles away. The underlying process is the same in both cases, however.

Certain types of rocks are more vulnerable to spheroidal weathering than others. Igneous rocks such as granite, diorite, and gabbro are particularly susceptible, for they contain large amounts of the mineral feldspar, which, when weathered chemically, produces new minerals of greater volume.

OTHER TYPES OF MECHANICAL WEATHERING. Plants also play a role in mechanical weathering. The roots of trees and shrubs growing in rock crevices sometimes exert enough pressure to dislodge previously loosened fragments of rock, much as tree roots heave and crack sidewalk pavements (Fig. 7-7).

More important, though, is the mechanical mixing of the soil by ants, worms, and rodents. Constant activity of this sort makes the soil particles more susceptible to chemical weathering (see below) and may even assist in the mechanical breakdown of the particles.

Finally, agents such as running water, glacier ice, wind, and ocean waves all help to reduce rock material to smaller and smaller fragments. The role of these agents in mechanical weathering will be discussed in later chapters.

Chemical weathering

Chemical weathering, sometimes called *decomposition,* is a more complex process than mechanical weathering. As we have

FIG. 7-6
These spheroidally weathered boulders of granite have been almost completely isolated from the bedrock. Photo by Sheldon Judson.

seen, mechanical weathering merely breaks rock material down into smaller and smaller particles, without changing the composition of the rock. Chemical weathering, however, actually transforms the original material into something different. The chemical weathering of the mineral feldspar, for example, produces the clay minerals, which have a different composition and different physical characteristics from those of the original feldspar. Sometimes the products of chemical weathering have no mineral form at all, as the salty solution that results from the transformation of the mineral halite, common salt.

PARTICLE SIZE AND CHEMICAL WEATHERING. The size of the individual particles of rock is an extremely important factor in chemical weathering, since substances can react chemically only where they come in contact with one another. The greater the surface area of a particle, the more vulnerable it is to chemical attack. If we were to take a pebble, for example, and grind it up into a fine powder, the total surface area exposed would be greatly increased. And as a result, the materials that make up the pebble would undergo more rapid chemical weathering.

Figure 7-8 shows how the surface area of a one-inch cube increases as we cut it up into smaller and smaller cubes. The initial cube has a surface area of six square inches and a volume of one cubic inch. If we divide the cube into smaller cubes, each ½ inch on a side, the surface area increases to

FIG. 7-7
A white birch tree growing in a crevice pries a large block from a low rock cliff in Hermosa Park, Colorado. Photo by U.S. Geol. Survey.

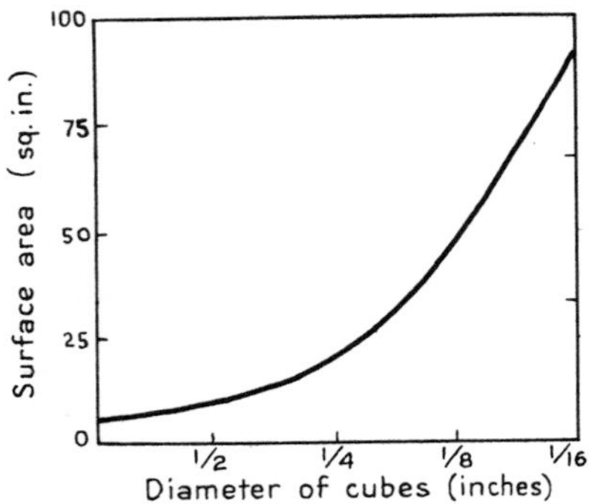

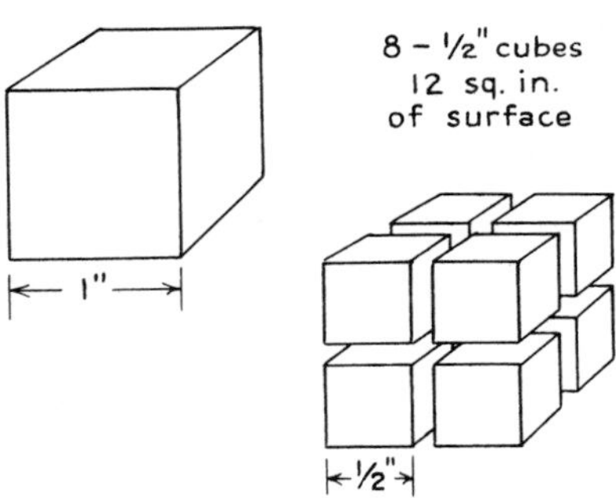

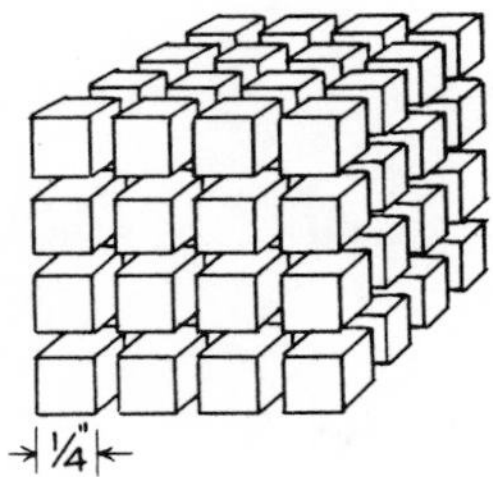

FIG. 7-8
Relation of volume, particle size, and surface area. In this illustration, a cube one inch square is divided into smaller and smaller units. The volume remains unchanged, but as the particle size decreases, the surface area increases. Because chemical weathering is confined to surfaces, the more finely a given volume of material is divided, the greater is the surface area exposed to chemical activity, and the more rapid is the process of chemical weathering.

12 square inches, though of course the total volume remains the same. Further subdivision into 1/4-inch cubes increases the surface to 24 square inches. And if we divide the original cube into units 1/16 inch on a side, the surface area increases to 96 square inches. As we have seen, this same process is performed by mechanical weathering: it reduces the size of the individual particles of rock, increases the surface area exposed, and thus promotes more rapid chemical weathering.

OTHER FACTORS IN CHEMICAL WEATHERING. The rate of chemical weathering is affected by other factors as well—the composition of the original mineral, for example. As we shall see later on, a mineral like quartz (SiO_2) responds much more slowly to chemical weathering than does a mineral like olivine $[(Fe,Mg)_2SiO_4]$. And copper water pipes last longer than iron water pipes, for copper "weathers" more slowly than iron.

Climate also plays a key role in chemical weathering. Moisture, particularly when it is accompanied by warmth, speeds up the rate of chemical weathering; conversely, dryness slows it down. Finally, plants and animals contribute directly or indirectly to chemical weathering, since their life processes produce oxygen, carbon dioxide, and certain acids that enter into chemical reactions with earth materials.

Chemical weathering of igneous rocks

In Chapter 6, we found that the most common minerals in igneous rocks are silicates, and that the most important silicates are quartz, the feldspars, and certain ferromagnesian minerals. Let us see how chemical weathering acts on each of these three types of silicate.

WEATHERING OF QUARTZ. Chemical weathering affects quartz very slowly, and for this reason we speak of quartz as a relatively stable mineral. When a rock such as granite, which contains a high percentage of quartz, decomposes, a great deal of unaltered quartz is left behind. The quartz grains (commonly called *sand grains*) found in the weathered debris of granite are the same as those that appeared in the unweathered granite.

When these quartz grains are first set free from the mother rock, they are sharp and angular. But since even quartz responds slowly to chemical weathering, the grains become more or less rounded as time passes. After many years of weathering, they look as though they had been abraded and worn by the action along a stream bed or a beach. And yet the change may have come about solely through chemical action.

WEATHERING OF FELDSPARS. In the Bowen reaction series (see "Formation of igneous rocks" in Chapter 6), we saw that when a magma cools to form an igneous rock like granite, the feldspars crystallize before the quartz. When granite is exposed to weathering at the earth's surface, the feldspars are also the first minerals to be broken down. Mineralogists and soil scientists still do not understand the precise process by which the feldspars weather, and some of the end-products of this action—the clay minerals—offer many puzzles. But the general direction and results of the process seem fairly clear.

The clay minerals are made up chiefly of aluminum silicate derived from the chemical breakdown of the original feldspar.

This combines with water to form hydrous aluminum silicate, which is the basis for another group of silicate minerals, the clays.

The decomposition of the feldspar orthoclase is a good example of the chemical weathering of the feldspar group of silicates. Two substances are essential to the weathering of orthoclase: carbon dioxide and water. The atmosphere contains small amounts of carbon dioxide and the soil contains much greater amounts. Since carbon dioxide is extremely soluble in water, it unites with rain water and water in the soil to form the weak acid, H_2CO_3, called *carbonic acid*. Now, when orthoclase comes into contact with water containing carbonic acid, the result is the formation of the soluble salt, potassium carbonate, along with amounts of silica, as shown in the following equation:

2 parts orthoclase	*plus*	1 part carbonic acid	*plus*	1 part water
$2K(AlSi_3O_8)$	+	H_2CO_3	+	H_2O
yield clay	*plus*	potassium carbonate	*plus*	4 parts silica
→ $Al_2Si_2O_5(OH)_4$	+	K_2CO_3	+	$4\ SiO_2$

In this reaction, the hydrogen ion from the water forces the potassium out of the orthoclase, disrupting its crystal structure. The hydrogen ion combines with the aluminum silicate radical of orthoclase to form the new clay mineral. (The process by which water combines chemically with other molecules is called hydration.) The disruption of the orthoclase crystal also yields a second product, the soluble salt, potassium carbonate, which is formed when the potassium ejected from the orthoclase combines with the carbonate ion of the carbonic acid. The third product, silica, is formed by the silicon and oxygen that are left over after the potassium has combined with the aluminum silicate to form the clay mineral.

The action of living plants may also bring about the chemical breakdown of orthoclase. A plant root in the soil is negatively charged and is surrounded by a swarm of hydrogen ions (H^+). If there happens to be a fragment of orthoclase lying nearby, these positive ions may change places with the potassium of the orthoclase and disrupt its crystal structure (see Fig. 7-10). Once again a clay mineral is formed, as in the equation above.

Now let us look more closely at each of the three products of the decomposition of orthoclase. First, the clay minerals. At the start, these minerals are very finely divided. In fact, they are sometimes of colloidal size, a size variously estimated as between two-tenths of a micron and one micron (8×10^{-6} in. and 4×10^{-5} in.; see Appendix B for explanation of powers of 10).

Immediately after it is formed, the aluminum silicate may possibly be amorphous—that is, its atoms are not arranged in any orderly pattern. It seems more probable, however, that even at this stage the atoms are arranged according to the definite pattern of a true crystal. In any event, as time passes, the small individual particles join together to form larger crystals which, when analyzed by such means as X-rays, exhibit the crystalline pattern of true minerals.

There are many different clay minerals and each has its own

FIG. 7-9
Deep chemical weathering has decomposed this simatic igneous rock almost beyond recognition. Wadesborough, North Carolina. Photo by U.S. Geol. Survey.

FIG. 7-10
The conversion of orthoclase to a clay mineral by plant roots. In this diagram, a swarm of hydrogen ions (positive) are shown surrounding a negatively charged plant rootlet. The suggestion has been made that a hydrogen ion from the rootlet may replace a potassium ion in a nearby orthoclase fragment and there bond with the oxygen within the original mineral, to begin the conversion of the orthoclase to clay. The potassium ion thus ejected replaces the hydrogen ion along the negatively charged rootlet and is eventually utilized in plant growth. Redrawn from W. D. Keller and A. F. Frederickson, "Role of Plants and Colloidal Acids in the Mechanism of Weathering," Am. J. Sci., CCL(1952), 603.

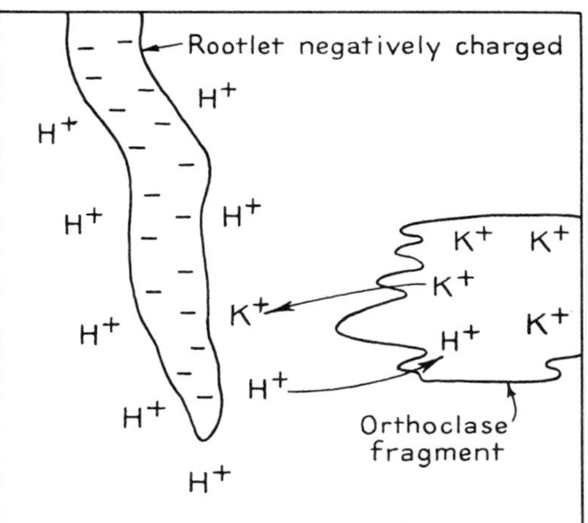

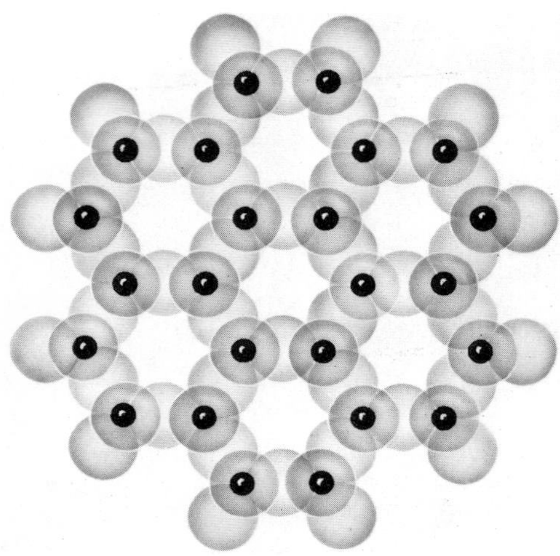

chemical behavior, physical structure, and evolution. Most of the clay minerals fall into three major groups: *kaolinite, montmorillonite,* and *illite.* The term kaolinite is derived from the Chinese *Kao-ling,* for "High Hill," the name of the mountain from which the first kaolinite was shipped to Europe for ceramic uses. The mineral montmorillonite was first described from samples collected near Montmorillon, a town in west-central France. The name illite was selected by geologists of the Illinois Geological Survey in honor of their state.

Like the micas shown in Fig. 4-11 (repeated left), the clay minerals are built up of silicon-oxygen tetrahedra linked together in sheets. These sheets combine in different ways with sheets composed of aluminum atoms and hydroxyl molecules. For this reason we refer to the clay minerals as hydrous aluminum silicates. In addition, montmorillonite may contain magnesium and some sodium and calcium, and illite contains potassium, occasionally with some magnesium and iron.

We still do not understand exactly what factors determine which clay minerals will form when a feldspar is weathered. Climate probably plays a key role, for we know that kaolinite tends to form as a result of the intense chemical weathering in warm, humid climates. And illite and montmorillonite seem to develop more commonly in cooler, drier climates. The history of the rock also seems to be influential. For example, when a soil forms from a sedimentary rock in which a clay has been incorporated, we often find that the soil contains the same type of clay as does the parent rock. The analysis of a number of sedimentary rocks and the soils developed on these rocks has shown that when illite is present in the original rock it is usually the dominant clay in the soil, regardless of climate. Clearly, then, both environment and inheritance seem to influence the type of clay that will develop from the chemical weathering of a feldspar.

Let us look back for a minute to the equation for the decomposition of orthoclase on page 79. Notice that the second product is potassium carbonate, which is soluble in water. We might expect that a soluble salt like this would be dissolved and carried off by water percolating through the ground, and that all of it would eventually find its way to the rivers and finally to the sea. Yet analyses show that not nearly as much potassium is present in river and ocean water as we would expect. What happens to the rest of the potassium? Some of it is used by growing plants before it can be carried away in solution, and some of it is absorbed by clay minerals or even taken into their crystal structure.

The third product resulting from the decomposition of orthoclase is silica, which appears either in solution (for even silica is slightly soluble in water) or as very finely divided quartz in the size range of the colloids. In the colloidal state, silica may exhibit some of the properties of silica in solution.

So far, we have been talking about the weathering of only orthoclase feldspar. But the products of the chemical weathering of plagioclase feldspars are very much the same. Instead of potassium carbonate, however, either sodium or calcium carbonate is produced, depending on whether the feldspar is the sodic albite or the calcic anorthite (see Table 7-1). As we found in Chapter 4 (see "Silicates"), the plagioclase feldspars almost invariably contain both sodium and calcium. The carbonates of sodium and calcium are soluble in water and may eventually reach the sea. We should note here, however, that calcium carbonate also forms the mineral calcite (see "Carbonate and sulfate materials" in Chapter 4). Calcite, in turn forms the greater part of limestone (a sedimentary rock) and marble (a metamorphic rock). Both limestone and marble are discussed in subsequent chapters.

WEATHERING OF FERROMAGNESIAN MINERALS. Now let us turn to the chemical weathering of the third group of common minerals in igneous rocks—the ferromagnesian silicates. The chemical weathering of these minerals produces the same products as the weathering of the feldspars: clay, soluble salts, and finely divided silica. But the presence of iron and magnesium in the ferromagnesian minerals makes possible certain other products as well.

The iron may be incorporated into one of the clay minerals or into an iron carbonate mineral. Usually, however, it unites with oxygen to form hematite, Fe_2O_3, one of the most common of the iron oxides. Hematite commonly has a deep red color, and in powdered form it is always red; this characteristic gives it its name, from the Greek, *haimatites,* "blood-like." Sometimes the iron unites with oxygen to form another iron oxide, *goethite,* FeO(OH), generally brownish in color. (Goethite was named after the German poet Goethe, in deference to his lively scientific interests.) Chemical weathering of the ferromagnesian minerals often produces a substance called *limonite,* yellowish to brownish in color and referred to in everyday lan-

TABLE 7-1
Chemical weathering products of common rock-forming silicate minerals

	MINERAL	COMPOSITION	IMPORTANT DECOMPOSITION PRODUCTS: MINERALS	IMPORTANT DECOMPOSITION PRODUCTS: OTHERS
	QUARTZ	SiO_2	Quartz grains	Some silica in solution.
FELDSPARS	Orthoclase	$K(AlSi_3O_8)$	Clay Quartz (finely divided)	Some silica in solution. Potassium carbonate (soluble).
FELDSPARS	Albite (sodic plagioclase) Anorthite (calcic plagioclase)	$Na(AlSi_3O_8)$ $Ca(Al_2Si_2O_8)$	Clay Quartz (finely divided) Calcite (from Ca)	Some silica in solution. Sodium and calicum carbonates (soluble).
FERROMAGNESIANS	Biotite Augite Hornblende	Fe, Mg, Ca silicates of Al	Clay Calcite Limonite Hematite Quartz (finely divided)	Some silica in solution. Carbonates of calcium and magnesium (soluble).
FERROMAGNESIANS	Olivine	$(Fe,Mg)_2SiO_4$	Limonite Hematite Quartz (finely divided)	Some silica in solution. Carbonates of iron and magnesium (soluble).

guage as just plain "rust." Limonite is not a true mineral, because its composition is not fixed within narrow limits, but the term is universally applied to the iron oxides of uncertain composition that contain a variable amount of water. Limonite and some of the other iron oxides are responsible for the characteristic colors of most soils.

What happens to the magnesium produced by the weathering of the ferromagnesian minerals? Some of it may be removed in solution as a carbonate, but most of it tends to stay behind in newly formed minerals, particularly in the illite and montmorillonite clays.

SUMMARY OF WEATHERING PRODUCTS. If we know the mineral composition of an igneous rock, we can determine in a general way the products that the chemical weathering of that rock will probably yield. The chemical weathering products of the common rock-forming minerals are listed in Table 7-1. These products include the minerals that make up most of our sedimentary rocks, and we shall meet them again in Chapter 8.

RATES OF WEATHERING

Some rocks weather very rapidly, others only slowly. Rate of weathering is governed by the type of rock and a variety of other factors, from minerals and moisture, temperature and topography, to plant and animal activity.

Rate of mineral weathering

On the basis of field observations and laboratory experiments, the minerals commonly found in igneous rocks can be arranged according to the order in which they are chemically decomposed at the surface. We are not sure of all the details, and different investigators report different conclusions, but we can make the following general observations:

1. Quartz is highly resistant to chemical weathering.
2. The plagioclase feldspars weather more rapidly than orthoclase feldspar.
3. Calcic plagioclase (anorthite) tends to weather more rapidly than sodic plagioclase (albite).
4. Olivine is less resistant than augite, and in many instances augite seems to weather more rapidly than hornblende.
5. Biotite mica weathers more slowly than the other dark minerals, and muscovite mica is more resistant than biotite.

Notice that these points suggest a pattern (Fig. 7-11) similar to that of Bowen's reaction series for crystallization from magma, discussed in Chapter 6 (illustrated in Fig. 6-5, shown as inset, right, for comparison). But there is one important difference: in weathering, the successive minerals formed do not react with one another as they do in a continuous reaction series.

The relative resistance of these minerals to decomposition may reflect the difference between the surface conditions under which they weather and the conditions that existed when they were formed. Olivine, for example, forms at high temperatures and pressures, early in the crystallization of a melt. Consequently, as we might expect, it is extremely unstable under the low temperatures and pressures that prevail at the surface, and it weathers quite rapidly. On the other hand, quartz forms late in the reaction series, under considerably lower temperatures and pressures. Since these conditions are more similar to those at the surface, quartz is relatively stable and is very resistant to weathering.

Now we can qualify slightly the definition of weathering given at the beginning of this chapter. We have found that weathering disrupts the equilibrium that existed while the minerals were still buried in the earth's crust, and that this disruption converts them into new minerals. Following Reiche,[1] we may revise our definition as follows: *Weathering is the response of materials that were once in equilibrium within the earth's crust to new conditions at or near contact with air, water, and living matter.*

Depth and rapidity of weathering

Most weathering takes place in the upper few feet or tens of feet of the earth's crust, where rock is in closest contact with air, moisture, and organic matter. But some factors operate well below the surface and permit weathering to penetrate to great depths. For instance, when erosion strips away great quantities of material from the surface, the underlying rocks are free to expand. As a result, parting planes or fractures—the joints that we spoke of earlier in the chapter—develop hundreds of feet below the surface.

Then, too, great quantities of water move through the soil and down into the underground, transforming some of the materials there long before they are ever exposed at the surface. Rock salt that is located deep below the surface in the form of sedimentary rock often undergoes exactly this transformation. If enough underground water is present, the salt is dissolved and carried off long before erosion can expose it.

Weathering is sometimes so rapid that it can actually be recorded. The Krakatoa eruption of August, 1883, described in Chapter 5, threw great quantities of volcanic ash into the air and deposited it to a depth exceeding 100 feet on the

1 Parry Reiche, "A Survey of Weathering Processes and Products," *U. of Nev Mexico Pubs. in Geology,* No. 3 (1950), p. 5.

FIG. 7-11
Relative rapidity of chemical weathering of the common igneous rock-forming minerals. The rate of weathering is most rapid at the bottom and decreases toward the top. Note that this table is in the same order as Bowen's reaction series (inset). The discrepancy in the rate of chemical weathering between, for instance, olivine and quartz, is explained by the fact that in the zone of weathering olivine is farther from its environment of formation than is quartz. It therefore reacts more rapidly than quartz to its new environment and thus weathers more rapidly.

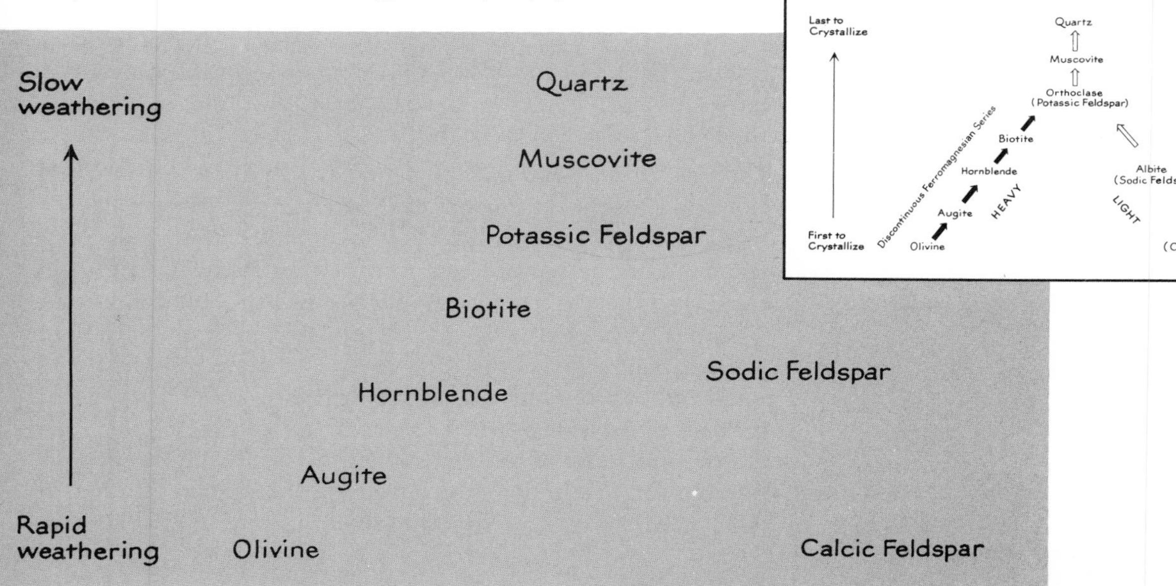

FIG. 7-12
Weathering of a marble headstone, Burying Ground of Christ Church, Cambridge, Massachusetts. The inscription, carved in 1818, is illegible. The monument illustrates the instability and rapid weathering of calcite (predominant mineral in marble) in a humid climate.
Photo by Sheldon Judson.

FIG. 7-13
Weathering of a slate headstone, Burying Ground of Christ Church, Cambridge, Massachusetts. The inscription date, 1693, testifies to its durability. The slate is composed largely of clay minerals formed in the zone of weathering and therefore relatively stable when exposed to additional chemical weathering.
Photo by Sheldon Judson.

nearby island of Long-Eiland. By 1928, 45 years later, a soil nearly 14 inches deep had developed on top of this deposit, and laboratory analyses showed that a significant change had taken place in the original materials. Chemical weathering had removed a measurable amount of the original potassium and sodium. Furthermore, either mechanical weathering or chemical weathering, or both, had broken down the original particles so that they were generally smaller than the particles in the unweathered ash beneath.

Graveyards provide many fine examples of weathering that has occurred within historic time. Calcite in the headstone pictured in Fig. 7-12 has weathered so rapidly that the inscription to the memory of Moses L. Gould, carved in 1818, is only partially legible after a century and a half. Examination of other marble slabs in the Burying Ground indicated that the earliest legible date was 1811.

Undoubtedly the rate of weathering has increased with time, for two reasons. First, continued weathering roughens the marble surface, exposing more and more of it to chemical attack and quickening the rate of decomposition. Second, as the number of factories and dwellings in Cambridge and neighboring towns increased, the amount of carbon dioxide in the atmosphere also increased. Consequently, rain water in the twentieth century carries more carbonic acid than it did in the nineteenth, and it attacks calcite more rapidly.

In contrast to the badly weathered marble is a headstone of slate erected in 1693 (Fig. 7-13). More than two and a half centuries later, the inscription is still plainly visible. Slate is usually a metamorphosed shale, which, in turn, is composed largely of clay minerals formed by the weathering of feldspars. The clay minerals in the headstone were originally formed in the zone of weathering. Consequently, they are relatively stable when exposed to additional chemical weathering. The slate headstone shows little sign of decomposition, because most of the minerals of which it is composed are still in an environment similar to that in which they were formed.

These examples show, then, that weathering often occurs rapidly enough to be measured during one's lifetime. Its rate is even precisely measurable in isolated, specific situations. But the numerous, variable factors of weathering make its exact rate usually difficult, if not impossible, to determine.

Differential weathering

Differential weathering is the process by which different sections of a rock mass weather at different rates. Almost all rock masses of any size weather in this manner. The results vary from the boldly sculptured forms of the Giant's Castle, Wisconsin, to the slightly uneven surface of a marble tombstone. Unequal rates of weathering are caused chiefly by variations in the composition of the rock itself. The more resistant zones stand out as ridges or ribs above the more rapidly weathered rock on either side.

A second cause of differential weathering is simply that the intensity of weathering varies from one section to another in the same rock. Figure 7-14 shows a sandstone memorial that has undergone mechanical weathering in certain spots. The rock is a coarse, red, homogeneous sandstone made up of quartz, feldspar, and mica, with some red iron oxides. The inner sides of the pillars have disintegrated so badly that the original fluting has been entirely destroyed, and the underside of the horizontal slab has scaled noticeably. Notice that these are the areas least accessible to the drying action of the sun. Consequently, moisture has tended to persist here, and frost action has pried off flakes and loosened individual grains.

Another example of differential chemical weathering is shown in Fig. 7-15. Here the limestone has been dissolved where the supply of water was abundant, but adjacent blocks of the same rock have been left relatively unaffected.

SOILS

So far, we have been discussing the ways in which weathering acts to break down existing rocks and to provide the material for new rocks. But weathering also plays a crucial role in the creation of the soils that cover the earth's surface and sustain all life. In fairly recent years, the study of soils has developed into the science of *pedology* (from the Greek, *pedon,* "soil," with *logos,* "reason," hence "knowledge of soil" or "soil science").[2]

Soil classification

In the early years of soil study in the United States, researchers thought that the parent material almost wholly determined the type of soil that would result from it. Thus, they reasoned, granite would weather to one type of soil, and limestone to another.

It is true that a soil reflects to some degree the material from which it developed, and in some instances one can even map the distribution of rocks on the basis of the types of soil that lie above them. But as more and more information became available, it became apparent that the bedrock is not the only factor determining soil type. Russian soil scientists, following the pioneer work of V. V. Dokuchaev (1846-1903), demonstrated that different soils develop over identical bedrock material in different areas when the climate varies from one area to another. The idea that climate exerts a major control over soil formation was introduced in this country in the 1920's by C. F. Marbut (1863-1935), for many years chief of the United States Soil Survey in the Department of Agriculture. Since that time, soil scientists have discovered that still other factors exercise important influences on soil development. For instance, the relief of the land surface plays a significant role. The soil on the crest of a hill is somewhat different from the soil on the slope, which, in turn, differs from the soil on the level ground at the foot of the hill; yet all three soils rest on identical bedrock. The passage of time is

[2] In the United States, the term pedology is sometimes confused with words based on *ped* and *pedi,* combining forms meaning "foot," or with words based on *ped* and *pedo,* combining forms meaning "boy, child," as in pediatrics, the medical science that treats of the hygiene and diseases of children. Consequently, there is a tendency in this country to use *soil science* instead of *pedology.*

FIG. 7-14
Differential weathering in a sandstone monument, Burying Ground of Christ Church, Cambridge, Massachusetts. Mechanical weathering has been concentrated along the inner faces of the vertically fluted columns. The more rapid disintegration here is due to differential exposure. Moisture remains longer on the inner faces, which are less accessible to the sun, and consequently frost action has been more effective here than on the outer faces. Photo by Sheldon Judson.

FIG. 7-15
Variation in intensity of chemical weathering on limestone blocks of similar composition, Harvard University, Cambridge, Massachusetts. Water with small amounts of carbonic acid has been concentrated along the center blocks as the water ran down the wall. Here the solution has been most rapid. Adjacent blocks of the same type of material have not been so often or so thoroughly wetted and are thus relatively unaffected by decomposition. Note the differences in the pattern of weathering from one block to the next. They are due to variations in solubility within each block. Photo by Sheldon Judson.

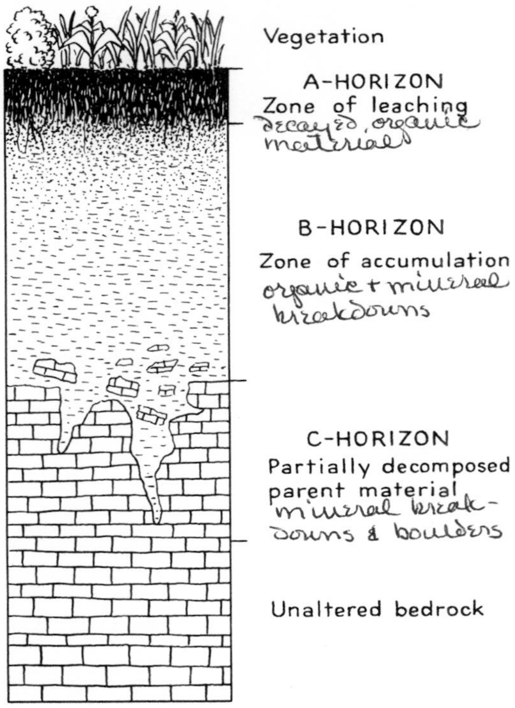

Vegetation

A-HORIZON
Zone of leaching

B-HORIZON
Zone of accumulation

C-HORIZON
Partially decomposed parent material

Unaltered bedrock

FIG. 7-16
The three major horizons of a soil. In many instances, it is possible to subdivide the zones themselves. Here the soil is shown as having developed from limestone.

another factor. A soil that has only begun to form differs from one that has been developing for thousands of years, although the climate, bedrock, and topography are the same in each instance. Finally, the type of vegetation in an area influences the type of soil that develops there. One type of soil will form beneath a pine forest, another type beneath a forest of deciduous trees, and yet another type on a grass-covered prairie.

Exactly what is a soil? It is a natural, surficial material that supports plant life. Each soil exhibits certain properties that are determined by climate and living organisms operating over periods of time on earth materials and on landscape of varying relief. Because all these factors are combined in various ways all over the land areas of the globe, the number of possible soil types is almost unlimited.

And yet certain valid generalizations can be made about soils. We know, for example, that the composition of a soil varies with depth. A natural or artificial exposure of a soil reveals a series of zones, each recognizably different from the one above. Each of these zones is called a *soil horizon* or, more simply, a *horizon*. The three major zones or horizons in a typical soil, shown in Fig. 7-16, may be described, from the bottom upward, as follows:

C-HORIZON. This is a zone of partially disintegrated and decomposed rock material. Some of the original bedrock minerals are still present, but others have been transformed into new materials. The C-horizon grades downward into the unweathered rock material.

B-HORIZON. This zone lies directly above the C-horizon. Weathering here has proceeded still further than in the underlying zone, and only those minerals of the parent rock that are most resistant to decomposition (quartz, for example) are still recognizable. The others have been converted into new minerals or into soluble salts. In moist climates, the B-horizon contains an accumulation of clayey material and iron oxides delivered by water percolating downward from the surface. In dry climates we generally find, in addition to the clay and iron oxides, deposits of more soluble minerals, such as calcite. This mineral, too, may have been brought down from above; but some is brought into the B-horizon from below, as soil water is drawn upward by high evaporation rates. Because material is deposited in the B-horizon, it is known as the "zone of accumulation" (see Fig. 7-16).

A-HORIZON. This is the uppermost zone—the one into which we sink a spade when we dig a garden. This is the zone from which the iron oxides have been carried to the B-horizon, and in dry climates it is the source of some soluble material that may be deposited in the B-horizon. The process by which these materials have been moved downward by soil water is called *leaching*, and the A-horizon is sometimes called the "zone of leaching" (Fig. 7-16). Varying amounts of organic material tend to give the A-horizon a gray to black color.

The three soil horizons have all developed from the underlying parent material. When this material is first exposed at the surface, the upper portion is subjected to intense weathering, and decomposition proceeds rapidly. As the decomposed material builds up, downward-percolating water begins to leach out some of the minerals and to deposit them lower down. Gradually, the A-horizon and the B-horizon build up. But weathering continues to go on, though at a slower rate now, on the underlying parent material, giving rise to the C-horizon. With the passage of time, the C-horizon reaches deeper and deeper into the unweathered material below, the B-horizon keeps moving downward, and the A-horizon, in turn, encroaches on the upper portion of the B-horizon. Finally, a "mature" soil is built up.

The thickness of the soil that forms depends on many factors. But in the northern United States and southern Canada, the material that was first exposed to weathering after the retreat of the last ice sheet some 10,000 years ago is now topped by a soil 2 to 3 feet thick. Farther south, where the surface was uncovered by the ice at an earlier time, the soils are thicker. And in some places the processes of weathering have extended to 2 or 3 scores of feet below the present surface.

N. US & Canada 2-3' thick

Some soil types

We can understand the farmer's interest in soil, but why is it important for the geologist to understand soils and the processes by which they are formed? There are several reasons.

First, soils provide clues to the environment in which they were originally formed. By analyzing an ancient soil buried in the rock record, we may be able to determine the climate and physical conditions that prevailed when it was formed.

Second, some soils are sources of valuable mineral deposits (see Chapter 22), and the weathering process often enriches otherwise low-grade mineral deposits, making them profitable to mine. An understanding of soils and soil-forming processes, therefore, can serve as a guide in the search for certain ores.

Third, since a soil reflects to some degree the nature of the rock material from which it has developed, we can sometimes determine the nature of the underlying rock by analyzing the soil.

But most important of all, soils provide the source of many of the sediments that are eventually converted into sedimentary rocks. And these, in turn, may be transformed into metamorphic rocks or, following another path in the rock cycle, may be converted into new soils. If we understand the processes and results of soil formation, we are in a better position to interpret the origin and evolution of many rock types.

The following pages will discuss three major types of soil. Two of them, the *pedalfers* and the *pedocals,* are typical of the middle latitudes. The third group, referred to as *laterites,* is found in tropical climates.

PEDALFER. A pedalfer is a soil in which iron oxides or clays, or both, have accumulated in the B-horizon. The name is derived from *pedon,* Greek for "soil," and the symbols Al and Fe for aluminum and iron. In general, soluble materials such as calcium carbonate or magnesium carbonate do not occur in the pedalfers. Pedalfers are commonly found in temperate, humid climates, usually beneath a forest vegetation. In the United States, most of the pedalfers lie east of a line that

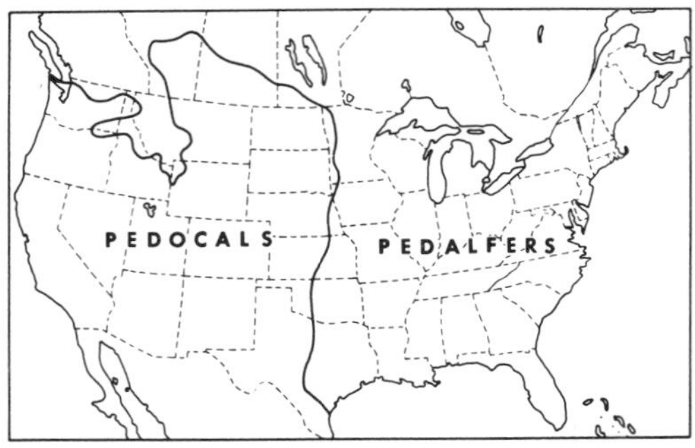

FIG. 7-17
Generalized distribution of pedalfer and pedocal soils in the United States and Canada. In the United States, the pedalfers have developed in the more humid climates to the east of the line that marks approximately 25 inches of precipitation per year. To the west of this line, where precipitation is generally less than 25 inches per year, pedocal soils predominate. In Canada and in the northern Rocky Mountains of the United States, temperature is more critical than precipitation in determining the distribution of the two soils. Here pedocals occur in areas where the average annual temperature is 40°F or less.

FIG. 7-18
A pedalfer soil that has developed on a granite. Note the transition from unaltered granite, upward through partially decomposed granite of the C-horizon, into the B-horizon, where no trace of the original granite structure remains, and finally into the A-horizon, just below the surface.

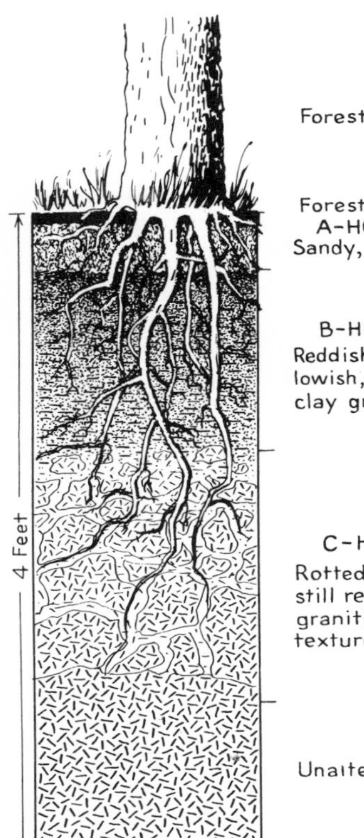

corresponds roughly to about 25 inches of rainfall a year. Northward in Canada, however, where the temperature is more important than the total rainfall in determining the distribution of pedalfers, the zone extends northwestward across Saskatchewan and Alberta coincident with a mean annual temperature of about 40°F or colder. Farther west, the pedalfers extend southward into the United States along the mountainous region of the Rockies, where the rainfall is somewhat higher and the temperatures lower than in the rest of western United States (see Fig. 7-17).

In the formation of pedalfers, certain soluble compounds, particularly those that contain sodium, calcium, and magnesium, are rapidly removed from the A-horizon by waters seeping into the soil from the surface. These soluble compounds proceed downward through the B-horizon and are carried off by ground water. The less soluble iron oxides and clay are deposited in the B-horizon, giving that zone a clayey character with a brownish to reddish color.

Using the information on the products of chemical weathering listed in Table 7-1, we can build up a picture of how a pedalfer develops from granite in temperate and humid areas. At some depth below the surface lies the unaltered granite. Directly above is the crumbly, partially disintegrated rock of the C-horizon. Here we can still identify the minerals that made up the original granite, although the feldspars have started to decompose and have become cloudy, and the iron-bearing minerals have been partially oxidized.

Moving upward to the B-horizon, the zone of accumulation, we find that here the feldspars have been converted to clay, and the material has a compact, clayey texture. Iron oxides or limonite stain the soil a reddish or brownish color. And since the grains of quartz released from the granite have undergone little change, we find some sand in this otherwise clayey zone.

The A-horizon, a few inches thick, has a grayish to ashen color, for the iron compounds have been leached from this zone and now color the B-horizon below. Furthermore, the texture of this zone is sandier, for most of the finer materials have also been moved downward to the B-horizon, and the soluble salts have been largely dissolved and removed by water. The very top of the A-horizon is a thin zone of dark, humic material. The final pedalfer soil is shown in Fig. 7-18.

Notice in Fig. 7-19 how the original minerals of the granite are transformed as weathering progresses. On the left we have quartz, plagioclase, and orthoclase, which were released directly from the granite. Then, as weathering progresses, we find that the amount of kaolinite increases at the expense of the original minerals. The initial rise in the amount of quartz and orthoclase indicates simply that these minerals tend to accumulate in the soil because of their greater resistance to decomposition. Iron oxides also increase with weathering as the iron-bearing silicates decompose.

There are several varieties of soils in the pedalfer group, including the red and yellow soils of the southeastern states, as well as *podsol* (from the Russian, "ashy gray soil"), and the gray-brown podsolic soils of the northeastern quarter of the

United States and of southern and eastern Canada. Prairie soils are transitional varieties between the pedalfers of the East and the pedocals of the West.

PEDOCALS. Pedocals are soils that contain an accumulation of calcium carbonate. Their name is derived from a combination of the Greek for *pedon,* "soil," with an abbreviation for calcium. The soils of this major group are found in the temperate zones where the temperature is relatively high, rainfall is low, and the vegetation is mostly grass or brush growth. In the United States, the pedocals are found generally to the west of the pedalfers; and in Canada, to the southwest.

In the formation of pedocals, calcium carbonate and, to a lesser extent, magnesium carbonate are deposited in the soil profile, particularly in the B-horizon. This process occurs in areas where temperature is high, rainfall scant, and the upper level of the soil is hot and dry most of the time. Water evaporates before it can remove carbonates from the soil. Consequently, these compounds are precipitated as *caliche* (ca-lee′-chee), a whitish accumulation made up largely of calcium carbonate. *Caliche* is a Spanish word, a derivative of the Latin *calix,* "lime." The occasional rain may carry the soluble material down from the A-horizon into the B-horizon, where it is later precipitated as the water evaporates. Soluble material may also move up into the soil from below. In this case, water beneath the soil or in its lower portion rises toward the surface through small, capillary openings. Then, as the water in the upper portions evaporates, the dissolved materials are precipitated.

Pedocals tend to develop under a growth of brush and grass, which also helps to concentrate the soluble carbonates by intercepting them before they can be moved downward in the soil. When the plants die, the carbonates are either added to the soil, where they are used by other plants, or are simply precipitated in the soil by high evaporation rates.

Because rainfall is light in the climates where pedocals form, chemical weathering proceeds only slowly, and clay is produced less rapidly than in more humid climates. For this reason, pedocals contain a lower percentage of clay minerals than do the pedalfer soils.

The pedocal group includes the black and chestnut-colored soils of southern Alberta and Saskatchewan in Canada and the northern plains of the United States, the reddish soils farther south, and the red and gray desert soils of the drier western states.

TROPICAL SOILS (LATERITES). The term *laterite* is applied to many tropical soils that are rich in hydrated aluminum and iron oxides. The name itself, from the Latin for "brick," suggests the characteristic color produced by the iron in these soils. The formation of laterites is not well understood. In fact, soil scientists are not even certain that the A-, B-, and C-horizons characteristic of the pedalfers and the pedocals have their counterparts in the laterites, even though these soils do exhibit recognizable zones.

In the development of the laterites, iron and aluminum accumulate in what is presumed to be the B-horizon. The

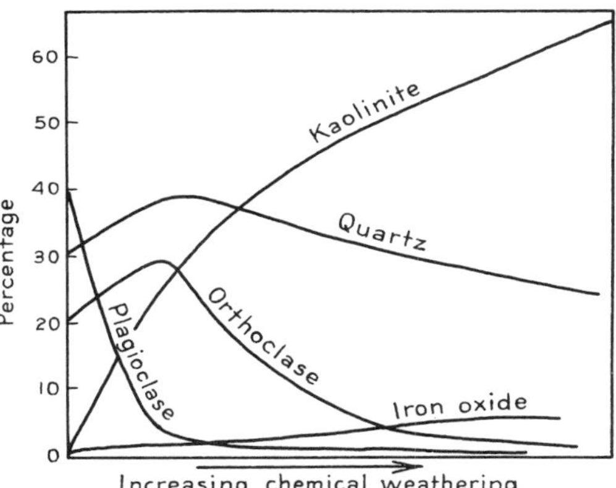

FIG. 7-19
Change in mineral percentages as a granite is subjected to increased chemical weathering. As weathering progresses, the orthoclase and plagioclase of the granite decrease in abundance and give rise to an increasing amount of clay (kaolinite). At the same time, the percentage of iron oxides increases at the expense of the original iron silicate minerals (not shown). Redrawn from S. S. Goldich, "A Study of Rock Weathering," J. Geol., XLVI (1938), 33.

FIG. 7-20
This podsol, a member of the pedalfer group of soils, occurs on Cape Cod, Massachusetts. The dark layer at the very top just beneath the plant cover is the humic zone in the upper part of the A-horizon. The light gray, leached zone below makes up the bulk of the A-horizon. The B-horizon is thin and shows up dark in the photograph because of the iron oxides that have accumulated there. This zone grades down into the C-horizon, the parent material, which is here an unconsolidated sandy deposit. Photo by Paul MacClintock.

aluminum is in the form of $Al_2O_3:nH_2O$, which is generally called *bauxite,* an ore of aluminum. This ore appears to be developed when intense and prolonged weathering removes the silica from the clay minerals and leaves a residuum of hydrous aluminum oxide—that is, bauxite. In some laterites, the concentration of iron oxides in the presumed B-horizon is so great that it is profitable to mine them for iron, as is done in certain districts of Cuba.

The term laterite is most properly applied only to the zone in which iron and aluminum have accumulated. As we have seen, this is the zone that may be equivalent to the B-horizon in more northerly soils. Overlying this zone, there is often a zone of crumbly loam, and below it is a light-colored, apparently leached zone that adjoins the parent material. Some soil scientists refer to these two zones as the A-horizon and the C-horizon, respectively.

SUMMARY OUTLINE

Weathering
- The response of surface or near-surface material to contact with water, air, and living matter

Mechanical weathering (disintegration)
- Reduction in size of fragments
- No change in composition
- Example: shattering of rocks by frost action

Chemical weathering (decomposition)
- Change in composition of earth material
- Example: development of clay from feldspar

Factors in chemical weathering
- Rate increases as size of particle decreases
- Rate increases as temperature and moisture increases
- Certain minerals weather more rapidly than others
- Example: olivine weathers more rapidly than quartz

Products of chemical weathering
- Igneous rocks of quartz + feldspar + ferromagnesian minerals yield clay + iron oxides + silica + soluble salts

Soil
- Naturally occurring surface material that supports life and generally is the product of weathering

Soil zones
- A-, B-, and C-horizons found from surface downward

Soil types
- Pedalfers (moist temperate climate)
- Pedocals (dry temperate climate)
- Laterites (moist tropical climate)

SELECTED REFERENCES

Goldich, S. S., "A Study in Rock Weathering," *Jour. Geol.,* XLVI (1938), pp. 17–58.

Keller, Walter D., *Chemistry in Introductory Geology*. Columbia, Mo.: Lucas Brothers, 1957.

———, *The Principles of Chemical Weathering* (rev. ed.). Columbia, Mo.: Lucas Brothers, 1959.

Lyon, T. L., H. O. Buckman, and N. C. Brady, *The Nature and Properties of Soils* (6th ed.). New York: The Macmillan Company, 1960.

Reiche, Parry, *A Survey of Weathering Processes and Products.* Albuquerque, N.M.: U. of New Mexico Press, 1950.

Soil, U.S. Department of Agriculture Yearbook, 1957. Washington, D.C.: Government Printing Office, 1957.

8

Sedimentary rocks

We have all dug our toes into a sandy beach, or picked our way over the gravels of a rushing stream, or perhaps slogged through the mud of a swamp. None of these—sand, gravel, or mud—immediately suggests hard, solid rock to us. Yet deposits of this sort, or materials very similar to them, are the stuff from which the great bulk of the rocks exposed at the earth's surface were formed. When we look down into the mile-deep Grand Canyon of the Colorado in Arizona, we see layer upon layer of rocks that were once unconsolidated deposits of sand, gravel, and mud. Over the course of time, these loose sediments have been hardened into rocks that we call *sedimentary rocks.*

The story of sedimentary rocks begins with the weathering processes discussed in Chapter 7, for the products of chemical and mechanical weathering are the raw materials of sedimentary rocks. Streams, glaciers, wind, and ocean currents move the weathered materials to new localities and deposit them as sand, gravel, or mud. To transform these sediments into rock is the final step in the development of sedimentary rocks.

Some sediments, particularly sand and gravel, are consolidated into rock by a process that actually cements the individual grains. Subsurface water trickling through the open spaces leaves behind a mineral deposit that serves to cement the grains firmly together, giving the entire deposit the strength we associate with rock. Other sediments, such as fine deposits of mud, are transformed into rock by the weight of overlying deposits, which press or compact them into a smaller and smaller space.

The sedimentary rock that results from either of these processes may eventually be exposed at the earth's surface. If the rock was formed beneath the bottom of the ocean, it may be exposed either by the slow withdrawal of the seas or by the upward motion of the sea floor, forming new areas of dry land.

It is extremely difficult to work out a concise, comprehensive definition of sedimentary rocks. The adjective *sedimentary,* from the Latin, *sedimentum,* means "settling." So we might expect sedimentary rocks to be formed when individual particles settle out of a fluid, like the water of a lake or an ocean. And many sedimentary rocks are formed in just that way. Fragments or minerals derived from the breakdown of rocks are swept into bodies of water where they settle out as unconsolidated sediments. Later, they are hardened into true rocks. But other rocks, such as rock salt, are made up of minerals left behind by the evaporation of large bodies of water. And these rocks are as truly sedimentary rocks as those formed from particles that have settled on an ocean floor. Still other sedimentary rocks are made up largely of the shells and hard parts of animals, particularly of invertebrate marine organisms.

Sedimentary rocks are often layered, or stratified. Unlike massive igneous rocks, such as granite, most sedimentary rocks are laid down in a series of individual beds, one on top of another. The surface of each bed is essentially parallel to the horizon at the time of deposition, and a cross section exposes a series of layers like those of a giant cake. True, some igneous rocks, such as those formed from lava flows, are also layered. By and large, however, *stratification is the single most characteristic feature of sedimentary rocks* (see Fig. 8-1).

About 75 per cent of the rocks exposed at the earth's surface are sedimentary rocks or metamorphic rocks derived from them. Yet sedimentary rocks make up only about 5 per cent by volume of the outer 10 miles of the globe. The other 95 per cent of the rocks in this 10-mile zone are, or once were, igneous rocks. The sedimentary cover is only as thick as a feather edge where it laps around the igneous rocks of the Adirondacks and the Rockies. In other places, it is thousands of feet thick. In the delta region of the Mississippi River, oil-drilling operations have cut into the crust more than 22,000 feet and have encountered nothing but sedimentary rocks. In the Ganges River basin of India, the thickness of the sedimentary deposits has been estimated at between 45,000 and 60,000 feet.

FIG. 8-1
The Colorado River, seen from Dead Horse Point, Utah. Erosion has exposed these flat-lying beds of sedimentary rocks that range in age from the Pennsylvanian (which ended about 280 million years ago) to the Triassic (which ended about 180 million years ago). The steep slopes are formed in sandstone and limestone, the gentler slopes in shale.
Photo by William C. Bradley.

FORMATION OF SEDIMENTARY ROCKS

We found in Chapter 6 that igneous rocks harden from molten material that originates some place beneath the surface, under the high temperatures and pressures that prevail there. In contrast, sedimentary rocks form at the much lower temperatures and pressures that prevail at or near the earth's surface.

Origin of material

The material from which sedimentary rocks are fashioned originates in two ways. First, the deposits may be accumulations of minerals and rocks derived either from the erosion of existing rock or from the weathered products of these rocks. Deposits of this type are called *detrital* (from the Latin for "worn down"), and sedimentary rocks formed from them are called *detrital sedimentary rocks.* Second, the deposits may be produced by chemical processes. We refer to these deposits as *chemical deposits* and to the rocks formed from them as *chemical sedimentary rocks.*

Gravel, sand, silt, and clay derived from the weathering and erosion of a land area are examples of detrital sediments. Let us take a specific example. The quartz grains freed by the weathering of a granite may be winnowed out by the running water of a stream and swept into the ocean. There they settle out as beds of sand, a detrital deposit. Later, when this deposit is cemented to form a hard rock, we have a sandstone, a detrital rock.

Chemically formed deposits are usually laid down by the precipitation of material dissolved in water. This process may take place either directly, through inorganic processes, or indirectly, through the intervention of plants or animals. The salt left behind after a salty body of water has evaporated is an example of a deposit laid down by inorganic chemical processes. On the other hand, certain organisms, such as the corals, extract calcium carbonate from sea water and use it to build up skeletons of calcite. When the animals die, their skeletons collect as a biochemical (from the Greek for "life," plus "chemical") deposit, and the rock that subsequently forms is called a *biochemical rock*—in this case, limestone.

Although we distinguish between the two general groups of sedimentary rocks—detrital and chemical—most sedimentary rocks are mixtures of the two. We commonly find that a chemically formed rock contains a certain amount of detrital material. In similar fashion, predominantly detrital rocks include some material that has been chemically deposited.

Geologists use various terms to describe the environment in which a sediment originally accumulated. For example, if a limestone contains fossils of an animal that is known to have lived only in the sea, the rock is known as a *marine* limestone. *Fluvial,* from the Latin for "river," is applied to rocks formed by deposits laid down by a river. *Aeolian,* derived from Aeolus, the Greek god of wind, describes rock made up of wind-deposited material. Rocks formed from lake deposits are termed *lacustrine,* from the Latin word for "lake."

Detrital and chemical, however, are the main divisions of sedimentary rocks based on the origin of material, and as we shall see later, they form the two major divisions in the classification of sedimentary rocks.

Sedimentation

The general process by which rock-forming material is laid down is called *sedimentation,* or deposition. The factors controlling sedimentation are easy to visualize. To have any deposition at all, there must obviously be something to deposit—another way of saying that a source of sediments must exist. We also need some process to transport this sediment. And, finally, there must be some place and some process for the deposition of the sedimentary material.

SOURCE OF MATERIAL. In talking about the rock cycle (Chapter 1), we mentioned that igneous rocks are the ultimate source of the sediments in sedimentary rocks, but that metamorphic rocks or other sedimentary rocks may serve as the immediate source.

In either case, after the rock material has been weathered, it is ready to be transported to some place of accumulation. Its movement is usually from a higher to a lower level. The energy

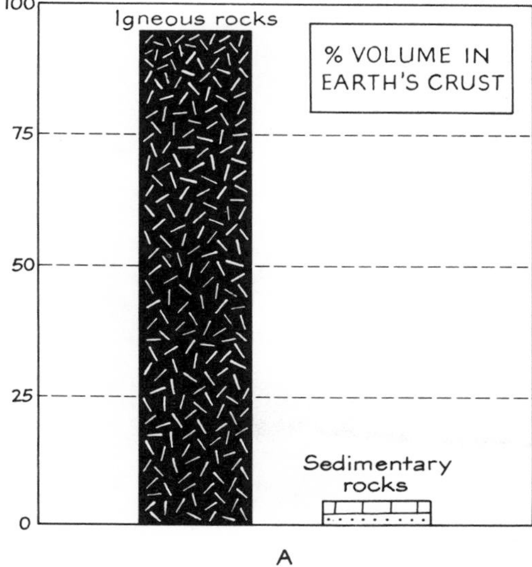

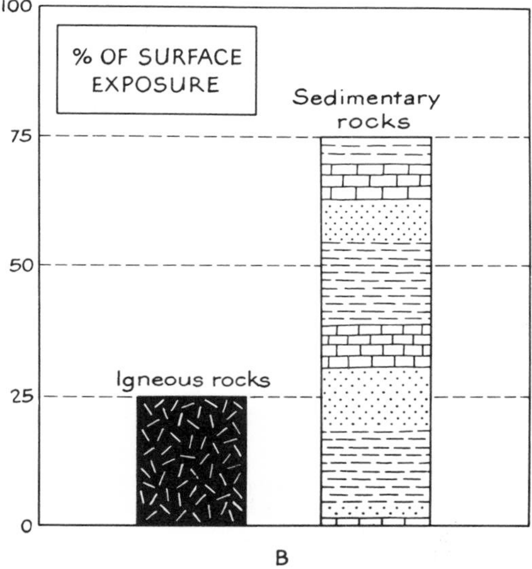

FIG. 8-2
Graphs showing relative abundance of sedimentary rocks and igneous rocks. Graph A *shows that the great bulk (95 per cent) of the outer 10 miles of the earth is made up of igneous rocks and that only a small percentage (5 per cent) is sedimentary. In contrast, Graph* B *shows that the areal extent of sedimentary rocks at the earth's surface is three times that of igneous rocks. Metamorphic rocks are considered with either igneous or sedimentary rocks, depending on their origin.*

FIG. 8-3
The environment of this quiet pond near Lexington, Massachusetts, favors the deposition of fine-grained sediments, largely mud. Compare with Fig. 8-4. Photo by Sheldon Judson.

FIG. 8-4
Exposed to the direct attack of ocean surf, the environment of this cliffed California coastline favors the deposition of coarse sand and gravel. Compare with Fig. 8-3, above. Photo by Sheldon Judson.

for this movement is provided by gravity, which makes possible not only the process of mass movement itself, but also the activity of such agents of transportation as running water and glacier ice. If gravity were free to go about its work without opposition, it would long ago have reduced the continents to smooth, low-lying landmasses. But working against the leveling action of gravity are energies within the earth that elevate the continents and portions of the sea floor (see Chapter 16). By constantly exposing new areas of the earth's surface to weathering, movements of this sort insure a continuing supply of material for the formation of sedimentary rocks.

The weathering of existing rock provides both detrital sediments and the soluble material that is eventually converted into chemical deposits. The nature of the rock that furnishes the sedimentary material has an effect on the nature of the sediments, and therefore on the rocks that form from them. For instance, material derived from a granite highland differs from material eroded from a limestone plain. Furthermore, the type of weathering that takes place also influences the type of sediments that develop. Thus the *chemical* weathering of a granitic landmass produces clay, soluble salts, iron oxides, and silica. But the *mechanical* weathering of the same granitic landmass produces bits of broken granite, and grains of the original quartz, feldspar, and ferromagnesian minerals that made up the granite.

METHODS OF TRANSPORTATION. Water—in streams and glaciers, underground and in ocean currents—is the principal means of transporting material from one place to another. Landslides and other movements induced by gravity also play a role, as does the wind, but we shall look more closely at these processes in Chapters 10 through 15.

PROCESSES OF SEDIMENTATION. Detrital material—material consisting of minerals and rock fragments—is deposited when its agent of transportation no longer has enough energy to move it farther. For example, a stream flowing along at a certain velocity possesses enough energy to move particles up to a certain maximum size. If the stream loses velocity, it also loses energy, and it is no longer able to transport all the material that it has been carrying along at the higher velocity. The solid particles, beginning with the heaviest, start to settle to the bottom. The effect is much the same when a wind that has been driving sand across a desert suddenly dies. A loss of energy accompanies the loss in velocity.

Material that has been carried along in solution is deposited in a different way: by precipitation, a chemical process by which dissolved material is converted into a solid and separated from the liquid solvent. As we have already noted, precipitation may be either biochemical or inorganic in nature.

Although at first glance the whole process of sedimentation seems quite simple, actually it is as complex as nature itself. Many factors are involved, and they can interact in a variety of ways. Consequently, the manner in which sedimentation takes place and the sediments that result from it differ greatly from one situation to another (see Figs. 8-3 and 8-4).

Think of the different ways in which materials settle out of water, for instance. A swift, narrow mountain stream may deposit coarse sand and gravel along its bed. But farther downstream, as the valley widens, the same stream may overflow its banks and spread silt and mud over the surrounding country. A lake provides a different environment, varying from the delta of the inlet stream to the deep lake bottom and the shallow, sandy shore zones. In the oceans, too—those great basins of sedimentation—environment and sedimentation differ from the brackish tidal lagoon to the zone of plunging surf, and out to the broad, submerged shelves of the continents and to the ocean depths beyond.

Mineral composition of sedimentary rocks

Sedimentary rocks, like igneous and metamorphic rocks, are accumulations of minerals. In sedimentary rocks, the three most common minerals are clay, quartz, and calcite, although, as we shall see, a few others are important in certain localities.

Rarely is a sedimentary rock made up of only a single mineral, although one mineral may predominate. Limestone, for example, is composed mostly of calcite, but even the purest limestone contains small amounts of other minerals, such as clay or quartz. The grains of many sandstones are predominantly quartz, but the cementing material that holds these grains together may be calcite, dolomite, or iron oxide. In general, we may say that most sedimentary rocks are mixtures of two or more minerals.

CLAY. Chapter 7 described how clay minerals develop from the weathering of the silicates, particularly the feldspars. These clays subsequently may be incorporated into sedimentary rocks; they may, for example, form an important constituent of mudstone and shale. Examination of recent and ancient marine deposits shows that the kaolinite and illite clays are the most common clays in sedimentary rocks, and that the montmorillonite clays are relatively rare.

QUARTZ. Another important component of sedimentary rocks is silica, including the very common mineral quartz, as well as a number of other forms such as chert, flint, opal, and chalcedony.

The mechanical and chemical weathering of an igneous rock such as granite sets free individual grains of quartz that eventually may be incorporated into sediments. These quartz grains produce the detrital forms of silica and account for most of the volume of the sedimentary rock sandstone. But silica in solution or in particles of colloidal size is also produced by the weathering of an igneous rock. This silica may be precipitated or deposited in the form of quartz, particularly as a cementing agent in certain coarse-grained sedimentary rocks. Silica may also be precipitated in other forms, such as *opal,* generally regarded as a hydrous silica ($SiO_2 \cdot nH_2O$). Opal is slightly softer than true quartz and has no true crystal structure.

Silica also occurs in sedimentary rocks in a form called *cryptocrystalline.* This term (from the Greek *kryptos,* "hid-

FIG. 8-5
Quartz grains of varying sizes and shapes are cemented together by hematite. The large quartz fragment is about half an inch long. Photo by Willard Starks.

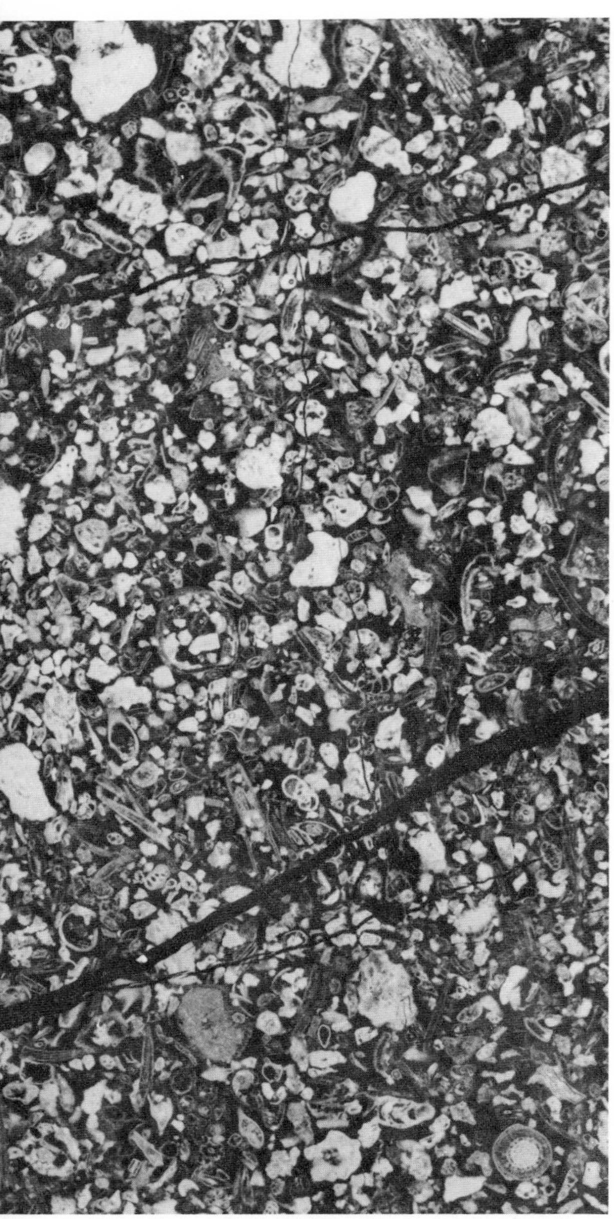

FIG. 8-6
Viewed under the microscope, some limestones are seen to have a clastic texture, as does this example from an ancient reef deposit in the Austrian Alps. The individual particles include the shells of one-celled marine animals called Foraminifera, as well as the fragments of other marine organisms and pellets of calcite. The particles are cemented together by clear calcite (dark). The black lines are also calcite that fills cracks in the rock. Photo by E. C. Bierwagen.

den," and crystalline) indicates that the crystalline structure of this type of silica is so fine that it cannot be seen under most ordinary microscopes. The microscope does reveal, however, that some cryptocrystalline silica has a granular pattern and that some has a fibrous pattern. To the naked eye, the surface of the granular form is somewhat duller than that of the fibrous form. Among the dull-surfaced or granular varieties is *flint,* usually dark in color. Flint is commonly found in certain limestone beds—the chalk beds of southern England, for example. *Chert* is similar to flint but tends to be lighter in color, and *jasper* is a red variety of granular cryptocrystalline form.

The general term *chalcedony* is often applied to the fibrous types of cryptocrystalline silica, which have a higher, more waxy luster than granular varieties. Sometimes the term is also used to describe a specific variety of brown, translucent cryptocrystalline silica.

Agate is a variegated form of silica, its bands of chalcedony alternating with bands of either opal or some variety of granular cryptocrystalline silica, such as jasper.

CALCITE. The chief constituent of the sedimentary rock limestone, calcite ($CaCO_3$) is also the most common cementing material in the coarse-grained sedimentary rocks. The calcium is derived from igneous rocks that contain calcium-bearing minerals, such as calcic plagioclase and some of the ferromagnesian minerals. Calcium is carried from the zone of weathering as calcium bicarbonate, $Ca(HCO_3)_2$, and is eventually precipitated as calcite, $CaCO_3$, through the intervention of plants, animals, or inorganic processes. The carbonate is derived from water and carbon dioxide.

OTHER MATERIALS IN SEDIMENTARY ROCKS. Accumulations of clay, quartz, and calcite, either alone or in combination, account for all but a very small percentage of the sedimentary rocks. But certain other materials occur in quantities large enough to form distinct strata. The mineral *dolomite,* $CaMg(CO_3)_2$, for example, usually is intimately associated with calcite, though it is far less abundant. It is named after an eighteenth-century French geologist, Dolomieu. When the mineral is present in large amounts in a rock, the rock itself is also known as dolomite. The mineral dolomite is easily confused with calcite; and since they often occur together, distinguishing them is important. Calcite effervesces freely in dilute hydrochloric acid; dolomite effervesces very slowly or not at all, unless it is finely ground or powdered. The more rapid chemical activity results from the increase in surface area, an example of the general principle discussed under "Chemical weathering" in Chapter 7.

The feldspars and micas are abundant in some sedimentary rocks. In Chapter 7, we found that chemical weathering converts these minerals into new minerals at a relatively rapid rate. Therefore, when we find mica and feldspar in a sedimentary rock, chances are that it was mechanical, rather than chemical, weathering that originally made them available for incorporation in the rock.

Iron produced by chemical weathering of the ferromagnesian minerals in igneous rocks may be caught up again in new minerals and incorporated into sedimentary deposits. The iron-bearing minerals that occur most frequently in sedimentary rocks are hematite, goethite, and limonite. In some deposits, these minerals predominate, but more commonly they act simply as coloring matter or as a cementing material.

Halite (NaCl) and gypsum ($CaSO_4 \cdot 2H_2O$) are minerals precipitated from solution by evaporation of the water in which they were dissolved. The salinity of the water—that is, the proportion of the dissolved material to the water—determines the type of mineral that will precipitate out. The gypsum begins to separate from sea water when the salinity (at 30°C) reaches a little over 3 times its normal value. Then, when the salinity of the sea water has increased to about 10 times its normal value, halite begins to precipitate.

Pyroclastic rocks, mentioned in Chapter 5, are sedimentary rocks composed mostly of fragments blown from volcanoes. The fragments may be large pieces that have fallen close to the volcano, or extremely fine ash that has been carried by the wind and deposited hundreds of miles from the volcanic eruption.

Finally, organic matter may be present in sedimentary rocks. In the sedimentary rock known as coal, plant materials are almost the only components. More commonly, however, organic matter is very sparsely disseminated through sedimentary deposits and the resulting rocks.

Texture

Texture refers to the general physical appearance of a rock—to the size, shape, and arrangements of the particles that make it up. There are two major types of texture in sedimentary rocks: clastic and nonclastic.

CLASTIC TEXTURE. The term *clastic* is derived from the Greek for "broken" or "fragmental," and rocks that have been formed from deposits of mineral and rock fragments are said to have clastic texture. The size and shape of the original particles have a direct influence on the nature of the resulting texture. A rock formed from a bed of gravel and sand has a coarse, rubble-like texture that is very different from the sugary texture of a rock developed from a deposit of rounded, uniform sand grains. Furthermore, the process by which a sediment is deposited also affects the texture of the sedimentary rock that develops from it. Thus, the debris dumped by a glacier is composed of a jumbled assortment of rock material ranging from particles of colloidal size to large boulders. A rock that develops from such a deposit has a very different texture from one that develops from a deposit of wind-blown sand, for instance, in which all the particles are approximately 0.15 to 0.30 mm in diameter.

Chemical sedimentary rocks may also show a clastic texture. A rock made up predominantly of shell fragments from a biochemical deposit has a clastic texture that is just as recognizable as the texture of a rock formed from sand deposits.

One of the most useful factors in classifying sedimentary rocks is the size of the individual particles. In practice, we

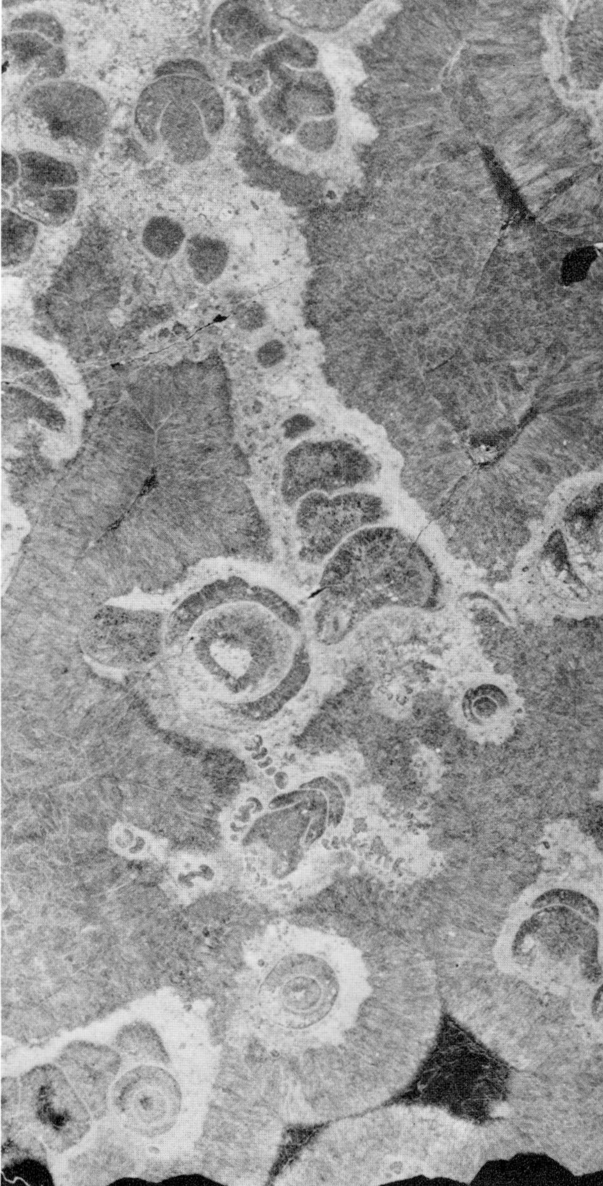

FIG. 8-7
Microscopic examination reveals a sequence of events involved in the formation of this limestone. The globular forms are fossils of unknown modern affinities and are called Cheilosporites. *Around them, white, halo-like zones of calcite were deposited by algae. Most of the pores were then almost completely filled by calcite that grew with a fibrous habit. Finally, a few remaining pores were filled with a clear, coarse variety of calcite, the very dark patches at the top and bottom. This limestone, then, represents two periods in which calcite was deposited organically and two later periods of inorganic deposition. Photo by E. C. Bierwagen.*

TABLE 8-1
Wentworth scale of particle sizes for clastic sediments

WENTWORTH SCALE SIZE	FRAGMENT	TO GET NEXT LARGER SIZE, MULTIPLY BY	APPROXIMATE EQUIVALENT
	Boulder		
256 mm			10 in.
	Cobble	4	
64 mm			2½ in.
	Pebble	16	
4 mm			5/32 in.
	Granule	2	
2 mm			5/64 in.
	Sand	32	
1/16 mm			.0025 in.
	Silt	16	.06 mm
1/256 mm	Dust		.00015 in.
	Clay		.004 mm

Modified after C. K. Wentworth, "A Scale of Grade and Class Terms for Clastic Sediments," *J. Geol.*, XXX (1922), 381.

usually express the size of a particle in terms of its diameter, rather than in terms of volume, weight, or surface area. When we speak of "diameter," we imply that the particle is a sphere, but it is very unlikely that any fragment in a sedimentary rock is a true sphere. In geological measurements, the term simply means the diameter that an irregularly shaped particle *would* have if it were a sphere of equivalent volume. Obviously, it would be a time-consuming, if not impossible, task to determine the volume of each sand grain or pebble in a rock, and then to convert these measurements into appropriate diameters. So the diameters we use for particles are only approximations of their actual sizes. They are accurate enough, however, for our needs.

Several scales have been proposed to describe particles ranging in size from large boulders to minerals of microscopic dimensions. The Wentworth scale, presented in Table 8-1, is used widely, though not universally, by American and Canadian geologists. Notice that although the term "clay" is used in the table to designate all particles below $\frac{1}{256}$ mm in diameter, the same term is used to describe certain minerals. To avoid confusion, we must always refer specifically to either "clay size" or "clay mineral," unless the context makes the meaning clear.

Since determining the size of particles calls for the use of special equipment, the procedure is normally carried out only in the laboratory. In examining specimens in the field, an educated guess based on careful examination usually suffices.

NONCLASTIC TEXTURE. Some, but not all, sedimentary rocks formed by chemical processes have a nonclastic texture in which the grains are interlocked. These rocks have somewhat the same appearance as igneous rocks with crystalline texture. Actually, most of the sedimentary rocks with nonclastic texture do have a crystalline structure, although a few of them, such as opal, do not.

The mineral crystals that precipitate from an aqueous solution are usually very small in size. Because the fluid in which they form has a very low density, they usually settle out rapidly and accumulate on the bottom as mud. Eventually, under the weight of additional sediments, the mud is compacted more and more. Now the size of the individual crystals may begin to increase. Their growth may be induced by added pressure causing the favorably oriented grains to grow at the expense of less favorably oriented neighboring grains. Or crystals may grow as more and more mineral matter is added to them from the saturated solutions trapped in the original mud. In any event, the resulting rock is made up of interlocking crystals and has a texture similar to that of crystalline igneous rocks. Depending upon the size of the crystals, we refer to these nonclastic textures as fine-grained, medium-grained, or coarse-grained. A coarse-grained texture has grains larger than 5 mm in diameter, and a fine-grained texture has grains less than 1 mm in diameter.

Lithification

The process of *lithification* converts unconsolidated rock-forming materials into consolidated, coherent rock. The term is derived from the Greek for "rock" and the Latin "to make." In the following section, we shall discuss the various ways in which sedimentary deposits are lithified.

CEMENTATION. In cementation, the spaces between the individual particles of an unconsolidated deposit are filled up by some binding agent. Of the many minerals that serve as cementing agents, the most common are calcite, dolomite, and quartz. Others include iron oxide, opal, chalcedony, anhydrite, and pyrite. Apparently, the cementing material is carried in solution by water that percolates through the open spaces between the particles of the deposit. Then some factor in the new environment causes the mineral to be deposited, and what was formerly an unconsolidated deposit is cemented into a sedimentary rock.

In coarse-grained deposits, there are relatively large interconnecting spaces between the particles. As we would expect, these deposits are very susceptible to cementation, because the percolating water can move through them with great ease. Deposits of sand and gravel are transformed by cementation into the sedimentary rocks sandstone and conglomerate, respectively.

COMPACTION AND DESICCATION. In a fine-grained clastic deposit of silt-sized and clay-sized particles, the pore spaces are usually so small that water cannot freely circulate through them. Consequently, very little cementing material manages to find its way between the particles. But deposits of this sort are lithified by two other processes: compaction and desiccation.

In *compaction,* the pore space between individual grains is gradually reduced by the pressure of overlying sediments or by pressures resulting from earth movement. Coarse deposits of sand and gravel undergo some compaction, but fine-grained deposits of silt and clay respond much more readily. As the individual particles are pressed closer and closer together, the thickness of the deposit is reduced and its coherence is increased. It has been estimated that deposits of clay-sized particles, buried to depths of 3,000 feet, have been compacted to about 60 per cent of their original volume.

In *desiccation,* the water that originally filled the pore spaces of water-laid clay and silt deposits is forced out. Sometimes this is the direct result of compaction. But desiccation also takes place when a deposit is simply exposed to the air and the water evaporates.

compaction or evaporation

CRYSTALLIZATION. The crystallization of certain chemical deposits is in itself a form of lithification. Crystallization also serves to harden deposits that have been laid down by mechanical processes of sedimentation. For example, new minerals may crystallize within a deposit, or the crystals of existing minerals may increase in size. New minerals sometimes are produced by chemical reactions among amorphous, colloidal materials in fine-grained muds. Exactly how and when these reactions occur is not yet generally understood. But the fact that new crystals *have* formed after the deposit was initially laid down becomes increasingly apparent as we make more and more detailed studies of sedimentary rocks. Furthermore,

FIG. 8-8
A conglomerate is a lithified gravel composed of rounded pebbles, as shown in this example. Largest pebble is about 2 inches long. Photo by G. K. Gilbert, U.S. Geol. Survey.

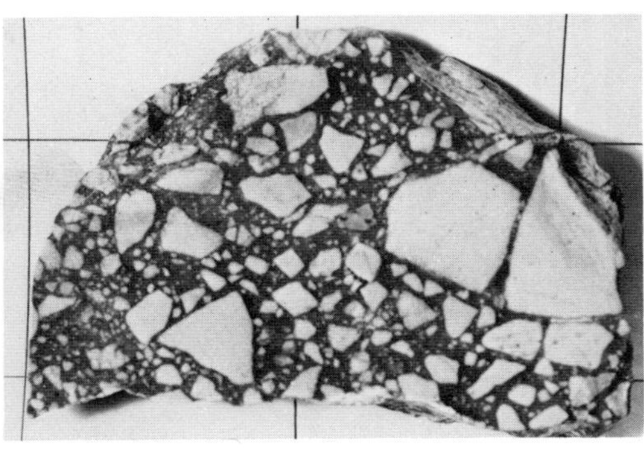

FIG. 8-9
A breccia is a lithified gravel containing many angular fragments. This specimen is from eastern Nevada. Background squares are 2 inches. Specimen in Princeton University Museum of Natural History. Photo by Willard Starks.

it seems clear that this crystallization promotes the process of lithification, particularly in the finer sediments.

TYPES OF SEDIMENTARY ROCKS

Classification

Having examined some of the factors involved in the formation of sedimentary rocks, we are in a better position to consider a classification for this rock family. The classification presented in Table 8-2 represents only one of many possible schemes, but it will serve our purposes very adequately. Notice that there are two main groups—detrital and chemical—based on the origin of the rocks, and that the chemical category is further split into inorganic and biochemical. All the detrital rocks have clastic texture, whereas the chemical rocks have either clastic or nonclastic texture. We use particle size to subdivide the detrital rocks, and composition to subdivide the chemical rocks.

Detrital sedimentary rocks

CONGLOMERATE. A *conglomerate* is a detrital rock made up of more or less rounded fragments, an appreciable percentage of which are of granule size (2 to 4 mm in diameter) or larger. If the fragments are more angular than rounded, the rock is called a *breccia*. Another type of conglomerate is *tillite,* a rock formed from deposits laid down directly by glacier ice (see Chapter 13). The large particles in a conglomerate are usually rock fragments, and the finer particles are usually minerals derived from pre-existing rocks (see Figs. 8-8 and 8-9).

SANDSTONE. A *sandstone* is formed by the consolidation of individual grains of sand size (between 1/16 mm and 2 mm in diameter). Sandstone is thus intermediate between coarse-grained conglomerate and fine-grained mudstone. Since the size of the grains varies from one sandstone to another, we speak of coarse-grained, medium-grained, and fine-grained sandstone.

Very often, but not always, the grains in a sandstone are composed of the mineral quartz. If the minerals are predominantly quartz and feldspar, the sandstone is called an

TABLE 8-2
Classification of sedimentary rocks

ORIGIN		TEXTURE	PARTICLE SIZE OR COMPOSITION	ROCK NAME
Detrital		Clastic	Granule or larger	Conglomerate
			Sand	SANDSTONE
			Silt and clay	MUDSTONE and SHALE
Chemical	Inorganic	Clastic and Nonclastic	Calcite, $CaCO_3$	Limestone
			Dolomite, $CaMg(CO_3)_2$	Dolomite
			Halite, NaCl	Salt
			Gypsum, $CaSO_4 \cdot 2H_2O$	Gypsum
	Biochemical		Calcite, $CaCO_3$	LIMESTONE
			Plant remains	Coal

arkose, a French word for the rock formed by the consolidation of debris derived from a mechanically weathered granite. Another variety of sandstone, called *graywacke,* is characterized by its hardness and dark color, and by angular grains of quartz, feldspar, and small fragments of rock set in a matrix of clay-sized particles.

MUDSTONE AND SHALE. Fine-grained detrital rocks composed of clay and silt-sized particles (less than 1/16 mm in diameter) are termed either *mudstone* or *shale.* Mudstones are fine-grained rocks with a massive or blocky aspect, whereas shales are fine-grained rocks that split into platy slabs more or less parallel to the bedding. The particles in these rocks are so small that it is difficult to determine the precise mineral composition of mudstone and shale. We do know, however, that they contain not only clay minerals, but also clay-sized and silt-sized particles of quarts, feldspar, calcite, and dolomite, to mention but a few.

FIG. 8-10
Alternating beds of sandstone and conglomerate dip inland from the sea cliff at Lobos State Park, near Carmel, California. Photo by Sheldon Judson.

Chemical rocks

LIMESTONE. Limestone is a sedimentary rock that is made up chiefly of the mineral calcite, $CaCO_3$, which has been deposited by either inorganic or organic chemical processes. Most limestones have a clastic texture; but nonclastic, particularly crystalline, textures are common.

Biochemically formed limestones are created by the action of plants and animals that extract calcium carbonate from the water in which they live. The calcium carbonate may be either incorporated into the skeleton of the organism or precipitated directly. In any event, when the organism dies, it leaves behind a quantity of calcium carbonate, and over a long period of time thick deposits of this material may be built up. Reefs, ancient and modern, are well-known examples of such accumulations. The most important builders of modern reefs are algae, molluscs, corals, and one-celled animals—the same animals whose ancestors built up the reefs of ancient seas—the reefs, now old and deeply buried, that are often valuable reservoirs of petroleum.

Chalk (from the Latin *calx,* "lime") is made up in part of biochemically derived calcite in the form of the skeletons or skeletal fragments of microscopic oceanic plants and animals. These organic remains are found mixed with very fine-grained calcite deposits of either biochemical or inorganic chemical origin. A much coarser type of limestone composed of organic remains is known as *coquina,* from the Spanish for "shellfish" or "cockle," and is characterized by the accumulation of many large fragments of shells.

Inorganically formed limestone is made up of calcite that has been precipitated from solution by inorganic processes. Some calcite is precipitated from the fresh water of streams, springs, and caves, although the total amount of rock formed in this way is negligible. When calcium-bearing rocks undergo chemical weathering, calcium bicarbonate, $Ca(HCO_3)_2$, is produced in solution. If enough of the water evaporates, or if the temperature rises, or if the pressure falls, calcite is precipitated from this solution. For example, most *dripstone,* or

FIG. 8-11
A massive bed of sandstone caps thinner beds of sandstone alternating with shaley beds. Near Wiley, Wyoming. Photo by Woodruff, U.S. Geol. Survey.

travertine, is formed in caves by the evaporation of water that is carrying calcium carbonate in solution. And *tufa* (from the Italian for "soft rock") is a spongy, porous limestone formed by the precipitation of calcite from the water of streams and springs.

Although geologists understand the inorganic processes by which limestone is formed by precipitation from fresh water, they are not quite sure how important these processes are in precipitation from sea water. Some observers have questioned whether they operate at all. On the floors of modern oceans and in rocks formed in ancient oceans, however, we do find small spheroidal grains called *oölites,* the size of sand and often composed of calcite. These grains are thought to be formed by the inorganic precipitation of calcium carbonate from sea water. The term oölite comes from the Greek for "egg," since an accumulation of oölites resembles a cluster of fish roe. Cross sections show that many oölites, though not all, have grown up around a mineral grain, or around a small fragment of shell that acts as a nucleus. Some limestones are made up largely of oölites. One, widely used for building, is the so-called Indiana or Spergen limestone.

DOLOMITE. In discussing the mineral dolomite, $CaMg(CO_3)_2$, we mentioned that when it occurs in large enough concentrations it forms a rock that is also called dolomite. The origin of dolomite, both mineral and rock, is still in dispute. Some geologists have held that most dolomite is precipitated directly from sea water, but the fact that no dolomite is known to be forming in modern seas has led most investigators to conclude that dolomite is not precipitated directly. Most dolomite rocks are probably formed from limestone, through the replacement of some of the calcium by magnesium.

EVAPORITES. An *evaporite* is a sedimentary rock composed of minerals that were precipitated from solution after the evaporation of the liquid in which they were dissolved. Rock salt (composed of the mineral halite, NaCl), and gypsum (composed of the mineral of the same name, $CaSO_4{\cdot}2H_2O$), are the most abundant evaporites. *Anhydrite* (from the Greek, *anydros,* "waterless") is an evaporite composed of the mineral of the same name, which is simply gypsum without the water, $CaSO_4$.

Most evaporite deposits seem to have been precipitated from sea water, according to a definite sequence. The less highly soluble minerals are the first to drop out of solution. Thus gypsum and anhydrite, both less soluble than halite, are deposited first. Then, as evaporation progresses, the more soluble halite is precipitated.

In the United States, the most extensive deposits of evaporites are found in Texas and New Mexico. Here gypsum, anhydrite, and rock salt make up over 90 per cent of the Castile formation, which has a maximum thickness of nearly 4,000 feet. In central New York State there are thick deposits of rock salt, and in central Michigan there are layers of rock salt and gypsum. Some evaporite deposits are mined for their mineral content, and in certain areas, particularly in the Gulf Coast states, deposits of rock salt have pushed upward toward

FIG. 8-12
Exposure of essentially flat-lying Pierre shale of Cretaceous age (which ended about 65 million years ago) on the Fort Totten Indian Reservation in east-central North Dakota. The shale splits into small, thin slabs parallel to the bedding, a characteristic known as fissility. The fracture planes (approximately at right angles to the bedding) and the fissility give the exposure a blocky appearance. The shovel is approximately 2½ feet long. Photo by Saul Aronow, U.S. Geol. Survey.

the surface to form salt domes containing commercially important reservoirs of petroleum (see Chapter 22).

COAL. Coal is a rock composed of combustible matter derived from the partial decomposition of plants. We shall consider coal as a biochemically formed sedimentary rock, although some geologists prefer to think of it as a metamorphic rock because it passes through various stages (see "Anthracite," in Chapter 18).

The process of coal formation begins with an accumulation of plant remains in a swamp. This accumulation is known as *peat,* a soft, spongy, brownish deposit in which plant structures are easily recognizable. Time, coupled with the pressure produced by deep burial and sometimes by earth movement, gradually transforms the organic matter into coal. During this process, the percentage of carbon increases as the volatile hydrocarbons and water are forced out of the deposit. Coals are ranked according to the percentage of carbon they contain. Peat, with the least amount of carbon, is the lowest ranking; then come lignite or brown coal, bituminous or soft coal, and finally anthracite or hard coal, the highest in percentage of carbon.

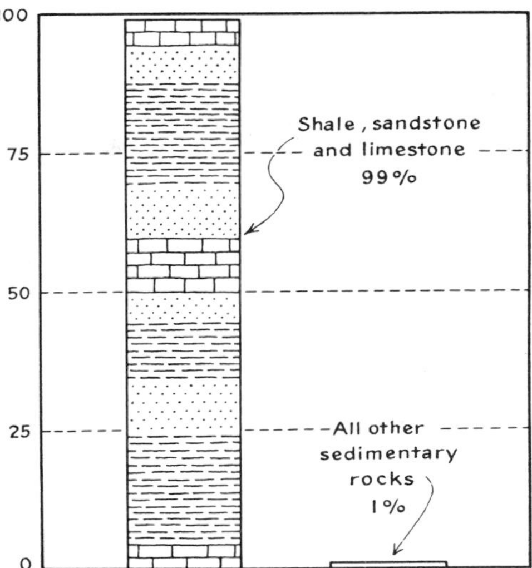

FIG. 8-13
Shale, sandstone, and limestone make up about 99 per cent of all the sedimentary rocks. All other sedimentary rocks total only 1 per cent.

Relative abundance of sedimentary rocks

Sandstone, mudstone and shale, and limestone constitute about 99 per cent of all sedimentary rocks. Of these, mudstone and shale are the most abundant; limestone is the least abundant. Although various estimates have been made of the abundance of each type, actual observations of rocks exposed on the continents suggest that mudstone and shale represent about 46 per cent of the total, sandstone about 32 per cent, and limestone about 22 per cent (see Figs. 8-13 and 8-14).

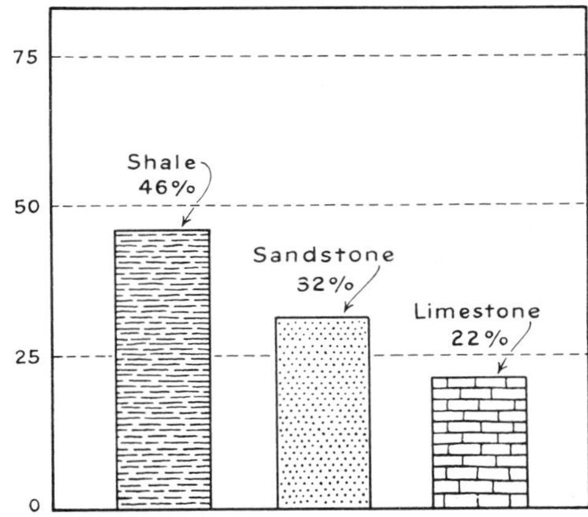

FIG. 8-14
Of shale, sandstone, and limestone, shale is relatively the most abundant and limestone the least abundant. Data from C. K. Leith and W. J. Mead, Metamorphic Geology (New York: Holt, Rinehart and Winston, Inc., 1915), p. 60.

FEATURES OF SEDIMENTARY ROCKS

We have mentioned that the stratification, or bedding, of sedimentary rocks is their single most characteristic feature. Now we shall look more closely at this feature, along with certain other characteristics of sedimentary rocks, including mud cracks and ripple marks, nodules, concretions, geodes, fossils, and color.

Bedding

The beds or layers of sedimentary rocks are separated by parallel *bedding planes,* along which the rocks tend to separate or break. The varying thickness of the layers in a given sedimentary rock reflects the changing conditions that prevailed when each deposit was laid down. In general, each bedding plane marks the termination of one deposit and the beginning of another. For example, let us imagine the bay of an ocean into which rivers normally carry fine silt from the nearby land. This silt settles out from the sea water to form a layer of mud. Now, heavy rains or melting snows may cause the rivers suddenly to flood and thereby pick up coarser material, such as sand, from the river bed. This material will be carried along and dumped into the bay. There it settles to the bottom and blankets the silt that was deposited earlier. The plane of con-

FIG. 8-15
Layered limestone of Mississippian age (which ended about 290 million years ago) along Beaver Creek Canyon in the Big Belt Mountains, Montana. The layers of rock are essentially horizontal and are separated from each other by bedding planes. Photo by Walcott, U.S. Geol. Survey.

FIG. 8-16
Inclined bedding in loosely cemented sandstone. Note the horizontal layers separated by thicker layers in which the bedding is inclined to the right. The hammer suggests the scale. Photo by David A. De Vries.

tact between the mud and the sand represents a bedding plane. If, later on, the silt and the sand are lithified into shale and sandstone, respectively, the bedding plane persists in the sedimentary rock. In fact, it marks a plane of weakness along which the rock tends to break.

Although deposits are usually laid down in horizontal beds, some are created at angles to the horizontal. For example, beds laid down on the surface of sand dunes are inclined (see "Deposition" in Chapter 14), and so are some of the beds that build up on deltas. A special type of inclined bedding is created by the alternate scouring and filling of a stream bed. If the velocity of a stream increases at some point along its course, it scours the sand and gravel from the bottom and carries them away. Then, if the velocity subsequently decreases, the depression is filled up again by sediments that tend to be laid down in inclined layers (see Figs. 8-16 and 8-17).

Mud cracks and ripple marks

Ripple marks are the little waves of sand that commonly develop on the surface of a sand dune, or along a beach, or on the bottom of a stream. *Mud cracks* are familiar on the dried surface of mud left exposed by the subsiding waters of a river. These features are often preserved in solid rock and provide us with clues to the history of the rock.

Mud cracks make their appearance when a deposit of silt or clay dries out and shrinks (see Fig. 8-18). The cracks outline roughly polygonal areas, making the surface of the deposit look like a section cut through a large honeycomb. Eventually, another deposit may come along to bury the first. If the deposits are later lithified, the outlines of the cracks may be accurately preserved for millions of years. Then, when the rock is split along the bedding plane between the two deposits, the cracks will be found much as they appeared when they were first formed, providing evidence that the original deposit underwent alternate flooding and drying.

Ripple marks preserved in sedimentary rocks also furnish clues to the conditions that prevailed when a sediment was orignally deposited. For instance, if the ripple marks are symmetrical, with sharp or slightly rounded ridges separated by more gently rounded troughs, we are fairly safe in assuming that they were formed by the back-and-forth movement of water such as we find along a sea coast outside the surf zone. These marks are called *ripple marks of oscillation* (see Fig. 8-19). If, on the other hand, the ripple marks are asymmetric, we can assume that they were formed by air or water moving more or less continuously in one direction. These marks are called *current ripple marks.*

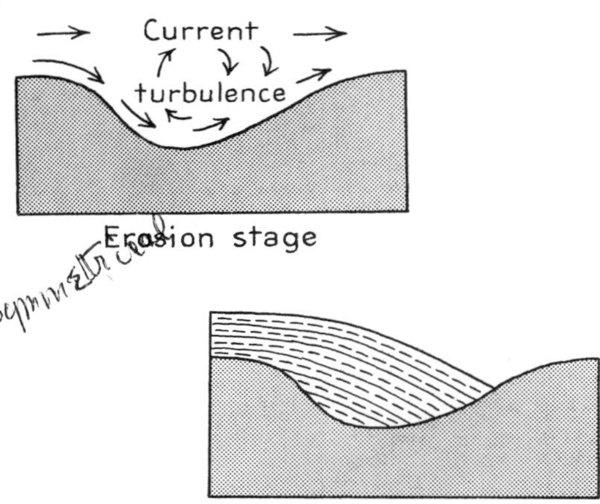

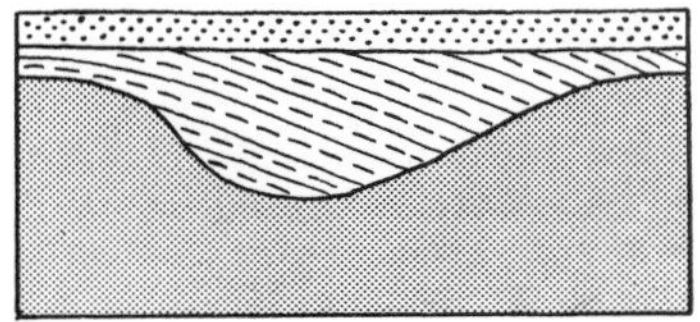

FIG. 8-17
Sequence in the formation of inclined bedding by alternate scouring and filling. A turbulent current first scours a depression in unconsolidated deposits. With a decrease in the velocity of the water, the stream begins to fill up the depression with inclined layers. Redrawn by permission from Robert R. Schrock, Sequence in Layered Rocks (New York: McGraw-Hill Book Company, 1948), p. 280.

Nodules, concretions, and geodes

Many sedimentary rocks contain structures that were formed only *after* the original sediment was deposited. Among these are nodules, concretions, and geodes.

A *nodule* is an irregular, knobby-surfaced body of mineral matter that differs in composition from the sedimentary rock in which it has formed. It usually lies parallel to the bedding planes of the enclosing rock, and sometimes adjoining nodules coalesce to form a continuous bed. Nodules average about one foot in maximum dimension. Silica, in the form of chert or flint, is the major component of these bodies. They are most commonly found in limestone or dolomite. Most nodules are thought to have formed when silica replaced some of the materials of the original deposit; some, however, may consist of silica that was deposited at the same time as the main beds were laid down.

A *concretion* is a local concentration of the cementing material that has lithified a deposit into a sedimentary rock. Concretions range in size from a fraction of an inch to several feet in maximum dimension. Most are shaped like simple spheres or disks, although some have fantastic and complex forms. For some reason, when the cementing material entered the unconsolidated sediment, it tended to concentrate around a common center point or along a common center line. The particles of the resulting concretion are cemented together more firmly than the particles of the host rock that surrounds it. The cementing material usually consists of calcite, dolomite, iron oxide, or silica—in other words, the same cementing materials that we find in the sedimentary rocks themselves.

Geodes, more eye-catching than either concretions or nodules, are roughly spherical, hollow structures that vary in diameter from a few inches to more than a foot (see Fig. 8-20). An outer layer of chalcedony is lined with crystals that project inward toward the hollow center. The crystals, often perfectly formed, are usually quartz, although crystals of calcite and dolomite have also been found and, more rarely, crystals of other minerals. Geodes are most commonly found in limestone, but they also occur in shale.

How does a geode form? First, a water-filled pocket develops in a sedimentary deposit, probably as a result of the decay of

FIG. 8-18
Polygonal pattern of mudcracks resulting from dessication of modern fine-grained sediments in a playa lake in Nevada. Scale shown by pocket knife. Photo by William C. Bradley.

some plant or animal that was buried in the sediments. As the deposit begins to consolidate into a sedimentary rock, a wall of silica with a jelly-like consistency forms around the water, isolating it from the surrounding material. As time passes, fresh water may enter the sediments. The water inside the pocket has a higher salt concentration than the water outside. In order to equalize the concentrations, there is a slow mixing of the two liquids through the silica wall or membrane that separates them. This process of mixing is called *osmosis.* So long as the osmotic action continues, pressure is exerted outward toward the surrounding rock. The original pocket expands bit by bit, until the salt concentrations of the liquids inside and outside are equalized. At this point, osmosis stops, the outward pressure ceases, and the pocket stops growing. Now the silica wall dries, crystallizes to form chalcedony, contracts, and cracks.

If, at some later time, mineral-bearing water finds its way into the deposit. It may seep in through the cracks in the wall of chalcedony. There the minerals are precipitated, and crystals begin to grow inward, toward the center, from the interior walls. Finally, we have a crystal-lined geode imbedded in the surrounding rock. Notice that the crystals in a geode grow inward, whereas in a concretion they grow outward.

FIG. 8-19
Ripple marks of oscillation on a slab of sandstone. The symmetrical nature of the ripples indicates that the current moved back and forth rather than continuously in one direction. Photo by Willard Starks.

FIG. 8-20
Two geodes broken open to show their internal structure. The dark outer layer of chalcedony is lined with milky-to-clear quartz crystals that project inward toward a hollow center. These structures are most commonly found in limestone, where they apparently form by the modification and enlargement of an original void. Specimen from the Geological Museum, Harvard University. Photo by Walter R. Fleischer.

Fossils

The word *fossil* (derived from the Latin *fodere,* "to dig up") originally referred to anything that was dug from the ground, particularly a mineral or some inexplicable form. It is still used in that sense occasionally, as in the term "fossil fuel" (see Chapter 22). But today the term "fossil" generally means any direct evidence of past life—for example, the bones of a dinosaur, the shell of an ancient clam, the footprints of a long-extinct animal, or the delicate impression of a leaf (see Fig. 8-21).

Fossils are usually found in sedimentary rocks, although they

FIG. 8-21
This limestone slab is marked by the impression of a large number of fossil brachiopods, a type of marine mollusc. Scale is given by 2-inch squares in the background. Specimen from Princeton University Museum of Natural History. Photo by Willard Starks.

sometimes turn up in igneous and metamorphic rocks. They are most abundant in mudstone, shale, and limestone, but are also found in sandstone, dolomite, and conglomerate. Fossils account for almost the entire volume of certain rocks, such as coquina and limestones formed from ancient reefs.

The remains of plants and animals are completely destroyed if they are left exposed on the earth's surface; but if they are somehow protected from destructive forces, they may become incorporated in a sedimentary deposit where they will be preserved for millions of years. In the quiet water of the ocean, for example, the remains of starfish, snails, and fish may be buried by sediments as they settle slowly to the bottom. If these sediments are subsequently lithified, the remains are preserved as fossils that tell us about the sort of life that existed when the sediments were laid down.

Fossils are also preserved in deposits that have settled out of fresh water. Countless remains of land animals, large and small, have been dug from the beds of extinct lakes, flood plains, and swamps.

The detailed story of the development of life as recorded by fossils is properly a part of historical geology, and we do not have time to trace it here, but in Chapter 9 we shall find that fossils are extremely useful in subdividing geologic time and constructing the geologic column.

Sedimentary facies

If we examine the environments of deposition that exist at any one time over a wide area, we find that they differ from place to place. Thus, the fresh-water environment of a river changes to a brackish-water environment as the river nears the ocean. In the ocean itself, marine conditions prevail. But even here the marine environment changes—from shallow water to deep water, for example. And as the environment changes, the nature of the sediments that are laid down also changes. The deposits in one environment show characteristics that are different from the characteristics of deposits laid down at the same time in another environment. This change in the "look" of the sediments is called a change in *sedimen-*

FIG. 8-22
Some sedimentary rocks are made up of extremely fine particles. This photo by electron miscroscope shows the structure of a limestone of Paleocene age from Zumaya, Spain. The magnification is about 10,000×. The geometric markings represent coccoliths, interlocking, en echelon plates of calcite that are developed by certain one-celled flagellate animals. Photo by S. Honjo.

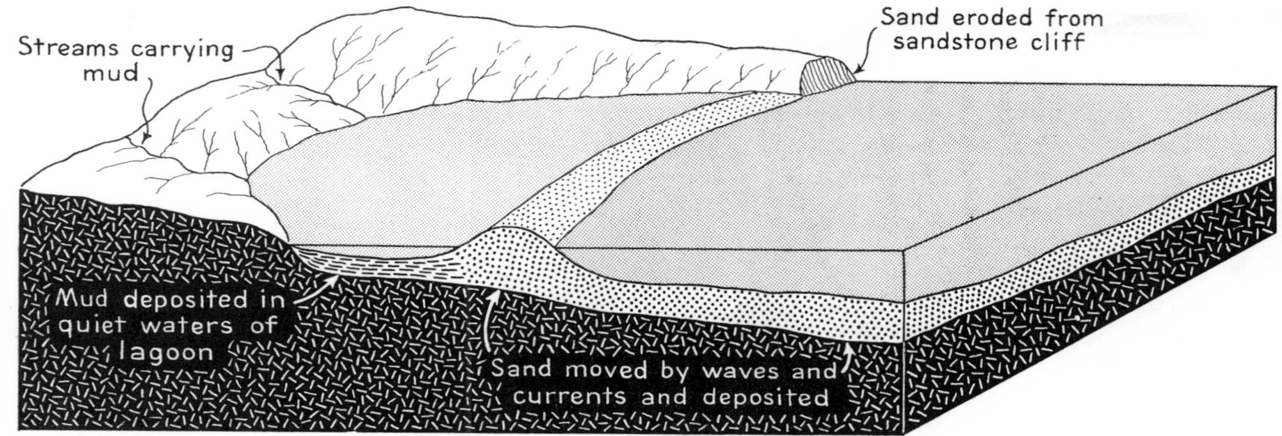

FIG. 8-23
Diagram to illustrate a change in sedimentary facies. Here, the fine-grained muds are deposited in a lagoon close to shore. A sand bar separates them from sand deposits farther away from shore. The sand in this instance has been derived from a sea cliff and transported by waves and currents.

tary facies; the latter word derives from the Latin for "aspect" or "form."

We may define sedimentary facies as an accumulation of deposits that exhibits specific characteristics and grades laterally into other sedimentary accumulations formed at the same time but exhibiting different characteristics. The concept of facies is widely used in studying sedimentary rocks and the conditions that gave rise to metamorphic rocks (see Chapter 18). The concept is not generally used in referring to igneous rocks, though there is no valid reason why it should not be used.

Let us consider a specific example of facies. Figure 8-23 shows a coastline where rivers from the land empty into a lagoon. The lagoon is separated from the open ocean by a

FIG. 8-24
Variation in facies of modern sediments off the coast of southern California. After Revelle and Shepard, in Recent Marine Sediments, Am. Assoc. Petroleum Geol. (1939), p. 246.

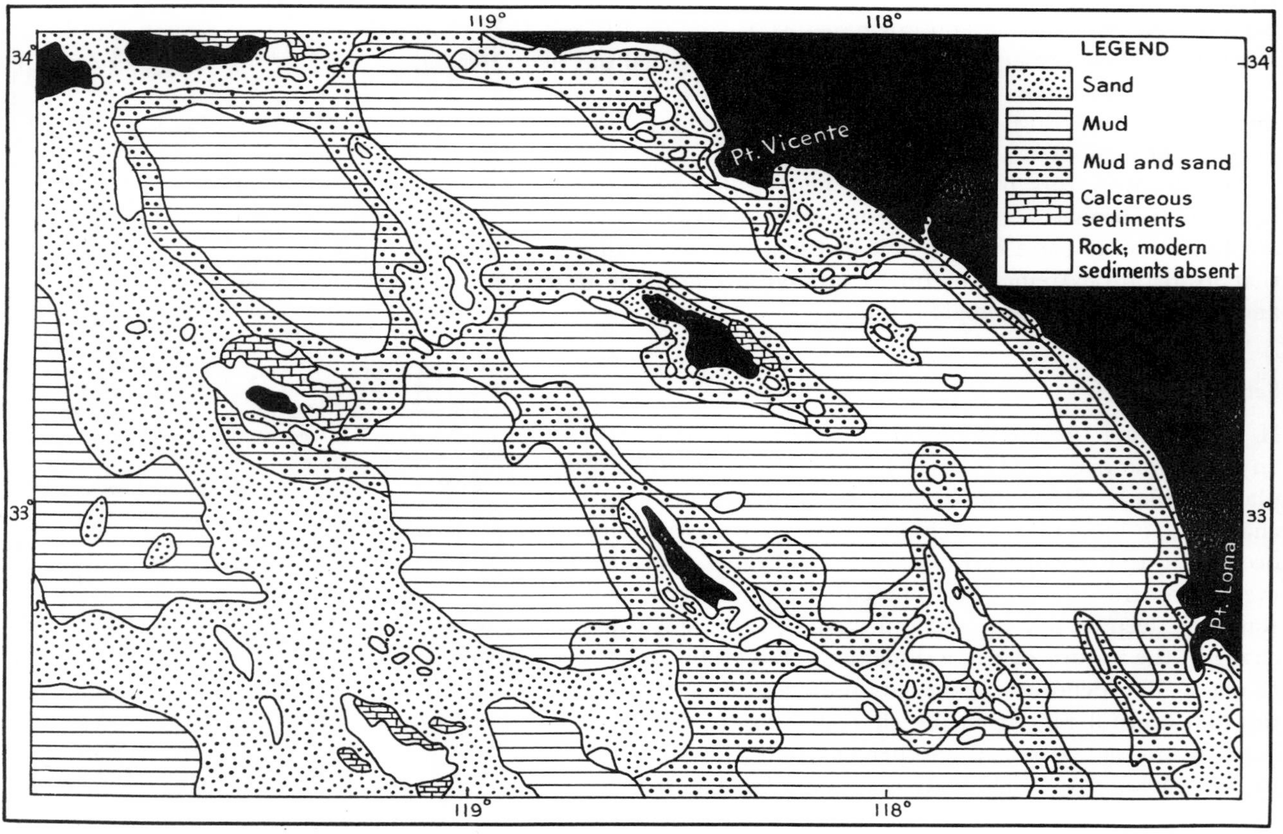

119° 118°
34° 34°
LEGEND
Sand
Mud
Mud and sand
Calcareous sediments
Rock; modern sediments absent
Pt. Vicente
33° 33°
Pt. Loma
119° 118°

sandbar. The fine silts and clays dumped into the quiet waters of the lagoon settle to the bottom as a layer of mud. At the same time, waves are eroding coarse sand from a nearby headland outside the lagoon. This sand is transported by currents and waves and deposited as a sandy layer seaward of the sandbar. Different environments exist inside and outside the lagoon; therefore, different deposits are being laid down simultaneously. Notice that the mud and the sand grade into each other along the sandbar. Now, imagine that these deposits were consolidated into rock and then exposed to view at the earth's surface. We would find a shale layer grading into sandstone—that is, one sedimentary facies is grading into another.

But the picture is not always so simple. Figure 8-24 shows the distribution of sediments off the coast of southern California. Here recent sediments range from sand, through a sandy mud, to mud, and in a few areas there are limy deposits. Where the sea floor is rocky, little or no recent sedimentation has taken place. Should the soft sediments become lithified, a sedimentary rock ranging from sandstone through sandy shale to shale and limestone would result.

Ancient sedimentary deposits show exactly this kind of variation in facies. Figure 8-25 pictures the actual pattern of rock types that have been identified in the middle portion of the Maquoketa formation in Illinois. Notice that the types include limestone, shale, limy shale, and a limy shale containing some sand.

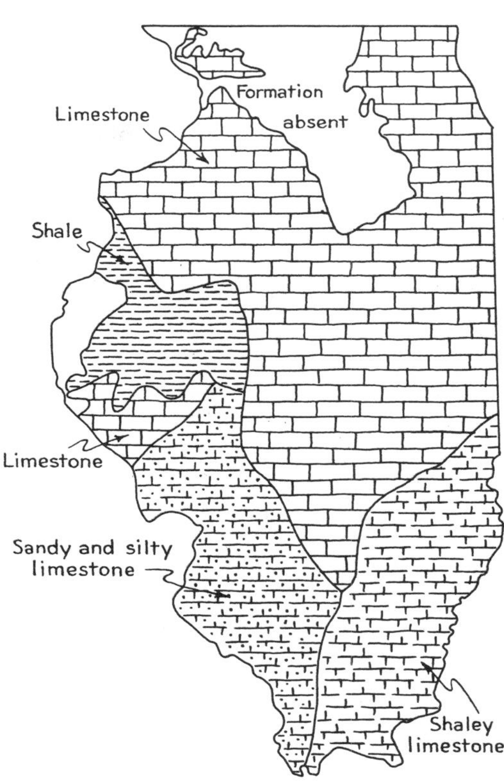

FIG. 8-25
Variation in facies of ancient sediments comprising the Maquoketa formation in Illinois. After E. P. DuBois, Illinois Geol. Survey, Report of Investigations #105 (1945), p. 10.

Color of sedimentary rocks

Throughout the western and southwestern areas of the United States, bare cliffs and steep-walled canyons provide a brilliant display of the great variety of colors exhibited by sedimentary rocks. The Grand Canyon of the Colorado River in Arizona cuts through rocks that vary in color from gray, through purple and red, to brown, buff, and green. Bryce Canyon in southern Utah is fashioned of rocks tinted a delicate pink, and the Painted Desert farther south in Arizona exhibits a wide range of colors, including red, gray, purple, and pink.

The most important sources of color in sedimentary rocks are the iron oxides. Hematite (Fe_2O_3), for example, gives rocks a red or pink color, and limonite or goethite produces tones of yellow and brown. Some of the green, purple, and black colors may be caused by iron, but in exactly what form is not completely understood. Only a very small amount of iron oxide is needed to color a rock. In fact, few sedimentary rocks contain more than 6 per cent of iron, and most contain very much less.

Organic matter, when present, may also contribute to the coloring of sedimentary rocks, usually making them gray to black. Generally, but not always, the higher the organic content, the darker the rock.

The size of the individual particles in a rock also influences the color, or at least the intensity of the color. For example, fine-grained clastic rocks are usually somewhat darker than coarse-grained rocks of the same mineral composition.

SUMMARY OUTLINE

Sedimentary rocks
- Cover 75 per cent of land surface
- Comprise 5 per cent of outer 10 miles of earth's crust

Origin of material
- Detrital sediments worn from land masses
- Chemical sediments precipitated from solution

Sedimentary deposits
- Vary with source of material, with methods of transportation, and with methods of deposition

Composition
- Clay, quartz, and calcite most important
- Most sedimentary rocks are mixtures of two or more minerals

Texture
- Size, shape, and arrangement of particles
- Clastic and nonclastic (chiefly crystalline)

Lithification
- Cementation, compaction and desiccation, and crystallization

Types of sedimentary rocks
- Detrital rocks have clastic texture and include conglomerate, sandstone, and mudstone and shale
- Chemical rocks have either clastic or nonclastic texture, and include limestone, dolomite, rock salt, gypsum, anhydrite, chert and flint, and coal

Relative abundance
- Mudstone and shale most abundant, sandstone less so, and limestone least abundant

Bedding or stratification
- Most characteristic feature of sedimentary rocks

Sedimentary facies
- An accumulation of deposits with specific characteristics, grading laterally into other sedimentary deposits with different characteristics

Color
- Iron oxides most important coloring matter

SELECTED REFERENCES

Pettijohn, F. J., *Sedimentary Rocks* (2nd ed.). New York: Harper & Row, Publishers, 1957.

Shrock, Robert R., *Sequence in Layered Rocks.* New York: McGraw-Hill Book Company, 1948.

Williams, Howel, Francis J. Turner, and Charles M. Gilbert, *Petrography.* San Francisco: W. H. Freeman and Co., 1954.

11/10/66

9

Geologic time

ABSOLUTE TIME
RADIOACTIVITY
SEDIMENTATION AND ABSOLUTE TIME
RELATIVE TIME
LAW OF SUPERPOSITION
CORRELATION OF SEDIMENTARY ROCKS
THE GEOLOGIC COLUMN
THE GEOLOGIC TIME SCALE
ABSOLUTE DATES IN THE GEOLOGIC TIME SCALE

Back in Chapter 1 we stressed the vastness of geologic time and emphasized that in order to understand fully the physical processes of geology we must constantly keep in mind this enormous stretch of time. In this chapter, we shall look at some of the ways of measuring geologic time and at how the geologic time-scale has been worked out.

We may think of geologic time in two ways: relative and absolute. *Relative time*—that is, whether one event in earth history came *before or after* another event—disregards years. *Absolute time* measures whether a geologic event took place a *few thousand years* ago, a *billion years* ago, or at some date even farther back in earth history.

Relative and absolute time in earth history have their counterparts in human history. In tracing the history of the earth, we may want to know whether some event, such as a volcanic eruption, occurred before or after another event, such as a rise in sea level, and how these two events are related in time to a third event, perhaps a mountain-building episode. In human history, too, we try to establish the relative position of events in time. In studying American history it is important to know that the Revolution preceded the War between the States, and that the Canadian-American boundary was fixed some time between these two events.

Sometimes, of course, events in both earth history and human history can be established in only relative terms. But our record becomes increasingly precise as we fit more and more events into an actual chronological calendar. If we did not know the date of the U.S.-Canadian boundary treaty—knew only that it was signed between the two wars—we could place it between 1783 and 1861. Recorded history, of course, provides us with the actual date, 1846.

Naturally, we would like to be able to date geologic events with precision. But so far this has been impossible, and the accuracy achieved in determining the dates of human history, at least written human history, will probably never be achieved in geologic dating. Still, we can determine approximate dates for many geologic events. Even though they may lack the pre-

FIG. 9-1
The dark areas in this specimen from Grafton, New Hampshire, are made up of the uranium-bearing mineral gummite. Compare with Fig. 9-2. Specimen in the Princeton University Museum of Natural History. Photo by Willard Starks.

cision of dates in recent human history, they are probably of the correct order of magnitude. We can say that the dinosaurs became extinct about 63 million years ago, and that about 11,000 years ago the last continental glacier began to recede from New England and the area bordering the Great Lakes.

ABSOLUTE TIME

We earthlings use two basic units of time: (1) a day, the interval required for our globe (in the present epoch) to complete one revolution on its axis and (2) a year, the interval required for the earth to complete one circuit of the sun. In geology, however, the problem is to determine how many of these units of time elapsed in the dim past when nobody was around to count and record them. Our most valuable clues in solving this problem are provided by the decay rates of radioactive minerals.

Radioactivity

The nuclei of certain elements spontaneously emit particles, and in so doing produce new elements. This process is known as *radioactivity*. Shortly after the turn of the present century, researchers suggested that minerals containing radioactive elements could be used to determine the age of other minerals in terms of absolute time (see Figs. 9-1 and 9-2).

Let us take a single radioactive element as an example of how this method works. Regardless of what element we use, we must know what products result from its radioactive decay. Let us choose uranium-238, ${}_{92}U^{238}$, which is known to yield helium and lead, ${}_{82}Pb^{206}$, as end products. We know, too, the rate at which uranium-238 decays. So far as we can determine, this rate is constant and unaffected by any known chemical or physical agency. The rate at which a radioactive element decays is expressed in terms of what we call its *half life*—the time required for half of the nuclei in a sample of that element to decay. The half life of uranium-238 is 4.56×10^9 years, which means that if we start with an ounce of uranium-238 there will be only half an ounce left after 4,560 million years. The history of an ounce of uranium-238 may be recorded as follows:

AGE *(in millions of years)*	${}_{82}Pb^{206}$ FORMED *(ounces)*	${}_{92}U^{238}$ REMAINING* *(ounces)*
100	.013	.985
1,000	.116	.825
2,000	.219	.747
3,000	.306	.646

* Sir James Jeans, *The Universe Around Us* (New York: The Macmillan Company, 1929), p. 144.

If you look carefully at these figures, you will see that at any instant during this process there is a unique ratio of lead-206 to uranium-238. This ratio depends on the length of time decay has been going on. Theoretically, then, we may find the age of a uranium mineral by determining how much lead-206 is present and how much uranium-238 is present. The ratio of lead to uranium then serves as an index to the age of the mineral.

One of the basic assumptions we have made in applying radioactivity to age determination is that the laws governing the rate of decay have remained constant over incredibly long periods of time, but we are justified in wondering whether this assumption is valid. Geology supplies one piece of confirming evidence in the form of *pleochroic* ("many-colored") *halos.* These are minute, concentric, spherical zones of dark or colored material no more than three-thousandths of an inch in diameter—the thickness of an ordinary sheet of paper—that form around inclusions of radioactive materials in biotite and in a few other minerals. If such a sphere is sliced through the center, the resulting sections show the pleochroic halos as rings. Each ring is a region in which alpha particles, shot out of the decaying radioactive mineral, came to rest and ionized the host material. The effect resembles that of light on a photographic film.

The energy possessed by an alpha particle depends on what element released it, and on the stage of decay at which the particle was released. The pleochroic halos have radii that correspond to the energy of present-day alpha particles. Apparently, the energy of an alpha particle today is the same as it was hundreds of millions of years ago. This fact implies that the fundamental constants of nuclear physics that govern the travel of alpha particles have not changed.

This evidence, of course, does not prove explicitly that the rate of decay has always been the same. But if the laws governing the energy of the particles have not changed, it is reasonable to assume that related laws governing the rate of decay have also continued unchanged.

Uranium-238 is not the only element found useful in the age determination of rock material; there are others. But the same basic idea prevails, whatever element we choose. If we discover a mineral that contains one or more radioactive elements, we may be able (after proper chemical analysis) to determine how many years ago the mineral was formed. If the mineral was formed at the same time as the rock in which it is enclosed, the age of the mineral will also give us the age of the rock.

Methods of determining age by radioactivity have produced literally hundreds of dates for events in earth history, and new ones are constantly being reported. By the mid-1960's, rocks from a number of localities had been dated as approximately 3.3 billion years old. Field relations show that other, still older rocks exist. A granite about 3.2 billion years old from Pretoria, South Africa, contains inclusions of a quartzite, positive indication that older, sedimentary rocks existed before the intrusion of the granite. The exact age of the earth itself is still undetermined, but several lines of evidence converge to suggest an age of about 4.5 billion years.

Modern science, then, has fully vindicated the assumptions made over a century and a half ago that geologic time *is* vast and that within earth history there *is* abundant time for slow processes to accomplish prodigious feats.

Most methods of age determination through radioactivity cannot be used to date recent events of geologic history—that is, events that occurred less than two million years ago. Radioactive potassium is an exception and has been used with good results in some instances. But for very recent geologic events

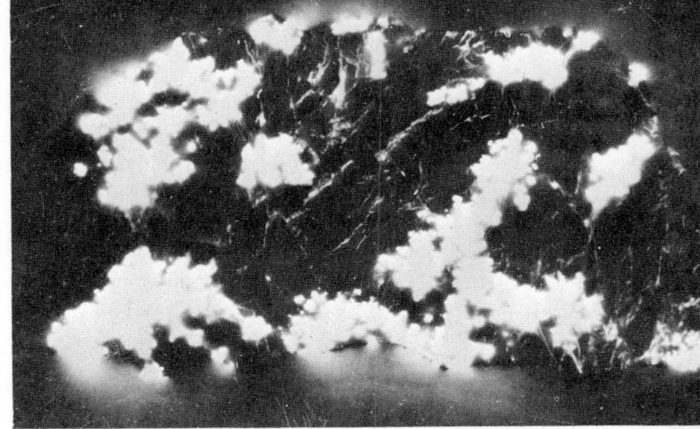

FIG. 9-2
A photograph of the same specimen as that in Fig. 9-1. In this photo the specimen was placed on a photographic plate. As the uranium and some of its radioactive daughter products decayed, the plate was exposed to the emission of particles. The white areas mark the location of the uranium-bearing minerals.

FIG. 9-3
This fragment of spruce log was part of a tree in a buried forest at Two Creeks, Wisconsin. Carbon-14 measurements of wood from the forest reveal that the trees died some 11,350 years ago, thereby establishing the date of the ice invasion. Our 2-inch squares again provide the scale. Photo by Willard Starks.

FIG. 9-4
Varves from glacial Lake Hackensack, northern New Jersey. Each pair of dark and light layers is thought to represent a single year of sedimentation in the old lake. Note the variable thickness of the varves. Photo by Paul MacClintock.

there is only one radioactive element that has been used with any real success, and that is the radioactive isotope of carbon, *carbon-14,* ${}_6C^{14}$. This isotope can be used only for organic material that is 50,000 years old or less (see Fig. 9-3).

The carbon-14 method, first developed at the University of Chicago by Willard F. Libby, works as follows. When neutrons from outer space, sometimes called cosmic rays, bombard nitrogen in the outer atmosphere, they knock a proton out of the nitrogen nucleus, thereby forming carbon-14.

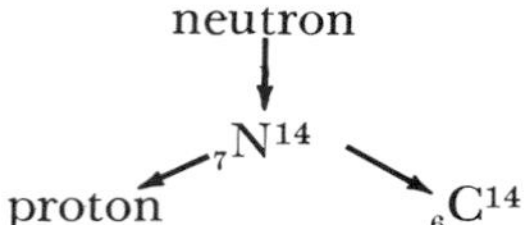

The carbon-14 combines with oxygen to form a special carbon dioxide, $C^{14}O_2$, which circulates in the atmosphere and eventually reaches the earth's surface, where it is absorbed by living matter. It has been found that the distribution of carbon-14 around the world is almost constant. Its abundance is independent of longitude, latitude, altitude, and the type of habitat of living matter.

There is, then, a certain small amount of carbon-14 in all living matter. And when the organism—whether it is a plant or an animal—dies, its supply of carbon-14 is, of course, no longer replenished by life processes. Instead, the carbon-14, with a half life of about 5,600 years, begins spontaneously to change back to $_7N^{14}$. The longer the time that has elapsed since the death of the organism, the less the amount of carbon-14 that remains. So when we find carbon-14 in a buried piece of wood or in a charred bone, by comparing the amount present with the universal modern abundance, we can work out the amount of time that has elapsed since the material ceased to take in $C^{14}O_2$—that is, since the organism died.

Radioactivity and sedimentary rocks

Until recently, radioactive minerals suitable for dating geologic events were sought chiefly in the igneous rocks. These rocks were usually the uranium- and thorium-bearing minerals. Even today the great bulk of the radioactively dated rocks are igneous in origin. The development of new techniques, however, particularly the use of radioactive potassium, has extended radioactive dating to some of the sedimentary rocks.

Some sandstones and, more rarely, the shales contain *glauconite,* a silicate mineral similar to biotite. Glauconite, formed in certain marine environments when the sedimentary layers are deposited, contains radioactive potassium, another geologic hourglass that reveals the age of the mineral and, hence, the age of the rock. The end products of the decay of radioactive potassium are argon and calcium.

Pyroclastic rocks are composed mostly or completely of volcanic ash. Biotite in these rocks includes radioactive potassium, and so offers a way of dating the biotite and sometimes the rock itself.

Sedimentation and absolute time

Another way of establishing absolute dates for sedimentary strata is to determine the rate of their deposit.

Certain sedimentary rocks show a succession of thinly laminated beds. Various lines of evidence suggest that, in some instances at least, each one of these beds represents a single year of deposition. So by counting the beds, we can determine the total time it took for the rock to be deposited.

Unfortunately, we have been able to link this kind of information to our modern calendar in only a very few places, such as the Scandinavian countries. Here the Swedish geologist Baron de Geer counted the annual deposits, or laminations, that formed in extinct glacial lakes. These laminations, called *varves* (see Fig. 9-4 and Chapter 13), enable us to piece together some of the geologic events of the last 20,000 years or so in the countries ringing the Baltic Sea.

Much longer sequences of laminated sediments have been found in other places, but they tell us only the *total length of time* during which sedimentation took place, not *how long ago* it happened, in absolute time. One excellent example of absolute time sequence is recorded in the Green River shales of Wyoming (see Figs. 9-5, 9-6). Here each bed, interpreted as an annual deposit, is less than .007 inch thick, and the total thickness of the layers is about 2,600 feet. These shales represent, then, approximately 6½ million years of time.

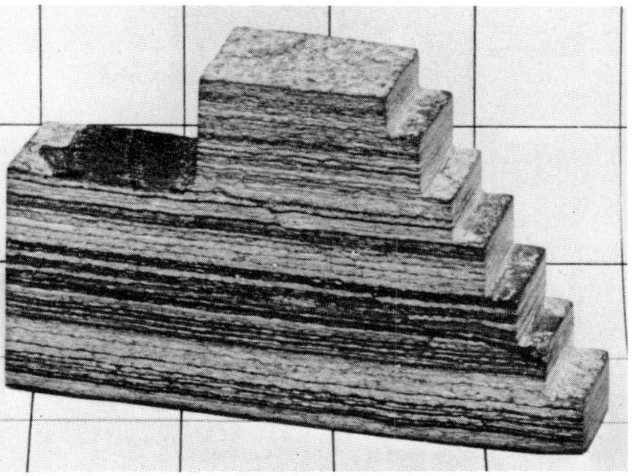

FIG. 9-5
The Green River shale in Wyoming is composed of minute, annual layers. Since each step in this block is 100 layers high, the entire block records 700 years of sedimentation. A portion of a fossil fish is seen on the large step on the left-hand side of the block. Counting the layers indicates that the fish died 471 years after the formation of the lowest layer. Specimen in the Princeton University Museum of Natural History. Photo by Willard Starks.

FIG. 9-6
An enlarged section of Green River shale showing, greatly magnified, the layered nature of the rock. The specimen represents about 100 years of time in a piece of rock about 0.39 inches thick. At this rate of accumulation, one foot of Green River shale represents approximately 3,360 years. Specimen from Princeton University Museum of Natural History. Photo by Fred Anderegg.

RELATIVE TIME

Before geologists knew how to determine absolute time, they discovered events in earth history that convinced them of the great length of geologic time. In putting these events in chronological order, they found themselves subdividing geologic time on a relative basis and using certain labels to indicate relative time. You have probably picked up a newspaper or magazine and have read of the discovery of a dinosaur that lived 100 million years ago during the Cretaceous period, or of the development of a new oil field in strata formed 280 million years ago in the Pennsylvanian period. "Cretaceous" and "Pennsylvanian" are terms used by geologists to designate certain units of *relative geologic time.* In this section, we shall look at how such units have been set up, and how absolute dates have been suggested for them.

Relative geologic time has been determined largely by the relative positions of sedimentary rocks. Remember that a given layer of sedimentary rock represents a certain amount of time—the time it took for the original deposit to accumulate. By arranging various sedimentary rocks in their proper chronological sequence, we are, in effect, arranging units of time in *their* proper order. Our first task in constructing a relative time-scale, then, is to arrange the sedimentary rocks in their proper order.

The Law of Superposition

The basic principle used to determine whether one sedimentary rock is older than another is very simple, and it is known as the *Law of Superposition.* Here is an example. A deposit of mud laid down this year in, say, the Gulf of Mexico, will rest on top of a layer that was deposited last year. Last year's deposit, in turn, rests on successively older deposits that extend backward into time for as long as deposition has been

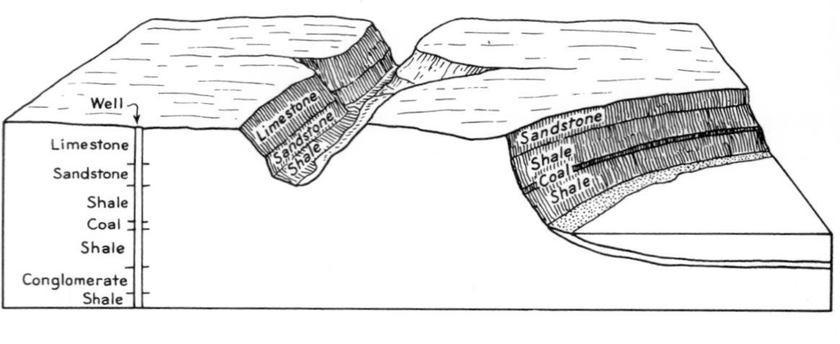

FIG. 9-7
Diagram to illustrate the data that might be used to correlate sedimentary rocks (right) in a sea cliff with those (center) in a stream valley and with those (left) encountered in a well-drilling operation. (See Fig. 9-8.)

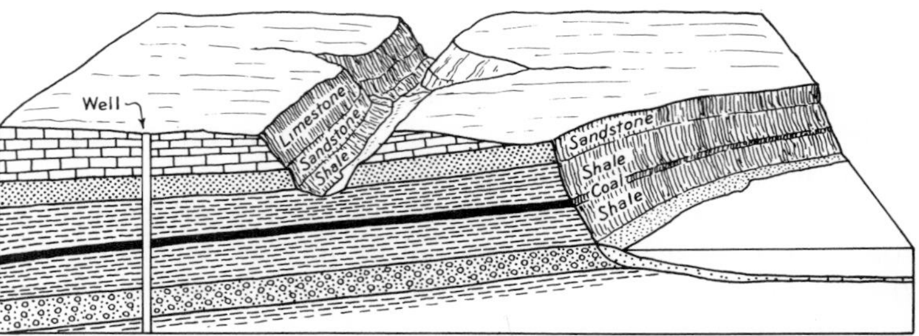

FIG. 9-8
Similar lithologies and sequences of beds in the three different localities shown in Fig. 9-7 suggest the correlation of rock layers shown in the diagram.

going on in the Gulf. If we could slice through these deposits, we would expose a chronologic record with the oldest deposit on the bottom and the youngest on top. This sequence would illustrate the Law of Superposition: *if a series of sedimentary rocks has not been overturned, the topmost layer is always the youngest and the lowermost layer is always the oldest.*

On first glance, this is an almost absurdly simple principle. For instance, in a cliff of sedimentary rocks, with one layer lying on top of another, it is perfectly obvious that the oldest is on the bottom and the youngest on top. We can quickly determine the relative age of any one layer in the cliff in relation to any other layer. The difficulty, however, lies in the fact that unknown hundreds of thousands of feet of sedimentary rock have been deposited during earth time. And there is no one cliff, no one area where *all* these rocks are exposed to our view. The rocks in one place may be older, or younger, or of the same age as those in some other place. The task is to find out how the rocks all around the world fit into some kind of relative time-scale.

Correlation of sedimentary rocks

Since we cannot find sedimentary rocks representing all of earth time neatly arranged in one convenient area, we must piece together the rock sequence from locality to locality. This process of tying one rock sequence in one place to another in some other place is known as *correlation,* from the Latin, "together" plus "relate."

CORRELATION BY PHYSICAL FEATURES. When sedimentary rocks show rather constant and distinctive features over a wide geographic area, we can sometimes connect sequences of rock layers from different localities. Figures 9-7 and 9-8 illustrate how this is done. Here is a series of sedimentary rocks exposed in a sea cliff. The topmost, and hence the youngest, is a sandstone. Beneath the sandstone we find first a shale, then a seam of coal, then more shale extending down to the level of the modern beach. We can trace these layers for some distance along the cliff face. But how are they related to other rocks farther inland?

Along the rim of a canyon that lies inland from the cliff we find that limestone rocks have been exposed. Are they older or younger than the sandstone in the cliff face? Scrambling down the canyon walls, we come to a ledge of sandstone that looks very much like the sandstone in the cliff. If it *is* the same, then the limestone must be younger, because it lies above it. The only trouble is that we cannot be certain that the two sandstone beds *are* the same. So we continue down to the bottom of the canyon, and there find some shale beds very similar to the shale beds exposed in the sea cliff beneath the sandstone. We feel fairly confident that the sandstone and the shale in the canyon are the same beds as the sandstone and upper shale in the sea cliff. But we must admit the possibility that we are dealing with different rocks.

In searching for further data, we find a well being drilled still farther inland, its rig cutting through the same limestone we saw in the canyon walls. As the bit cuts deeper and deeper, it encounters sandstone, then shale, then a coal seam, more shale, and then a bed of conglomerate before the drilling finally stops in another shale bed. This sequence duplicates the one we observed in the sea cliff, and also reveals a limestone and an underlying conglomerate and shale that we have not seen before. We may now feel justified in correlating the sandstone in the sea cliff with that in the canyon and that in the well hole: the limestone is the youngest rock in the area; the conglomerate and lowest shale are the oldest rocks. This correlation is shown in Fig. 9-8.

Many sedimentary formations are correlated in just this way, especially when physical features are our only keys to rock correlation. But as we extend the range of our correlation over a wider and wider area, physical features become more and more difficult to use. Clearly, it is impossible to use physical characteristics to determine the relative age of two sequences of layered rocks in, say, England and the eastern United States. Fortunately, we have another method of correlation—a method that involves the use of fossils.

CORRELATION BY FOSSILS. Around the turn of the nineteenth century, an English surveyor and civil engineer named William Smith (1769-1839) became impressed with the relationship of rock strata to the success of various engineering projects—particularly the building of canals. As he investigated rock strata from place to place, he noticed that many of them contained fossils. Furthermore, he observed that the same rock layer usually contained the same fossils, whereas the fossils in rock layers above or below were different. Eventually, Smith became so skillful that confronted with a fossil, he could name the rock from which it had come.

At about the same time, two French geologists, Georges Cuvier (1769-1832) and Alexandre Brongniart (1770-1847), were studying and mapping the fossil-bearing strata that surround Paris. They, too, found that certain fossils were restricted to certain rock layers; and they, also, had used the Law of Superposition to arrange the rocks of the Paris area in chronologic order, just as Smith had done in England. Then Cuvier and Brongniart arranged their collection of fossils in the same order as the rocks from which the fossils had been dug. They discovered that the fossil assemblages varied in a systematic way with the chronologic positions of

FIG. 9-9
William Smith (1769-1839), British civil engineer, discovered that the same rock layer usually contained the same assemblage of fossils, whereas rocks above and below that layer contained different assemblages of fossils. Reproduced from F. D. Adams, Birth and Development of the Geological Sciences (1954), by permission of Dover Publications, Inc., New York.

FIG. 9-10
Georges Cuvier (1769-1832), French paleontologist and natural historian, studied the fossils in the Paris area. Together with Alexandre Brongniart, he found that the fossils in rocks varied systematically with the relative age of the rocks as determined by the Law of Superposition. Reproduced from F. D. Adams, op. cit., by permission of Dover Publications, Inc., New York.

the rocks. In comparing the fossil forms with modern forms of life, Cuvier and Brongniart discovered that the fossils from the higher rock layers bore a closer resemblance to modern forms than did the fossils from rocks lower down.

From all these observations, it became evident that the *relative age* of a layer of sedimentary rock could be determined by the nature of the fossils it contained. This fact has been verified time and again by other workers throughout the world. *It has become an axiom in geology that fossils are a key to correlating rocks, and that rocks containing the same fossil assemblages are similar in age.*

But when we apply this axiom to actual situations involving the use of fossils for correlation, certain complications arise. For instance, it is obvious that in our modern world the distribution of living forms varies with the environment. This fact was presumably as true in the past as it is now. We found in discussing facies of sedimentary rocks that different sediments were laid down in different places at the same time. Plants and animals also reflect changes in environment, particularly if they happen to live on the sea bottom. Organisms living in an area where mud is being deposited are different from those living in an area where sand is being laid down. Thus we find somewhat different fossils in a bed of shale (formed from mud), than we do in a bed of sandstone (formed from sand).

If both the physical features and the fossils are different, how can we correlate the rocks in two different areas? There are two possible ways. First, we may actually be able to see that two different rock types, with their differing fossils, grade into each other laterally as we follow the beds along a cliff face. Secondly, we may find that a few fossils occur in both environments. In an oceanic environment, for instance, some forms float or swim over a wide geographic area that takes in more than one condition of deposition on the sea floor. The remains of these swimming or floating forms may settle to the bottom, to be incorporated in different kinds of sediment forming on the ocean floor.

THE GEOLOGIC COLUMN

Using the Law of Superposition and the concept that fossils are an index to time, geologists have made chronological arrangements of sedimentary rocks from all over the world. They have pictured the rocks as forming a great column, with the oldest at the bottom and the youngest at the top. The pioneer work in developing this pattern was carried out in the British Isles and in western Europe, where modern geology had its birth. There geologists recognized that the change in the fossil record between one layer and the next was not gradual but sudden. It seemed as if whole segments recording the slow change of plants and animals had been left out of the rock sequence. These breaks or gaps in the fossil record served as boundaries between adjoining strata. The names assigned to the various groups of sedimentary rocks are given in the geologic column of Table 9-1.

Notice that the oldest rocks are called "Precambrian," a general term applied to all the rocks that lie beneath the

Cambrian rocks. Although the Precambrian rocks represent the great bulk of geologic time, we have yet to work out satisfactory subdivisions for them, because there is an almost complete absence of fossil remains, so plentiful in Cambrian and younger rocks. Without fossils to aid them, geologists have been forced to base their correlations on the physical features of the rocks and on dates obtained from radioactive minerals. Physical features have been useful for establishing local sequences of Precambrian rocks, but these sequences cannot be extended to worldwide subdivisions. On the other hand, radioactive dates are not yet numerous enough to permit subdivisions of the Precambrian rocks, although such dates will become increasingly important as more are assembled.

We have said that the geologic column was originally separated into different groups of rocks on the basis of apparent gaps in the fossil record. But as geologic research progressed, and as the area of investigation spread from Europe to other continents, new discoveries narrowed the gaps in the fossil record. It is now apparent that the change in fossil forms has been continuous, and that the original gaps can be filled in with data from other localities. This increase in information

TABLE 9-1
The geologic column.

A: *Some geologists prefer to divide the Cenozoic System into two systems, the Quaternary and the Tertiary. The Quaternary System of this division includes the Pleistocene Epoch, and the Tertiary System includes the Paleocene through the Pliocene epochs.*
B: *This column indicates the dominant life forms found in different rock units. It does not give the time range of the forms listed. For example, fish are known from pre-Silurian rocks and obviously exist today. But when the Silurian and Devonian rocks were being formed, fish represented the most advanced form of animal life.*

Eras	SYSTEM (Periods)	SERIES (Epochs)	SOME ASPECTS OF THE LIFE RECORD (b)	
Cenozoic	Cenozoic (a)	Pleistocene	Flowering plants; Mammals	Man
		Pliocene		
		Miocene		Grasses become abundant
		Oligocene		
		Eocene		Horses first appear
		Paleocene		
Mesozoic	Cretaceous	(Many	Conifer and cycad plants; Reptiles	Extinction of dinosaurs
	Jurassic	series		Birds first appear
	Triassic	are		Dinosaurs first appear
Paleozoic	Permian	distinguished	Amphibia	
	Pennsylvanian	but	Spore-bearing land plants	Coal-forming swamps
	Mississippian	are not		
	Devonian	necessary	Fish	
	Silurian	here)		First vertebrates appear (fish)
	Ordovician		Marine plants; Marine invertebrates	First abundant fossil record (marine invertebrates)
	Cambrian			
Precambrian rocks (abundant, but worldwide subdivisions not generally agreed upon)			Marine plants; Marine invertebrates	Scanty fossil record Primitive marine plants and invertebrates One-celled organisms

has made it more and more difficult to draw clear boundaries between groups of rocks. And yet, despite the increasing number of "boundary" problems, the broad framework of the geologic column is still valid.

THE GEOLOGIC TIME SCALE

The names in the geologic column refer to rock units that have been arranged in a chronological sequence from oldest to youngest. Since each of the units was formed during a definite interval of time, they provide us with a basis for setting up time divisions in geologic history.

TABLE 9-2
The geologic timetable. Modified from J. Laurence Kulp in Science, CXXX, April 14, 1961.

ERAS	PERIODS	EPOCHS	MILLIONS OF YEARS DURATION	MILLIONS OF YEARS BEFORE THE PRESENT
CENOZOIC	Cenozoic	Pleistocene	1,000,000	
		Pliocene	12,000,000	
		Miocene	12,000,000	
		Oligocene	11,000,000	
		Eocene	22,000,000	
		Paleocene	5,000,000	63,000,000
MESOZOIC	Cretaceous		72,000,000	
	Jurassic		46,000,000	
	Triassic		49,000,000	230,000,000
PALEOZOIC	Permian		50,000,000	
	Pennsylvanian		30,000,000	
	Mississippian		35,000,000	
	Devonian		60,000,000	
	Silurian		20,000,000	
	Ordovician		75,000,000	
	Cambrian		100,000,000	600,000,000
	Precambrian time			

Oldest rocks dated 3,300,000,000 years

Origin of earth 4-5,000,000,000 years

In effect, the terms we apply to time units are the terms that were originally used to distinguish rock units. Thus we speak either of Cambrian *time* or of Cambrian *rocks*. *When we speak of time units, we are referring to the geologic time scale. When we speak of rock units, we are referring to the geologic column.*

The geologic time scale is given in Table 9-2. Notice the terms *eras, periods,* and *epochs* across the top of the table. These are general time terms. Thus we can speak of the Paleozoic Era, or the Permian Period, or the Pleistocene Epoch. In Table 9-1 the terms *system* and *series,* used as general terms for rock units, correspond to the time units, period and epoch, respectively. There is no generally accepted rock term that is equivalent to the "era" of the geologic time scale, although the term "group" is sometimes used.

Absolute dates in the geologic time scale

We have found that the geologic time scale is made up of units of relative time and that these units can be arranged in proper order without the use of any designations of absolute time. This relative time scale has been constructed on the basis of *sedimentary* rocks. As we noted earlier, geologists have only recently been able to date some sedimentary rocks by radioactive methods and most dates have come from the igneous rocks. How can the dates obtained from igneous rocks be fitted in with the relative time units from sedimentary rocks?

In order to insert the absolute age of igneous rocks into the geologic time scale, we must know the relative time relationships between the sedimentary and igneous rocks. The basic rule here is called the *Law of Crosscutting Relationships,* which states that *a rock is younger than any rock that it cuts across.*

Let us consider the example given in Fig. 9-11, a hypothetical section of the earth's crust with both igneous and sedimentary rocks exposed. The sedimentary rocks are arranged in three assemblages, numbered *1, 3,* and *5,* from oldest to youngest. The igneous rocks are numbered *2* and *4,* also from oldest to youngest.

The sedimentary rocks labeled *1* are the oldest rocks in the diagram. First, they were folded by earth forces; then, a dike of igneous rock was injected into them. Since the sedimentary rocks had to be present before the dike could cut across them, they must be older than the dike. After the first igneous intrusion, erosion beveled both the sedimentary rocks and the dike, and across this surface were deposited the sedimentary rocks labeled *3*. At some later time, the batholith, labeled *4,* cut across all the older rocks. In time, this batholith and the sedimentary rocks, *3,* were also beveled by erosion, and the sedimentary rocks labeled *5* were laid across this surface. We now

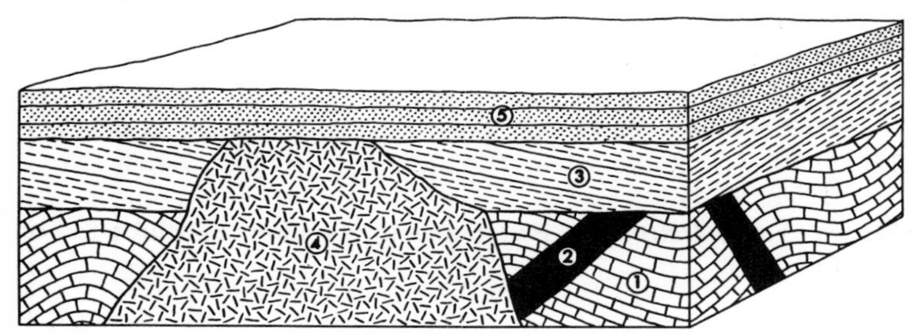

FIG. 9-11
This diagram illustrates the Law of Crosscutting Relationships, which states that a rock is younger than any rock that it cuts. The rock units are arranged in order of decreasing age from 1 to 5. The manner in which radioactive ages of the igneous rock (#2 and #4 of the diagram) are used to give approximate ages in terms of years for the sedimentary rocks (#1, #3, and #5 of the diagram) is discussed in the text and in Table 9-3.

have established the relative ages of the rocks, from oldest to youngest, as *1, 2, 3, 4,* and *5.*

Now, if we can date the igneous rocks by means of radioactive minerals, we can fit these dates into the relative time sequence. If we establish that the batholith is 230 million years old, and that the dike is 310 million years old, the ages of the sedimentary rocks may be expressed in relation to the known dates, and the final arrangement will be as shown in Table 9-3.

TABLE 9-3
Relative, absolute, and approximate ages of rocks (see Fig. 9-11 and text).

EVENT	AGE (*in millions of years*) RELATIVE	ABSOLUTE	APPROXIMATE
Sedimentary rocks	*5* (Youngest)	—	Younger than 230
Erosion		—	
Batholith	*4*	230	
Sedimentary rocks	*3*	—	Older than 230, younger than 310
Erosion		—	
Dike	*2*	310	
Folding		—	Older than 310
Sedimentary rocks	*1*	—	

By this general method, approximate dates have been assigned to the relative time units of the geologic time scale, as shown in Table 9-2. These dates may be revised and refined as new techniques for dating develop. One of the most exciting developments in this field lies in the direct application of dating methods to the radioactive minerals of sedimentary rocks, as suggested earlier.

SUMMARY OUTLINE

Geologic time
- Either relative or absolute

Absolute time
- Determined by decay of radioactive elements, chiefly in igneous rocks, but also in sedimentary rocks, to some extent

Relative time
- Determined chiefly by relative position of sedimentary rocks

Law of Superposition
- Determines relative age of a rock layer in any one sequence of sedimentary rocks

Correlation
- Process of relating, in time, one sequence of sedimentary rocks with another
- Usually accomplished on basis of physical characteristics or fossil content of rocks

Fossils
- Key to relative time
- Rocks with similar fossils are of similar age

Geologic column
- Chronologic sequence of rocks, from oldest to youngest

Geologic time scale
- Chronologic sequence of units of earth time

Absolute dates in geologic time scale
- From igneous rocks and sedimentary rocks
- Position in time scale of events dated from igneous rocks is determined by relation of the igneous rocks to sedimentary rocks

SELECTED REFERENCES

Bradley, W. H., *The Varves and Climate of the Green River Epoch.* Washington, D.C.: U.S. Geol. Survey, Professional Paper 158, 1929.

Knopf, Adolph, "Measuring Geologic Time," *Sci. Monthly,* XVC, No. 5 (1957), 225–236.

———, "The Geologic Records of Time," in *Time and Its Mysteries,* Series III. New York: N. Y. Univ. Press, 1949, pp. 33–59.

Kulp, J. Laurence, "Geologic Time Scale," *Science,* CXXXIII, No. 3459 (1961), 1105–14.

Libby, W. F., "Radiocarbon Dating," *Am. Scientist,* XLIV, No. 1 (1956), 98–112.

Zeuner, F. E., *Dating the Past* (3rd ed.). London: Methuen & Co., Ltd., 1952.

Mass movement of surface material

FACTORS OF MASS MOVEMENT

BEHAVIOR OF MATERIAL

RAPID MOVEMENTS

LANDSLIDES

MUDFLOWS

EARTHFLOWS

TALUS

SLOW MOVEMENTS

CREEP

SOLIFLUCTION

ROCK GLACIERS

When rocks are exposed at the earth's surface, weathering immediately sets to work to establish an equilibrium between the rock material and its new environment. Other factors join forces with the processes of weathering; gravity, for example, acts to move the products of weathering, and even unweathered bedrock, to lower and lower levels. This movement of surface material caused by gravity is known as *mass movement*. Sometimes it takes place suddenly in the form of great landslides and rock falls from precipitous cliffs (see Fig. 10-1), but often it occurs almost imperceptibly, as the slow creep of soil across gently sloping fields. Mass movement, then, is one type of adjustment that earth materials make to their physical environment; it is one of the many ways in which gravity acts to wear down the land masses of the earth. Other geological agents, such as surface water, underground water, wind, ice, and waves, all work hand in hand with gravity to bring about the constant *gradation,* or leveling, of the land.

But while all these agents are working on the surface of the earth to lower it to ocean level, counteragents are working beneath the surface. These internal forces are constantly bending, breaking, and heaving the earth's crust, raising the land above the oceans and exposing it to erosion. This conflict has been going on throughout earth history—and luckily so, for otherwise the continents would have become flat, featureless "pancakes" millions of years ago.

In the next several chapters, we shall consider in some detail the external agents that erode the land masses of the earth. As we begin this study, remember that mass movement is only one of the many processes that work counter to the internal forces of the earth. Remember, too, that the processes of erosion and transportation discussed in the next few chapters occupy a definite place in the rock cycle that we traced earlier. It is under the impetus of gravity that the products of weathering begin their long trek to a resting place, though perhaps only a temporary one, on the floor of the sea.

FIG. 10-1
A large slab of massive Wingate sandstone has fallen and shattered at the foot of this precipitous cliff, where the San Juan River now begins to move away the fragments. Photo by William C. Bradley.

FACTORS OF MASS MOVEMENT

Gravity provides the energy for the downslope movement of surface debris and bedrock. But several other factors, particularly water, augment gravity and ease its work.

Immediately after a heavy rainstorm, you may have witnessed a landslide on a steep hillside or on the bank of a river. Movement of this sort is often mistakenly attributed to the "lubricating action" of water. But water does not "grease the skids" in the strict sense of the phrase. With many minerals water actually acts not as a lubricant but as an *anti*lubricant. We must conclude that heavy rains do not promote movement by "lubrication."

Water does aid in downslope movements, however. In many unconsolidated deposits, the pore spaces between individual grains are filled partly with moisture and partly with air. And so long as this condition persists, the surface tension of the moisture gives a certain cohesion to the soil. But when a heavy rain comes along and forces all the air out of the pore spaces, this surface tension is completely destroyed. The cohesion of the soil is reduced, and the whole mass becomes more susceptible to downslope movement. The presence of water also adds weight to the soil on a slope, although this added weight is probably not a very important factor in promoting mass movement.

Water that soaks into the ground and completely fills the pore spaces in the slope material contributes to instability in another way. The water in the pores is under pressure, which tends to push apart individual grains or even whole rock units and to decrease the internal friction or resistance of the material to movement. Here again, water assists in mass movement.

Gravity can move material only when it is able to overcome the material's internal resistance against being set into motion. Clearly, then, any factor that reduces this resistance to the point where gravity can take over contributes to mass movement. The erosive action of a stream, an ocean, or a glacier may so steepen a slope that the earth material no longer can resist the pull of gravity and is forced to give in to mass movement. In regions of cold climate, alternate freezing and thawing of earth materials may be enough to set them in motion. The impetus needed to initiate movement may also be furnished by earthquakes, excavations or blasting operations, or even by the gentle activities of burrowing animals and growing plants.

BEHAVIOR OF MATERIAL

Once material has been set in motion down a slope, it may behave as (1) an elastic solid or an aggregation of elastic solids, (2) a plastic substance, or (3) a fluid.

An elastic solid is a substance that undergoes a change in shape or volume when *stress* (defined as "force per unit area") is applied to it, but the substance returns to its original condition when the stress is removed. An elastic solid breaks only when the stress applied to it is greater than its strength to resist.

FIG. 10-2
The beginning of slump or slope failure along the sea cliffs at Gay Head, Massachusetts. Note that the slump block is tilted back slightly, away from the ocean. This slump block eventually moved downward and outward toward the shore along a curving plane, a portion of which is represented by the face of the low scarp in the foreground. Photo from Gardner Collection, Harvard University.

A plastic substance undergoes continuous change of shape after the stress applied to it passes a critical point. If a slope is steep enough, masses of earth sometimes behave as a plastic substance, creeping slowly but continuously downhill under the influence of gravity.

Finally, a fluid offers little or no resistance to the stresses that tend to change its shape. And masses of earth sometimes behave in just this way, flowing down even the most gradual slope.

We could actually study any type of mass movement and classify it on the basis of these three types of movement. But we would have to assemble an excessive amount of technical data, and we would find the picture complicated by the fact that material often behaves in different ways during any one movement. So we shall simply classify mass movement as either *rapid* or *slow*.

RAPID MOVEMENTS

Catastrophic and destructive movements of rock and soil, the most spectacular and easily recognized examples of mass movement, are popularly known as "landslides." But the geologist subdivides this general term into slump, rock slides, debris slides, mudflows, and earthflows.

Landslides

Landslides include a wide range of movements, from the slipping of a stream bank to the sudden, devastating release of a whole mountainside. Some landslides involve only the unconsolidated debris lying on bedrock; others involve movement of the bedrock itself.

SLUMP. Sometimes called *slope failure, slump* is the downward and outward movement of rock or unconsolidated material traveling as a unit or as a series of units. Slump usually occurs where the original slope has been sharply steepened, either artificially or naturally. The material reacts to the pull of gravity as if it were an elastic solid, and large blocks of the slope move downward and outward along curved planes.

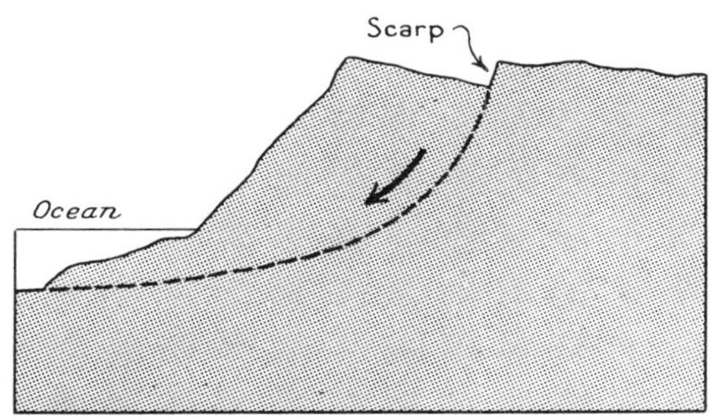

FIG. 10-3
This diagrammatic cross section shows the type of movement found in a slump similar to that pictured in Fig. 10-2. A block of earth material along the steepened cliff has begun to move downward along a plane that curves toward the ocean.

FIG. 10-4
Aerial photograph of the Gros Ventre rockslide in northwestern Wyoming. The lake in the lower left of the picture has been dammed by a landslide that moved down into the valley of the Gros Ventre River. The area from which the material slid is about a mile and a half long and is well marked by the white scar down the center of the photograph. The adjoining slopes appear dark because of a vegetative cover of trees and bushes, a cover that has not yet re-established itself in the slide area.
Photo by U.S. Army Air Force.

The upper surface of each block is tilted backward as it moves.

Figure 10-2 shows a slump beginning at Gay Head, Massachusetts. The action of the sea has cut away the unconsolidated material at the base of the slope, steepening it to a point where the earth mass can no longer support itself. Now the large block has begun to move along a single curving plane, as suggested in Fig. 10-3.

Once a slump has been started, it is often helped along by rainwater collecting in basins between the tilted blocks and the original slope. The water drains down along the plane on which the block is sliding and promotes further movement.

ROCK SLIDES. The most catastrophic of all mass movements are rock slides—sudden, rapid slides of bedrock along planes of weakness. A great rock slide occurred in 1925 on the flanks of Sheep Mountain, along the Gros Ventre River in northwestern Wyoming, not far from Yellowstone National Park (see Fig. 10-4). An estimated 50 million cubic yards of rock and debris plunged down the valley wall and swept across the valley floor. The nose of the slide rushed some 350 feet up the opposite wall and then settled back, like liquid being sloshed in a great basin. The debris formed a dam between 225 and 250 feet high across the valley, the dammed-up river creating a lake almost 5 miles long. The spring floods of 1926 raised the water level to the lip of the dam, and in mid-May the water flooded over the top. So rapid was the downcutting of the dam that the lake level was lowered about 50 feet in 5 hours. During the flood that followed, several lives were lost in the town of Kelly, in the valley below.

The Gros Ventre slide was a long time in the making, and there was probably nothing that could have been done to prevent it. Conditions immediately before the slide are shown

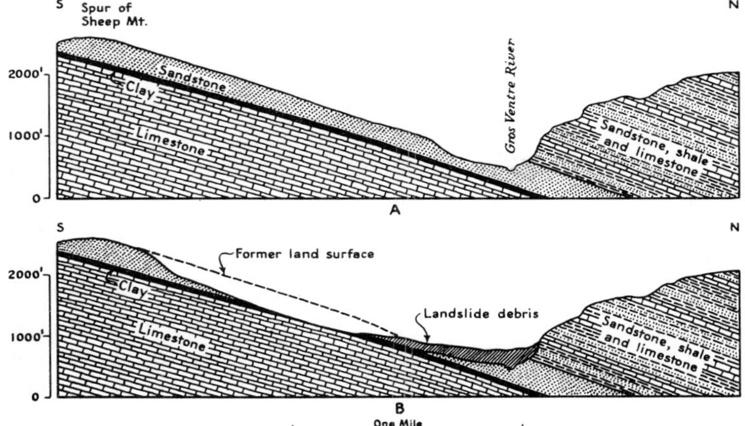

FIG. 10-5
Diagrams to show the nature of the Gros Ventre slide. A *shows the conditions existing before the slide took place.* B *represents the area of the slide and the location of the debris in the valley bottom. Note that the sedimentary beds dip into the valley from the south. The large section of sandstone slid downward along the clay bed. Redrawn from William C. Alden, "Landslide and Flood at Gros Ventre, Wyoming," Transactions, Am. Inst. of Mining and Metallurgical Engineers, LXXVI (1928), p. 348.*

in the first of the two diagrams in Fig. 10-5. In this part of Wyoming, the Gros Ventre valley cuts through sedimentary beds inclined between 15° and 21° to the north. The slide occurred on the south side of the valley wall, where the beds dip into the valley. Notice that the sandstone bed is separated from the limestone strata by a thin layer of clay. Before the rock slide occurred, the sandstone bed near the bottom of the valley had been worn thin by erosion. The melting of winter snows and the heavy rains that fell during the spring of 1925 furnished an abundant supply of water that seeped down to the thin layer of clay, soaking it and reducing the adhesion between it and the overlying sandstone. When the sandstone was no longer able to hold its position on the clay bed, the rock slide roared down the slope. The lower diagram of Fig. 10-5 suggests the amount of material that was moved from the spur of Sheep Mountain to its resting place on the valley floor.

Another rock slide, in 1903, killed 70 people in the coal-mining town of Frank, Alberta, when some 40 million cubic yards of rock crashed down from the crest of Turtle Mountain, which rises over 3,000 feet above the valley. Mining activities may have triggered this movement, but natural causes were basically responsible for it.

As Fig. 10-6 shows, Turtle Mountain has been sculptured from a series of limestone, sandstone, and shale beds that dip southwestward away from the valley. The diagram reveals four factors that contributed to the slide: (1) the steepness of the mountain, (2) the series of joints or fractures that dip down through the limestone strata, (3) the weak shale strata

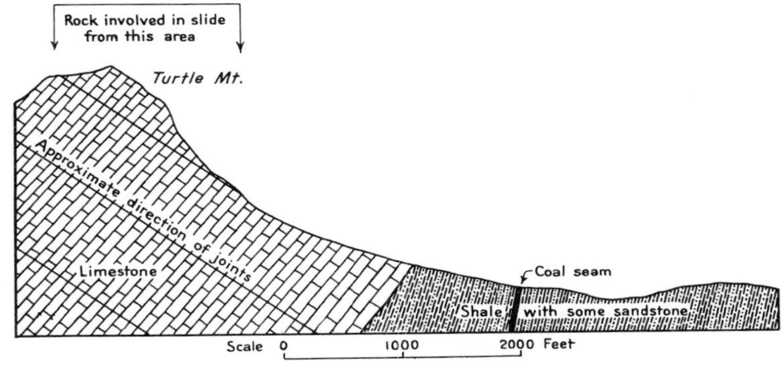

FIG. 10-6
A cross section to show the conditions at Turtle Mountain that brought on the Frank, Alberta, landslide. Redrawn from R. A. Daly and others, "Report of the Committee to Investigate Turtle Mt., Frank, Alberta," Department of Mines, Geol. Survey of Canada, Memoir 27 (1912), Fig. 5.

FIG. 10-7
The Madison River Canyon before the landslide of August, 1959. The slide began on the forested valley wall on the far side of the river. The debris clogged the river channel to form a lake. The spot where this fisherman once stood is now under 100 feet of water. Compare with Fig. 10-8. Photo by Montana Power Co.

FIG. 10-8
An aerial view of the Madison Canyon after the landslide. An outlet channel for the newly formed lake has been cut across the landslide dam. Photo by William C. Bradley.

that underlie the limestone and form the base of the mountain, and (4) the coal-mining operations in the valley.

The steep valley wall enhanced the effectiveness of gravity, and the joints served as potential planes of movement. The weak shale beds at the base of the mountain undoubtedly underwent slow plastic deformation under the weight of the overlying limestone. And as the shale was deformed, the limestone settled lower and lower. The settling action may have been helped along by the coal-mining operations in the valley, as well as by frost action, rain, melting snows, and earthquake tremors that had shaken the area two years before. In any event, the stress finally reached the point where the limestone beds fractured and the great mass of rock hurtled down into the valley.

This time the rock material behaved in three different ways. The shales underwent plastic deformation, producing a condition of extreme instability on the mountain slope. When the strata that still held the limestone mass on the slope sheared in the manner of an elastic solid, the slide actually began. Once under way, the rock debris bounced, ricocheted, slid, and rolled down the mountain slope to the valley, where it moved onward like a viscous fluid with a series of waves spreading out along its front.

A more recent rock slide occurred in southwestern Montana a few minutes before midnight on August 17, 1959. An earthquake whose focus was located just north of West Yellowstone, Montana, triggered a rock slide in the mouth of the Madison Canyon, about 20 miles to the west. An estimated 80 million tons of rock slide from the south wall of the canyon down to the valley bottom, where it dammed up a lake 5 miles long and 100 feet deep. At least a score of people lost their lives in the Madison River Campground area below the slide (see Figs. 10-7 and 10-8).

DEBRIS SLIDES. A *debris slide* is a small, rapid movement of largely unconsolidated material that slides or rolls downward and produces a surface of low hummocks with small, intervening depressions. Movements of this sort are common on grassy slopes, particularly after heavy rains, and in unconsolidated material along the steep slopes of stream banks and shorelines.

WARNINGS OF LANDSLIDES. We usually think of a landslide as breaking loose without warning, but it is more accurate to say that people in the area simply fail to detect the warnings.

For example, a disastrous rock slide at Goldau, Switzerland, in 1806, wiped out a whole village, killing 457 people. The few who lived to tell the tale reported that they themselves had no warning of the coming slide, but that animals and insects in the region may have been more observant or more sensitive. For several hours before the slide, horses and cattle seemed to be extremely nervous, and even the bees abandoned their hives. Some slight preliminary movement probably took place before the rock mass actually broke loose.

During the spring of 1935, slides took place in clay deposits along a German superhighway that was being built between Munich and Salzburg. The slides came as a complete surprise to the engineers, but for a full week the workmen had been murmuring, "Der Abhang wird lebendig" (the slope becomes alive).

Landslides like the one on Turtle Mountain are often preceded by slowly widening fissures in the rock near the upward limit of the future movement.

There is some evidence that landslides may recur periodically in certain areas. In southeastern England, not far from Dover, extensive landslides have been occurring once every 19 to 20 years. Some observers feel that there may be some correlation between such periodical mass movement and periods of excessive rainfall. On steep slopes in very moist tropical or semitropical climates, for instance, landslides do seem to follow a cyclic pattern. First, a landslide strips the soil and vegetation from a hill slope. In time, new soil and vegetation develop, the old scar heals, and when the cover reaches a certain stage, the landsliding begins again. Although landslides may occur in cycles, our data are as yet far too scanty to support firm conclusions.

Mudflows

A *mudflow* is a well-mixed mass of rock, earth, and water that flows down valley slopes with the consistency of newly mixed concrete. In mountainous, desert, and semiarid areas, mudflows manage to transport great masses of material.

The typical mudflow originates in a small, steep-sided gulch or canyon where the slopes and floor are covered by unconsolidated or unstable material. A sudden flood of water, from cloudbursts in semiarid country or from spring thaws in mountainous regions, flushes the earth and rocks from the slopes and carries them to the stream channel. Here the debris blocks the channel until the growing pressure of the water becomes great enough to break through. Then the water and debris begin their course down-valley, mixing together with a rolling motion along the forward edge of the flow. The advance of the flow is intermittent, for sometimes it is slowed or halted by a narrowing of the stream channel; at other times it surges forward, pushing obstacles aside or carrying them along with it.

Eventually, the mudflow spills out of the canyon mouth and spreads across the gentle slopes below. No longer confined by the valley walls or the stream channel, it splays out in a great tongue, spreading a layer of mud and boulders that ranges from a few inches to several feet in thickness. Mudflows can move even large boulders weighing 85 tons or more for hundreds of feet, across slopes as gentle as 5°.

Earthflows

Earthflows are a combination of slump and the plastic movement of unconsolidated material. They move slowly but perceptibly and may involve from a few to several million cubic yards of earth material. Some of the material behaves like an elastic solid, and some like a plastic substance, depending on its position in the moving mass.

The line at which a slump pulls away from the the slope

FIG. 10-9
An earthflow in a roadcut near Dallas, Texas, shows the sharp scar high on the slope and, farther down, the area of soil movement by flow. Compare with Fig. 10-10. Photo by C. W. Brown.

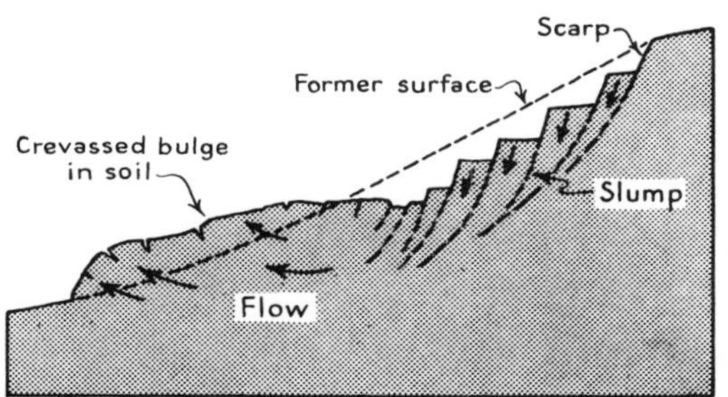

FIG. 10-10
In this diagram of an earthflow, note the scarp and slump blocks that have pulled from the flow in the upper section. In the downslope section, the flowing has expressed itself at the surface by bulging and cracking the sod.

is marked by an abrupt scarp or cliff, as shown in Fig. 10-9. Notice that the slump zone is made up of a series of blocks that move downward and outward, tilting the original surface back toward the slope. Farther down, the material tends to flow like a liquid, often beneath the vegetative cover. At the downslope limit of an earthflow, the sod often bulges out and fractures (see Fig. 10-10). Earthflows occur in unconsolidated material lying on solid bedrock and are usually helped along by the presence of excessive moisture.

FIG. 10-11
Soil creep is shown in this sloping roadcut along the Pennsylvania Turnpike east of Bedford. Note that the traces of the steeply dipping beds, still preserved in the partially decomposed zone immediately below the sod, have been bent downslope. Photo by Elliott A. Riggs.

Talus

Strictly speaking, a *talus* is a slope built up by an accumulation of rock fragments at the foot of a cliff or a ridge. The rock fragments are sometimes referred to as *rock waste* or *slide-rock*. In practice, however, talus is widely used as a synonym for the rock debris itself.

In the development of a talus, rock fragments are loosened from the cliff and clatter downward in a series of free falls, bounces, and slides. As time passes, the rock waste finally buils up a heap or sheet of rock rubble. An individual talus resembles a half-cone with its apex resting against the cliff face in a small gulch. A series of these half-cones often forms a girdle around high mountains, completely obscuring their lower portions. Eventually, if the rock waste accumulates more rapidly than it can be destroyed or removed, even the upper cliffs become buried, and the growth of the talus stops. The slope angle of the talus varies with the size and shape of the rock fragments. Although angular material can maintain slopes up to 50°, rarely does a talus ever exceed angles of 40°.

A talus is subject to the normal process of chemical weathering, particularly in a moist climate. The rock waste is decomposed, especially toward its lower limit, or toe, and the material there may grade imperceptibly into a soil.

SLOW MOVEMENTS

Slow mass movements of unconsolidated material are harder to recognize and less fully understood than rapid movements; yet they are extremely important in the sculpturing of the land surface. Since they operate over long periods of time, they are probably responsible for the transportation of more material than are rapid and violent movements of rock and soil.

Before the end of the nineteenth century, William Morris Davis aptly described the nature of slow movements.

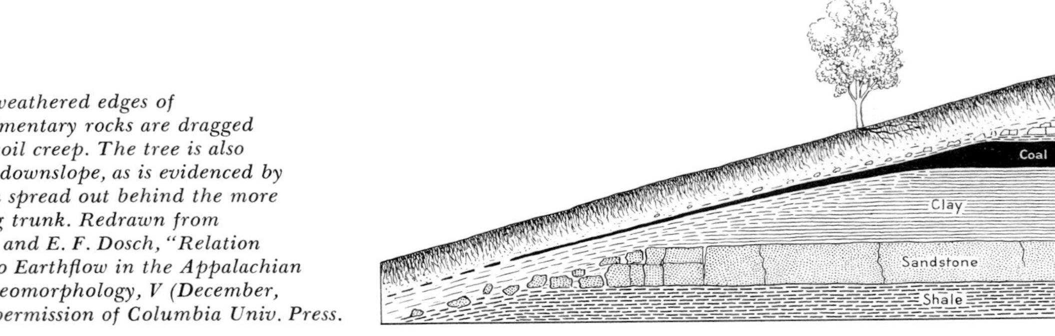

FIG. 10-12
The partially weathered edges of horizontal sedimentary rocks are dragged downslope by soil creep. The tree is also moving slowly downslope, as is evidenced by the root system spread out behind the more rapidly moving trunk. Redrawn from C. F. S. Sharpe and E. F. Dosch, "Relation of Soil-Creep to Earthflow in the Appalachian Plateaus," J. Geomorphology, V (December, 1942), 316, by permission of Columbia Univ. Press.

The movement of land waste is generally so slow that it is not noticed. But when one has learned that many land forms result from the removal of more or less rock waste, the reality and the importance of the movement are better understood. It is then possible to picture in the imagination a slow washing and creeping of the waste down the land slopes; not bodily or hastily, but grain by grain, inch by inch; yet so patiently that in the course of ages even mountains may be laid low.[1]

Creep

In temperate and tropical climates, a slow downward movement of surface material known as *creep* operates even on gentle slopes with a protective cover of grass and trees. It is hard to realize that this movement is actually taking place. Since the observer sees no break in the vegetative mat, no large scars or hummocks, he has no reason to suspect that the soil is in motion beneath his feet.

Yet this movement can be demonstrated by exposures in soil profile (see Fig. 10-11), by the behavior of tree roots, of large blocks of resistant rock, and of man-built objects such as fences. Figure 10-12 shows a section through a hillside underlain by flatlying beds of shale, limestone, clay, sandstone, and coal. The slope is covered with rock debris and soil. But notice that the beds near the base of the soil bend downslope and thin out rapidly. These beds are being pulled downslope by gravity and are strung out in ever-thinning bands that may extend for hundreds of feet. Eventually, they approach the surface and lose their identity in the zone of active chemical weathering.

The same diagram shows other evidence that the soil is moving. Although when viewed from the surface the tree appears to be growing in a normal way, it is actually creeping slowly down the slope. Since the surface of the soil is moving more rapidly than the soil beneath it, the roots of the tree are unable to keep up with the trunk. Consequently, they are spread out like great streamers along the slope.

We can find other evidence of the slow movement of soil in displaced fences and tilted telephone poles and gravestones. On slopes where resistant rock layers crop up through the soil, fragments are sometimes broken off and distributed down the slope by the slowly moving soil.

Many other factors cooperate with gravity to produce creep. Probably the most important is moisture in the soil, which works to weaken the soil's resistance to movement. In fact, any process that causes a dislocation in the soil brings about an adjustment of the soil downslope under the pull of gravity. Thus, the burrows of animals tend to fill downslope, and the same is true of cavities left by the decay of organic material, such as the root system of a dead tree. The prying action of swaying trees, the tread of animals, and even of men, may also aid in the motion. The end result of all these processes, aided by the influence of gravity, is to produce a slow and inevitable downslope creep of the surface cover of debris and soil.

[1] William Morris Davis, *Physical Geography* (Boston: Ginn & Company, 1898), p. 261.

FIG. 10-13
Beds of silt, sand, and clayey gravel have been contorted by differential freezing and thawing during the more rigorous climates of glacial times. The gravel at the base of the exposure is clayey, gravelly till deposited directly by glacier ice. Above this are the highly contorted beds of water-laid sand (dark) and silt (light), which were originally flat-lying. The modern soil has developed across the contortions. The white of the silt bands is due to precipitation of calcium carbonate from soil water. The brush hook is about 18 inches long. Exposure north of city of Devils Lake, east-central North Dakota. Photo by Saul Aronow, U.S. Geol. Survey.

Solifluction

The term *solifluction* (from the Latin *solum,* "soil," and *fluere,* "to flow") refers to the downslope movement of debris under saturated conditions in high latitudes where the soil is strongly affected by alternate freezing and thawing. Solifluction is most pronounced in areas where the ground freezes to great depths. But even moderately deep seasonal freezing promotes solifluction.

Solifluction takes place during periods of thaw. Since the

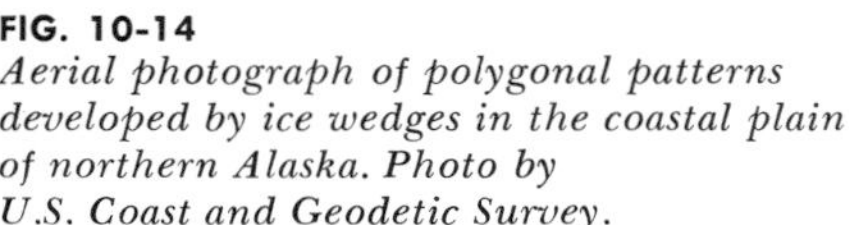

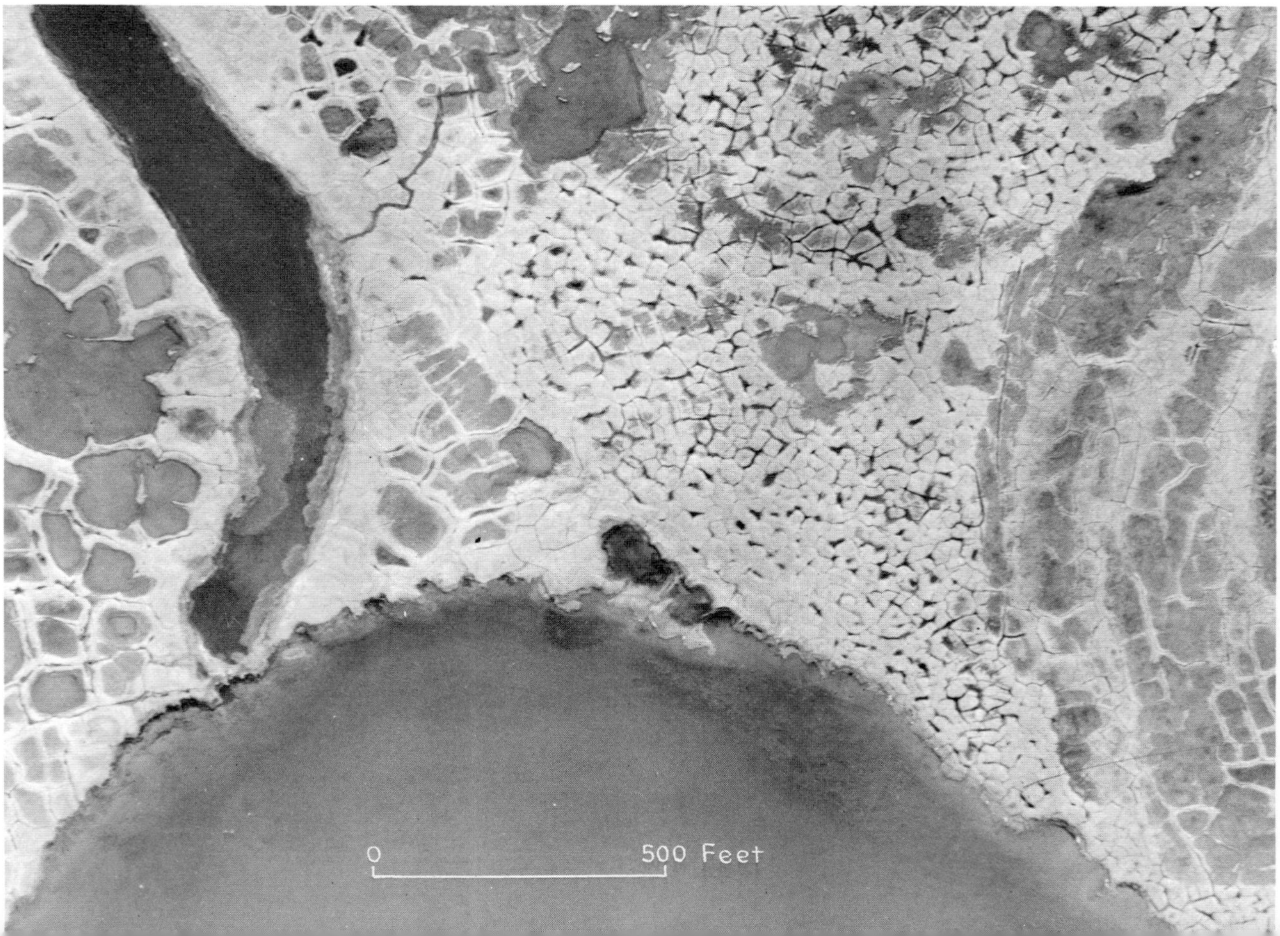

FIG. 10-14
Aerial photograph of polygonal patterns developed by ice wedges in the coastal plain of northern Alaska. Photo by U.S. Coast and Geodetic Survey.

ground thaws from the surface downward, the water that is released cannot percolate into the subsoil and adjacent bedrock, which are still frozen and therefore impermeable to water. As a result, the surface soil becomes sodden and water-laden and tends to flow down even the gentlest slopes. Solifluction is an important process in the reduction of land masses in arctic climates, where it transports great sheets of debris from higher to lower elevations.

During the glacier advances of the Pleistocene, a zone of intense frost action and solifluction bordered the southward moving ice. In some places we can still find the evidence of these more rigorous climates preserved in distorted layers of earth material just below the modern soil (see Fig. 10-13).

Frost action plays queer tricks in the soils of the higher elevations and latitudes. Strange polygonal patterns made up of rings of boulders surrounding finer material, stripes of stones strewn down the face of hillsides, great tabular masses of ice within the soil, and deep ice wedges that taper downward from the surface—all are found in areas where the ground is deeply frozen (see Fig. 10-14). The behavior of frozen ground is one of the greatest barriers to the settlement of arctic regions. The importance of these regions has increased in recent years, and studies begun by Scandinavian and Russian investigators are now being intensively pursued by American scientists.

FIG. 10-15
This rock glacier in Silver Basin, near Ouray, Colorado, is no longer moving. When the climate was cold enough to allow the formation of interstitial ice in the voids between the coarse fragments, the mass moved an estimated 1 to 3 feet per year. Its enormity may be judged in contrast to the trees that appear diminutive in the foreground. Photo by Cross, U.S. Geol. Survey.

Rock glaciers

Rock glaciers are long tongues of rock waste that form in the valleys of certain mountainous regions. Though they consist almost entirely of rock, they bear a striking resemblance to ice glaciers. A typical rock glacier is marked by a series of rounded ridges, suggesting that the material has behaved as a viscous mass.

Observations on active rock glaciers in Alaska indicate that movement takes place because of interstitial ice within the mass. Favorable conditions for the development of glaciers include a climate cold enough to keep the ground continuously frozen, steep cliffs to supply debris, and coarse blocks that allow for large interstitial spaces. Measurements on modern glaciers over an eight-year period showed that the front moved 1.6 feet per year and that on the surface the average maximum movement was 2.6 feet per year.

SUMMARY OUTLINE

Mass movement
Movement of bedrock and unconsolidated material in response to pull of gravity

Behavior of material
As an elastic solid, as a plastic substance, or as a fluid

Factors in mass movement
Saturation of material with water
Steepening of slope by erosion
Earthquakes
Activity of animals (including man)

Rapid movements
Landslides, mudflows, earthflows, and talus development

Slow movements
Creep, solifluction, rock glaciers

SELECTED REFERENCES

Andersson, J. G., "Solifluction, a Component of Subaerial Denudation," *J. Geol.,* XIV (1906), 91–112.

Daly, R. A., W. G. Miller, and G. S. Rice, *Report of the Committee to Investigate Turtle Mt., Frank, Alberta.* Department of Mines, Geological Survey Branch, Canada, Memoir 27, 1912.

Muller, S. W., *Permafrost or Permanently Frozen Ground and Related Engineering Problems.* Ann Arbor, Mich.: J. W. Edwards, Inc., 1947.

National Academy of Sciences, *Memoir 18.* Washington, D.C., 1924.

Roy, Chalmer J. and Keith M. Hussy, "Mass-wasting on Table Mountain, Fremont County, Colorado," *Am. J. Sci.,* CCI (1952), 35–45.

Sharpe, C. F. S., *Landslides and Related Phenomena.* New York: Columbia Univ. Press, 1938.

——— and E. F. Dosch, "Relation of Soil Creep to Earthflow in the Appalachian Plateaus," *J. Geomorphology,* V (1942), 312–24.

Tabor, Stephen, "Perennially Frozen Ground in Alaska: Its Origin and History," *Geol. Soc. Am. Bull.,* LIV (1943), 1433–1548.

Terzaghi, Karl, "Mechanism of Landslides," *Geol. Soc. Am. Bull.,* Berkey Volume (1950), 83–123.

Wahrhaftig, Clyde and Allan Cox, "Rock Glaciers in the Alaska Range," *Geol. Soc. Am. Bull.,* LXX (1959), 383–436.

White, Sidney E., "Processes of Erosion on Steep Slopes of Oahu, Hawaii," *Am. J. Sci.,* CCIIIL (1949), 168–86.

Wooley, R. R., *Cloudburst Floods in Utah, 1850–1938.* Washington, D.C.: U.S. Geol. Survey, Water Supply Paper 994, 1946.

11 Running water

Through millions of years of earth history, agencies of erosion have been working constantly to reduce the land masses to the level of the seas. Of these agencies, running water is the most important. Year after year, the streams of the earth move staggering amounts of debris and dissolved material through their valleys to the great settling basins, the oceans.

"All the rivers run into the sea, yet the sea is not full: unto the place from whence the rivers come, thither they return again," reads Ecclesiastes 1:7. And thither they still return, for in the final analysis the water that runs off the slopes of the land in thin sheets, and then travels on in rills, streams, and rivers, is derived from the oceans. There is one exception: volcanic eruptions apparently bring water to the surface from deep beneath the earth. But once it has reached the surface, this water also follows the general pattern of water movement from sea to land and back again to the sea, a pattern that we call the *hydrologic cycle* (Fig. 11-1).

PRECIPITATION AND STREAM FLOW

Once water has fallen on the land as precipitation, it follows one of the many paths that make up the hydrologic cycle. By far the greatest part is evaporated back to the air directly, or is taken up by the plants and transpired (breathed back) by them to the atmosphere. A smaller amount follows the path of *runoff,* the water that flows off the land. And the smallest amount of precipitation soaks into the ground through *infiltration.*

Figure 11-2 shows how infiltration, runoff, and evaporation-transpiration vary in six widely separated localities in the United States. In the examples given, between 54 and 97 per cent of the total precipitation travels back to the atmosphere through transpiration and evaporation. About 2 to 27 per cent drains into streams and oceans as runoff, and between 1 and 20 per cent finds it way into the ground through infiltration.

In the next several chapters we shall consider water at various stages of the hydrologic cycle. In Chapter 12 we look

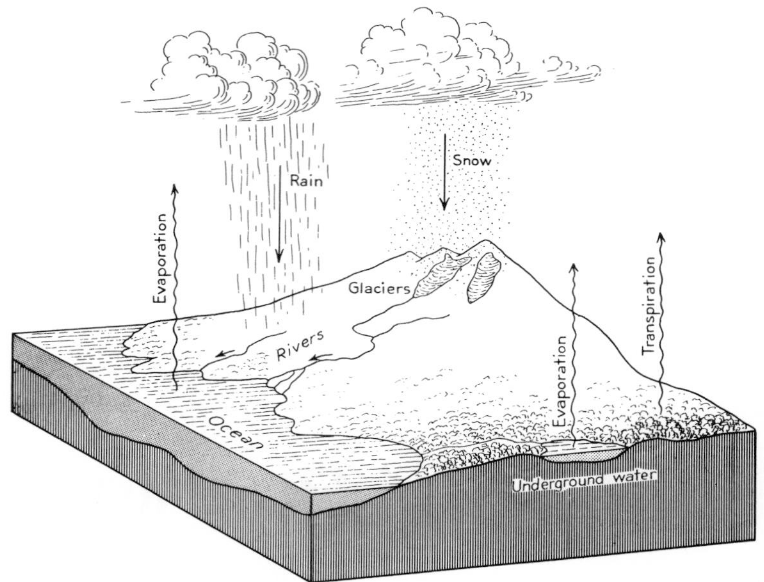

FIG. 11-1
In the hydrologic cycle, water evaporated into the atmosphere reaches the land as rain or snow. Here it may be temporarily stored in glaciers, lakes, or the underground before returning by the rivers to the sea. Or some may be transpired or evaporated directly back into the atmosphere before reaching the sea.

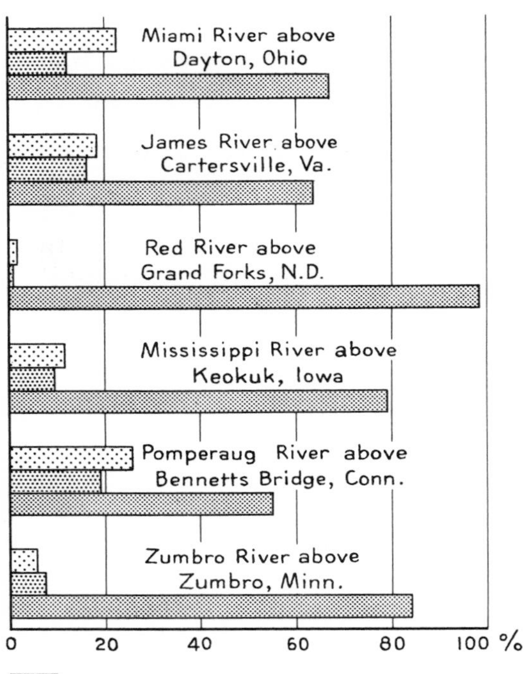

FIG. 11-2
Distribution of precipitation in selected drainage basins. Notice that in all cases 50 per cent or more of all moisture that falls is returned to the atmosphere by evaporation and transpiration. Run-off from the surface is comparatively small, and infiltration of water in the underground is still less. Data from W. G. Hoyt and others, Studies of Relation of Rainfall and Run-off in the United States. Washington, D.C.: U.S. Geol. Survey, Water Supply Paper 772, 1936.

at the water that infiltrates into the ground; in Chapter 13 we study water that has been impounded on the land as glacier ice, a condition that represents a temporary halting of the water's progress through the cycle. Chapter 15 deals with water stored in oceans. But in this chapter we shall concentrate on the nature and effects of runoff. Bearing in mind the ways in which water that falls as precipitation proceeds through the hydrologic cycle, we can express the amount of runoff by the following generalized formula:

Runoff = Precipitation − (Infiltration + Evaporation and Transpiration)

LAMINAR AND TURBULENT FLOW. When water moves slowly along a smooth channel, or through a tube with smooth walls, it follows straight-line paths that are parallel to the channel or walls. This type of movement is called *laminar flow.*

If the rate of flow increases, however, or if the confining channel becomes rough and irregular, this smooth, streamline movement is disrupted. The water in contact with the channel is slowed down by friction, whereas the rest of the water tends to move along as before. As a result (see Fig. 11-3), the water is deflected from its straight paths into a series of eddies and swirls. This type of movement is known as *turbulent flow.* Water in streams usually flows along in this way, its turbulent flow being highly effective both in eroding a stream's channel and in transporting materials.

When a stream reaches an exceptionally high velocity along a sharply inclined stretch or over a waterfall, the water moves in plunging, jetlike surges. This type of flow, closely related to turbulent flow, is called *jet* or *shooting flow.*

VELOCITY, GRADIENT, AND DISCHARGE. The velocity of a stream is measured in terms of the distance its water travels in a unit of time, usually in feet per second. A velocity of half a foot per second (about 0.3 miles per hour) is relatively low, and a velocity of 25 to 30 feet per second (about 17 to 20 miles per hour) is relatively high.

A stream's velocity is determined by many factors, including the amount of water passing a given point, the nature of the stream banks, and the *gradient* or slope of the stream bed. In general, a stream's gradient decreases from its headwaters toward its mouth; as a result, a stream's longitudinal profile is more or less concave toward the sky (Fig. 11-4). We usually express the gradient of a stream as the number of feet the stream descends during each mile of flow. The Mississippi River from Cairo, Illinois, to the mouth of the Red River in Arkansas has a low gradient, for along this stretch the drop varies between only one-tenth and one-half foot per mile. On the other hand, the Arkansas River in its upper reaches through the Rocky Mountains in central Colorado has a high gradient, for there the drop averages 40 feet per mile. The gradients of other rivers are even higher. The upper 12 miles of the Yuba River in California, for example, have an average gradient of 225 feet per mile; and in the upper 4 miles of the Uncompahgre River in Colorado, the gradient averages 350 feet per mile.

The velocity of a stream is checked by friction along the banks and bed of its channel and, to a much smaller extent, by friction with the air above. So if we were to study a cross section of a stream, we would find that the velocity would vary from point to point. Along a straight stretch of a channel, the greatest velocity is achieved toward the center of the stream at, or just below, the surface, as shown in Fig. 11-5.

We have, then two opposing forces: the *forward flow* of the water under the influence of gravity, and the *friction* developed along the walls and bed of the stream. These are the two forces that create different velocities. Zones of maximum turbulence occur where the different velocities come into closest contact. These zones are very thin, since the velocity of the water increases very rapidly as we move into the stream away from its walls and bed; but within these thin zones of great turbulence, a stream shows its highest potential for erosive action (see Fig. 11-6).

There is one more term that will be helpful in our discussion of running water. This is *discharge,* the quantity of water that passes a given point in a unit of time. It is usually measured in cubic feet per second, abbreviated *c.f.s.* Discharge varies not only from one stream to another, but also within a single stream from time to time and from place to place along its course. Discharge usually increases downstream as more and more tributaries add their water to the main channel. Spring floods may so greatly increase a stream's discharge that its normally peaceful course becomes a raging torrent.

THE ECONOMY OF A STREAM

Elsewhere, we have seen that earth processes tend to seek a balance, to establish an equilibrium, and that there is, in the words of James Hutton, "a system of beautiful economy in the works of nature." We found, for example, that weathering is a response of earth materials to the new and changing conditions they meet as they are exposed at or near the earth's surface. On a larger scale, we found that the major rock groups

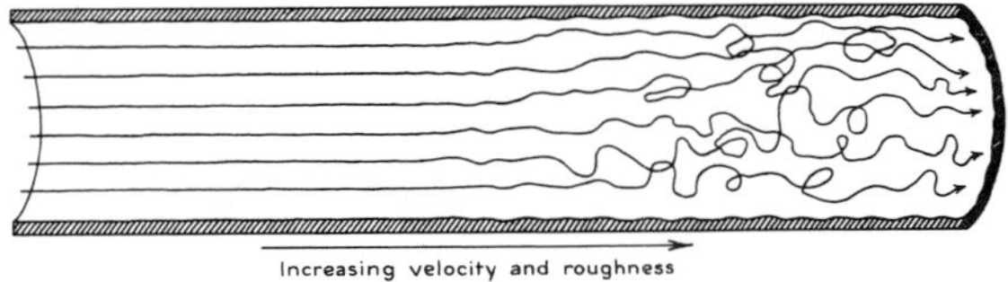

FIG. 11-3
Diagram showing laminar and turbulent flow of water through a section of pipe. Individual water particles follow paths depicted by the black lines. In laminar flow, the particles follow paths parallel to the containing walls. With increasing velocity or increasing roughness of the confining walls, laminar flow gives way to turbulent flow. The water particles no longer follow straight lines but are deflected into eddies and swirls. Most water flow in streams is turbulent.

FIG. 11-4
In longitudinal profile (from mouth to headwaters), a stream valley is concave to the sky. Irregularities along the profile indicate variations in rates of erosion. Redrawn from Henry Gannett, Profiles of Rivers in the United States. Washington, D.C.: U.S. Geol. Survey, Water Supply Paper 44, 1901.

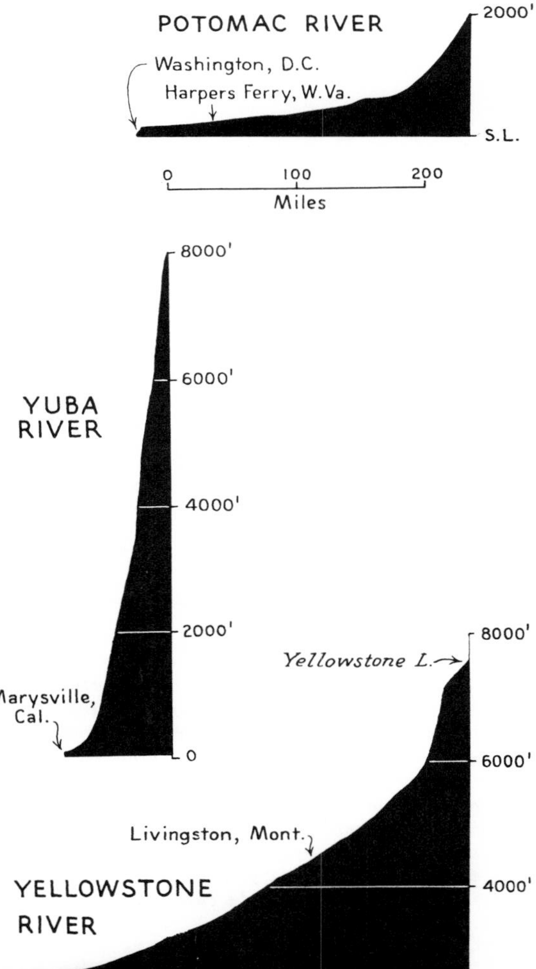

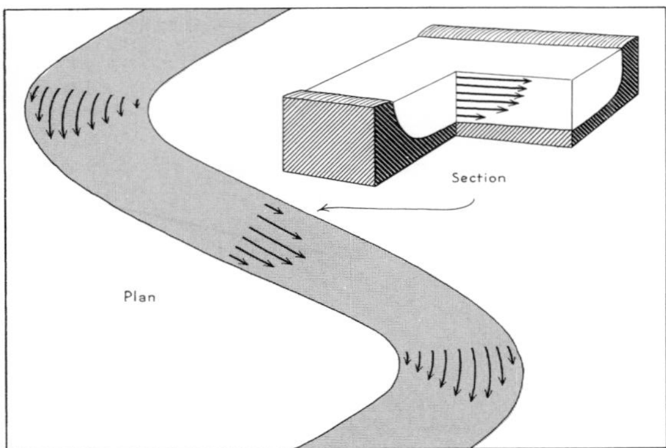

FIG. 11-5
Velocity variations in a stream. Both in plan view and in cross section, the velocity is slowest along the stream channel, where the water is slowed by friction. On the surface, it is most rapid at the center in straight stretches and toward the outside of a bed where the river curves. Velocity increases upward from the river bottom.

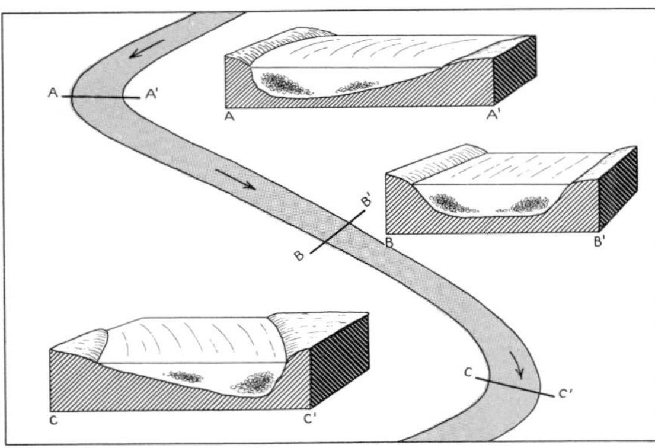

FIG. 11-6
Zones of maximum turbulence in a stream are shown by the shaded areas in the sections through a river bed. They occur where the change between the two opposing forces—the forward flow and the friction of the stream channel—is most marked. Note that the maximum turbulence along straight stretches of the river is located where the stream banks join the stream floor. On bends, the two zones have unequal intensity; the greater turbulence is located on the outside of a curve.

—igneous, sedimentary, and metamorphic—reflect certain environments and that as these environments change, members of one group may be transformed into members of another group. These changes were traced in what we called the rock cycle (Fig. 1-9). Water running off the land in streams and rivers is no exception to this universal tendency of nature to seek equilibrium.

Adjustments of discharge, velocity, and channel

Just a casual glance tells us that the behavior of a river during flood stage is very different from its behavior during the low-water stage. For one thing, a river carries more water and moves more swiftly in flood time. Furthermore, the river is generally wider during flood, its level is higher, and we would guess, even without measuring, that it is also deeper. We can relate the discharge of a river to its width, depth, and velocity as follows:

$$\textit{Discharge}\ (\text{c.f.s.}) = \begin{matrix}\text{Channel}\\ \text{width}\\ \text{(ft)}\end{matrix} \times \begin{matrix}\text{Channel}\\ \text{depth}\\ \text{(ft)}\end{matrix} \times \begin{matrix}\text{Water}\\ \text{velocity}\\ \text{(ft/sec)}\end{matrix}$$

In other words, if the dicharge at a given point along a river increases, then the width, depth, or velocity, or some combination of these factors must also increase. Leopold and Maddock [1] have shown that variations in width, depth, and velocity are neither random nor unpredictable. In most streams, if the discharge increases, then the width, depth, and velocity each increase at a definite rate. The stream maintains a balance between the amount of water it carries on the one hand, and its depth, width, and velocity on the other. Moreover, it does so in an orderly fashion, as shown in Fig. 11-7.

Let us turn now from the behavior of a stream at a single locality to the changes that take place along its entire length. From our own observation, we know that the discharge of a stream increases downstream as more and more tributaries contribute water to its main channel. We also know that the width and depth increase as we travel downstream. But if we go beyond casual observation and gather accurate data on the width, depth, velocity, and discharge of a stream from its headwaters to its mouth for a particular stage of flow —say flood or low-water—we would find again that the changes follow a definite pattern and that depth and width increase downstream as the discharge increases (Fig. 11-8). And, surprisingly enough, we would also find that the stream's *velocity* increases toward its mouth. This is contrary to our expectations, for we know that the gradients are higher upstream, which suggests that the velocities in the steeper headwater areas would also be higher. But the explanation for this seeming anomaly is simple: in order to handle the greater discharge downstream, a stream must not only deepen and widen its channel, but must also increase its velocity.

[1] *The Hydraulic Geometry of Stream Channels and Some Physiographic Implications.*

Adjustments of gradient

The gradient of a stream decreases along its course from headwaters to mouth, producing an over-all profile that is concave to the sky. If it were not for this gradual flattening of the profile, the increased discharge downstream would produce velocities fantastically higher than those observed in nature. A concave slope tends to decrease the rate at which stream velocity increases.

The actual profile of a stream is determined by the particular conditions the stream meets along its course. In its attempt to establish a balance between discharge on the one hand, and channel characteristics, velocity, and gradient on the other, the stream reduces its gradient and increases its velocity, width and depth as it flows downstream. The resulting profile or gradient is an expression of the equilibrium that is set up along each section of the stream.

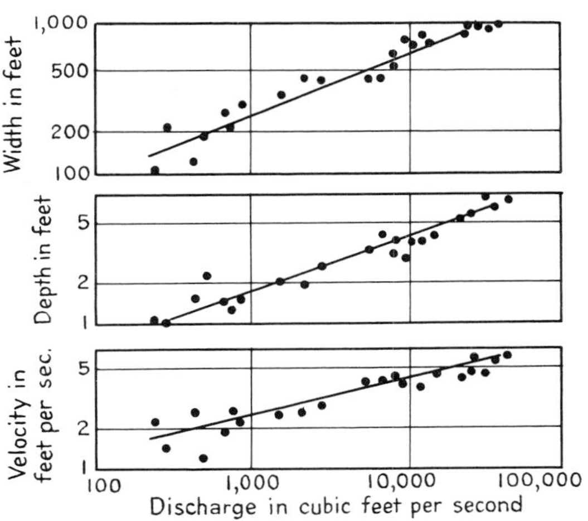

FIG. 11-7
As the discharge of a stream increases at a given gauging station, so do its velocity, width, and depth. They increase in an orderly fashion, as shown by these graphs based on data from a gauging station in the Cheyenne River near Eagle Butte, South Dakota. Redrawn from Luna B. Leopold and Thomas Maddock, The Hydraulic Geometry of Stream Channels and Some Physiographic Implications. Washington, D.C.: U.S. Geol. Survey, Professional Paper 252, 1953, p. 5.

FIG. 11-8
Stream velocity and depth and width of a channel increase as the discharge of a stream increases downstream. Measurements in this example were made at mean annual discharge along a section of the Mississippi-Missouri river system. Ibid., p. 13.

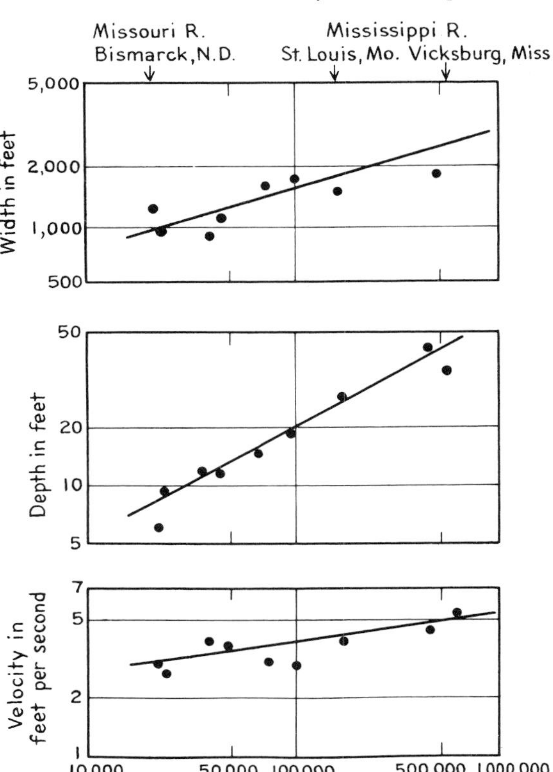

Base level of a stream

Base level is a key concept in the study of stream activity. The *base level* of a stream is defined as the lowest point to which a stream can erode its channel. Anything that prohibits the stream from lowering its channel serves to create a base level. For example, the velocity of a stream is checked when it enters the standing, quiet waters of a lake. Consequently, the stream loses its ability to erode, and it cannot cut below the level of the lake. Actually, the lake's control over the stream is effective along the entire course upstream, for no part of the stream can erode beneath the level of the lake—at least until the lake has been destroyed. But in a geologic sense, every lake is temporary. So when the lake has been destroyed, perhaps by the downcutting of its outlet, it will no longer control the stream's base level, and the stream will be free to continue its downward erosion. Because of its impermanence, the base level formed by a lake is referred to as a *temporary base level.* But even after a stream has been freed from one temporary base level, it will be controlled by others farther downstream. And its erosive power is always influenced by the ocean, which is the *ultimate base level.* Yet, as we shall see in later chapters, the ocean itself is subject to changes in level, so even the ultimate base level is not fixed.

The base level of a stream may be controlled not only by lakes, but also by layers of resistant rock and the level of the main stream into which a tributary drains (see Fig. 11-9).

ADJUSTMENT TO CHANGING BASE LEVEL. We have defined base level as the lowest level to which a stream can erode its channel. If for some reason the base level is either raised or lowered, the stream will adjust the level of its channel to adapt to the new situation.

Let us see what happens when we raise the base level of a stream by building a dam and creating a lake across its course. The level of the lake serves as a new base level, and the gradient of the stream above the dam is now less steep than it was originally. As a result, the stream's velocity is reduced. Since

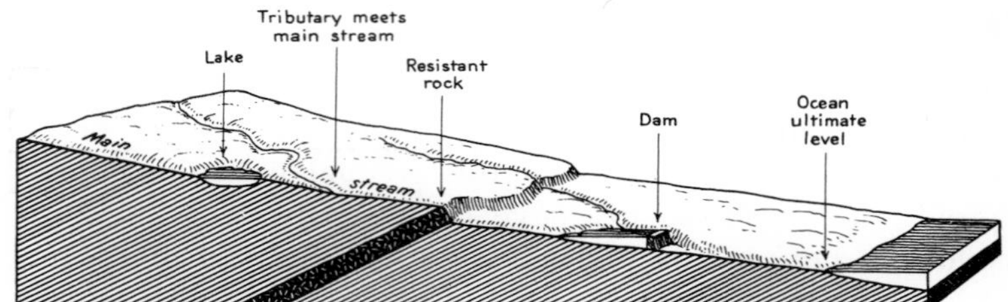

FIG. 11-9
Base level for a stream may be determined by natural and artificial lakes, by a resistant rock stratum, by the point at which a tributary stream enters a main stream, and by the ocean. Of these, the ocean is considered ultimate base level; others are temporary base levels.

the stream can no longer carry all the material supplied to it, it begins to deposit sediments at the point where it enters the lake. As time passes, a new river channel is formed with approximately the same slope as the original channel, but at a higher level (see Fig. 11-10).

What happens when we *lower* the base level by removing the dam and hence the lake? The river will now cut down through the sediments it deposited when the lake still existed. In a short time, the profile of the channel will be essentially the same as it was before we began to tamper with the stream.

In general, then, we may say that a stream adjusts itself to a rise in base level by building up its channel through sedimentation, and that it adjusts to a fall in base level by eroding its channel downward.

WORK OF RUNNING WATER

The water that flows along through river channels does several jobs: (1) it transports debris, (2) it erodes the river channel deeper into the land, and (3) it deposits sediments at various points along the valley or delivers them to lakes or oceans. Running water may help to create a chasm like that of the Grand Canyon of the Colorado, or in flood time, it may spread mud and sand across vast expanses of valley flats, or it may build deltas like those at the mouths of the Nile and Mississippi rivers.

The nature and extent of these activities depend on the kinetic energy of the stream, and this in turn depends on the amount of water in the stream and the gradient of the stream channel. A stream expends its energy in several ways. By far the greatest part is used up in the friction of the water with the stream channel, and in the friction of water with water in the turbulent eddies we discussed above. Relatively little of the stream's energy remains to erode and transport material. Deposition takes place when energy decreases and the stream can no longer move the material it has been carrying.

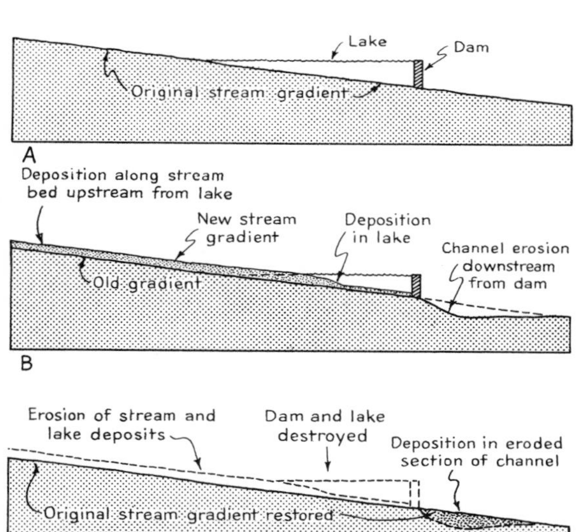

FIG. 11-10
A stream adjusts its channel to changing base level. Construction of a dam across a stream raises its base level, imposes a lower velocity on the stream above the dam, and thus causes deposition in this section of the channel. Failure of the dam lowers base level, increases the velocity, and causes erosion of the previously deposited sediments.

Transportation

The material that a stream picks up directly from its own channel—or that is supplied to it by slope wash, tributaries, or mass movement—is moved downstream toward its eventual goal, the ocean. The amount of material that a stream carries at any one time, which is called its *load,* is usually less than its *capacity*—that is, the total amount it is capable of carrying under any given set of conditions (see Fig. 11-11). The maximum size of particle that a stream can move measures the *competency* of a stream. Experiments have shown that the diameter of a particle that a stream can move varies approximately with the square of the velocity. Thus, a stream with a velocity of one-quarter of a mile per hour can move coarse sand particles of about 0.02 inch diameter. If the velocity doubles to half a mile per hour, then the diameter of a particle that can be moved increases to about 0.08 inch, and a stream flowing at a velocity of one mile an hour can move a pebble about 0.32 inch in diameter.

There are three ways in which a stream can transport material: by (1) solution, (2) suspension, and (3) bed load.

SOLUTION. In nature, no water is completely pure. We have already seen that when water falls and filters down into the ground, it dissolves some of the soil's compounds. Then the water may seep down through openings, pores, and crevices in the bedrock and dissolve additional matter as it moves along. Much of this water eventually finds its way to streams at lower levels. The amount of dissolved matter contained in water varies with climate, season, and geologic setting and is measured in terms of parts of dissolved matter per million parts of water. Sometimes the amount of dissolved material exceeds 1,000 parts per million, but usually it is much less. By far the most common compounds found in solution in running water, particularly in arid regions, are calcium and magnesium carbonates. In addition, streams carry small amounts of chlorides, nitrates, sulfates, and silica, with perhaps a trace of potassium. It has been estimated that the total load of dissolved material delivered to the seas every year by the streams of the United States is about 270,000,000 tons. All the rivers of the world are thought to dump about 3 billion tons of dissolved material into the oceans each year.

SUSPENSION. Particles of solid matter that are swept along in the turbulent current of a stream are said to be in *suspension*. This process of transportation is controlled by two factors: (1) the turbulence of the water, and (2) a characteristic known as *terminal velocity* of each individual grain. Terminal velocity is the constant rate of fall that a grain eventually attains when the acceleration caused by gravity is balanced by the resistance of the fluid through which the grain is falling. In this case, the fluid is water. If we drop a grain of sand into a quiet pond, it will settle toward the bottom at an ever-increasing rate until the friction of the water on the grain just balances this rate of increase. Thereafter, it will settle at a constant rate, its terminal velocity. If we can set up a force that will equal or exceed the terminal velocity of the grain, we can succeed in keeping it in suspension. Turbulent water supplies such a force. The eddies of turbulent water move in a series of orbits, and grains caught in these eddies will be buoyed up, or held in suspension, so long as the velocity of the turbulent water is equal to, or greater than, the terminal velocity of the grains.

Terminal velocity increases with the size of the particle, assuming that its general shape and density remain the same. The bigger a particle, the more turbulent the flow needed to keep it in suspension. And since turbulence increases when the velocity of streams flow increases, it follows that the greatest amount of material is moved during flood time when

FIG. 11-11
These converging rivers in British Columbia illustrate the different loads carried by two streams. The Frazer River enters from the upper right, milky with suspended sediment derived largely from the melting of mountain glaciers. Its load is high but probably somewhat less than capacity. The Thompson River, entering from the lower right, is relatively clear and carries a very small load, much less than its capacity. Photo by Elliott A. Riggs.

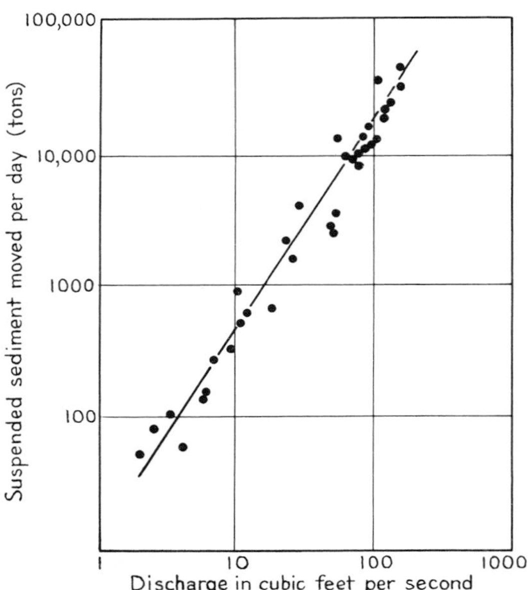

FIG. 11-12
The suspended load of a stream increases very rapidly during floods, as illustrated by this graph based on measurements in the Rio Puerco near Cabezon, New Mexico. Redrawn from Luna B. Leopold and John P. Miller, Ephemeral Streams—Hydraulic Factors and Their Relation to the Drainage Net. Washington, D.C.: U.S. Geol. Survey, Professional Paper 282-A, 1956, p. 11.

velocities and turbulence are highest. The graph in Fig. 11-12 shows how the suspended load of a stream increases as the discharge increases. In just a few hours or a few days during flood time, a stream transports more material than it does during the much longer periods of low or normal flow. Observations of the area drained by Coon Creek, at Coon Valley, Wisconsin, over a period of 450 days, showed that 90 per cent of the stream's total suspended load was carried during an interval of 10 days, slightly over 2 per cent of total time.

Silt and clay-sized particles are distributed fairly evenly through the depth of a stream, but coarser particles in the sand-size range are carried in greater amounts lower down in the current, in the zone of greatest turbulence.

BED LOAD. Materials in movement along a stream bottom constitutes the stream's *bed load,* in contrast to its suspended load and solution load. Since it is difficult to observe and measure the movement of the bed load, we have little data on the subject. Measurements on the Niobrara River near Cody, Nebraska, however, have shown that at discharges between 200 and 1,000 c.f.s., the bed load averaged about 50 per cent of the total load. Particles in the bed load move along in three ways: by saltation, rolling, or sliding.

The term *saltation* has nothing to do with salt. It is derived from the Latin *saltare,* "to jump." A particle moving by saltation jumps from one point on the stream bed to another. First it is picked up by a current of turbulent water and flung upward; then, if it is too heavy to remain in suspension, it drops to the stream floor again at some spot downstream.

Some particles are too large and too heavy to be picked up, even momentarily, by water currents. But they may be pushed and shoved along the stream bed, and depending on their shape, they move forward either by *rolling* or by *sliding.*

Erosion

A stream does more than simply transport material that has been brought to it by other agencies of erosion, for it is an effective agent of erosion in itself. In various ways, an actively eroding stream may remove material from its channel or banks.

DIRECT LIFTING. In turbulent flow, as we have seen, water travels along paths that are not parallel to the bed. The water eddies and whirls, and if an eddy is powerful enough, it dislodges particles from the stream channel and lifts them into the stream. Whether or not this will happen in a given situation depends on a number of variables that are difficult to measure. But if we assume that the bed of a stream is composed of particles of uniform size, then the graph in Fig. 11-13 gives us the approximate stream velocities that are needed to erode particles of various sizes, such as clay, silt, sand, granules, and pebbles. A stream bed composed of medium-sized sand grains, for example, can be eroded by a stream with a velocity of less than 1 foot per second. As the fragments become larger and larger, ranging from coarse sand to granules, to pebbles, increasingly higher velocities are required to move them, as we would expect.

But what we might *not* expect is that higher stream velocities are needed to erode smaller particles of clay and silt size. The reason is that smaller particles tend to pack together more firmly; and the more firmly packed a deposit is, the more resistant it is to erosion. Moreover, the individual particles may be so small that they do not project high enough into the stream to be swept up by the turbulent water.

Notice, too, in Fig. 11-13, that once a particle has been dislodged from the stream bed, it will continue to be carried along even though the stream's velocity decreases somewhat. In other words, it takes less velocity (hence, less energy) to keep a particle in movement than it does to erode the particle and start it moving.

ABRASION, IMPACT, AND SOLUTION. The solid particles carried by a stream may themselves act as erosive agents, for they are capable of abrading (wearing down) the bedrock itself or larger fragments in the bed of the stream. When the bedrock is worn by abrasion, it usually develops a series of smooth, curving surfaces, either convex or concave. Individual cobbles or pebbles on a stream bottom are sometimes moved and rolled about by the force of the current, and as they rub together they become rounder and smoother.

The impact of large particles against the bedrock or against other particles knocks off fragments that are added to the load of the stream.

Some erosion also results from the solution of channel debris and bedrock in the water of the stream. Most of the dissolved matter carried by a stream, however, is probably contributed by the underground water that drains into it.

CAVITATION. At very high stream velocities, above 25 or 30 feet per second, a highly effective erosive process known as *cavitation* sometimes comes into play. From the Latin meaning "hollow," *cavitation* refers to the sudden collapse of vapor bubbles in the water of a stream. If a bubble is in contact with the stream bed at the moment when the collapse occurs, an extremely strong impact is produced. Obvious difficulties frustrate measurement of the exact strength of the impact; but various experiments, as well as theoretical considerations, suggest that the minimum impact may be as much as 1,500 or 2,000 pounds per square inch—a very effective erosive force. In fact, in one experiment, cavitation eroded away 18 inches of a concrete spillway during a 23-hour period.

Since very high velocities are needed to produce cavitation in streams, however, this process probably occurs only in the jet and shooting flow of waterfalls and rapids.

SLOPE EROSION BY RUNNING WATER. So far, we have considered the erosion that takes place only along a stream channel—certainly the most conspicuous form of erosion by water—but the total area covered by stream channels is only a very small proportion of the total land surface drained by streams, perhaps about 1 per cent. Furthermore, most of the flood water carried by streams originates as runoff from the neighboring slopes. The runoff, flowing as a sheet of water called *slope wash* or in closely spaced, shallow channels called *rills* is sometimes powerful enough to overcome the soil's resistance to erosion, and it manages to transport a great deal of material downslope toward the stream channels.

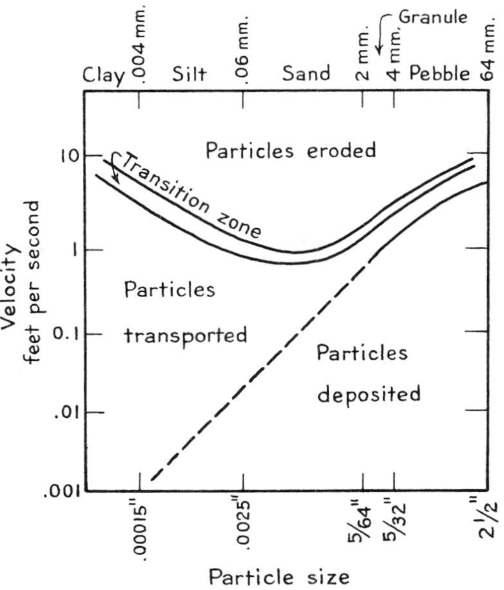

FIG. 11-13
This diagram shows the velocities at which a stream erodes, transports, and deposits particles of different sizes. Redrawn from Filip Hjultröm, Studies of the Morphological Activity of Rivers as Illustrated by the River Fyris. Upsala: Upsala Geol. Inst. Bull. 25, 1935, p. 298.

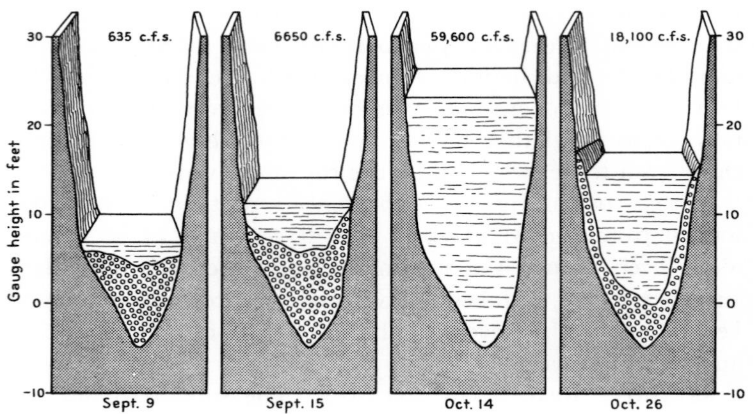

FIG. 11-14
Changes in the channel of the San Juan River near Bluff, Utah, during a flood in 1941. On September 9 and 15, periods of moderate discharge, the river flowed on a bed of gravel within the larger bedrock channel. On October 14, flood waters swelled to 59,600 c.f.s. and swept the gravel downstream, exposing the bedrock abrasion. With the subsidence of the flood, new gravel deposits brought from upstream began to build up the gravel bed of the river. Width of river on September 9 was approximately 150 feet. Redrawn from Leopold and Maddock, op. cit., p. 32.

The muddy water running off a plowed field or a newly graded slope during a heavy rain is a familiar example of the erosive power of runoff. In an area of 100 square miles with 100 miles of streams, it has been estimated that a sheet of water one-fourth of an inch thick will produce a runoff of 22,000 cubic feet per second. If this same sheet of water carried 10 per cent of solid matter by volume and flowed for 6 hours, it would remove between one-fourth and one-third of an inch of soil. To quote the author of this estimate:

Little drops of water,
Little grains of sand,
Run away together
And destroy the land.[2]

Although the importance of slope erosion by running water is often overlooked, it must play a significant role in the general process of erosion. We shall refer to it again later in this chapter.

TIME OF MOST RAPID EROSION. We have found that, other things being equal, the greater the stream's velocity the greater its erosive power. Obviously, then, the greatest erosive (and transporting) power of any stream is developed during flood time. When a stream is at flood stage, the water level rises and the channel is deepened. The fast-moving water picks up the layer of sand and gravel that usually lies on the bedrock of the stream channel during nonflood stages and sweeps it downstream. If the flood is great enough, the bedrock itself is exposed and eroded. A new layer of debris collects as the flood waters subside, but by that time great masses of material have been moved downstream toward the oceans, and the bedrock channel of the stream has been permanently lowered. Figure 11-14 illustrates this action.

In general, then, we may say that erosion is most effective during flood periods.

Deposition

As soon as the velocity of stream falls below the point necessary to hold material in suspension, the stream begins to deposit its suspended load. Deposition is a selective process. First, the coarsest material is dropped; then, as the velocity (and

[2] Robert E. Horton, "Sheet Erosion—Present and Past," *Trans. Am. Geophys. Union,* XXII (1941), 300.

hence the energy) continues to slacken, finer and finer material settles out. We shall consider stream deposits in more detail elsewhere in this chapter, but another look at Fig. 11-13 will show the size of particles that settle out at different velocities. Thus, when the velocity of a stream falls below 1 foot per second, pebble-sized particles can no longer be carried, and they begin to fall to the bottom. At a velocity of about 0.1 foot per second, medium-sized sand grains are dropped; and below 0.01 foot per second, silt begins to settle out.

FEATURES OF VALLEYS

Cross-valley profiles

Earlier in this chapter we mentioned the longitudinal profile of a stream (Fig. 11-4). Now let us turn to a discussion of the cross-valley profile—that is, the profile of a cross section at right angles across the stream's valley. In Fig. 11-15A, notice

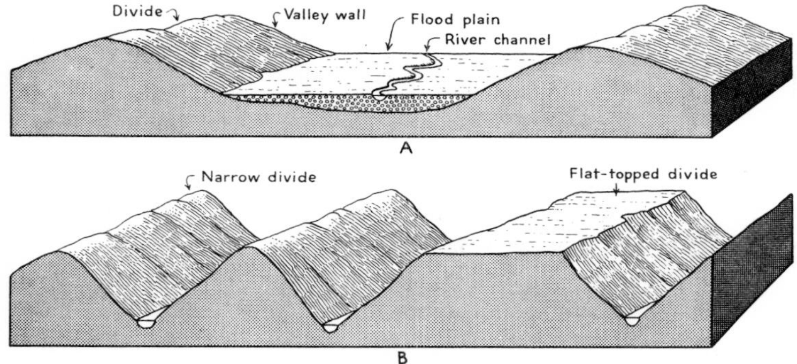

FIG. 11-15
Cross-sectional sketches of typical stream valleys. The major features of valleys in cross section include divides, valley walls, river channel, and, in some instances, a flood plain. Divides may be either flat-topped or broadly rounded.

that the channel of the river runs across a broad, relatively flat *flood plain.* During flood time, when the channel can no longer accommodate the increased discharge, the stream overflows its banks and floods this area. On either side of the flood plain, *valley walls* rise to crests called *divides,* separations between the central valley and the other valleys on either side. In B, no flood plain is present, for the valley walls descend directly to the banks of the river. This diagram also illustrates two different shapes of divide. One is broad and flat, the other is narrow, almost knife-edged. Both are in contrast to the broadly convex divides shown in A.

Drainage basins

A *drainage basin* is the entire area from which a stream and its tributaries receive their water. The Mississippi and its tributaries drain a tremendous section of central United States reaching from the Rockies to the Appalachians, and each tributary of the Mississippi has its own drainage area, which forms a part of the larger basin. Every stream, even the smallest brook, has its own drainage basin, shaped differently from stream to stream, but characteristically pear-shaped, with the main stream emerging from the narrow end (see Fig. 11-16).

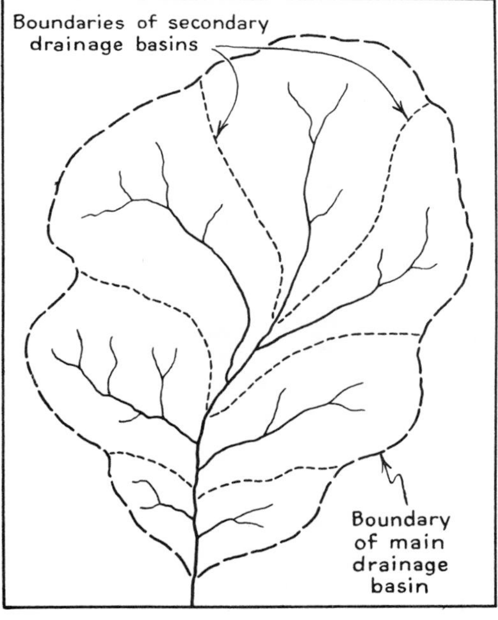

FIG. 11-16
Each stream, no matter how small, has its own drainage basin, the area from which the stream and its tributaries receive water. This basin displays a pattern reminiscent of a tree leaf and its veins.

Enlargement of valleys

We cannot say with assurance how running water first fashioned the great valleys and drainage basins of the continents,

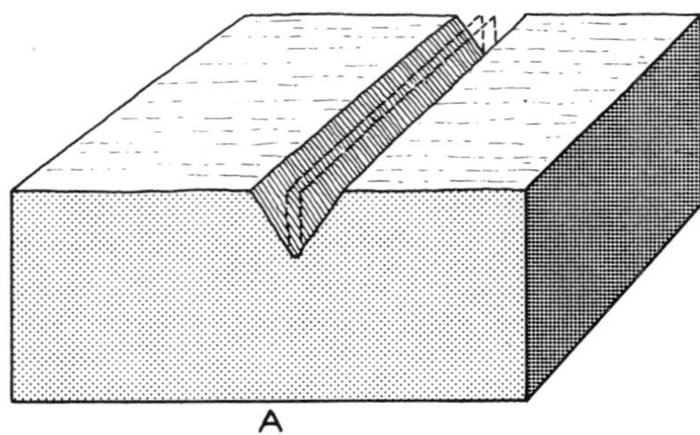

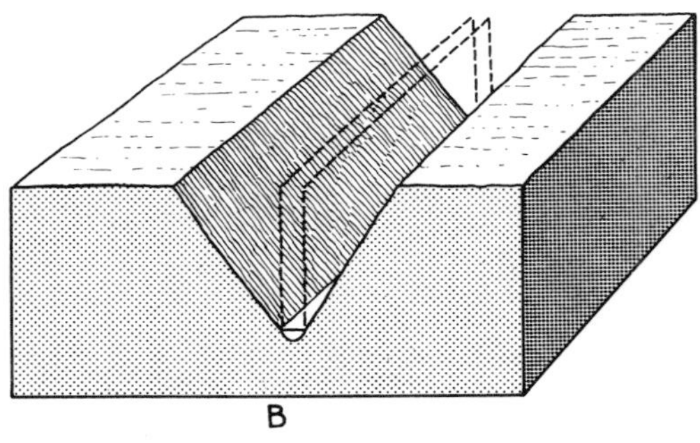

FIG. 11-17
If a stream of water were the only agent in valley formation, we might expect a vertically-walled valley no wider than the stream channel, as suggested by the dotted lines in A *and* B. *Mass movement and slope wash, however, are constantly wearing away the valley walls, carving slopes that flare upward and away from the stream channel, as shown in the diagrams.*

FIG. 11-18
Erosion by a small stream has fashioned vertically-walled Labyrinth Canyon, Utah, in beds of massive sandstone. The stream is the major agent in formation of the valley. Mass movement and other agents of slope modification have yet to lower the angle of valley walls. Cf. Fig. 11-17. Photo by William C. Bradley.

for the record has been lost in time. But we do know that certain processes are now at work in widening and deepening valleys, and it seems safe to assume that they also operated in the past.

If a stream were left to itself in its attempt to reach base level, it would erode its bed straight downward, forming a vertically walled chasm in the process. But since the stream is not the only agent at work in valley formation, the walls of most valleys slope upward and outward from the valley floor. In time, the cliffs of even the steepest gorge will be angled away from the axis of its valley.

As a stream cuts downward and lowers its channel into the land surface, weathering, slope wash, and mass movement come into play, constantly wearing away the valley walls, pushing them farther back. Under the influence of gravity, material is carried down from the valley walls and dumped into the stream, to be moved onward toward the seas. The result is a valley whose walls flare outward and upward from the stream in a typical cross-valley profile (Fig. 11-17).

The rate at which valley walls are reduced and the angles that they assume depend on several factors. If the walls are made up of unconsolidated material that is vulnerable to erosion and mass movement, the rate will be rapid. But if the walls are composed of resistant rock, the rate of erosion will be very slow, and the walls may rise almost vertically from the valley floor (see Fig. 11-18).

In addition to cutting downward into its channel, a stream also cuts from side to side, or laterally, into its banks. In the early stages of valley enlargement, when the stream is still far above its base level, downward erosion is dominant. Later, as the stream cuts its channel closer and closer to base level, downward erosion becomes progressively less important. Now a larger percentage of the stream's energy is directed toward eroding its banks. As the stream swings backs and forth, it forms an ever-widening flood plain on the valley floor, and the valley itself becomes broader and broader.

We shall return to the progressive development of a valley later on, when we consider the cycle of erosion. But first, let us examine some specific features of valleys.

Features of narrow valleys

WATERFALLS AND RAPIDS. Waterfalls are among the most fascinating spectacles of the landscape. Thunderous and powerful as they are, however, they are actually short-lived features in the history of a stream. They owe their existence to some sudden drop in the river's longitudinal profile—a drop that may be eliminated with the passing of time.

Waterfalls are caused by many different conditions. Niagara Falls, for instance, is held up by a relatively resistant bed of dolomite underlain by beds of nonresistant shale (Fig. 11-19). This shale is easily undermined by the swirling waters of the Niagara River as they plunge over the lip of the falls. When the undermining has progressed far enough, the dolomite collapses and tumbles to the base of the falls. The same process is repeated over and over again as time passes, and the falls slowly retreat upstream. Historical records suggest that the Horseshoe or Canadian Falls (by far the larger of the two falls at Niagara) have been retreating at a rate of four to five feet per year, while the smaller American Falls have been eroded away about two or three inches per year. The seven miles of gorge between the foot of the falls and Lake Ontario are evidence of the headward retreat of the falls through time.

Yosemite Falls in Yosemite National Park, California, plunge 2,565 feet over the Upper Falls, down an intermediate zone of cascades, and then over the Lower Falls. The falls leap from the mouth of a small valley high above the main valley of the Yosemite. The Upper Falls alone measure 1,430 feet, nine times the height of Niagara. During the ice age, glaciers scoured the main valley much deeper than they did the side valley. Then, when the glacier ice melted, the main valley was left far below its tributary, which now joins it after a drop of nearly half a mile. (See "Hanging valleys," in Chapter 13).

FIG. 11-19
Niagara Falls tumbles over a bed of dolomite, underlain chiefly by shale. As the less resistant shale is eroded, the undermined ledge of dolomite breaks off, and the lip of the falls retreats. Redrawn from G. K. Gilbert, Niagara Falls and Their History. (New York: American Book Company, 1896), p. 213.

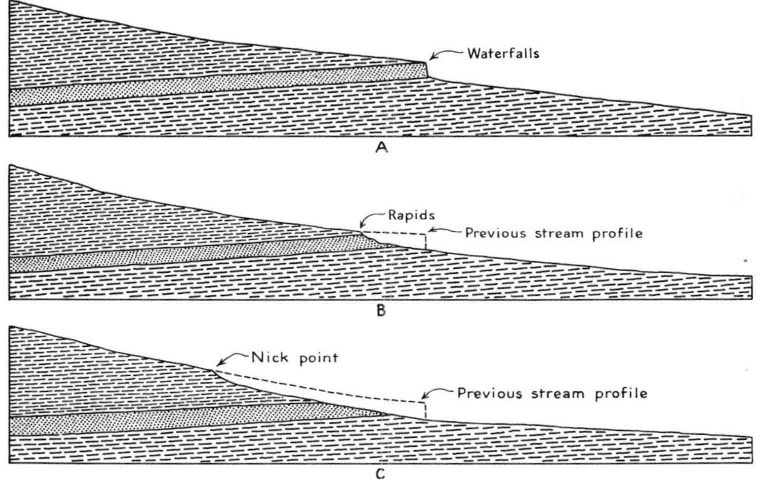

FIG. 11-20
Rapids may represent a stage in the destruction of waterfalls, as suggested in this diagram.

The Victoria Falls of Africa's Zambezi River were caused by yet another set of conditions. Here the Zambezi drops over a resistant bed of lava 295 feet to the gorge below. The gorge itself follows a zigzag course excavated by the retreating falls along zones of weakness in the rock. These zones are the result of intersecting fractures in the beds of lava.

Rapids, like waterfalls, occur at a sudden drop in the stream channel. Although rapids do not plunge straight down as waterfalls do, the underlying cause of formation is often the same. In fact, many rapids have developed directly from preexisting waterfalls (see Fig. 11-20).

POTHOLES. As the bedrock channel of a stream is eroded away, *potholes* sometimes develop (see Fig. 11-21). These are deep holes, circular to elliptical in outline, and a few inches to scores of feet in depth. They are most often observed in the stream channel during low water or along the bedrock walls, where they have been left stranded after the stream has cut its channel downward. Potholes are most common in narrow valleys, but they often occur in broad valleys as well.

A pothole begins as a shallow depression in the bedrock

FIG. 11-21
This nearly dry stream bed is marked by a series of potholes. Coarse sand and gravel, caught up in the eddies of turbulent water, served as the cutting materials that carved the holes. Photo by Paul MacClintock.

channel of a stream. Then, as the swirling, turbulent water drives sand, pebbles, and even cobbles round and round the depression, the continued abrasion wears the pothole ever deeper, as if the bedrock were being bored by a giant drill (see Fig. 11-22). The initial depression may be caused by ordinary abrasion, by some irregularity in the bedrock, or by cavitation.

Features of broad valleys

If conditions permit, the various agents working toward valley enlargement ultimately produce a broad valley with a wide level floor. During periods of normal or low water, the river running through the valley is confined to its channel. But during high water it overflows its banks and spreads out over the flood plain.

A flood plain that has been created by the lateral erosion and the gradual retreat of the valley walls is called an *erosional flood plain* and is characterized by a thin cover of gravel, sand, and silt a few feet or a few scores of feet in thickness. On the other hand, the floors of many broad valleys are underlain by deposits of gravel, sand, and silt hundreds of feet thick. These thick deposits are laid down as changing conditions force the river to drop its load across the valley floor. Such a flood plain, formed by the building up of the valley floor, or aggradation, is called a *flood plain of aggradation*. Flood plains of aggradation are much more common than erosional flood plains and are found in the lower reaches of the Mississippi, Nile, Rhône, and Yellow rivers, to name but a few.

Both erosional flood plains and flood plains of aggradation exhibit the following characteristic features.

MEANDERS. The channel of the Menderes River in Asia Minor curves back on itself in a series of broad hairpin bends. In fact, the very name of the river is derived from the Greek *maiandros*, "a bend." Today, all such bends are called *meanders* (me-an′-ders), and the zone along a valley floor that encloses a meandering river is called a *meander belt* (see Figs. 11-23, 11-24).

Both erosion and deposition are involved in the formation of a meander. First, some obstruction swings the current of a stream against one of the banks, and then the current is deflected over to the opposite bank. Erosion takes place on the outside of each bend, where the turbulence is greatest. The material detached from the banks is moved downstream, there to be deposited in zones of decreased turbulence—either along the center of the channel or on the inside of the next bend. As the river swings from side to side, the meander continues to grow by erosion on the outside of the bends and by deposition on the inside. Growth ceases when the meander reaches a critical size, a size that increases with an increase in the size of the stream.

Because a meander is eroded more on its downstream side than on its upstream side, the entire bend tends to move slowly down-valley. This movement is not uniform, however, and under certain conditions the downstream sweep of a series of meanders is distorted into cutoffs, meander scars, and oxbow lakes.

FIG. 11-22
A cluster of pebbles in a pothole exposed at low water stage in the bed of the Blackstone River, Blackstone, Massachusetts. Photo by Alden, U.S. Geol. Survey.

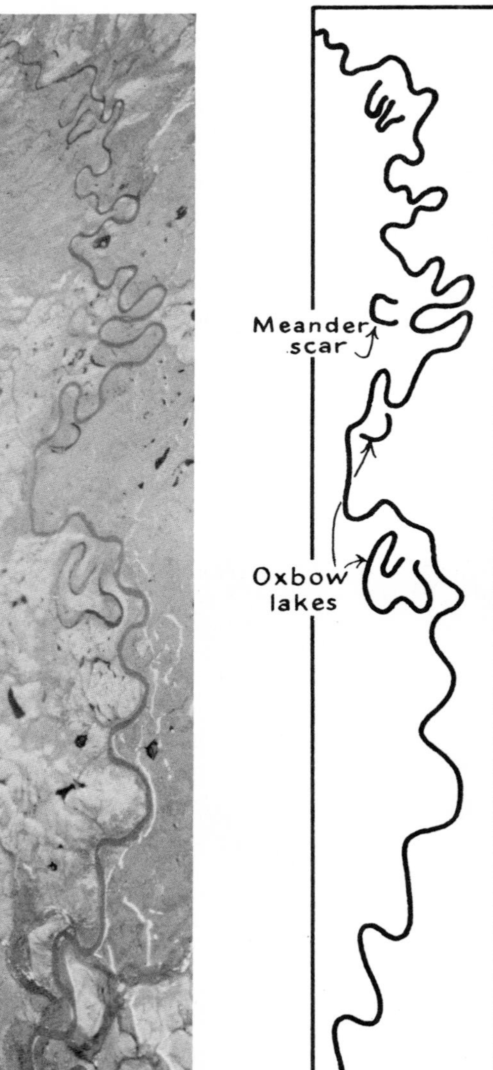

FIG. 11-23
Aerial photograph and a drawing of meanders in an Alaskan stream. Note the oxbow lakes. Photo by U.S. Army Air Force.

In its down-valley migration, a meander sometimes runs into a stretch of land that is relatively more resistant to erosion. But the next meander upstream continues to move right along, and gradually the neck between them is narrowed. Finally, the river cuts a new, shorter channel, called a *neck cutoff,* across the neck. The abandoned meander is called an *oxbow,* because of its characteristic shape. Usually both ends of the oxbow are gradually silted in, and the old meander becomes completely isolated from the new channel. If the abandoned meander fills up with water, an *oxbow lake* results. Although a cutoff will eliminate a particular meander, the stream's tendency toward meandering still exists, and before long the entire process begins to repeat itself.

We found that a meander grows and migrates by erosion on the outside of the bend and by deposition on the inside. This deposition on the inside leaves behind a series of low ridges and troughs. Swamps often form in the troughs, and during flood time the river may develop an alternate channel through one of the troughs. Such a channel is called a *chute cutoff,* or simply a chute (see Figs. 11-25, 11-26).

The meandering river demonstrates a unity in ways other than the balance of erosion and deposition. The length of a meander, for example, is proportional to the width of the river, and this is true regardless of the size of the river. It holds for channels a few feet wide as well as those as large as that of the Mississippi. As shown in Figure 11-27, this principle also is true of the Gulf Stream, even though this "river" is unconfined by solid banks. A similar relationship holds between the length of the meander and radius of curvature of the meander (Fig. 11-27).

BRAIDED STREAMS. On some flood plains, particularly where large amounts of debris are dropped rapidly, a stream may build up a complex tangle of converging and diverging channels separated by sand bars or islands. A stream of this sort is called a *braided stream.* When the velocity is checked either by a decrease in the stream's gradient or by a loss of water through infiltration into porous deposits, the energy of the stream also falls. Consequently, a large part of the stream's suspended load is suddenly dropped. The deposited material deflects the current into different channels, in search of an easier course. The braided pattern is commonly found on alluvial fans, glacial outwash deposits, and along certain rapidly depositing rivers.

NATURAL LEVEES. In many flood plains, the water surface of the stream is held above the level of the valley floor by banks of sand and silt known as *natural levees,* a name derived from the French verb *lever,* "to raise." These banks slope gently, almost imperceptibly, away from their crest along the river toward the valley wall. The low-lying flood plain adjoining a natural levee, may contain marshy areas known as *back swamps.* Levees are built up during flood time, when the water spills over the river banks onto the flood plain. Since the muddy water rising over the stream bank is no longer confined by the channel, its velocity and turbulence drop immediately, and much of the suspended load is deposited close to the river; but some is carried farther along,

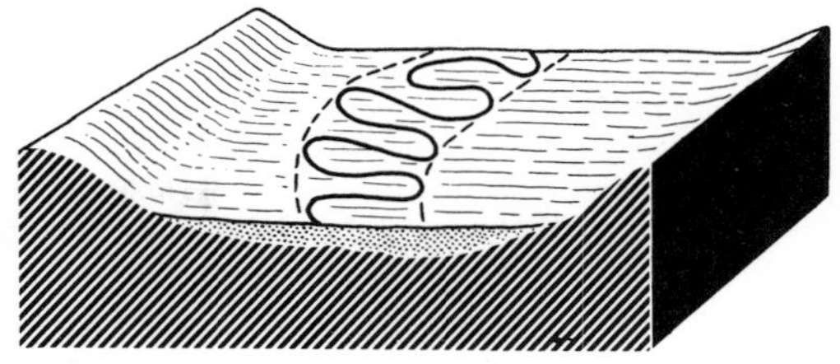

FIG. 11-24
The meander belt is the portion of the floodplain that encloses a meandering stream.

FIG. 11-25
This oxbow lake near Weslaco, Texas, was once a part of the meandering Rio Grande, which lies in the distance. An old bend in the river was cut through at the neck, became isolated from the river, and filled with water. Photo by Standard Oil Co. (N.J.).

FIG. 11-26
Erosion takes place on the outside of a meander bend, whereas deposition is most marked on the inside. If the neck of a meander is eroded through, an oxbow forms. A chute originates along the inside of a meander where irregular deposition creates ridges and troughs as the meander migrates.

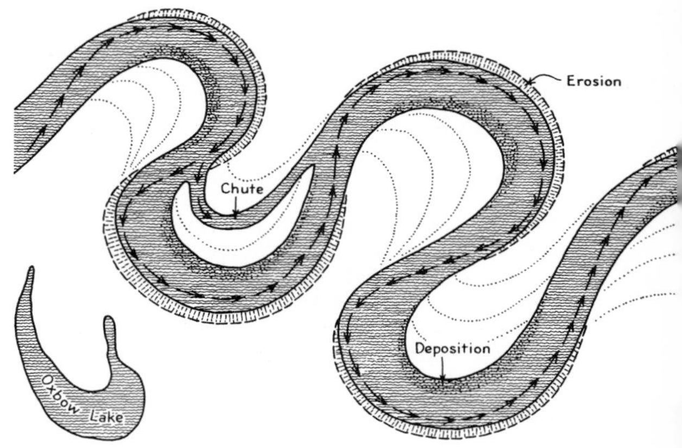

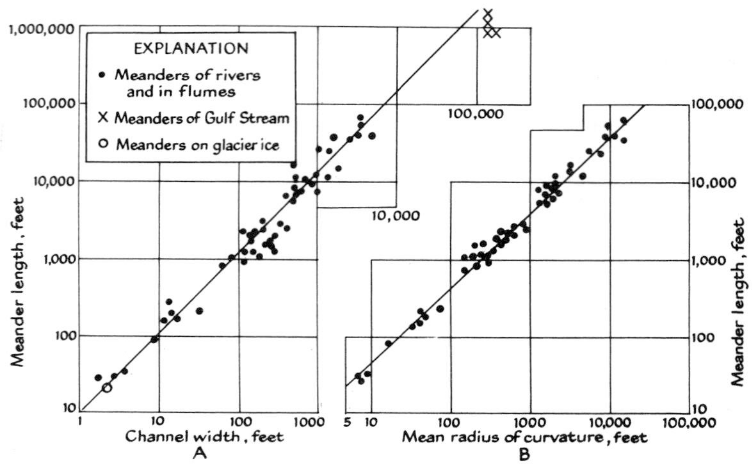

FIG. 11-27
A: Length of the meander increases with the widening meandering stream. B: A similar orderly relationship exists between length of the meander and the mean radius of curvature of the meander. Redrawn from Luna B. Leopold and M. Gordon Wolman, "River Meanders," Geol. Soc. Am. Bull., LXXI (1960), p. 773.

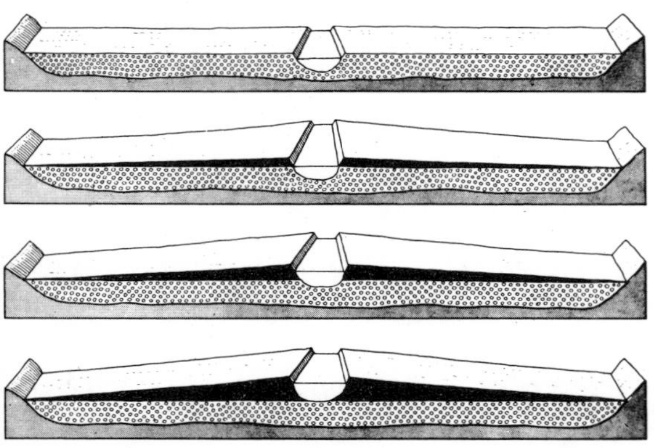

FIG. 11-28
Natural levees, characteristic of many aggrading streams. These highly exaggerated diagrams show building up of wedge-shaped layers of silt that taper away from the stream banks toward valley walls. As the banks are built up, the floor of the stream channel also rises.

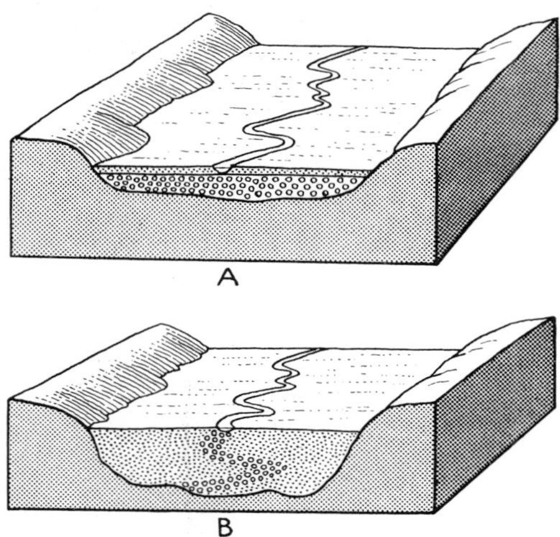

FIG. 11-29
Deposits underlying the flood plain of a slowly aggrading river or beneath a flood plain formed by erosion differ from those beneath a rapidly aggrading river's flood plain. A: Deposits are those to be expected beneath an erosional flood plain or one being slowly aggraded. Coarse river channel deposits underlie the entire flood plain and are veneered with fine-grained sediments. B: The type of deposit beneath the flood plain of a rapidly aggrading river, the great bulk being fine-grained sediments deposited during flood periods. Coarse channel deposits may form a ribbon of gravel within the finer deposits.

to be deposited across the flood plain. The deposit of one flood is a thin wedge tapering away from the river; but over many years, the cumulative effect produces a natural levee that is considerably higher alongside the river bank than away from it (Fig. 11-28). On the Mississippi delta, for instance, the levees stand 15 to 20 feet above the back swamps.

Although natural levees tend to confine a stream within its channel, each time the levees are raised slightly, the bed of the river is also raised. In time, the level of the bed is raised above the level of the surrounding flood plain. If the river manages to escape from its confining walls during a flood, it will assume a new channel across the lowest parts of the flood plain toward the back swamps.

A tributary stream entering a river valley with high levees may be unable to find its way directly into the main channel, so it will flow down the back-swamp zone and may run parallel to the main stream for many miles before finding a place to enter. Because the Yazoo River typifies this situation by running 200 miles parallel to the Mississippi, all rivers following similar courses are known as *yazoo-type* rivers.

FLOOD-PLAIN DEPOSITS. The floors of most flood plains are covered by two and sometimes three different types of deposit. The coarsest material is deposited directly by the stream along its channel. During flood periods, finer sand, silt, and clay are spread across the flood plain, away from the river banks. In addition, relatively small amounts of debris of various types and sizes move down the valley walls under the influence of slope wash and mass movement and are spread along the sides of the valley floor. The distribution of the channel and flood deposits across a flood plain depends on the rate at which a stream builds up its valley floor.

A meandering stream is constantly shifting its channel, and over a period of time it may succeed in occupying every possible position across the plain. A cross section through the flood plain developed by such a stream reveals a cover of gravel capped by fine-grained sediments deposited during overbank flow (see Fig. 11-29, A). This pattern of sediments is typical of erosional flood plains and of very slowly aggraded flood plains.

But a meandering stream that builds up its flood plain at

a rapid rate has less opportunity to occupy each spot across the valley floor. Consequently, its flood plain will be covered for the most part by fine sediments deposited during times of overflow. A cross section reveals an irregular band of coarse material, marking successive positions of the channel (see Fig. 11-29, B). Rapidly aggraded flood plains show this pattern of deposition.

DELTAS AND ALLUVIAL FANS. For centuries, the Nile River has been depositing sediments as it empties into the Mediterranean Sea, forming a great triangular plain with its apex upstream. This plain came to be called a *delta* because of the similarity of its shape to the Greek letter Δ (see Figs. 11-30, 11-31).

Whenever a stream flows into a body of standing water, such as a lake or an ocean, its velocity and transporting power are quickly stemmed. If it carries enough debris and if conditions in the body of standing water are favorable, a delta will gradually be built up. An ideal delta is triangular in plan, with the apex pointed upstream, and with the sediments arranged according to a definite pattern. The coarse material is dumped first, forming a series of dipping beds called *foreset beds.* But the finer material is swept farther along to settle across the sea or lake floor as *bottomset beds.* As the delta extends farther and farther out into the water body, the stream must extend its channel to the edge of the delta. As it does so, it covers the delta with *topset beds,* which lie across the top of the foreset beds (see Fig. 11-32).

Very few deltas, however, show either the perfect delta shape or this regular sequence of sediments. Many factors, including lake and shore currents, varying rates of deposition, the settling of delta deposits as a result of their compaction, and the down-warping of the earth's crust, all conspire to modify the typical form and sequence.

Across the top of the delta deposits, the stream spreads seaward in a complex of channels radiating from the apex. These *distributary channels* shift their position from time to time as they seek more favorable gradients.

Deltas are characteristic of many of the larger rivers of the world, including the Nile, Mississippi, Ganges, Rhine, and Rhône. On the other hand, many rivers have no deltas, either because the deposited material is swept away as soon as it is dumped or because the streams do not carry enough detrital material to build up a delta.

An *alluvial fan* is the land counterpart of a delta. These fans are typical of arid and semiarid climates but they may form in almost any climate if conditions are right. A fan marks a sudden decrease in the carrying power of a stream as it descends from a steep gradient to a flatter one—for example, when the stream flows down a steep mountain slope onto a

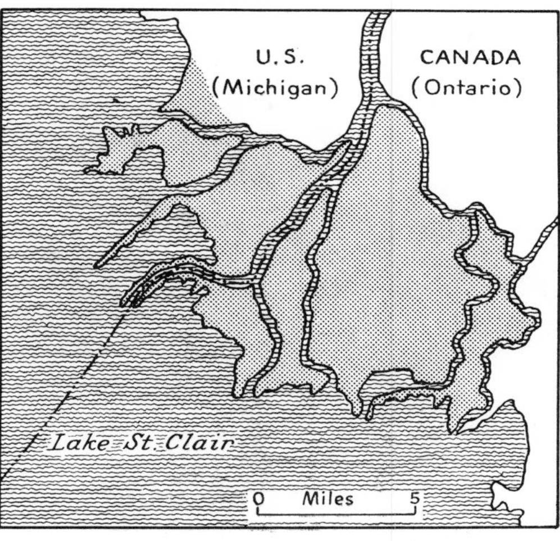

FIG. 11-30
The delta (shaded area) of the St. Clair River in Lake St. Clair has the classic shape of a delta as well as its distributary channels. Redrawn from Leon J. Cole, "The Delta of the St. Clair River," Geological Survey of Michigan, IX (1903), Pt. 1, Plate 1.

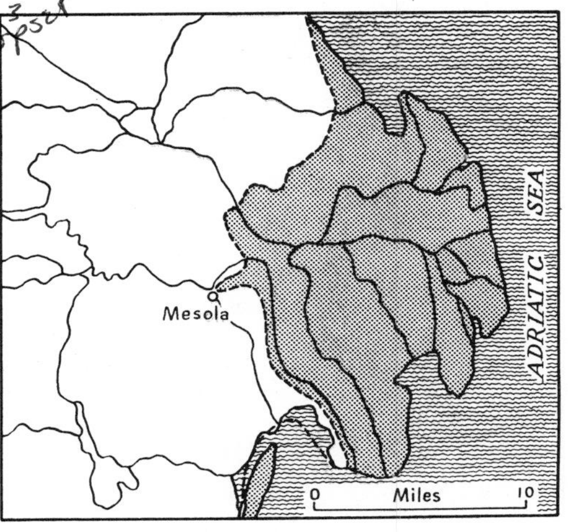

FIG. 11-31
The rapid growth of some deltas is represented by the delta of the Po River, Italy. The entire land area on the map above is within the delta area. The stippled section of the delta was built between 1559 and 1869.

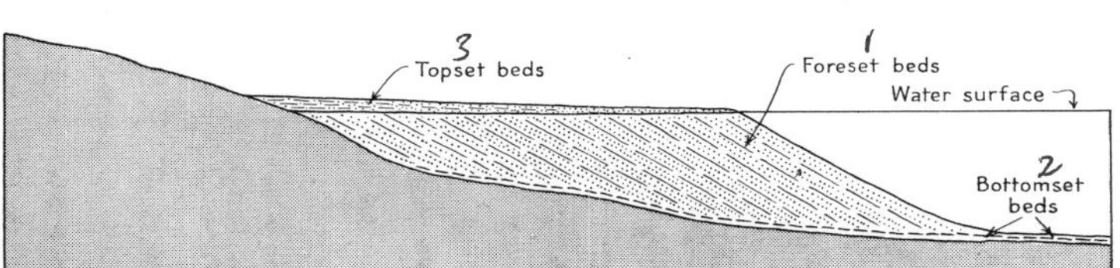

FIG. 11-32
The ideal arrangement of sediments beneath a delta. Some of the material deposited in a water body is laid on the bottom of the lake or sea as bottomset beds. Other material is dumped in inclined foreset beds, built farther and farther into the body of water and partly covering the bottomset beds. Over the foreset beds the stream lays down topset beds.

FIG. 11-33
An alluvial fan is the land counterpart of a delta. In this example in Death Valley, California, the streams flow only during the rare rains, carrying debris from the steep gulches along the cliff face. As the velocity of the streams is checked on the flat valley floor, material is deposited to form the alluvial fan. Photo by Sheldon Judson.

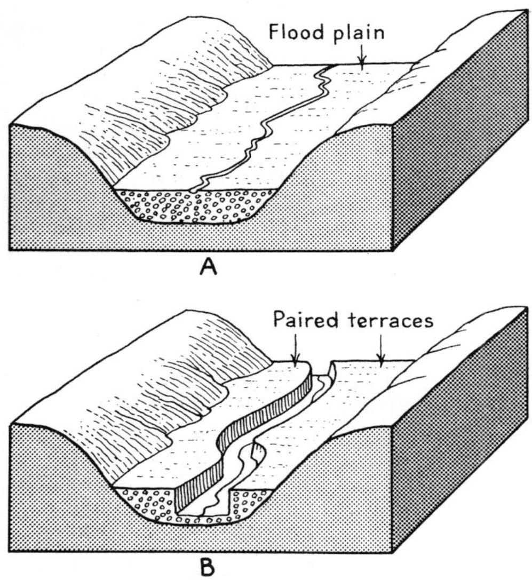

FIG. 11-34
One example of the formation of paired terraces. In A, *the stream has partially filled its valley and has created a broad flood plain. In* B, *some change in conditions has caused the stream to erode into its own deposits; the remnants of the old flood plain stand above the new river level as terraces of equal height. This particular example is referred to as a cut-and-fill terrace. (See also Fig. 11-35.)*

plain. As the velocity is checked, the stream rapidly begins to dump its load. In the process, it builds up its channel, often with small natural levees along its banks. Eventually, as the levees continue to grow, the stream may flow above the general level. Then, during a time of flood, it seeks a lower level and shifts its channel to begin deposition elsewhere. As this process of shifting continues, an alluvial fan builds up (Fig. 11-33).

STREAM TERRACES. A *stream terrace* is a relatively flat surface running along a valley, with a steep bank separating it either from the flood plain or from a lower terrace. It is a remnant of the former channel of a stream that now has cut its way down to a lower level.

The so-called *cut-and-fill terrace* is created when a stream first clogs a valley with sediments and then cuts its way down to a lower level (see Figs. 11-34, 11-35). The initial aggradation may be caused by a change in climate that leads either to an increase in the stream's load or a decrease in its discharge. Or the base level of the stream may rise, reducing the gradient and causing deposition. In any event, the stream chokes the valley with sediment and the flood plain gradually rises. Now, if the equilibrium is upset and the stream begins to erode, it will cut a channel down through the deposits it has already laid down. The level of flow will be lower than the old flood plain, and at this lower level the stream will begin to carve out a new flood plain. As time passes, remnants of the old flood plain may be left standing on either side of the new one. Terraces that face each other across the stream at the same elevation are referred to as *paired terraces.*

Sometimes the downward erosion by streams creates *unpaired terraces* rather than paired ones. If the stream swings back and forth across the valley, slowly eroding as it moves, it may encounter resistant rock beneath the unconsolidated deposits. The exposed rock will then deflect the stream and prevent further erosion. A single terrace is left behind, with no corresponding terrace on the other side of the stream (see Fig. 11-36).

Terraces, either paired or unpaired, may be cut into bedrock as well. A thin layer of sand and gravel usually rests on the beveled bedrock of these terraces.

EVIDENCE THAT A STREAM CUTS ITS OWN VALLEY

So far, we have been assuming that every stream has created its own valley. True, we have seen that other processes, such as slope wash and mass movement, have helped in valley enlargement; but we have taken it for granted that they rely on the streams to transport the material they produce and to create and maintain slopes on which they can operate. This assumption has not always been accepted, however. In fact, during the early nineteenth century, geologists devoted a great deal of time to demonstrating that valleys were not great, original furrows in the earth's surface, along which the rivers flow merely for want of a better place to go. Today, we are confident that most valleys have been created by the streams that flow through them and by the processes that these streams have encouraged. Let us review some of the evidence for this belief.

Most of us have observed at first hand the direct results of running water during a heavy rain. For instance, we can watch the actual headward erosion of small gullies in miniature drainage basins. What we are observing here is really a small stream in the process of forming and extending its valley. Merely by dipping up a cupful of water we can see evidence of the load carried by the stream, and we know that this debris must have come from the drainage basin of the stream. Erosion is going on as we watch, and the valley is growing larger as the stream moves the eroded material downvalley.

We know from observing modern streams that abrasion wears and polishes the beds and banks of bedrock and sometimes drills potholes deep into the rock floor. When we find these marks of stream activity high above the channel of a modern stream, it is logical to assume that they were made by the stream when it was flowing at this higher level, and that the stream has since cut downward and deepened its valley.

As we have seen, a terrace records the fact that a stream once flowed at a higher level. And when we find terraces covered with sand and gravel high above a modern stream, again it is reasonable to assume that the stream has cut its way down to a lower level.

Along the walls of many streams, we can observe beds of rocks formed from layers of sediments that were laid down in ancient seas, and we can match individual beds from one valley wall to the other. We know that these beds were laid down originally as continuous sheets and that some agency subsequently removed large sections of them. Barring evidence of crustal movement, we conclude that the stream flowing along the bottom of the valley has been responsible.

These and other arguments make it reasonably clear that a stream has created the valley through which it flows. No one argument or bit of evidence is final proof, of course. In fact, we know that some valleys were formed by earth movement (Chapter 16) and were deepened by glaciers (Chapter 13). Still, the weight of evidence points to the likelihood that most valleys have been formed by stream activity.

CYCLE OF EROSION

From the beginning of the twentieth century, the concept that stream valleys, indeed entire regions, progress through a series of stages has influenced geologists in their attempts to explain the development of the landscape. This so-called *cycle of erosion* has been abused by over-enthusiastic advocates and bitterly attacked by critics. As in most violent controversies, the truth probably lies somewhere between the extremes.

The cycle of erosion does provide us with a qualitative description of river valleys and areas, but difficulties arise when

FIG. 11-35
A Roman mausoleum, partially buried in stream deposits, is exposed in this stream bank just north of Rome, Italy. In A.D. 50, when the mausoleum was built, the stream flowed at the same level as it does today, but the steep banks were not then present. Sometime after the third century A.D., this stream began to build up its flood plain until the valley floor stood at a level marked by the top of the modern bank. Thereafter the stream cut down to its present level, re-exposing the partially buried structure and leaving its old valley floor and flood plain standing as a low terrace. (See also Fig. 11-34.) Photo by C. T. Stifter.

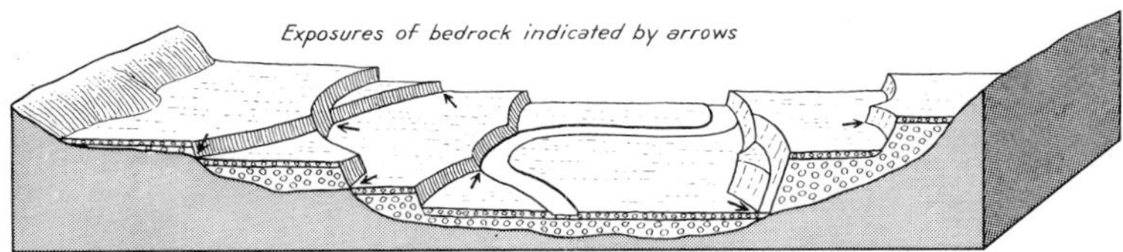

FIG. 11-36
Unpaired terraces do not match across the stream that separates them. Here is one way in which they may form. The stream has cut through unconsolidated deposits within the valley. As it eroded downward, it also swept laterally across the valley and created a sloping surface. Lateral migration was stopped locally when the stream encountered resistant bedrock (see arrows) beneath the softer valley fill. This bedrock not only deflected the stream back across the valley but also protected remnants of the valley fill from further stream erosion and allowed them to be preserved as terraces. Because they are portions of a surface sloping across the valley, however, no single remnant matches any other on the opposite side of the river.

FIG. 11-37
Terraces along the Madison River, Montana. The various levels have been formed by the river as it simultaneously swung laterally across, and cut downward into, deposits of sand and gravel laid down in front of a now vanished glacier farther upstream. Photo by William C. Bradley.

FIG. 11-38
The canyon of the Yellowstone is typical of a youthful valley. The valley walls slope directly to the river banks to give it a V-shape. The river rapids are also characteristic of a stream in a youthful valley. Photo by Tozier.

we try to assign quantitative values to it. As a device that enables us to paint a word picture of a stream valley or a region, it has great value. And, just as important, the concept has led geologists into a quantitative investigation of the nature of streams and the development of landforms, an investigation that has only just begun.

The cycle of a stream valley

The cycle of a stream valley is divided into three main stages comparable to the ages of man: *youth, maturity,* and *old age.* Each of these stages has certain characteristics. But just as it is difficult to say at what moment a man passes from youth to maturity, or from maturity to old age, so it is impossible to draw sharp lines between stages in the life of a stream valley.

Probably the most characteristic feature of a youthful stream valley is the stream's active and rapid erosion of its channel. At this stage, the valley walls come right down to (or almost to) the stream bank and form a V-shaped cross-valley profile. There is no flood plain, or only a very narrow one. The stream's gradient is steep, marked by falls and rapids, and tributaries tend to be few and small (see Fig. 11-38).

In a mature valley, the rate of downward cutting slows. The gradient is smooth, and most of the falls and rapids have been eliminated. A flood plain begins to form as valley-widening progresses more rapidly than valley-deepening. Across this flood plain a stream may begin to meander. At this stage, the valley has reached its greatest depth (see Fig. 11-39).

The distinction between maturity and old age is largely a matter of degree. In old age, valley-widening, though slow, still dominates downward cutting, and the flood plain is wider than the meander belt. Oxbow lakes, meander scars, and natural levees are more common now than they were during the stream's maturity.

The factor that controls the progress of a stream valley from youth to old age is the base level. The closer a valley approaches base level, the further it has progressed through its aging cycle.

No one has ever observed a valley as it went through this complete cycle, of course, but there are valleys that represent different stages in the cycle. And we sometimes find that a valley has reached different stages of development at different points along its course—maturity in its lower reaches, for example, and youth toward its headwaters.

INTERRUPTIONS IN THE CYCLE OF A STREAM VALLEY. A stream valley moves smoothly through its life cycle only if the stream's base level remains constant. Any significant movement of the base level, either up or down, will interrupt the cycle. For example, if sea level falls, or if earth movements raise and warp the land, the stream will begin to cut its channel deeper and adjust its profile to the new base level. A youthful V-shaped valley, then, may develop within a broad, mature valley, setting off a new cycle of erosion. If the new base level remains constant for a long enough time, all evidence of the original cycle will be destroyed, and the valley will pass from youth to maturity to old age.

What happens when earth movements result in the uplifting of a mature stream valley? If the stream has progressed to the meandering stage before uplift occurs, it may be able to incise its channel into the underlying bedrock in a pattern of *entrenched meanders*. In other words, the new valley will be youthful, but it will continue to follow the old pattern established by the stream before the change in base level occurred.

When a stream is forced by changing conditions to begin a new cycle of erosion, we say that it has been *rejuvenated* (see Fig. 11-40).

Interruptions in the cycle of erosion may occur in still other ways. For example, if the base level rises, a river will deposit its load in an attempt to create a new profile. As a result, a youthful valley may become clogged with sediment and take on some of the features of old age. Such a valley, however, is not strictly within the old-age stage of the cycle of erosion, for its seeming age stems from deposition rather than erosion.

FIG. 11-39
A stream meanders across the floodplain of a small, mature valley near Steamboat Springs, Colorado. Photo by Sheldon Judson.

The cycle of a region

The concept of the cycle of erosion has been applied to the evolution of a whole region as well as to the evolution of a stream valley. And again the controlling factor is base level, although here we are dealing with a base level that includes a great many drainage basins. We can think of the base level of a region as a plane or a surface extending inland from the ocean and rising very gently beneath the major drainage basins. Erosion of the land works down toward this imaginary surface, though it is probably never reached.

As with a stream valley, so, too, the life cycle of a region progresses through youth, maturity, and old age. The regional cycle is thought to begin with the rapid uplift of a land mass, followed by a period of stability in which streams, mass movement, and slope wash combine to reduce the elevated mass ever lower toward the regional base level.

During the youthful stage of a region, its streams cut rapidly downward, and the difference in elevation between valley bottoms and hilltops (known as *relief*) increases rapidly. The streams have not yet extended into all portions of the land mass, and they are still separated by broad divides. Maturity begins as the streams and related agencies dissect the land more deeply, causing the broad divides of youth to disappear. With maturity, the region achieves its maximum relief, and the divides between the streams are narrowed until most of their surface is sloping. The major streams have now adjusted their profiles to the conditions that exist along their courses, and they maintain this adjustment during the rest of the cycle. It is during maturity that the streams of a region etch out the greatest variety of land features from rocks of differing resistance and structure, molding valleys and lowlands in the areas underlain by the weakest rocks and hills, and leaving highlands in the areas underlain by the strongest rocks (see Fig. 11-41).

As a region passes slowly through maturity into old age, its streams wander freely across the wide valley, with little regard for differences in the resistance of the rocks that underlie the

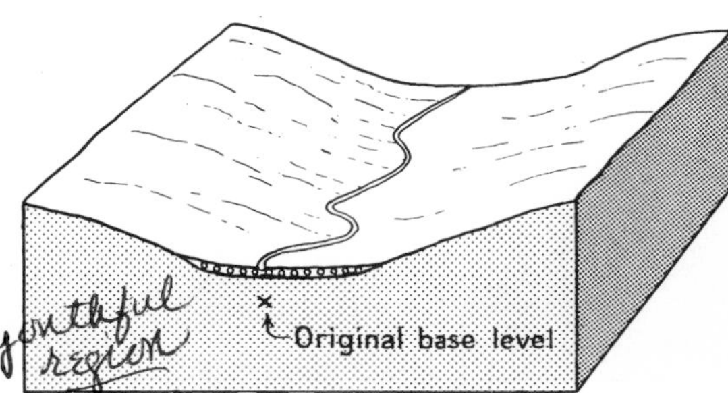

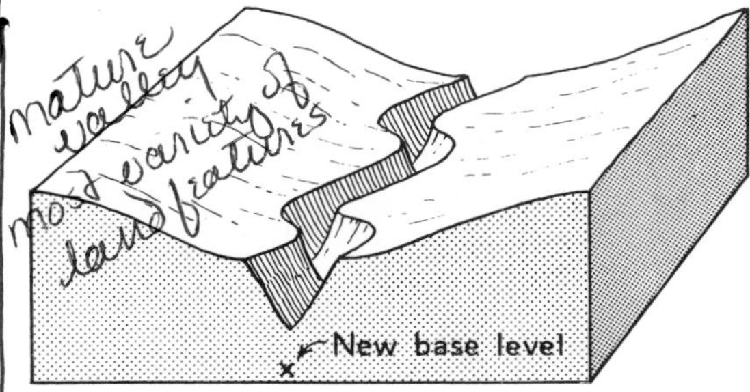

FIG. 11-40
The rejuvenation of a mature valley. In the upper diagram, a mature valley has formed in respect to the base level X. In the lower diagram the base level is pictured as having dropped. As a result, the stream has incised its channel, and a youthful valley has been formed within the older mature valley.

FIG. 11-41
Mature country along the flanks of the Humboldt Range, Nevada, as seen from Star Peak. The land is intricately dissected and is all in slope. Photo by E. N. Cameron.

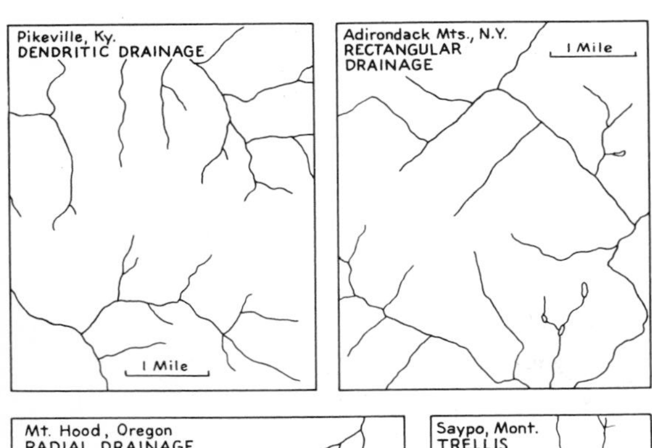

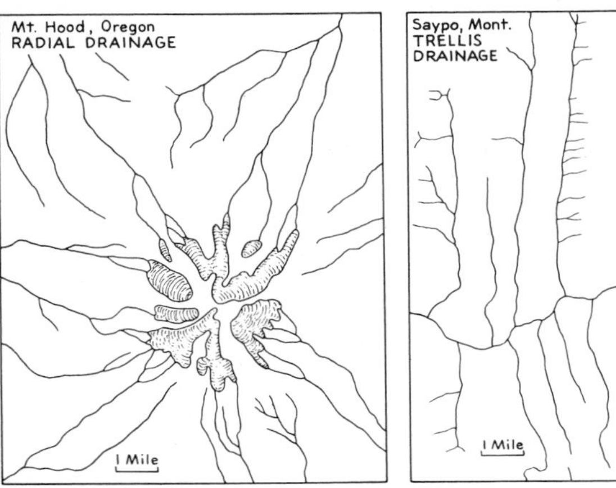

FIG. 11-42
The over-all pattern developed by a stream system depends in part on the nature of the bedrock, and in part on the history of the area. See text for discussion.

surface. The divides are now low and widely spaced. Theoretically the cycle progresses until the land has been reduced to a gently rolling plain very close to base level. Such a surface is termed a *peneplain,* from the Latin *paene,* "almost," with the English "plain." A few hills may rise above this surface, representing areas where erosion has not been able to reduce the original land mass completely. These residuals left unconsumed by erosion are called *monadnocks,* after Mt. Monadnock, in New Hampshire, which has been interpreted as a residual standing above an ancient peneplain that has been uplifted and dissected. Monadnocks may survive either because they are composed of rock relatively resistant to erosion or because they stand in areas protected from the action of streams.

INTERRUPTIONS IN THE REGIONAL CYCLE. A change in base level interrupts the cycle of erosion for a region just as it interrupts the cycle for a stream. If the land moves upward, or the sea downward, a new cycle is set under way and the area is rejuvenated. Remnants of the earlier cycle will be preserved, however, until erosion in the new cycle succeeds in destroying them.

Objections to the cycle of erosion

This whole concept of the erosion cycle has been subjected to numerous criticisms—many of them well grounded. For instance, the cycle of erosion as originally conceived and as we have described it is the result of erosion in a humid climate. Yet humid climates cover only a fraction of the earth's surface. The erosional processes of other climates would presumably produce a somewhat different sequence of events. And we can ask whether the cycle of erosion as we have pictured it ever takes place in a desert climate (see Chapter 14), either hot or cold. Or we can ask what the cycle of erosion would be like in the humid tropics or in the steppes.

Also, the cycle of erosion is postulated as starting with rapid uplift, followed by a period of no movement during which the uplifted land mass progresses from youth through maturity to old age. But suppose the uplift were slow or intermittent and took place over many millions of years. Would the cycle of erosion then proceed in the manner we have described or in some other way?

If the cycle of erosion for a region carries through to completion—that is, to the formation of a peneplain—we should have examples of peneplains in the world today. Yet we have no examples of large areas that have been graded to the level of the modern seas. The nearest thing we have to a convincing example are surfaces of low relief that are now buried beneath younger rocks—as, for example, deep within the Grand Canyon, or along the eastern seaboard. But even with these examples we are still in doubt, since we do not yet know enough about the nature of these ancient, buried surfaces.

These criticisms and others do throw into question certain details of the cycle of erosion. But the concept still serves the valuable purpose of indicating that streams and land masses go through a progressive development. Furthermore, it is very useful to have terms such as *youth, maturity,* and *old age* in describing the general nature of a valley or a region.

STREAM PATTERNS AND STREAM TYPES

The over-all pattern developed by a system of streams and tributaries depends partly on the nature of the underlying rocks and partly on the history of the streams. Almost all streams follow a branching pattern in the sense that they receive tributaries; the tributaries, in turn, are joined by still smaller tributaries. But the manner of branching varies widely (see Fig. 11-42).

A stream that resembles the branching habit of a maple, oak, or similar deciduous tree is called *dendritic,* "tree-like." A dendritic pattern develops when the underlying bedrock is uniform in its resistance to erosion and exercises no control over the direction of valley growth. This situation occurs when the bedrock is composed either of flat-lying sedimentary rocks or massive igneous or metamorphic rocks. The streams can cut as easily in one place as another; thus the dendritic pattern is, in a sense, the result of the random orientation of the streams.

Another type of stream pattern is *radial:* streams radiate outward in all directions from a high central zone. Such a pattern is likely to develop on the flanks of a newly formed volcano, where the streams and their valleys radiate outward and downward from various points around the cone.

A *rectangular* pattern occurs when the underlying bedrock is criss-crossed by fractures that form zones of weakness particularly vulnerable to erosion. The master stream and its tributaries then follow courses marked by nearly right-angle bends.

Some streams, particularly in a belt of the Appalachian Mountains running from New York to Alabama, follow what is known as a *trellis* pattern. This pattern, like the rectangular one, is caused by zones in the bedrock that differ in their resistance to erosion. The trellis pattern usually, though not always, indicates that the region is underlain by alternate bands of resistant and nonresistant rock.

In the Appalachian Mountains, the trellis pattern may have started to form when flat-lying sedimentary rocks were first folded, then exposed to erosion, and finally worn down to a surface of old age—a peneplain. Streams flowing across this surface were close to base level and were probably affected very little by the differing resistance of the rocks beneath. As a result, they probably flowed in a dendritic pattern. The next stage was the uplift of the area, when base level was lowered and the streams began to cut downward. As the land rose, the main stream was able to maintain its original course and to cut its valley into the bands of resistant and nonresistant rock athwart its course. The smaller, less competent tributaries, however, were strongly influenced by the nature of the rock in the rising land mass. So they shifted their courses to zones underlain by the weaker rocks, such as limestone or shale, and entered the main stream at high angles to produce the trellis pattern (Fig. 11-43).

We can classify streams on the basis of their particular his-

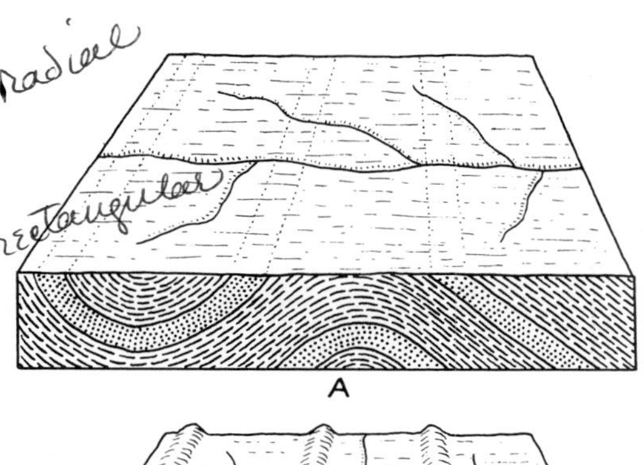

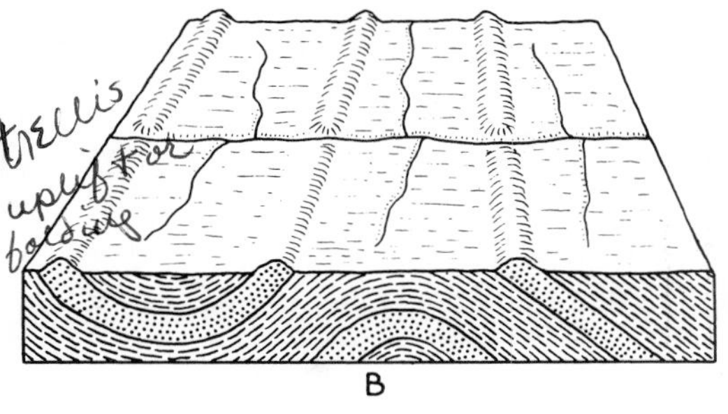

FIG. 11-43
One type of trellis pattern development. In A, *folded rocks of differing resistance have been beveled by stream erosion. The streams on this old-age surface have a dendritic pattern and are unaffected by the bedrock. In* B, *the land is pictured as having risen, and the streams have thus been rejuvenated. Erosion by the main stream has managed to keep pace with uplift, and the stream has cut through both resistant and nonresistant beds. This is called an antecedent stream, and the passes through the resistant rock are called water gaps. The tributary streams, unable to erode so rapidly, have taken new courses along the less resistant beds and now enter the main stream nearly at right angles, thus producing a trellis pattern. These tributary streams are now called subsequent streams.*

tory of development. Streams that take their courses as a consequence of the original slope of the land they flow through are known as *consequent streams.* Streams flowing in a radial pattern down the flanks of volcanoes exemplify one kind of consequent stream.

In discussing the development of trellis stream patterns, we mentioned that the main stream maintained the course it originally followed before uplift. Because its present course anteceded the uplift, such a stream is called an *antecedent stream.* But the tributaries of an antecedent stream usually alter their

FIG. 11-44
An aerial photograph of a water gap in North Africa. The master stream cuts through the ridge of resistant rock. Photo by U.S. Army Air Force.

courses subsequent to the uplift, and the modern, altered courses are conveniently labeled *subsequent streams*. The tributaries in the trellis pattern are examples of subsequent streams, flowing in zones of less resistant rock. Continued erosion leaves the more resistant rocks standing as ridges or hills above narrowed segments of the valleys and antecedent streams. These stretches of valley are called *water gaps* (see Fig. 11-44).

Water gaps are also created in other ways. Picture an area of hills and valleys carved by differential erosion from rocks of varying resistance. Then imagine sediments covering this landscape so that the valleys and hills are buried beneath the debris. Any streams that flow over the surface of this cover will establish their own courses across the buried hills and valleys. When these streams erode downward, some of them may encounter an old ridge crest. If such a stream has enough erosional energy, it may cut down through the resistant rock of the hill. The course of the stream is thus superimposed across the old hill, and we call the stream a *superimposed stream*. Differential erosion may excavate the sedimentary fill from the old valleys, but the main, superimposed stream flows through the hill in a new narrow gorge or water gap. An example of such a gap is that followed by the Big Horn River through the northern end of the Big Horn Mountains in Montana.

We have found that a stream does not maintain a constant course through time. And one of the most interesting shifts in stream direction comes about as the result of *stream piracy*, or *stream capture*. In this process, one stream actually steals the headwater portions of a neighboring stream, in the following manner. If one of two streams in adjacent valleys is able to deepen its valley more rapidly than the other, it may also extend its valley headward until it breaches the divide between them. When this happens, the more rapidly eroding stream captures the upper portion of the neighboring stream. The capturing stream is called the *pirate stream,* and the stream that has lost its upper section is called the *beheaded stream.*

stream piracy

Fig. 11-45 diagrams this activity. At some time in the past, two streams, the Potomac River and Beaver Dam Creek, flowed through the Blue Ridge, each in its own water gap. The ancestral Shenandoah River joined the Potomac, as it does today, just before the Potomac entered its gap at Harpers Ferry. As time passed, the Shenandoah deepened its valley more rapidly than did Beaver Dam Creek, and eventually extended itself headward through the divide separating its valley from that of Beaver Dam Creek. Now the waters of the Upper Beaver Dam no longer flowed through the gap in the Blue Ridge but were diverted into the Shenandoah River. Here the Shenandoah is the pirate stream, and the shortened Beaver Dam Creek is the beheaded stream. At the time of capture, the old water gap of Beaver Dam Creek was abandoned and is now locally known as Snickers Gap. The general term, however, for an abandoned water gap such as this is *wind gap*.

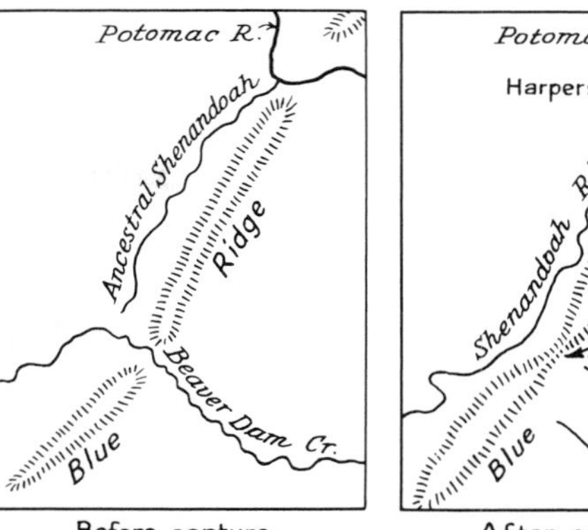

FIG. 11-45
The Shenandoah River has captured the upper reaches of Beaver Dam Creek. The Shenandoah deepened its valley more rapidly than did the Beaver Dam and eventually breached the divide between them. The upper section of the Beaver Dam was thus diverted to the Shenandoah. Snickers is the abandoned water gap of the old Beaver Dam Creek through the Blue Ridge. The general name for such an abandoned water gap is "wind gap."

SUMMARY OUTLINE

Hydrologic cycle
- Pattern of water circulation: from oceans to atmosphere to land to oceans

Runoff = Precipitation − (Infiltration + Evaporation and Transpiration)

Laminar and turbulent flow

Water in a stream has velocity, flows down a gradient, and is measured in terms of discharge

At any one spot, the channel width and depth and the water velocity increase with increasing discharge

In adjusting to discharge, the gradient decreases downstream while width and depth of channel and water velocity increase

Base level of a stream
- The point below which it cannot erode
- Lowered base level = Erosion
- Raised base level = Deposition

Transportation
- Load, capacity, and competence
- Material moved in solution and suspension and as bed load

Erosion
- Direct lifting; abrasion, impact, and solution; cavitation; slope erosion
- Most rapid erosion during flood

Deposition
- Decreased velocity (hence decreased energy) = Deposition

Valley features
- Flood plains, divides, and valley walls

Valley widened by stream erosion in channel and by mass movement and slope erosion on valley walls

Narrow valleys
- Waterfalls, rapids, and potholes

Broad valleys
- Flood plains, meanders, braided streams, natural levees, and stream terraces

Most valleys cut by the streams that flow through them

Cycle of erosion
- Youth, maturity, and old age
- Cycle applies to valleys and regions
- Changes in base level interrupt cycle

Objections to cycle of erosion do not invalidate the concept of progressive development of landforms through time

Stream patterns and types reflect nature of underlying rocks and stream history

SELECTED REFERENCES

Davis, William Morris, "The Geographical Cycle," *Geog. J.*, XIV (1899), 481–504.

———, "Base Level, Grade and Peneplain," *J. Geol.*, X (1902), 77–111.

Hjulstrem, Filip, "Transportation of Detritus by Running Water," in *Recent Marine Sedients, A Symposium,* ed. Parker D. Trask. Tulsa: Am. Assoc. Petroleum Geol., 1939, pp. 3–31.

Hoyt, William G. and Walter B. Langbein, *Floods.* Princeton: Princeton University Press, 1955.

Kuenen, P. H., *Realms of Water.* New York: John Wiley & Sons, Inc., 1955.

Leopold, Luna B., "Rivers," *American Scientist,* L (1962), 511–37.

———, Gordon Wolman, and John P. Miller, *Fluvial Processes in Geomorphology*. San Francisco: W. H. Freeman & Co., 1964.

U.S. Dept. of Agriculture, *Water, The Yearbook of Agriculture, 1955.* Washington, D.C.: Government Printing Office, 1955.

Underground water

12

Tremendous quantities of water lie exposed in rivers, lakes, oceans, and—in the solid state—in glaciers on the earth's surface. But beneath the surface, hidden from our sight, is another great store of water. Underground reservoirs in the United States contain far more usable water than all our surface reservoirs and lakes combined, and we depend on this underground supply for about one-fifth of our total water needs.

BASIC DISTRIBUTION

Underground water, subsurface water, and *subterranean water* are all general terms used to refer to water in the pore spaces, cracks, tubes, and crevices of the consolidated and unconsolidated material beneath our feet. The study of underground water is largely an investigation of these openings and of what happens to the water that finds its way into them. In the preceding chapter, we found that most of the water beneath the surface comes from rain and snow that fall on the face of the earth. Part of this water soaks directly into the ground, and part of it drains away into lakes and streams and thence into the underground.

Zones of saturation and aeration

Some of the water that moves down from the surface is caught by rock and earth materials and is checked in its downward progress. The zone in which this water is held is known as the *zone of aeration,* and the water itself is called *suspended water.* The spaces between particles in this zone are filled partly with water and partly with air. Two forces operate to prevent suspended water from moving deeper into the earth: (1) the molecular attraction exerted on the water by the rock and earth materials, and (2) the attraction exerted by the water particles on one another (see Figs. 12-1, 12-2).

The zone of aeration can be subdivided into three belts: (1) *belt of soil moisture,* (2) *intermediate belt,* and (3) *capillary fringe.* Some of the water that enters the belt of soil moisture from the surface is used by plants, and some is evaporated

zone of aeration

back into the atmosphere. But some water also passes down to the intermediate belt, where it may be held by molecular attraction (as suspended water). Little movement occurs in the intermediate belt, except when rain or melting snow sends a new wave of moisture down from above. In some areas, the intermediate belt is missing, and the belt of soil moisture lies directly above the third belt, the capillary fringe. Water rises into the capillary fringe from below, to a height ranging from a few inches to five or even ten feet.

Beneath the zone of aeration lies the *zone of saturation.* Here the openings in the rock and earth materials are completely filled with *ground water,* and the surface between the zone of saturation and the zone of aeration is called the *ground-water table,* or simply the *water table.* The level of the water table fluctuates with variations in the supply of water coming down from the zone of aeration, with variations in the rate of discharge in the area, and with variations in the amount of ground water drawn off by plants and human beings.

It is the water below the water table, within the zone of saturation, that we shall focus on in this chapter.

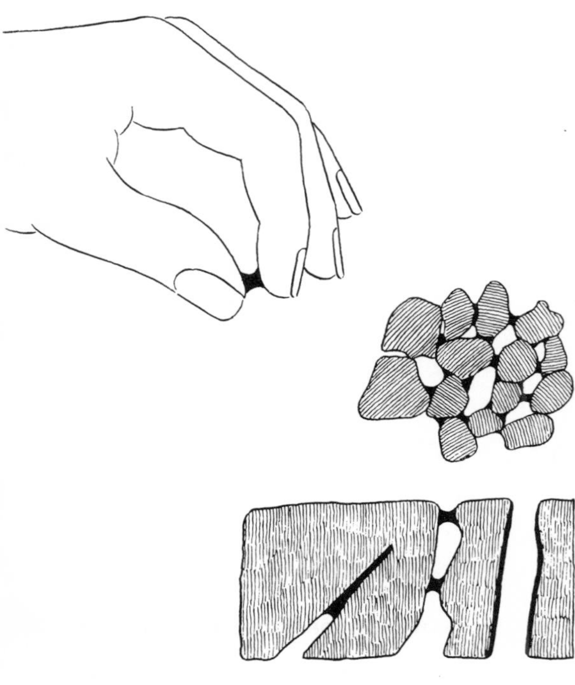

FIG. 12-1
A drop of water held between two fingers illustrates the molecular attraction that holds suspended water in the zone of aeration. Surface tension of the water is great enough to prevent its downward movement to the zone of saturation.

FIG. 12-2
Underground water's two major zones: zone of aeration and zone of saturation. The water table marks the upper surface of the zone of saturation. Within the zone of aeration is a belt of soil moisture, the source of moisture for many plants. From here, also, some moisture is evaporated back to the atmosphere. In many instances, this belt lies above an intermediate belt where water is held by molecular attraction and little movement occurs except during periods of rain or melting snow. In the capillary fringe, just above the water table, water rises a few inches to several feet from the zone of saturation, depending on the size of the interstices.

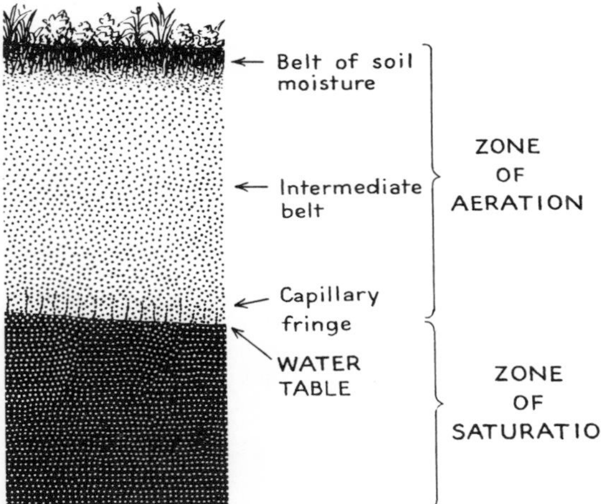

The water table

The water table is an irregular surface of contact between the zone of saturation and the zone of aeration. Below the water table lies the ground water; above it lies the suspended water. The thickness of the zone of saturation differs from one place to another, and the level of the water table fluctuates accordingly. In general, the water table tends to follow the irregularities of the ground surface, reaching its highest elevation beneath hills and its lowest elevation beneath valleys. Although the water table reflects variations in the ground surface, the irregularities in the water table are less pronounced.

In looking at the topography of the water table, let us consider an ideal situation. Figure 12-3 shows a hill underlain by completely homogeneous material. Assume that, initially, this material contains no water at all. Then a heavy rainfall comes along, and the water soaks slowly downward, filling the interstices at depth. In other words, a zone of saturation begins to develop. As more and more water seeps down, the upper limit of this zone continues to rise. The water table remains horizontal until it just reaches the level of the two valley bottoms on either side of the hill. Then, as additional water seeps down to the water table, some of it seeks an outlet into the valleys. But this added water is "supported" by the material through which it flows, and the water table is prevented from maintaining its flat surface. The water is slowed by the friction of its movement through the interstices and even, to some degree, by its own internal friction. Consequently, more and more water is piled up beneath the hill, and the water table begins to reflect the shape of the hill. The water flows away most rapidly along the steeper slope of the water table near the valleys, and most slowly on its gentler slope beneath the hill crest.

We can modify the shape of the ground-water surface by providing an artificial outlet for the water. For example, we can drill a well on the hill crest and extend it down into the saturated zone. Then, if we pumped out the ground water that flowed into the well, we would create a dimple in the water table. The more we pumped, the more pronounced the depression—called a *cone of depression*—would become.

Returning to our ideal situation, we find that if the supply of water from the surface were to be completely stopped, the water table under the hill would slowly flatten out as water discharged into the valleys. Eventually it would almost reach the level of the water table under the valley bottoms; then the flow would stop. This condition is common in desert areas where the rainfall is sparse.

MOVEMENT OF UNDERGROUND WATER

The preceding chapter stated that the flow of water in surface streams could be measured in terms of so many feet per second. But in dealing with the flow of underground water, we must change our scale of measurement; for here, although the water does move, it usually moves very, very slowly. So we find that "feet per day" and, in some places, even "feet per year" provide a better scale of measurement. The main reason for this slow rate of flow is that the water must travel through small, confined passages if it is to move at all. It will be worthwhile, then, for us to consider the porosity and permeability of earth materials.

Porosity

The *porosity* of a rock is measured by the percentage of its total volume that is occupied by voids or interstices. The more porous a rock is, the greater the amount of open space it contains. Through these open spaces, underground water must find its way.

Porosity differs from one material to another. What is the porosity of a rock made up of particles and grains derived from pre-existing rocks? Here porosity is determined largely by the shape, size, and assortment of these rock-building units. A sand deposit composed of rounded quartz grains with fairly uniform size has a high porosity. But if mineral matter enters the deposit and cements the grains into a sandstone, the porosity is reduced by an amount equal to the volume of the cementing agent. A deposit of sand, poorly sorted with finer particles of silt and clay mixed in, has low porosity, because the smaller particles fill up much of the space between the larger particles.

Even a dense, massive rock such as granite may become porous as a result of fracturing. And a soluble massive rock such as limestone may have its original planes of weakness enlarged by solution.

Clearly then, the range of porosity in earth materials is extremely great. Recently deposited muds (called *slurries*) may hold up to 90 per cent by volume of water, whereas unweathered igneous rocks such as granite, gabbro, or obsidian may

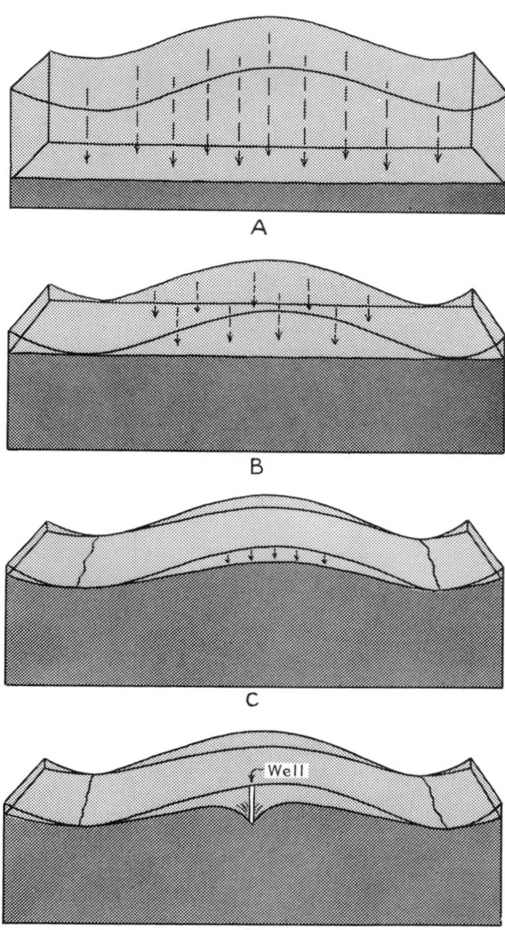

FIG. 12-3
Ideally, the water table is a subdued reflection of the surface of the ground. In A *and* B, *the water table rises as a horizontal plane until it reaches the level of the valley bottoms on either side of the hill. Thereafter, as more water soaks into the ground, it seeks an outlet toward the valleys. Were the movement of the water not slowed down by the material making up the hill, it would remain essentially horizontal. The friction caused by the water's passing through the material (and even to some extent the internal friction of the water itself) results in a piling up of water beneath the hill; the bulge is highest beneath the crest and lowest toward the valleys (*C*). The shape of the water table may be altered by pumping water from a well (*D*). The water flows to this new outlet and forms a cone of depression.*

hold only a fraction of 1 per cent. Unconsolidated deposits of clay, silt, sand, and gravel have porosities ranging from about 20 to as much as 50 per cent. But when these deposits have been consolidated into sedimentary rocks by cementation or compaction, their porosity is sharply reduced. Average porosity values for individual rock types have little meaning because of the extreme variations within each type. In general, however, a porosity of less than 5 per cent is considered low; from 5 to 15 per cent represents medium porosity; and over 15 per cent is considered high.

Permeability

Whether or not we find a supply of fresh ground water in a given area depends on the ability of the earth materials to transmit water, as well as on their ability to contain it. The ability to transmit underground water is termed *permeability*.

The rate at which a rock transmits water depends not only on its total porosity, but also on the size of the interconnections between its openings. For example, although a clay may have a higher porosity than a sand, the particles that make up the clay are minute flakes and the interstices between them are very small. Therefore, water passes more readily through the sand than through the more porous clay, simply because the molecular attraction on the water is much stronger in the tiny openings of the clay. The water moves more freely through the sand because the passageways between particles are relatively large and the molecular attraction on the water is relatively low. Of course, no matter how large the interstices of a material are, there must be connections between them if water is to pass through. If they are not interconnected, the material is impermeable.

A permeable material that actually carries underground water is called an *aquifer*, from the Latin for "water" and "to bear." Perhaps the most effective aquifers are unconsolidated sand and gravel, sandstone, and some limestones. The permeability of limestone is usually due to solution that has enlarged the fractures and bedding planes into open passageways. The fractured zones of some of the denser rocks such as granite, basalt, and gabbro also act as aquifers, although the permeability of such zones decreases rapidly with depth (see discussion of joints in Chapter 16). Clay, shale, and most metamorphic and crystalline igneous rocks are generally poor aquifers.

Since the flow of underground water is usually very slow, it is largely laminar; in contrast, the flow of surface water is largely turbulent. There is one exception, however: the turbulent flow of water in large underground passageways formed in such rocks as cavernous limestone.

In laminar flow, the water near the walls of interstices is presumably held motionless by the molecular attraction of the walls. Water particles farther away from the walls move more rapidly, in smooth, threadlike patterns, for the resistance to motion decreases toward the center of an opening. The most rapid flow is reached at the very center.

The energy that causes underground water to flow is derived from gravity. Gravity draws water downward to the water table; from there it flows through the ground to a point of discharge in a stream, lake, or spring. Just as surface water needs a slope to flow on, so must there be a slope for the flow of ground water. This is the slope of the water table, the *hydraulic gradient*. It is measured by dividing the length of flow (from the point of intake to the point of discharge) into the vertical distance between these two points, a distance called *head*. Therefore, hydraulic gradient is expressed as h/l, where h is head and l is length of flow from intake to discharge. Thus, if h is 10 feet and l is 100 feet, the hydraulic gradient is 0.1 or 10 per cent.

An equation to express the rate of water movement through a rock was proposed by the French engineer Henri Darcy in 1856. What is now known as Darcy's Law is essentially the same as his original equation. The law may be expressed as follows:

$$V = P\frac{h}{l}$$

where V is velocity, h is head, l the length of flow, and P a coefficient of permeability that depends on the nature of the rock in question. But since h/l is simply a way of expressing the hydraulic gradient, we may say that in a rock of constant permeability, the velocity of water will increase as the hydraulic gradient increases. Remembering that the hydraulic gradient and the slope of the ground-water table are the same thing, we may also say that the velocity of ground water varies with the slope of the water table. Other things being equal, the steeper the slope of the water table, the more rapid the flow. In ordinary aquifers, the rate of water flow has been estimated as not faster than 5 feet per day and not slower than 5 feet per year. It is true, however, that rates of over 400 feet a day and as low as a few inches a year have been recorded.

The movement of underground water down the slope of the water table is only a part of the picture, for the water is also in motion at depth. Water moves downward from the water table in broad looping curves toward some effective discharge agency, such as a stream, as suggested in Fig. 12-4. The water feeds into the stream from all possible directions, including straight up through the bottom of the channel. We can explain this curving path as a compromise between the force of gravity and the tendency of water to flow laterally in the direction of the slope of the water table. This tendency toward lateral flow is actually the result of the movement of water toward an area of lower pressure, the stream channel in Fig. 12-4. The resulting movement is neither directly downward

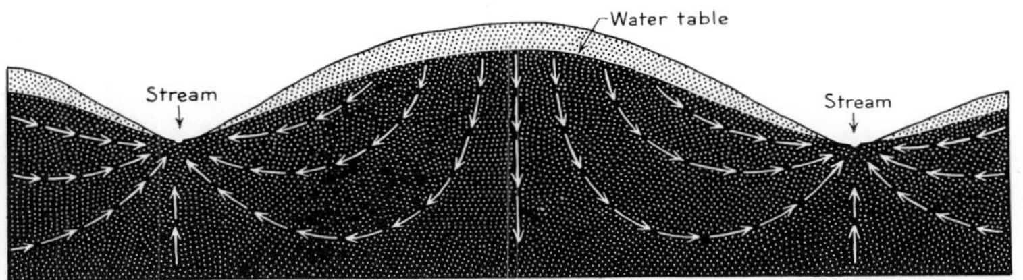

FIG. 12-4
The flow of ground water through uniformly permeable material is suggested here. Movement is not primarily along the ground-water table; rather, particles of water define broadly looping paths that converge toward the outlet and may approach it from below. Redrawn from M. King Hubbert, "The Theory of Ground-water Motion," J. Geol., XLVIII (1940) 930.

nor directly toward the channel, but is rather along curving paths to the stream.

GROUND WATER IN NATURE

So far, we have assumed that ground water is free to move on indefinitely through a uniformly permeable material of unlimited extent. Actually, subsurface conditions fall far short of this ideal situation. Some layers of rock material are more permeable than others, and the water tends to move rapidly through these beds in a direction more or less parallel to bedding planes. Even in a rock that is essentially homogeneous, the ground water tends to move in some preferred direction.

Simple springs and wells

Underground water moves freely downward from the surface until it reaches an impermeable layer of rock or until it arrives at the water table. Then it begins to move laterally. Sooner or later it may flow out again at the surface of the ground in an opening called a *spring*.

Springs have attracted the attention of men throughout history. In early days they were regarded with superstitious awe and were sometimes selected as sites for temples and oracles. To this day, many people feel that spring water possesses special medicinal and therapeutic values. Water from "mineral springs" contains salts in solution that were picked up by the water as it percolated through the ground. The same water pumped up out of a well would be regarded merely as hard and not very desirable for general purposes.

Springs range from intermittent flows that disappear when the water table recedes during a dry season, through pint-sized trickles, to an effluence of 900 million gallons daily, the abundant discharge of springs along a 10-mile stretch of Fall River, California.

This wide variety of spring types is the result of underground conditions that vary greatly from one place to another. As a general rule, however, a spring results wherever the flow of ground water is diverted to a discharge zone at the surface (see Fig. 12-5). For example, a hill made up largely of permeable rock may contain a zone of impermeable material, as shown in Fig. 12-6. Some of the water percolating downward will be blocked by this impermeable rock, and a

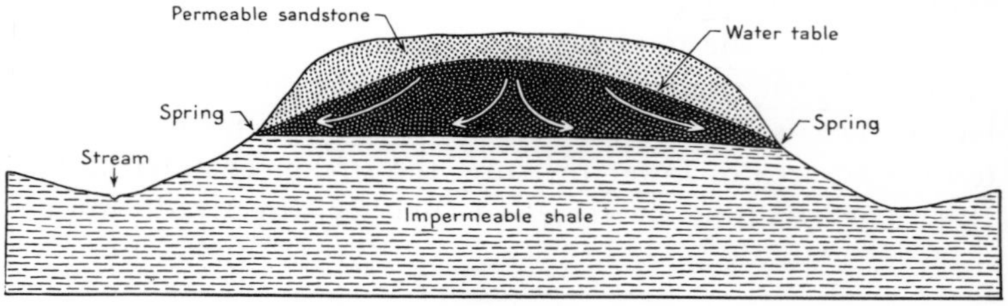

FIG. 12-5
Nature seldom, if ever, provides uniformly permeable material. In this diagram, a hill is capped by permeable sandstone and overlies impermeable shale. Water soaking into the sandstone from the surface is diverted laterally by the impermeable beds. Springs result where the water table intersects the surface at the contact of the shale and sandstone.

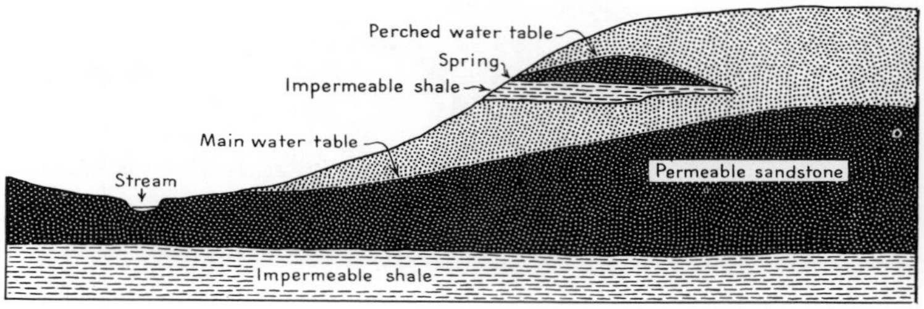

FIG. 12-6
A perched water table results when ground water collects over an impermeable zone and is separated from the main water table.

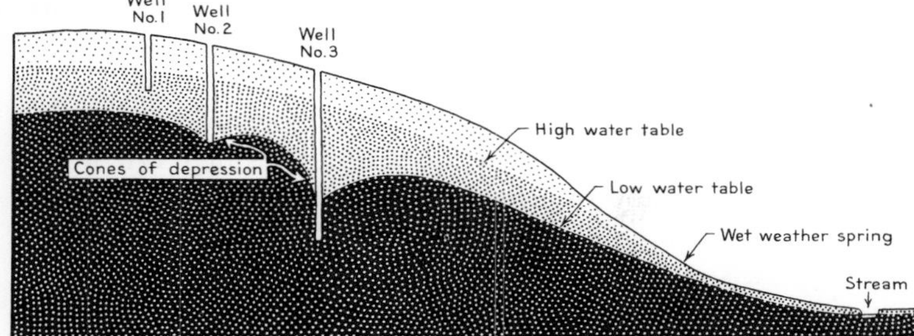

FIG. 12-7
To provide a reliable source, a well must penetrate deep into the zone of saturation. In this diagram, Well No. 1 reaches only deep enough to tap the ground water during periods of high water table; a seasonal drop of this surface will dry up the well. Well No. 2 reaches to the low water table, but continued pumping may produce a cone of depression that will reduce effective flow. Well No. 3 is deep enough to produce reliable amounts of water, even with continued pumping during low water-table stages.

small saturated zone will be built up. Since the local water level here is actually above the main water table, it is called a *perched water table.* The water that flows laterally along this impermeable rock may emerge at the surface as a spring. Springs are not confined to points where a perched water table flows from the surface, and it is clear that if the main water table intersects the surface along a slope, then a spring will form.

Even in impermeable rocks, permeable zones may develop as a result of fractures or solution channels. If these openings fill with water and are intersected by the ground surface, the water will issue forth as a spring.

A spring is the result of a natural intersection of the ground surface and the water table. But a well is an artificial opening cut down from the surface into the zone of saturation. A well is productive only if it is drilled into permeable rock and penetrates below the water table. The greater the demands that are made on a well, the deeper it must be drilled below the water table. Continuous pumping creates the cone of depression previously described, which distorts the water table and may reduce the flow of ground water into the well (see Fig. 12-7). Wells drilled into fractured crystalline rock, such as granite, may produce a good supply of water at relatively shallow depths. But we cannot increase the yield of such wells appreciably by deepening them, since the number and size of the fractures commonly decrease the farther down we go (see Fig. 12-8).

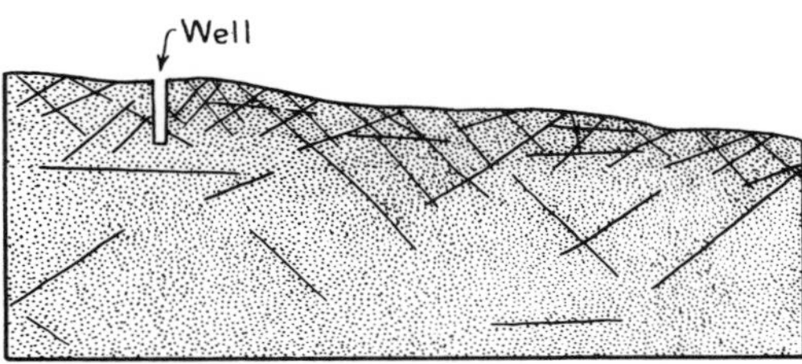

FIG. 12-8
Wells may produce water from a fractured zone of impermeable rocks such as granite. The supply, however, is likely to be limited, not only because the size and number of fractures decrease with depth, but also because the fractures do not interconnect.

Wells drilled into limestone that has been riddled by large solution passages may yield a heavy flow of water part of the time and no flow the rest of the time, simply because the water runs out rapidly through the large openings. Furthermore, water soaking down from the surface flows rapidly through limestone of this sort and may make its way to a well in a very short time. Consequently, water drawn from the well may be contaminated, because there has not been enough time for impurities to be filtered out as the water passes from the surface to the well. In sandstone, on the other hand, the rate of flow is slow enough to permit the elimination of impurities even within a very short distance of underground flow. Harmful bacteria are destroyed in part by entrapment, in part by lack of food and by temperature changes, and in part by hostile substances or organisms encountered along the way, particularly in the soil.

By applying Darcy's Law, we can estimate the amount of water that a well will probably yield. The quantity of water passing through a given section in a unit of time is determined by the area of the section it passes through, and by the velocity of the flow. Therefore,

$$V = Q/A$$

where V is velocity, Q is quantity of water per unit time, and A is the area of the cross section through which the water flows. For h/l in the original equation for Darcy's Law, we substitute the symbol i to represent hydraulic gradient. We then have a statement of Darcy's Law that gives quantity of water in terms of permeability, hydraulic gradient, and area of cross section:

$$V = P\frac{h}{l} = Pi = Q/A$$

or

$$Q = PiA$$

Therefore, we can calculate the rate of discharge for a given well if we know the permeability of the bed, P, the hydraulic gradient, i, and the cross section through which the water passes, A; this last figure is taken as the area of the well wall receiving water from the surrounding rock. In actual practice, the most difficult problem in applying this formula is determining the hydraulic gradient.

ARTESIAN WATER

Contrary to common opinion, artesian water does not necessarily come from great depths. But other definite conditions characterize an artesian water system: (1) the water is contained in a permeable layer, the aquifer, inclined so that one end is exposed to receive water at the surface; (2) the aquifer is capped by an impermeable layer; (3) the water in the aquifer is prevented from escaping either downward or off to the sides; and (4) there is enough head to force the water above the aquifer wherever it is tapped. If the head is great enough, the water will flow out to the surface either as a well or a spring.

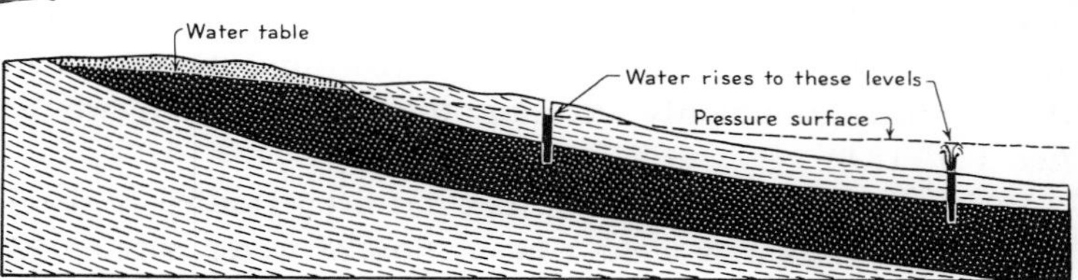

FIG. 12-9
The wells in the diagram meet the conditions that characterize an artesian system: (1) an inclined aquifer, (2) capped by an impermeable layer, (3) with water prevented from escaping either downward or laterally, and (4) sufficient head to force the water above the aquifer wherever it is tapped. In the well at the right, the head is great enough to force water out at the surface.

The term "artesian" is derived from the name of a French town, Artois (originally called *Artesium* by the Romans), where this type of well was first studied.

A classic example of an artesian water system is found in western South Dakota, where the Black Hills have punched up through a series of sedimentary rocks, bending their edges up to the surface. One of these sedimentary rocks, a permeable sandstone of Cretaceous age, carries water readily and is sandwiched between impermeable layers. Water entering the sandstone around the Black Hills moves underground eastward across the state, reaching greater and greater depths as it travels along. When we drive a well into this aquifer, we tap water that is under the pressure exerted by all the water piled up between the well and the Black Hills.

Increasing demands on this source of supply have been exceeding the replenishment rate for years. During a 35-year period the pressure fell off so sharply that the level of water in a well near Pierre, on the Missouri River, dropped 300 feet. From 1920 to 1935, the rate of decline was 6 feet per year at the town of Chamberlain.

Thermal springs

Springs that bring warm or hot water to the surface are called *thermal springs, hot springs,* or *warm springs.* A spring is usually regarded as a thermal spring if the temperature of its water is about 15°F higher than the mean temperature of the air. There are over a thousand thermal springs in the western mountain regions of the United States, 46 in the Appalachian Highlands of the east, six in the Ouachita area in Arkansas, and three in the Black Hills of South Dakota.

Most of the western thermal springs derive their heat from masses of magma that have pushed their way into the crust almost to the surface and are now cooling. In the eastern group, however, the circulation of the ground water carries it to depths great enough for it to be warmed by the normal increase in earth heat (see "Thermal gradient" in Glossary).

The well-known spring at Warm Springs, Georgia, is heated in just this way. Long before the Civil War, this spring was used as a health and bathing resort by the people of the region. Then, with the establishment of the Georgia Warm Springs Foundation for the treatment of victims of infantile paralysis, the facilities were greatly improved. Rain falling on Pine Mountain, about two miles south of Warm Springs, enters a rock formation known as the Hollis. At the start of its journey downward, the average temperature of the water is about 62°F. It percolates through the Hollis formation northward under Warm Springs at a depth of a few hundred feet and then follows the rock as it plunges into the earth to a depth of 3,800 feet, a mile farther north. Normal rock temperatures in the region increase 1°F per 100 feet of depth, and the water is warmed as it descends along the bottom of the Hollis bed. At 3,800 feet, the bed has been broken and shoved against an impervious layer that turns the water back. This water is now hotter than the water coming down from above, and it moves upward along the top of the Hollis formation, cooling somewhat as it goes. Finally it emerges in a spring at a temperature of 88°F.

Less than a mile away is Cold Spring, whose water comes from the same rainfall on Pine Mountain. A freak of circulation, however, causes the water at Cold Spring to emerge before it can be conducted to the depths and warmed. Its temperature is only about 62°F.

Geysers

A *geyser* (guy'zir) is a special type of thermal spring that ejects water intermittently with considerable force. The word geyser comes from the name of a spring of this type in Iceland, *geysir,* probably based on the verb *geysa,* "to rush furiously."

Although the details of geyser action are still not understood, we do know that, in general, a geyser's behavior is

FIG. 12-10
Thermal springs in Yellowstone National Park. The small pool-covered terraces are composed of travertine. Photo by Tozier.

FIG. 12-11
Old Faithful in Yellowstone National Park is America's most widely known geyser. The periodic eruption of a geyser is due to the particular pattern of its plumbing and its proximity to a liberal source of heat and ground water. Photo by Barton W. Knapp.

caused by the arrangement of its plumbing and the proximity of a good supply of heat. Here is probably what happens. Ground water moving downward from the surface fills a natural pipe, or conduit, that opens upward to the surface. Hot igneous rocks, or the gases given off by such rocks, gradually heat the column of water in the pipe and raise its temperature toward the boiling point. Now, the higher the pressure on water, the higher its boiling point. And since water toward the bottom of the pipe is under the greatest pressure, it must be heated to a higher temperature than the water above before it will come to a boil. Eventually the column of water becomes so hot that either a slight increase in temperature or a slight decrease in pressure will cause it to boil. At this critical point, the water near the base of the pipe is heated to the boiling point. The water then passes to steam and, as it does so, expands, pushing the water above it toward the surface. But this raising of the heated column of water reduces the pressure acting upon it, and it, too, begins to boil. The energy thus developed throws the water and steam high into the air, producing the spectacular action characteristic of many geysers. After the eruption has spent itself, the pipe is again filled with water and the whole process begins anew.

We can compare this theoretical cycle with that of Old Faithful Geyser in Yellowstone National Park (see Fig. 12-11). The first indication of a coming eruption at Old Faithful is the quiet flow of water in a fountain some four to eight feet high. This preliminary activity lasts for a few seconds and then subsides. It represents the first upward push of the column of water described in our theoretical case. This push reduces the pressure and thereby lowers the boiling point of the water in the pipe. Consequently, the water passes to steam; and less than a minute after the preliminary fountain, the first of the violent eruptions takes place. Steam and boiling water are thrown 120 to 170 feet into the air. The entire display lasts about four minutes. Emptied by the eruption, the tube then gradually refills with ground water, the water is heated, and in approximately one hour the same cycle is repeated. The actual time between eruptions at Old Faithful averages about 65 minutes but may be from 30 to 90 minutes.

RECHARGE OF GROUND WATER

As we have seen, the ultimate source of most underground water is precipitation that finds its way below the surface

FIG. 12-12
Steam rises from a myriad of vents in Yellowstone's Geyser Basin. Photo by William C. Bradley.

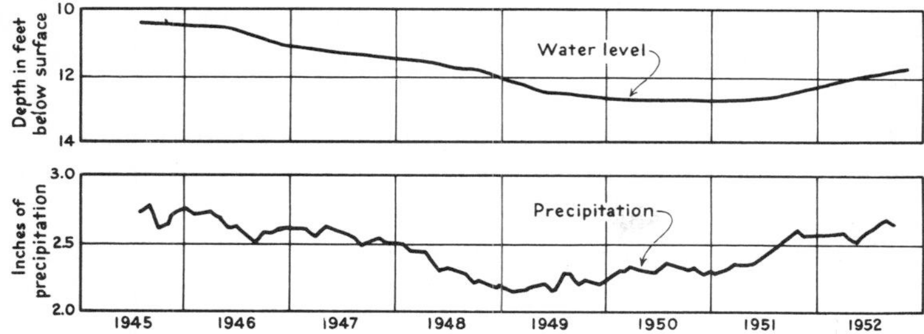

FIG. 12-13
Relationship between the water level in an observation well near Antigo, Wisconsin, and precipitation, as shown by records from 1945 to 1952. The water table reflects the changes in precipitation. The graphs represent 3-year running monthly averages. For example, 2.3 inches of precipitation for May means that precipitation averaged 2.3 inches per month from May 1947 to May 1950, inclusive. From A. H. Harder and William J. Drescher, Ground Water Conditions in Southwestern Langlade County, Wisconsin. Washington, D.C.: U.S. Geol. Survey, Water Supply Paper, 1954.

through either natural means or through artificial means.

Some of the water from precipitation seeps into the ground, reaches the zone of saturation, and raises the water table. Continuous measurements over long periods of time at many places throughout the United States show an intimate connnection between water level and rainfall (see Fig. 12-13). Since water moves relatively slowly in the zone of aeration and the zone of saturation, fluctuations in the water table usually lag a little behind fluctuations in rainfall.

Several factors control the amount of water that actually reaches the zone of saturation. For example, rain that falls during the growing season must first replenish moisture used up by plants or passed off through evaporation. If these demands are great, very little water will find its way down to recharge the zone of saturation. Then, too, during a very rapid, heavy rainfall, most of the water may run off directly into the streams instead of soaking down into the ground. A slow, steady rain is much more effective than a heavy, violent rain in replenishing the supply of ground water. High slopes, lack of vegetation, or the presence of impermeable rock near the surface may promote run-off and reduce the amount of water that reaches the zone of saturation. It is true, however, that some streams are themselves sources for the recharge of underground water. Water from the streams leaks into the zone of saturation, sometimes through a zone of aeration (see Fig. 12-14).

In many localities, the natural recharge of the underground supplies cannot keep pace with man's demands for ground water. Consequently, attempts are sometimes made to recharge these supplies artificially. On Long Island, New York, for example, water that has been pumped out for air-conditioning purposes is returned to the ground through special recharging wells or, in winter, through idle wells that are used in summer for air-conditioning. In the San Fernando Valley, California, surplus water from the Owens Valley aqueduct is fed into the underground in an attempt to keep the local water table at a high level.

CAVES AND RELATED FEATURES

Caves are probably the most spectacular examples of the handiwork of underground water. In dissolving great quantities of solid rock in its downward course, the water fashions large rooms, galleries, and underground stream systems as the years pass. In many caves, the water deposits calcium carbonate as it drips off the ceilings and walls, building up fantastic shapes of a material known as *dripstone* (see Fig. 12-15).

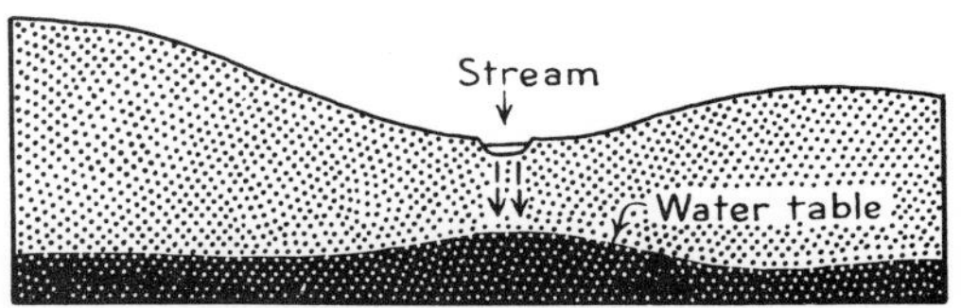

FIG. 12-14
The ground water may be recharged by water from a surface stream leaking into the underground.

Caves of all sizes tend to develop in highly soluble rocks

such as limestone ($CaCO_3$), and small ones occur in the sedimentary rock dolomite [$CaMg(CO_3)_2$]. Rock salt ($NaCl$), gypsum ($CaSO_4 2H_2O$), and similar rock types are the victims of such rapid solution that underground caverns usually collapse under the weight of overlying rocks before erosion can open them at the surface.

Calcite, the main component of limestone, is very insoluble in pure water. But when the mineral is attacked by water containing small amounts of carbonic acid, it undergoes rapid chemical weathering; and most natural water does contain carbonic acid (H_2CO_3), the combination of water with carbon dioxide. The carbonic acid reacts with the calcite to form calcium bicarbonate, $Ca(HCO_3)_2$, a soluble substance that is then removed in solution. If not redeposited, it eventually reaches the ocean.

Let us look more closely at underground water as it brings about the decay of calcite. Calcite contains the complex carbonate ion, $(CO_3)^{2-}$ (built by packing three oxygen atoms around a carbon atom) and the calcium ion, Ca^{2+}. These two ions are arranged in much the same way as sodium and chlorine in forming salt or halite (Fig. 4-1, repeated left). The weathering or solution of calcite takes place when a hydrogen ion, H^+, approaches a carbonate ion, $(CO_3)^{2-}$. Since the attraction of hydrogen for oxygen is stronger than the attraction of carbon for oxygen, the hydrogen ion pulls away one of the oxygen atoms of the carbonate ion and, with another hydrogen ion, forms water. The two other oxygen atoms remain with the carbon atom as carbon dioxide gas. The calcium ion, Ca^{2+}, now joins with two negative bicarbonate ions, $(HCO_3)^-$, to form calcium bicarbonate in solution. We can express these activities as follows:

Two parts water + Two parts carbon dioxide *yield* Two parts carbonic acid

$$2H_2O + 2CO_2 \rightleftharpoons 2H_2CO_3$$

Two parts carbonic acid *yield* Two hydrogen ions + Two bicarbonate ions

$$2H_2CO_3 \rightleftharpoons 2H^+ + 2(HCO_3)^-$$

Two hydrogen ions + Two bicarbonate ions + Calcite *yield* Water + Carbon dioxide + Calcium bicarbonate in solution

$$2H^+ + 2(HCO_3)^- + CaCO_3 \rightleftharpoons H_2O + CO_2 + Ca^{2+} + 2(HCO_3)^-$$

The first signs of solution in limestone usually appear along original lines of weakness, such as bedding surfaces or fractures. As water seeps into these areas, it dissolves some of the rock and enlarges the openings. The dissolved material is moved onward by the underground water and is either redeposited or discharged into streams. As time passes, the openings grow larger and larger, until finally they form large passageways. Whether this cave-forming activity goes on above the water table, at the water table, or at some distance beneath it is a question that is still being argued. Most investigators, however, believe that caves are usually formed below the water table and are exposed later on, when the water table in the area is lowered by downward-cutting surface streams.

Regardless of where caves are originally formed, we know

that the weird stone formations so characteristic of most of them must have developed above the water table, when the caves were filled with air. These bizarre shapes are composed of calcite deposited by underground water that has seeped down through the zone of aeration. They develop either as *stalactites,* looking like stoney icicles hanging from the cave roof (Greek, *stalactos,* "oozing out in drops") or as *stalagmites,* heavy posts growing up from the floor (Greek, *stalagmos,* "a dropping or dripping"). When a stalactite and stalagmite meet, a *column* is formed.

A stalactite forms as water charged with calcium bicarbonate in solution seeps through the cave roof. Drop after drop forms on the ceiling and then falls to the floor. But during the few moments that each drop clings to the ceiling, a small amount of evaporation takes place; some carbon dioxide is lost, and a small amount of calcium carbonate is deposited. Over the centuries, a large stalactite may gradually develop. Part of the water that falls to the cave floor runs off, and part is evaporated. This evaporation again causes the deposition of calcite, and a stalagmite begins to grow upward to meet the stalactite hanging down from above.

On the ground surface above soluble rock material, depressions sometimes develop that reflect areas where the underlying rock has been carried away in solution. These depressions, called *sinkholes* or merely *sinks,* usually form when the surface collapses into a large cavity beneath. Surface water may then drain through the sinkholes to the underground, or if their subterranean outlets become clogged, they may fill with water to form lakes. An area with numerous sinkholes is said to display *karst topography,* from the name of a plateau

FIG. 12-15
The floor of this section of the Luray Caverns, Virginia, is partially flooded by a lake. Both stalagmites and stalactites are present. Photo by permission of the Luray Caverns, Virginia.

in Yugoslavia and northeastern Italy where this type of landscape is extensively developed.

CEMENTATION AND REPLACEMENT

All underground water carries a certain amount of mineral matter in solution. Some of this matter, particularly the iron and silica compounds, is picked up as the water passes through the soil and down to the zone of saturation. The water also acquires calcium bicarbonate from the soil and from any limestone through which it passes. Later on, in new surroundings in the underground, this dissolved material may be deposited again. In fact, the common calcareous, siliceous, and iron oxide cements of the coarse-grained and medium-grained sedimentary rocks are derived in large part from minerals precipitated out of water that percolates beneath the surface.

Sometimes the dissolved material carried by underground water may replace other material. Thus silica in solution may replace the organic matter in buried logs and produce petrified wood, the original woody structure of the log faithfully preserved in quartz, as in the Petrified Forest in Arizona.

Meteoric, juvenile, and connate water

Most underground water is derived from precipitation, and, fittingly, it is called *meteoric water*, from the Greek word meaning "high in the air." But some underground water originates within the earth itself, from sources related to igneous activity. It may appear at the surface during volcanic eruptions or simply accumulate below the surface after the crystallization of a magma. Appropriately known as *juvenile water*, this young, new water is entering into the hydrologic cycle for the first time.

The third type of underground water is *connate water*, water that was trapped in sedimentary deposits at the time of their formation. It takes its name from the Latin meaning "born at the same time." Actually, connate water was not *created* at the same time as the sedimentary rocks that hold it, but it did form a part of the original deposits. Thus, sand laid down on an ancient sea floor may be converted to a sandstone; and if conditions permit, the sea water trapped during deposition may be sealed off in the rock. An example of connate water is the salt water that is often brought up from oil fields (see Chapter 21).

Connate water in marine rocks is salty, reflecting the nature of its origin but differing in composition from modern sea water, for several reasons. Part of the material carried in solution by the ancient sea water may have been precipitated as a cement, or it may have entered into chemical combination with other minerals in the sedimentary rock. Or the original connate water may have become somewhat diluted by the slow infiltration of fresh, unsalty ground water. Finally, it may be that the chemical composition of ancient seas differed from that of modern seas.

Not all salty water in the underground is connate, however. Fresh ground water may become salty as it flows down through beds of rock salt, and some salty water may seep from the ocean into the rocks along the shore.

SUMMARY OUTLINE

Underground water
Distributed in zone of aeration and in underlying zone of saturation

Porosity
Total percentage of void space in earth material

Permeability
Ability of earth material to transmit water

Water table
Irregular surface between zone of saturation and zone of aeration

Movement of ground water
Mostly very slow laminar flow
Movement under influence of gravity
Darcy's Law:

$$V = P\frac{h}{l}$$

Aquifer
Water-bearing zone composed of permeable earth material

Wells
Wells draw water from zone of saturation
Artesian wells are those in which water rises above top of aquifer

Springs
Result of natural intersection of ground surface and water table

Thermal springs
Derive heat from cooling igneous rocks or by normal increase of earth's heat with depth
Geysers are thermal springs marked by periodic, violent eruptions

Recharge of ground water
Natural or artificial

Caves
Solution of limestone
Carbonic acid + water + limestone = solution of limestone
Stalactites grow from ceiling; stalagmites grow from floor

Karst topography
Landscape pockmarked by sink holes

Cementation and replacement
Cementation of sediments to form solid rock; e.g., sand cemented by mineral matter to form sandstone
Replacement of material; e.g., wood replaced by mineral matter to form petrified wood

Sources of underground water
Meteoric, juvenile, and connate

SELECTED REFERENCES

Bretz, J Harlan, "Vadose and Phreatic Features of Limestone Caverns," *J. Geol.*, L (1942), 675–811.

Holland, H. D., and others, "On Some Aspects of the Chemical Evolution of Cave Waters," *J. Geol.*, LXXII (1964), 36–67.

Hubbert, M. King, "The Theory of Ground Water Motion," *J. Geol.*, XLVIII (1940), 785–944.

Meinzer, O. E., *The Occurrence of Ground Water in the United States*. Washington, D.C.: U.S. Geol. Survey Water-Supply Paper 489, 1923.

———, *Ground Water in the United States, A Summary*. Washington, D.C.: U.S. Geol. Survey Water-Supply Paper 836–D, 1939.

———, ed., *Hydrology* (*Physics of the Earth*, IX). New York: McGraw-Hill Book Company, 1942.

Todd, D. K., *Ground Water Hydrology*. New York: John Wiley & Sons, Inc., 1959.

Tolman, C. F., *Ground Water*. New York: McGraw-Hill Book Company, 1937.

13 Glaciation

The seas and rivers of moving ice known as glaciers have attracted inquisitive men deep into the arctic, antarctic, and mountainous regions of the world. There they have discovered that glaciers are active agents of erosion, transportation, and deposition, and that these impressive masses of ice were far more widespread in the past than they are now. Geologists have learned, too, that the ice of the last great glacial period has modified and molded great stretches of landscape in what are now the temperate zones.

FORMATION OF GLACIER ICE

A *glacier* is a mass of ice that has been formed by the recrystallization of snow, and that flows forward, or has flowed at some time in the past, under the influence of gravity. This definition eliminates the pack ice formed from sea water in polar latitudes and—by convention—icebergs, even though though they are large fragments broken from the seaward end of glaciers.

Like surface streams and underground reservoirs, glaciers depend on the oceans for their nourishment. Some of the water drawn up from the oceans by evaporation falls on the land in the form of snow. If the climate is right, part of the snow may last through the summer without melting. Gradually, as the years pass, the accumulation may grow deeper and deeper, until at last a glacier is born.

In areas where the winter snowfall exceeds the amount of snow that melts away during the summer, stretches of perennial snow known as *snowfields* cover the landscape. At the lower limit of a snowfield lies the *snow line*. Above the snow line, glacier ice may collect in the more sheltered areas of the snowfields. The exact position of the snow line varies from one climatic region to another. In polar regions, for example, it reaches down to sea level, but near the equator it recedes to the mountain tops. In the high mountains of East Africa, it ranges from elevations of 15,000 to 18,000 feet. The highest snow lines in the world are in the dry regions known as the "horse latitudes" between 20° and 30° north and south of the equator. Here the snow line reaches higher than 20,000 feet.

Fresh snow falls as a feathery aggregate of complex and beautiful crystals with a great variety of patterns. All the crystals are basically hexagonal, however, and all reflect their internal arrangement of hydrogen and oxygen atoms (see Fig. 13-1). Snow is not frozen rain; rather, it forms from the condensation of water vapor at temperatures below the freezing point.

After snow has been lying on the ground for some time, it changes from a light, fluffy mass to a heavier, granular material called *firn,* or *névé* (nay-vay). "Firn" derives from a Greek adjective meaning "of last year," and "névé" is a French word from the Latin for "snow." Solid remnants of large snow banks, those tiresome vestiges of winter, are largely firn.

Several processes are at work in the transformation of snow into firn. The first is sublimation, a general term for the process of a solid material passing into the gaseous state without first becoming a liquid. In sublimation, molecules of water vapor escape from the snow, particularly from the edges of the flakes. Some of the molecules attach themselves to the center of the flakes, where they adapt themselves to the structure of the snow crystals. Then, as time passes, one snowfall follows another, and the granules that have already begun to grow as a result of sublimation are packed tighter and tighter together under the pressure of the overlying snow.

Water has the unique property of increasing in volume when it freezes; conversely it decreases in volume as the ice melts. But the cause and effect may be interchanged: if added pressure on the ice squeezes the molecules closer together and reduces its volume, the ice may melt. In fact, if the individual granules are in contact, they begin to melt with only a slight increase in pressure. The resulting meltwater trickles down and refreezes on still lower granules at points where they are not yet in contact. And all through this process the basic hexagonal structure of the original snow crystals is maintained.

Gradually, then, a layer of firn granules, ranging from a fraction of a millimeter to approximately three or four millimeters in diameter, is built up. The thickness of this layer varies, but 100 feet seems to be average on many mountain glaciers.

The firn itself undergoes further change as continued pressure forces out most of the air between the granules, reduces the space between them, and finally transforms it into *glacier ice,* a true solid composed of interlocking crystals. It is usually opaque and takes on a blue-gray color from the air and the fine dirt that it contains.

The ice crystals that make up glacier ice are minerals; the mass of glacier ice, made up of many interlocking crystals, is a metamorphic rock, for it has been transformed from snow into firn and eventually into glacier ice. Later, we will see that glacier ice itself undergoes further metamorphism.

FIG. 13-1
Snowflakes exhibit a wide variety of patterns, all hexagonal and all reflecting the internal arrangement of hydrogen and oxygen. It is from snowflakes that glacier ice eventually forms.

Classification of glaciers

The glaciers of the world fall into three principal classifications: (1) valley glaciers, (2) piedmont glaciers, and (3) ice sheets.

Valley glaciers are streams of ice that flow down the valleys of mountainous areas (see Fig. 13-2). Like streams of running water, they vary in width, depth, and length. A branch of the Hubbard Glacier in Alaska is 75 miles long, whereas some of the valley glaciers that dot the higher reaches of our western mountains are only a few hundred yards in length. Valley glaciers that are nourished on the flanks of high mountains and that flow down the mountain sides are sometimes called *mountain glaciers* or *Alpine glaciers*. Very small mountain glaciers are referred to as *cliff glaciers, hanging glaciers,* or *glacierets*. A particular type of valley glacier sometimes grows up in areas where large masses of ice are dammed by a mountain barrier along the coast. Some of the ice escapes through valleys in the mountain barrier to form an *outlet glacier,* as it has done along the coasts of Greenland and Antarctica.

Piedmont glaciers form when two or more glaciers emerge from their valleys and coalesce to form an apron of moving ice on the plains below.

Ice sheets are broad, moundlike masses of glacier ice that tend to spread radially under their own weight. The Vatna Glacier of Iceland is a small ice sheet measuring about 75 miles by 100 miles and 750 feet in thickness. A localized sheet of this sort is sometimes called an *icecap*. The term *continental glacier* is usually reserved for great ice sheets that obscure the mountains and plains of large sections of a continent, such as those of Greenland and Antarctica (see Fig. 13-3). On Greenland, ice exceeds 10,000 feet in thickness near the center of the

FIG. 13-2
Valley glaciers in the high mountains of the Caucasus. Photo by Vittorio Sella.

ice caps. The greatest known thickness of ice in Antarctica is more than 14,000 feet, in Marie Byrd Land.

FIG. 13-3
Isolated peaks protrude through the Antarctic icecap. Photo by F. J. Rootes.

Distribution of modern glaciers

Modern glaciers cover approximately 10 per cent of the land area of the world. They are found in widely scattered locations in North and South America, Europe, Asia, Africa, Antarctica, Greenland, many of the north polar islands, and on the Pacific islands of New Guinea and New Zealand. A few valley glaciers are located almost on the equator. Mt. Kenya in East Africa, for instance, only half a degree from the equator, rises over 17,000 feet into the tropical skies and supports at least ten valley glaciers.

The total land area covered by existing glaciers is estimated at 5,780,000 square miles, of which the Greenland and Antarctica ice sheets account for about 96 per cent. The Antarctica ice sheet covers approximately 4,860,000 square miles, and the Greenland sheet covers about 670,000 square miles. Small icecaps and numerous mountain glaciers scattered around the world account for the remaining 4 per cent.

Nourishment and wastage of glaciers

When the weight of a mass of snow, firn, and ice above the snow line becomes great enough, movement begins and a glacier is created. The moving stream flows downward across the snow line until it reaches an area where the loss through evaporation and melting is so great that the forward edge of the glacier can push no farther. A glacier, then, can be divided into two zones: (1) *a zone of accumulation* and (2) *a zone of wastage* (see Fig. 13-4).

The position of the front of a glacier depends on the relationship between the glacier's rate of nourishment and its rate of wastage. When nourishment just balances wastage, the front becomes stationary and the glacier is said to be in equilibrium. This balance seldom lasts for long, however, for a slight change in either nourishment or wastage will cause the front to advance or recede.

Today, most of the glaciers of the world are receding. With only a few exceptions, this process has been going on since the latter part of the nineteenth century, and since 1920 the rate has speeded up. A striking feature of modern glaciers is that they follow the same general pattern of growth and wastage the world over and serve as indicators of widespread climatic changes.

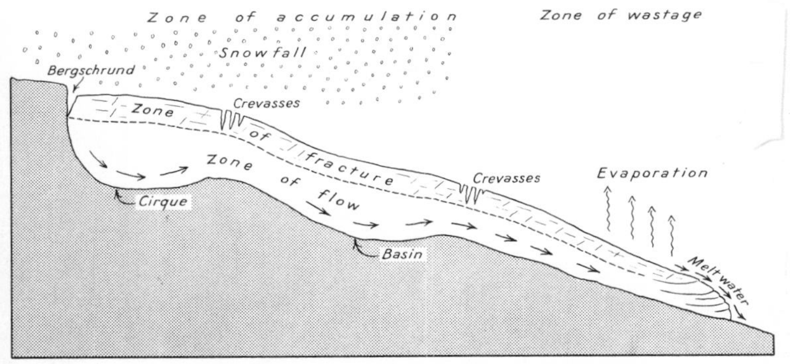

FIG. 13-4
A glacier is marked by a zone of accumulation and a zone of wastage. Within a glacier, ice may lie either in the zone of fracture or deeper in the zone of flow. A valley glacier originates in a basin, the cirque, and is separated from the headwall of the cirque by a large crevasse, the bergschrund.

Valley glaciers are nourished not only in the zone of accumulation, but also by great masses of snow that avalanche down the steep slopes along their course. In fact, according to one interpretation, avalanches caused by earthquakes have enabled a glacier to advance in a single month as far as it would have if it had been fed by the normal snowfall of several years.

Below the snow line, wastage takes place through a double process of evaporation and melting known as *ablation*. If a glacier terminates in a body of water, great blocks of ice break off and float away in a process called *calving*. This is the action that produces the icebergs of the polar seas.

Glacier movement

Except in rare cases, glaciers move only a few inches or at most a few feet a day. That they actually do move, however, can be demonstrated in several ways. The most conclusive test is to measure the movement directly, by emplacing a row of stakes across a valley glacier. As time passes, the stakes move downvalley with the advancing ice, the center stakes more rapidly than those near the valley walls. A second source of evidence is provided by the distribution of rock material on the surface of a glacier. When we examine the boulders and cobbles lying along a valley glacier, we find that many of them could not have come from the walls immediately above, and that the only possible source lies upvalley. We can infer, then,

FIG. 13-5
A glacier formed from snow gathered near Dent d'Herens, the 13,690-foot peak on the right, flows past Matterhorn, the 14,780-foot peak on the left, and carries rock debris down the valley. Photo by Vittorio Sella.

that the boulders must have been carried to their present position on the back of the glacier. Another indication of glacier movement is that when a glacier melts, it often exposes a rock floor that has been polished, scratched, and grooved. It is simplest to explain this surface by assuming that the glacier actually moved across the rock floor, using embedded debris to polish, scratch, and groove it.

Clearly, then, a glacier does move (see Fig. 13-5). In fact, different parts of it move at different rates. But though we know a good bit about how a glacier flows forward, certain phases are not yet clearly understood. In any event, we can distinguish two zones of movement: (1) an upper zone between 100 and 200 feet thick, which reacts like a brittle substance—that is, it breaks sharply rather than undergoing gradual, permanent distortion, and (2) a lower zone, which, because of the pressure of the overlying ice, behaves like a plastic substance (see "Behavior of material" in Chapter 10). The first is the *zone of fracture;* the second is the *zone of flow.*

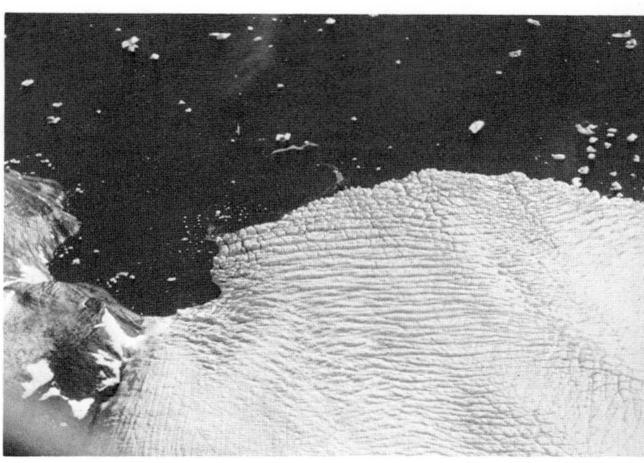

FIG. 13-6
Aerial photograph of crevassed ice along the northwestern coast of Greenland. Note the icebergs that have calved off the forward edge of the glacier. Photo by George McGill.

As plastic deformation takes place in the zone of flow, the brittle ice above is carried along. But the zone of flow moves forward at different rates—faster in some parts, more slowly in others—and the rigid ice in the zone of fracture is unable to adjust itself to this irregular advance. Consequently, the upper part of the glacier cracks and shatters, giving rise to a series of deep, treacherous *crevasses* (see Figs. 13-4, 13-6).

A glacier attains its greatest velocity somewhere above the valley floor, in midstream, for the sides and bottom are retarded by friction against the valley walls and beds. In this respect the movement of an ice stream resembles that of a stream of water.

The mechanics of ice flow are still a matter of study—a study made difficult by the fact that we cannot actually observe the zone of flow, since it lies concealed within the glacier. Yet the ice from the zone of flow eventually emerges at the snout of the glacier, and there it can be studied. We find that by the time it has emerged it is brittle; but it retains the imprint of movement by flow. The individual ice crystals are now several inches in size; in contrast, crystals in ice newly formed from firn measure but a fraction of an inch. We can conclude that the ice crystals have grown by recrystallization as they passed through the zone of flow. The ice at the snout is also marked by bands that represent shearing and differential movement within the glacier. Recrystallization has taken place along many of the old shear planes, and along others the debris carried forward by the ice has been concentrated. These observations suggest that some movement in the zone of flow has taken place as a result of shearing.

RESULTS OF GLACIATION

Movement of material

Glaciers have special ways of eroding, transporting, and depositing earth materials. A valley glacier, for example, acquires debris by means of frost action, landsliding, and avalanching.

Fragments pried loose by frost action clatter down from neighboring peaks and come to rest on the back of the glacier. And great snowbanks, unable to maintain themselves on the steep slopes of the mountainsides, avalanche downward to the glacier, carrying along quantities of rock debris and rubble. This material is buried beneath fresh snow or avalanches, or else tumbles into gaping crevasses in the zone of fracture and is carried along by the glacier.

When a glacier flows across a fractured or jointed stretch of bedrock, it may lift up large blocks of stone and move them off. This process is known as *plucking,* or *quarrying.* The force of the ice flow itself may be strong enough to pick up the blocks, and the action may be helped along by the great pressures that operate at the bottom of a glacier. Suppose the moving ice encounters a projection of rock jutting up from the valley floor. As the glacier ice forces itself over and around the projection, the pressure on the ice is increased and some of the ice around the rock may melt. This meltwater trickles toward a place of lower pressure, perhaps into a crack in the rock itself. There it refreezes, forming a strong bond between the glacier and the rock. Continued movement by the glacier may then tear the block out of the valley floor.

At the heads of valley glaciers, plucking and frost action sometimes work together to pry rock material loose. Along the back walls of the collection basins of mountain glaciers, great hollows called *cirques* (pronounced sirks) or *amphitheaters* develop in the mountainside. As the glacier begins its movement downslope, it pulls slightly away from the back wall, forming a crevasse known as a *bergschrund.* One wall of of the bergschrund is formed by the glacier ice; the other is formed by the nearly vertical cliff of bedrock. During the day, meltwater pours into the bergschrund and fills the openings in the rock. At night, the water freezes, producing pressures great enough to loosen blocks of rock from the cliff. Eventually, these blocks are incorporated into the glacier and are moved away from the headwall of the cirque.

The streams that drain from the front of a melting glacier are charged with *rock flour,* very fine particles of pulverized rock. So great is the volume of this material that it gives the water a characteristically grayish-blue color similar to that of skim milk. Here, then, is further evidence of the grinding power of the glacier mill.

Glaciers also pick up rock material by means of abrasion. As the moving ice drags rocks, boulders, pebbles, sand, and silt across the glacier floor, the bedrock is cut away as though by a great rasp or file. And the cutting tools themselves are abraded. It is this mutual abrasion that produces rock flour and gives a high *polish* to many of the rock surfaces across which a glacier has ridden. But abrasion sometimes produces scratches, or *striations,* on both the bedrock floor and on the grinding tools carried by the ice (see Fig. 13-7). More extensive abrasion creates deep gouges, or *grooves,* in the bedrock. The striations and grooves along a bedrock surface show the direction of the glacier's movement. At Kelleys Island, in Lake

FIG. 13-7
Rock fragments embedded in glacier ice often gouge scratches or striations in bedrock as the ice moves across it. This exposure in northeastern Wisconsin reveals that ice movement was parallel to the orientation of the striations. Photo by Raymond C. Murray.

Erie north of Sandusky, Ohio, the bedrock is marked by grooves 1 to 2 feet deep, and 2 to 3 feet wide. In the Mackenzie Valley west of Great Bear Lake in Canada, grooves as wide as 150 feet have been described with an average depth of 50 feet and lengths ranging from several hundred feet to over a mile.

Erosional effects

The erosional effects of glaciers are not limited to the fine polish and striations mentioned above, however. For glaciers also operate on a much grander scale, producing spectacularly sculptured peaks and valleys in the mountainous areas of the world.

CIRQUES. As we have seen, a cirque is the basin from which a mountain glacier flows, the focal point for the glacier's nourishment. After a glacier has disappeared and all its ice has melted away, the cirque is revealed as a great amphitheater or bowl, with one side partially cut away. The back wall rises a few hundred feet to over 3,000 feet above the floor, often as an almost vertical cliff. The floor of a cirque lies below the level of the low ridge separating it from the valley of the glacier's descent. The lake that forms in the bedrock basin of the cirque floor is called a *tarn* (see Fig. 13-9).

A cirque begins with an irregularity in the mountainside formed either by preglacial erosion or by a process called *nivation,* a term that refers to erosion beneath and around the edges of a snow bank. Nivation works in the following way. When seasonal thaws melt some of the snow, the meltwater seeps down to the bedrock and trickles along the margin of the snowbank. Some of the water works its way into cracks in the bedrock where it freezes again, producing pressures that loosen and pry out fragments of the rock. These fragments are moved off by solifluction, by rill wash, and perhaps by mass wasting, forming a shallow basin. As this basin gradually grows deeper, a cirque eventually develops. Continued accumulation of snow leads to the formation of firn; and if the basin becomes deep enough, the firn is transformed into ice. Finally the ice begins to flow out of the cirque into the valley below, and a small glacier is born.

The actual mechanism by which a cirque is enlarged is still a matter of dispute. Some observers claim that frost action and plucking on the cirque wall within the bergschrund are enough to produce precipitous walls thousands of feet in height. Others, however, point out that the bergschrund, like all glacier crevasses, remains open only in the zone of fracture, about 200 feet at most. Below that depth, pressures cause the ice to deform plastically, closing the bergschrund.

This debate has led to the development of the so-called *meltwater hypothesis* to explain erosion along the headwalls below the base of the bergschrund. The chief proponent of this theory explains "that meltwater periodically descends the headwalls of cirques, melts its way down behind the ice and into crevices in the rock, and there freezes at night and during cold spells. The material thus broken loose is then re-

FIG. 13-8
Valley glaciers flow from cirques on the flanks of Mt. Deborah, Alaska. Photo by U.S. Army Air Force.

FIG. 13-9
When glacier ice melts from a cirque, the resulting basin is often filled with water. A lake so formed is called a tarn. The tarn in this photograph is Lake Marie, in the Snowy Range, west of Centennial, Wyoming. Photo by Barton W. Knapp.

moved by the glacier, and cirque erosion proceeds mainly by this form of headwall recession." [1]

HORNS, ARETÊS, AND COLS. A *horn* is a spire of rock formed by the headward erosion of a ring of cirques around a single high mountain. When the glaciers originating in these cirques finally disappear, they leave a steep, pyramidal mountain outlined by the headwalls of the cirques. The classic example of a horn is the famous Matterhorn of Switzerland (see Figs. 13-5, 13-10).

An *arête* (pronounced a-ret′, from the French for "fishbone," "ridge," or "sharp edge") is formed when a number of cirques gnaw into a ridge from opposite sides. The ridge becomes knife-edged, jagged, and serrated (see Fig. 13-10).

A *col* (from the Latin *collum,* "neck"), or pass, is fashioned when two cirques erode headward into a ridge from opposite sides. When their headwalls meet, they cut a sharp-edged gap in the ridge.

Cirques

A

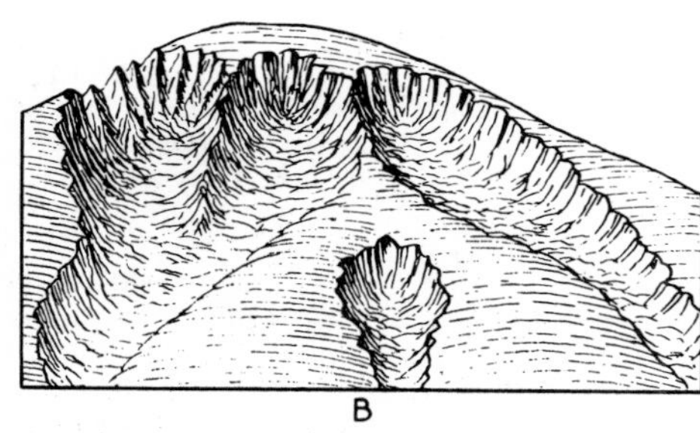

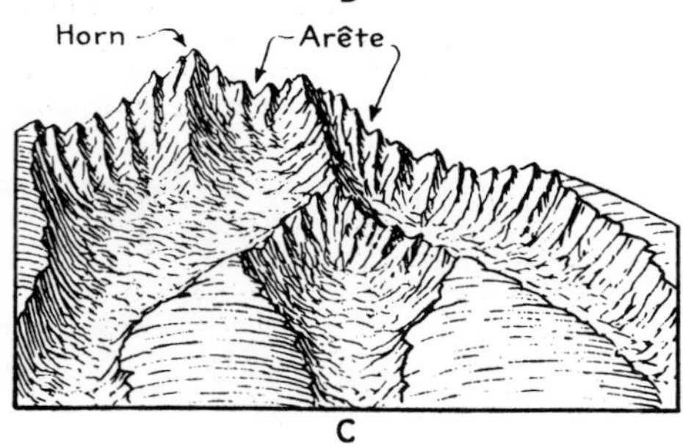

FIG. 13-10
The progressive development of cirques, horns, arêtes, and cols. In the first diagram, valley glaciers have produced cirques; but since erosion has been moderate, much of the original mountain surface has been unaffected by the ice. The result of more extensive glacial erosion is shown in the second diagram. In the final drawing, glacial erosion has affected the entire mass and has produced not only cirques but also a matterhorn and jagged, knife-edged arêtes. Redrawn from William Morris Davis, "The Colorado Front Range," Annals Assoc. Am. Geo., I (1911), 57.

GLACIATED VALLEYS. Rather than fashioning their own valleys, glaciers probably follow the course of pre-existing valleys, modifying them in a variety of ways; but usually the valleys have a broad *U-shaped* cross profile, whereas mountain valleys created exclusively by streams have narrow, V-shaped cross profiles. Since the tongue of an advancing glacier is relatively broad, it tends to broaden and deepen the V-shaped stream valleys, transforming them into broad, U-shaped troughs. And since the moving body of ice has difficulty manipulating the curves of a stream valley, it tends to straighten and simplify the course of the original valley. In this process of straightening, the ice snubs off any spurs of land that extend into it from either side. The cliffs thus formed are shaped like large triangles or flatirons with their apex upward, and are called *truncated spurs* (see Figs. 13-11, 13-12, 13-13).

Glaciers also give a mountain valley a characteristic longitudinal profile from the cirque downward. The course of a glaciated valley is marked by a series of *rock basins,* probably formed by plucking in areas where the bedrock was shattered or closely jointed. Between the basins are relatively flat stretches of rock that was more resistant to plucking. As time passes, the rock basins may fill up with water, producing a string of lakes that are sometimes referred to as *pater noster* lakes because they resemble a string of beads.

Hanging valleys are another characteristic of mountainous areas that have undergone glaciation. The mouth of a hanging valley is left stranded high above the main valley through which a glacier has passed. As a result, streams from hanging valleys plummet into the main valley in a series of falls and plunges. Hanging valleys may be formed by processes other than glaciation, but they are almost always present in mountainous areas that formerly supported glaciers and are thus very characteristic of past valley glaciation.

What has happened to leave these valleys stranded high above the main valley floor? During the time when glaciers

[1] W. V. Lewis, "The Function of Meltwater in Cirque Formation: A Reply," *Geog. Review,* XIL (1949), 110.

still moved down the mountains, the greatest accumulation of ice would tend to travel along the central valley. Consequently, the erosive action there would be greater than in the tributary valleys, with their relatively small glaciers, and the main valley floor would be cut correspondingly deeper. This action would be even more pronounced where the main valley was underlain by rock that was more susceptible to erosion than the rock under the tributary valleys. Finally, some hanging valleys were probably created by the straightening and widening action of a glacier on the main valley. In any event, the difference in level between the tributary valleys and the main valley does not become apparent until the glacier has melted away.

Cutting deep into the coasts of Alaska, Norway, Greenland, Labrador, and New Zealand are deep, narrow arms of the sea —*fiords* (see Fig. 13-14). Actually, these inlets are stream valleys that were modified by glacier erosion and then partially filled by the sea. The deepest known fiord, in Patagonia, has a maximum depth of about 4,250 feet.

Some valleys have been modified by continental glaciers rather than by the valley glaciers that we have been discussing so far. The valleys occupied by the Finger Lakes of central New York State are good examples. These long, narrow lakes lie in basins that were carved out by the ice of a continental glacier. As the great sheet of ice moved down from the north, its progress seems to have been checked by the northern scarp of the Appalachian Plateau. But some of the ice moved on up the valleys that had previously drained the plateau. The energy concentrated in the valleys was so great that the ice was able to scoop out the basins that are now filled by the Finger Lakes.

ASYMMETRIC ROCK KNOBS AND HILLS. Glacier erosion of bedrock in many places produces small, rounded, asymmetric hills with gentle, striated, and polished slopes on one side and steeper slopes lacking polish and striations on the opposite side. An assemblage of these undulating knobs is referred to as *rôches moutonnées,* from the French for "rocks" plus

A

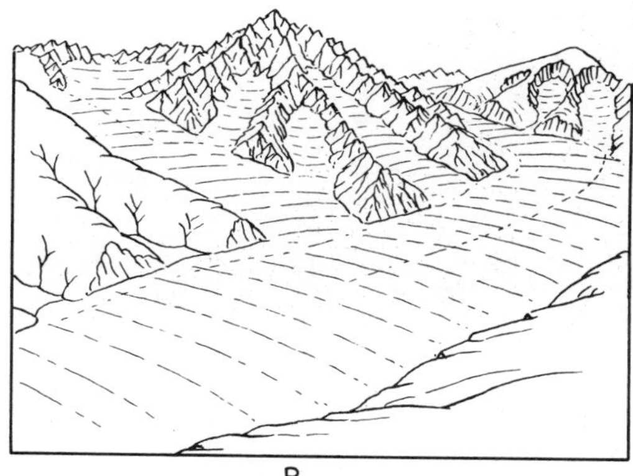

B

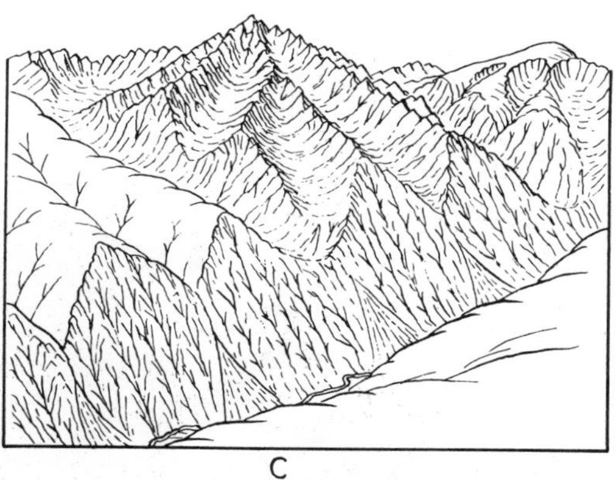

C

FIG. 13-11
A mountainous area before, during, and after glaciation. Redrawn from William Morris Davis, "The Sculpture of Mountains by Glaciers," Scottish Geoprahical Magazine, XXII (1906), 80, 81, and 83.

FIG. 13-12
A long valley glacier with many tributaries, in Alaska. Photo by U.S. Army Air Force.

FIG. 13-13
This valley in the Beartooth Mountains, Montana, shows the typical U-shaped profile of a glaciated valley. Compare with Fig. 11-38. Photo by George McGill.

FIG. 13-14
Glaciated valleys have been flooded by the sea (black) to produce these fiords along the coast of Greenland. Redrawn from Louise A. Boyd and others, "The Fiord Region of East Greenland," Am. Geog. Society, Special Publication No. 18 (1935), p. xii.

"curved." The now-gentle slope faced the advancing glacier and was eroded by abrasion. The opposite slope has been steepened by the plucking action of the ice as it rode over the knob.

Large individual hills have the same asymmetric profiles as the smaller hills. Here, too, the gentle slope faced the moving ice.

Types of glacial deposits

The debris carried along by a glacier is eventually deposited, either because the ice that holds it melts or, less commonly, because the ice smears the debris across the land surface.

The general term *drift* is applied to all deposits that are laid down directly by glaciers or that, as a result of glacial activity, are laid down in lakes, oceans, or streams. The term dates from the days when geologists thought that the unconsolidated cover of sand and gravel blanketing much of Europe and America had been made to drift into its present position either by the sea or by icebergs. Drift can be divided into two general categories: *stratified* and *unstratified.*

DEPOSITS OF UNSTRATIFIED DRIFT. Unstratified drift laid down directly by glacier ice is called *till.* It is composed of rock fragments of all sizes mixed together in random fashion, ranging all the way from boulders weighing several tons to tiny clay and colloid particles (see Fig. 13-15). Many of the large pieces are striated, polished, and faceted as a result of the wear they underwent while being transported by the glaciers (see Figs. 13-16—13-18). Some of the material picked up along the way was smeared across the landscape during the glacier's progress, but most of it was dumped when the rate of wastage began to exceed the rate of nourishment and the glacier gradually melted away.

The type of till varies from one glacier to another. Some tills, for instance, are known as *clay tills,* because clay-sized particles predominate with only a scattering of larger units. Many of the most recent tills in northeastern and eastern Wisconsin are of this type. But in many parts of New England the tills are composed for the most part of large rock fragments and boulders. Deposits of this sort are known as *boulder tills,* or *stony tills.*

Some till deposits seem to have been worked over by meltwater. The materials have begun to be sorted out according to size, and some of the finer particles may even have been washed away. This is the sort of winnowing action we would expect to find near the nose of a melting glacier, where floods of meltwater wash down through the deposits.

Till is deposited by receding glaciers in a great variety of topographic forms, including moraines, drumlins, erratics, and boulder trains.

Moraines. Moraine is a general term used to describe many of the landforms that are composed largely of till.

A *terminal moraine,* or *end moraine,* is a ridge of till that marks the utmost limit of a glacier's advance. These ridges vary in size from ramparts hundreds of feet high to very low,

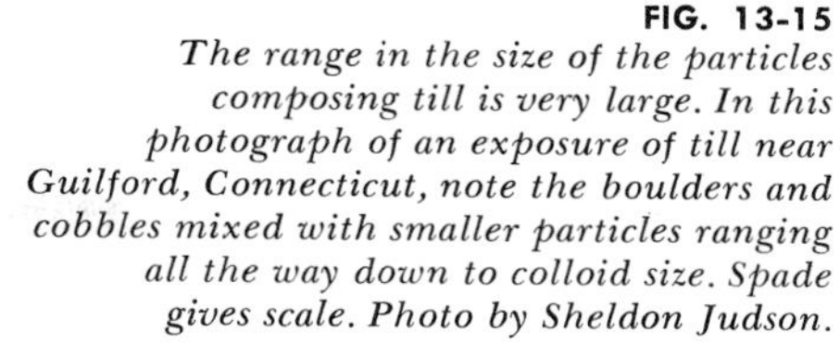

FIG. 13-15
The range in the size of the particles composing till is very large. In this photograph of an exposure of till near Guilford, Connecticut, note the boulders and cobbles mixed with smaller particles ranging all the way down to colloid size. Spade gives scale. Photo by Sheldon Judson.

interrupted walls of debris. A terminal moraine forms when a glacier reaches the critical point of equilibrium—the point at which it wastes away at exactly the same rate as it is nourished. Although the front of the glacier is now stable, ice continues to push downward from above, delivering a continuous supply of rock debris. As the ice melts in the zone of wastage, the debris is dumped and the terminal moraine grows. At the same time, water from the melting ice pours down over the till and sweeps part of it out in a broad flat fan that butts against the forward edge of the moraine like a giant ramp (Fig. 13-16).

The terminal moraine of a mountain glacier is crescent-shaped, with the convex side extending downvalley. The terminal moraine of a continental ice sheet is a broad loop or series of loops traceable for many miles across the countryside.

Behind the terminal moraine, and at varying distances from it, a series of smaller ridges known as *recessional moraines* may build up. These ridges mark the position where the glacier front was stabilized temporarily during the retreat of the glacier.

Not all the rock debris carried by a glacier finds its way to the terminal and recessional moraines, however. A great deal of till is laid down as the main body of the glacier melts, to form gently rolling plains across the valley floor. Till in this form, called a *ground moraine,* may be a thin veneer lying on the bedrock, or it may form a deposit scores or even hundreds of feet thick, partially or completely clogging preglacial valleys.

Finally, valley glaciers produce two special types of mo-

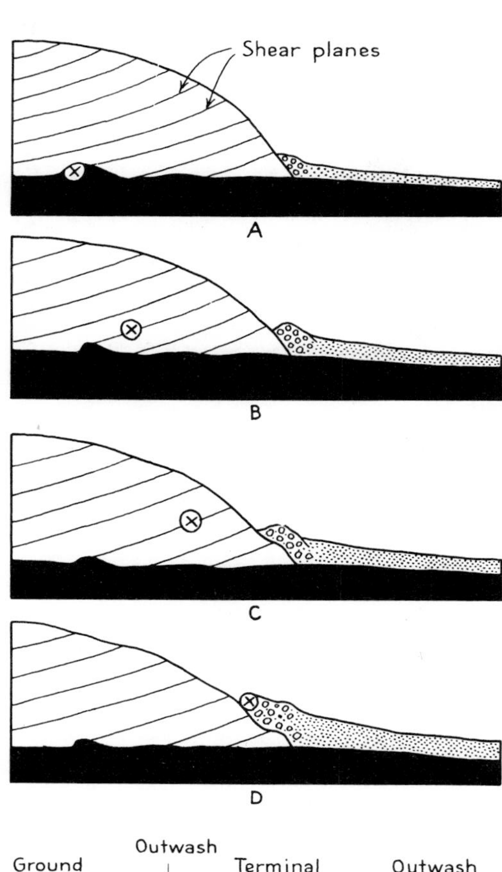

FIG. 13-16
A sequence of diagrams to suggest the growth of a terminal moraine at the edge of a stable ice front. The progressive movement of a single particle (X) is shown. In A, *it is moved by the ice from the bedrock floor. Forward motion of ice along a shear plane carries it ever closer to the stabilized ice margin, where finally it is deposited as a part of the moraine in diagram* D. E *represents the relation of the terminal moraine, ground moraine, and outwash after the final melting of the glacier.*

FIG. 13-17
Ice-transported boulder of granite gneiss near city of Devils Lake, east-central North Dakota. The subangular, relatively smooth facet is typical of glacially transported boulders. Photo by Saul Aronow, U.S. Geol. Survey.

FIG. 13-18 *(right)*
Stones from till, marked by facets and striations. Specimens from northern Illinois. Squares are 2 inches. Photo by Willard Starks.

FIG. 13-19
Low aerial photo shows irregular topography of morainal deposits along western base of Madison Range, Montana. A tree-lined river winds through the hummocked, grass-covered till. Distance across the photograph is about one-quarter mile. Photo by William C. Bradley.

FIG. 13-20
Map of part of the drumlin field area south and east of Charlevoix, Michigan. Ice moved toward the south-southeast. Redrawn from Frank Leverett and F. B. Taylor, "The Pleistocene of Indiana and Michigan and the History of the Great Lakes," U.S. Geol. Survey, Monograph 53 (1915), p. 311.

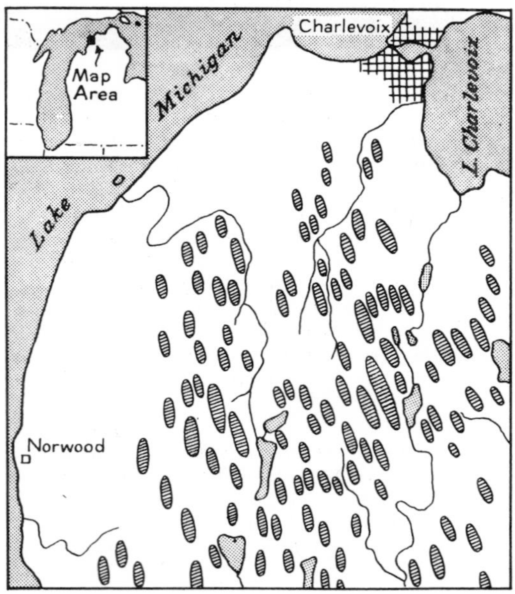

raines. While a valley glacier is still active, large amounts of rubble keep tumbling down from the valley walls, collecting along the side of the glacier. When the ice melts, all this debris is stranded as a ridge along each side of the valley, forming a *lateral moraine.* At its downvalley end, the lateral moraine grades into the terminal moraine.

The other special type of deposit produced by valley glaciers is a *medial moraine,* created when two valley glaciers join to form a single ice stream; material formerly carried along on the edges of the separate glaciers is combined in a single moraine near the center of the enlarged glacier. A streak of this kind builds up whenever a tributary glacier joins a larger glacier in the main valley. Although medial moraines are very characteristic of living glaciers, they are seldom preserved as topographic features after the disappearance of the ice.

Drumlins. Drumlins are smooth, elongated hills composed largely of till. The ideal drumlin shape has an asymmetric profile with a blunt nose pointing in the direction from which the vanished glacier advanced, and with a gentler, longer slope pointing in the opposite direction. Drumlins range from 25 to 200 feet in height, the average somewhat less than 100 feet. Most drumlins are between a quarter-mile and a half-mile in length, usually several times longer than they are wide.

In most areas, drumlins occur in clusters, or *drumlin fields.* In the United States, these are most spectacularly developed in New England, particularly around Boston; in eastern Wisconsin; in west-central New York State, particularly around Syracuse; in Michigan (Fig. 13-20); and in certain sections of Minnesota. In Canada, extensive drumlin fields are located in western Nova Scotia and in northern Manitoba and Saskatchewan; Fig. 13-21 shows a drumlin field in British Columbia.

Just how drumlins were formed is still not clear. Since their shape is a nearly perfect example of streamlining, it seems probable that they were formed deep within active glaciers in the zone of plastic flow.

Erratics and boulder trains. A stone or a boulder that has been carried from its place of origin by a glacier and left stranded on bedrock of different composition is called an

FIG. 13-21
This aerial photograph shows the drumloidal patterns of hills and intervening grooves formed parallel to the flow of glacier ice on the Nechako Plateau, British Columbia. Weedon Lake is 5½ miles long. View is northeast in the direction of ice movement. Photo by U.S. Army Air Force.

erratic. The term is used whether the stone is embedded in a till deposit or rests directly on the bedrock. Some erratics weigh several tons, and a few are even larger. Near Conway, New Hampshire, there is a granite erratic 90 feet in maximum dimension, weighing close to 10,000 tons. Although most erratics have traveled only a limited distance, many have been carried along by the glacier for hundreds of miles. Chunks of native copper torn from the Upper Peninsula of Michigan, for example, have been transported as far as southeastern Iowa, a distance of nearly 500 miles, and to southern Illinois, a distance of over 600 miles.

Boulder trains consist of a series of erratics that have come from the same source, usually with some characteristic that makes it easy to recognize their common origin. The trains appear either as a line of erratics stretching downvalley from their source or else in a fan-shaped pattern with the apex near the place of origin. By mapping boulder trains that have been left behind by continental ice sheets, we can get an excellent indication of the direction of the ice flow (Fig. 13-22).

DEPOSITS OF STRATIFIED DRIFT. Stratified drift is ice-transported material that has been washed and sorted by glacial meltwaters according to particle size. Since water is a much more selective sorting agent than ice, deposits of stratified drift

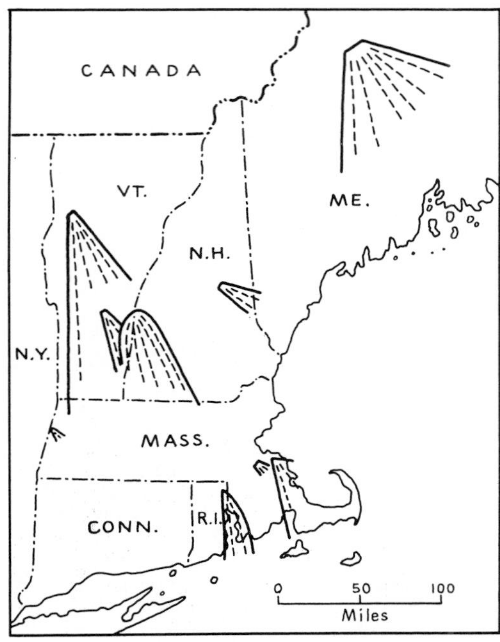

FIG. 13-22
The boulder trains plotted on this map indicate the general direction of ice movement across New England. The apex of the fan indicates the area from which the boulders were derived; the fan itself covers the area across which they were deposited. Redrawn from J. W. Goldthwait in R. F. Flint, "Glacial Map of North America," Geol. Soc. Am., Special Paper No. 60 (1945).

are laid down in recognizable layers, unlike the random arrangements of particles typical of till. Stratified drift occurs in outwash and kettle plains, eskers, kames, and varves—all discussed below.

Outwash sand and gravel. The sand and gravel that are carried outward by meltwater from the front of a glacier are referred to as *outwash* (see Fig. 13-23). As a glacier melts, streams of water heavily loaded with reworked till, or with material *washed* directly from the ice, weave a complex, braided pattern of channels across the land in front of the glacier. These streams, choked with clay, silt, sand, and gravel, rapidly lose their velocity and dump their load of debris as they flow away from the ice sheet. In time, a vast apron of bedded sand and gravel is built up that may extend for miles beyond the ice front. If the zone of wastage happens to be located in a valley, the outwash deposits are confined to the lower valley and compose a *valley train.* But along the front of a continental ice sheet, the outwash deposits stretch out for miles, forming what is called an *outwash plain* (see Fig. 13-24).

Kettles. Sometimes a block of stagnant ice becomes isolated from the receding glacier during wastage and is partially or completely buried in till or outwash before it finally melts. When it disappears, it leaves a *kettle,* a pit or depression in the drift (Fig. 13-25). These depressions range from a few feet to several miles in diameter, and from a few feet to over 100 feet in depth. Many outwash plains are pockmarked with kettles and are referred to as *pitted outwash plains.* As time passes, water sometimes fills the kettles to form lakes or swamps, features found through much of Canada and northern United States.

Eskers and crevasse fillings. Winding, steep-walled ridges of stratified gravel and sand, sometimes branching and often discontinuous, are called *eskers.* They usually vary in height from about 10 to 50 feet, although a few are over 100 feet high. Eskers range from a fraction of a mile to over 100 miles in length, but they are only a few feet wide. Most investigators (but not all) believe that eskers were formed by

FIG. 13-23
Modern outwash in front of an Alaskan glacier shows deposits of sand and gravel. A braided stream pattern is barely discernible in the middle distance. Photo by Joseph H. Hartshorn, U.S. Geol Survey.

FIG. 13-24
This outwash plain in North Dakota was produced by a now-vanished glacier. It is underlain by stratified sand and gravel. The crop is flax. Photo by Saul Aronow, U.S. Geol. Survey.

the deposits of streams running through tunnels beneath stagnant ice. Then, when the body of the glacier finally disappeared, the old stream deposits were left standing as a ridge.

Crevasse fillings are similar to eskers in height, width, and cross profile; but unlike the sinuous and branching pattern of eskers, they run in straight ridges. As their name suggests, they were probably formed by the filling of a crevasse in stagnant ice.

Kames and kame terraces. In many areas, stratified drift has built up low, relatively steep-sided hills called *kames,* either as isolated mounds or in clusters. Unlike drumlins, kames are of random shape and the deposits that make them up are stratified. They were formed by the material that collected in openings in stagnant ice. In this sense they are similar to crevasse fillings, but without the linear pattern.

A *kame terrace* is a deposit of stratified sand and gravel that has been laid down between a wasting glacier and an adjacent valley wall. When the glacier disappears, the deposit stands as a terrace along the side of the valley (see Fig. 13-28).

Varves. A *varve* is a pair of thin sedimentary beds, one coarse and one fine. This couplet of beds is usually interpreted as representing the deposits of a single year and is thought to form in the following way. During the period of summer thaw, waters from a melting glacier carry large amounts of clay, fine sand, and silt out into lakes along the ice margin. The coarser particles sink fairly rapidly and blanket the lake floor with a thin layer of silt and silty sand. But as long as the lake is unfrozen, the wind creates currents strong enough to keep the finer clay particles in suspension. When the lake freezes over in the winter, these wind-generated currents cease, and the fine particles sink through the quiet water to the bottom, covering the somewhat coarser summer layer. A varve is usually a fraction of an inch thick, though thicknesses of two or three inches and, in rare instances, of a foot or more are known (see Fig. 9-4).

COMPARISON OF VALLEY AND CONTINENTAL GLACIATION FEATURES. Some of the glacial features that we have been discussing are more common in areas that have undergone valley glaciation; others usually occur only in regions that have been overridden by ice sheets; many other features, however, are found in both types of area. Table 13-1 lists and compares the features that are characteristic of the two types.

DEVELOPMENT OF THE GLACIAL THEORY

Geologists have made extensive studies of the behavior of modern glaciers and have carefully interpreted the traces left by glaciers that disappeared thousands of years ago. On the

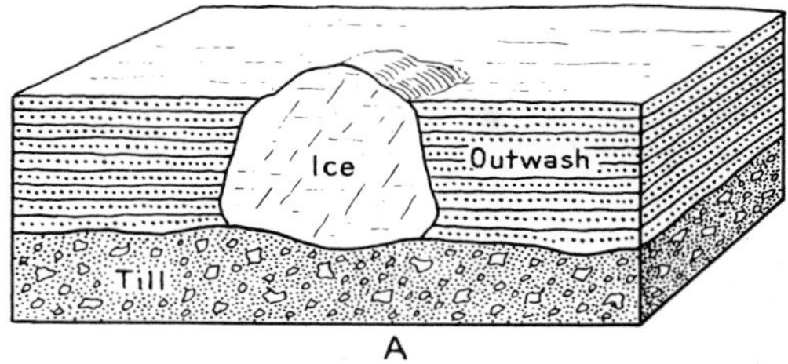

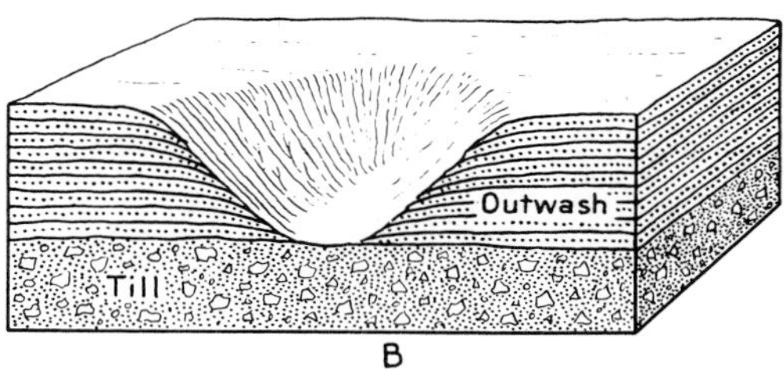

FIG. 13-25
Sequence in the formation of a kettle. A block of stagnant ice is almost buried by outwash in A. *The eventual melting of the ice produces a depression, as shown in* B. *In some instances, outwash may completely bury the ice block. Some kettles are formed in till.*

FIG. 13-26
The top of this esker ridge near Lake Ivanhoe, Northwest Territory, Canada, stands about 75 feet above the surrounding countryside. Photo by R. A. Noel.

FIG. 13-27
This isolated kame in eastern Wisconsin was formed by the partial filling of an opening in stagnant glacier ice. The melting of the ice has left this steep-sided hill of stratified material. Photo by Raymond C. Murray.

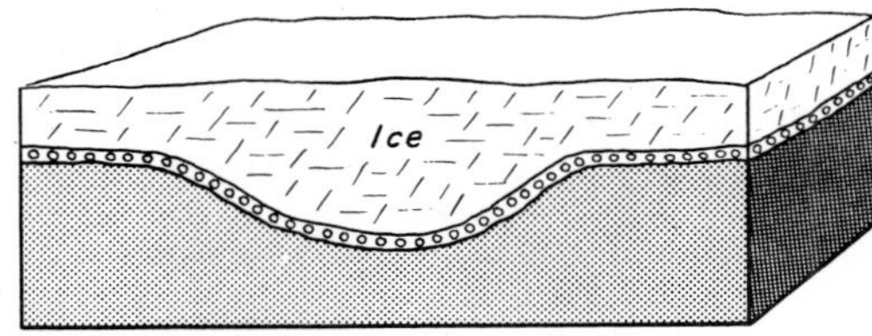

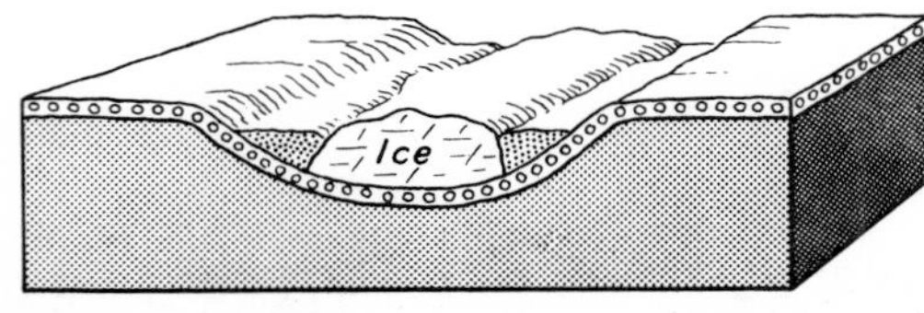

FIG. 13-28
The sequence in the development of a kame terrace. Ice wasting from an irregular topography lingers longest in the valleys. While the ice still partially fills one of these valleys, outwash may be deposited between it and the valley walls. The final disappearance of the ice leaves the outwash in the form of terraces along the sides of the valley.

basis of their studies, they have developed *the glacial theory* that *in the past great ice sheets covered large sections of the earth where no ice now exists, and that existing glaciers once extended far beyond their present limits.*

The beginnings

The glacial theory took many years to evolve, years of trying to explain the occurrence of erratics and the vast expanses of drift strewn across northern Europe, the British Isles, Switzerland, and adjoining areas. The exact time when inquisitive minds first began to seek an explanation of these deposits is shrouded in the past. But by the beginning of the eighteenth century, explanations of what we now know to be glacial deposits and features were finding their way into print. According to the most popular early hypothesis, a great inundation had swept these deposits across the face of the land with cataclysmic suddenness, or else had drifted them in by means of floating icebergs. Then, when the flood receded, the material was left stranded in its present location.

By the turn of the nineteenth century, a new theory was in the air—the theory of ice transport. We do not know who first stated the idea or when it was first proposed, but it seems quite clear that it was not hailed immediately as a great truth. As the years passed, however, more and more observers became intrigued with the idea. The greatest impetus came from Switzerland, where the activity of living glaciers could be studied on every hand.

In 1821, J. Venetz, a Swiss engineer delivering a paper before the Helvetic Society, presented the argument that Swiss glaciers had once expanded on a great scale. It has since been established that from about 1600 to the middle of the eighteenth century there actually was a time of moderate but persistent glacier expansion in many localities. Abundant evidence in the Alps, Scandinavia, and Iceland indicates that the climate was milder during the Middle Ages than it is at the present, that communities existed and farming was carried on in places later invaded by advancing glaciers or devastated by glacier-fed streams. We know, for example, that a silver mine in the valley of Chamonix was being worked during the Middle Ages and that it was subsequently buried by an advancing glacier, where it lies to this day. And the village of St. Jean de Perthuis has been buried under the Brenva Glacier since about 1600.

Although Venetz' idea did not take hold immediately, by 1834 Jean de Charpentier was arguing in its support before the same Helvetic Society. Yet the theory continued to have more opponents than defenders. It was one of the skeptics, Jean Louis Rodolphe Agassiz, who did more than anyone else to develop the glacial theory and bring about its general acceptance.

Agassiz

Louis Agassiz (1807-1873), a young zoologist, had listened to Charpentier's explanation; afterwards, he undertook to demonstrate to his friend and colleague the error of his ways.

During the summer of 1836, the two men made a trip together into the upper Rhône Valley to the Getrotz Glacier. Before the summer was over, it was Agassiz who was convinced of his error. In 1837, he spoke before the Helvetic Society championing the glacial theory and suggesting that during a "great ice age" not only the Alps but much of northern Europe and the British Isles were overrun by a sea of ice.

Agassiz' statement of the glacial theory was not accepted immediately, but in 1840 he visited England and won the support of leading British geologists. In 1846 he arrived in America, where in the following year he became professor of zoology at Harvard College and later founded the Museum of Comparative Zoology. In this country, he convinced geologists of the validity of the glacial theory; by the third quarter of the nineteenth century the theory was firmly entrenched. The last opposition died with the turn of the century.

Proof of the glacial theory

What proof is there that the glacial theory is valid? The most important evidence is that certain features produced by glacier ice are produced by no other known process. Thus Agassiz and his colleagues found isolated stones and boulders quite alien to their present surroundings. They noticed, too, that boulders were actually being transported from their original location by modern ice. Some of the boulders they observed were so large that rivers could not possibly have moved them, and others were perched on high places that a river could have reached only by flowing uphill. They also noticed that when modern ice melted it revealed a polished and striated pavement unlike the surface fashioned by any other known process. To explain the occurrence of these features in areas where no modern glaciers exist, they postulated that the ice once extended far beyond its present limits.

Notice that the development of this theory sprang from a concept that we mentioned earlier: "The present is the key to the past." The proof of glaciation lies not in the authority of the textbook or the lecture. It lies in observing modern glacial activity directly and in comparing the results of this activity with features and deposits found beyond the present extent of the ice.

TABLE 13-1
Features of valley and continental glaciations

FEATURES	VALLEY	CONTINENTAL
Striations, polish, etc.	Common	Common
Cirques	Common	Absent
Horns, arêtes, cols	Common	Absent
U-shaped valley, truncated spurs, hanging valleys	Common	Rare
Fiords	Common	Absent
Till and stratified drift	Common	Common
Terminal moraine	Common	Common
Recessional moraine	Common	Common
Ground moraine	Common	Common
Lateral moraine	Common	Absent
Medial moraine	Common, easily destroyed	Absent
Drumlins	Rare or absent	Locally common
Erratics	Common	Common
Kettles	Common	Common
Eskers, crevasse fillings	Rare	Common
Kames	Common	Common
Kame terraces	Common	Present in hilly country

Theory of multiple glaciation

Even before universal acceptance of the glacial theory, which spoke of a single Great Ice Age, some investigators were coming to the conclusion that the ice had advanced and retreated not just once but several times in the recent geologic past. By the early twentieth century, a broad fourfold division of the Ice Age, or Pleistocene, had been demonstrated in this country and in Europe. According to this theory, each major glacial advance was followed by a retreat and a return to climates that were sometimes even warmer than that of the present. In the United States, each glacial period is named for a midwestern state where deposits of that particular period were first studied or where they are well exposed: Nebraskan, Kansan, Illinoian, and Wisconsin (Fig. 13-29).

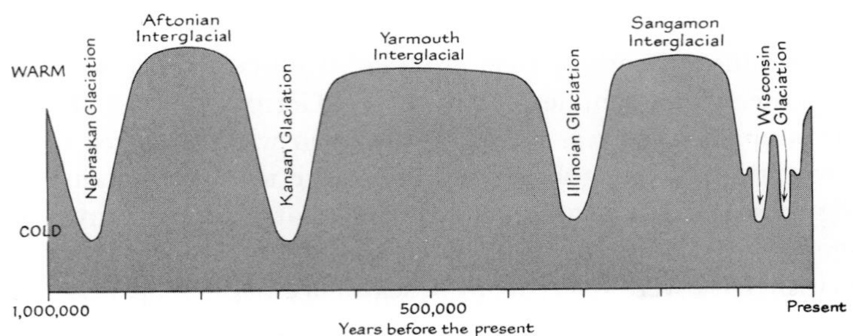

FIG. 13-29
Investigation of the glacial and interglacial deposits shows that the Great Ice Age or Pleistocene has been marked by four major advances of continental glaciers separated by periods of ice recession.

This subdivision of the Ice Age was built on a great variety of evidence from widely scattered localities. All the evidence cited, however, points in the same direction: that in each period a glaciation took place, that it was followed by an interval during which the glacier wasted and disappeared, and that finally a younger glacier moved forward. Some of the lines of evidence used to support this concept are suggested in Fig. 13-30. Needless to say, all this evidence is seldom present in any one exposure of glacial material, nor does our hypothetical example represent all the evidence that could be assembled to demonstrate multiple glaciation.

On the basis of the evidence summarized in Fig. 13-30, we can build up the following arguments in support of at least two major periods of glaciation:

(1) Two different till types are present: a lower, gray till and an upper, red till. Since the composition of the two tills differs, they must have been deposited by ice from two different sources. The most logical explanation would be that the gray till was laid down first by glacier ice moving in from a given direction over rock material that was predominantly gray. When the glacier melted, it laid down the gray till. Then a second glacier moved in from a different direction, over rock material that was predominantly red. When this second glacier melted, it laid down the red till on top of the gray.

(2) Cut into the surface of the gray till are old stream channels that must have been formed after the disappearance of the first glacier and before the appearance of the second.

(3) The forest bed buried between the red and the gray till indicates that a forest must have grown up after the disappearance of the first glacier and before the appearance of the second.

(4) Soils shown in the diagram indicate multiple glaciation in two different ways. In the first place, notice that the soil developed on the gray till is buried by red till. Again, the reasoning applied in numbers 2 and 3 also holds true here. The now-buried soil must have formed in an ice-free interval between two glaciations.

But there is also another convincing argument. Notice that the soil developed on the red till is much thinner than that

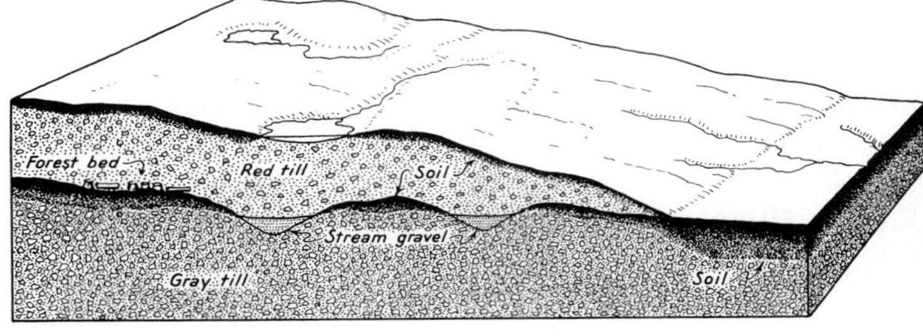

FIG. 13-30
This diagram depicts some of the evidence that points to multiple glaciation. See text for discussion.

developed on the *unburied* gray till. We can say that the thickness of a soil is, in a general way, an index to the length of time it has undergone weathering. Therefore, the unburied gray till must have undergone a longer period of weathering than did the red till. We can explain this difference in weathering periods if the red till is younger and was laid down long after the gray till was deposited. It then follows that there was an older glaciation represented by the deeply weathered till and a younger glaciation represented by the less deeply weathered till.

(5) The topography of the two tills is different, indicating two distinct glaciations. Notice that there are water-filled kettles on the surface of the red till but not on the well-drained gray-till surface. Originally, the gray till was probably marked by kettles just as the red is now. But during the long period of weathering, the kettles were filled, the low hills were worn down, and an efficient drainage system was built up. We can conclude that the gray till arrived long before the ice that deposited the red till, and that a considerable period of time passed between the two glaciers.

Extent of Pleistocene glaciers

During the maximum advance of the glaciers of Wisconsin age (the last of the four great ice advances during the Pleistocene), over 15 million square miles of the earth's surface—nearly 27 per cent of the present land areas—were probably buried by ice. Glaciers covered about 5.7 million square miles of North America, and Greenland was also under a great mass of ice, as it is now. In Europe, an ice sheet spread southward from Scandinavia across the Baltic and into Germany and Poland, and the Alps and the British Isles supported their

FIG. 13-31
The extent of Pleistocene glaciation (white areas) in the Northern Hemisphere. Redrawn from Ernst Antevs, "Maps of the Pleistocene Glaciations," Geol. Soc. Am. Bull., XL (1929), 636.

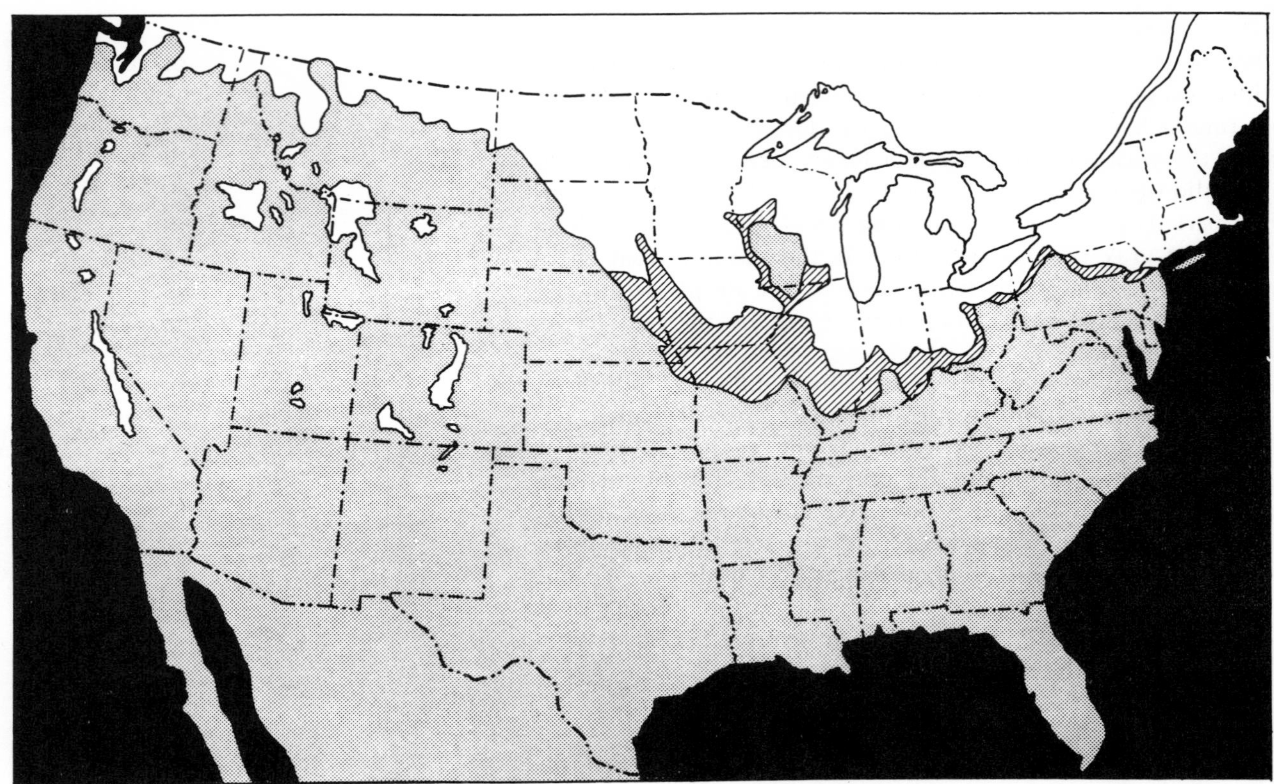

FIG. 13-32
The extent of Pleistocene glaciation in the United States. Unshaded zones indicate area covered at various times during the Wisconsin glaciation. Diagonal lines represent area glaciated during pre-Wisconsin stages but not covered by the later Wisconsin ice. Gray area unglaciated.
Generalized from R. F. Flint, "Glacial Map of North America," Geol. Soc. Am., Special Paper No. 60 (1945).

own icecaps. Eastward in Asia, the northern plains of Russia were covered by glaciers, as were large sections of Siberia and of the Kamchatka Peninsula, and the high plateaus of Central Asia (see Fig. 13-31).

In eastern North America, ice moved southward out of Canada to New Jersey, and in the Midwest it reached as far south as St. Louis. The western mountains were heavily glaciated by small icecaps and valley glaciers. The southernmost glaciation was in the Sierra Blanca of south-central New Mexico. The maximum extent of the Wisconsin glaciation in the United States and the maximum limit of glaciation during the Pleistocene are shown in Fig. 13-32.

Figure 13-32 also shows an area in southwestern Wisconsin and northwestern Illinois, touching upon the Minnesota and Iowa borders—the "Driftless Area" that was surrounded by glacier ice but that was itself unglaciated. Although this country was never completely encircled by ice at any one time, during one glacial stage the ice advanced to one edge of the area, and then withdrew. Then in another glacial stage a second glacier approached from another direction and left its terminal moraine. Eventually, all the country around the Driftless Area had been glaciated at one time or another.

INDIRECT EFFECTS OF GLACIATION

The glaciers that diverted rivers, carved mountains, and covered half a continent with debris also gave rise to a variety of indirect effects that were felt far beyond the glaciers' immediate margins. Not all these effects are completely understood, even today.

Changing sea level

The water that is now locked up in the ice of glaciers originally came from the oceans. It was transferred landward by evaporation and winds, precipitated as snow, and finally converted to firn and ice. If all this ice were suddenly to melt, it would find its way back to the ocean basins and would raise the sea level between 70 and 200 feet, according to different estimates. A rise of this magnitude would transform the outline of the earth's land masses and would submerge towns and cities along the coasts. For the last several thousand years, melting glaciers have been raising the sea level (see Fig. 13-33), and modern records of sea level indicate that the sea is still rising. Along the Atlantic coastline of the United States, the rate of rise prior to the early 1920's was about 3½ inches per century. Thereafter, the rate of rise increased rapidly to about 24 inches per century. This sudden change in rate is coincident with a marked quickening of the retreat of present-day glaciers. It is tempting to see a cause and effect in this coincidence between the increased rate of the rise of sea level and the more rapid melting of glacier ice.

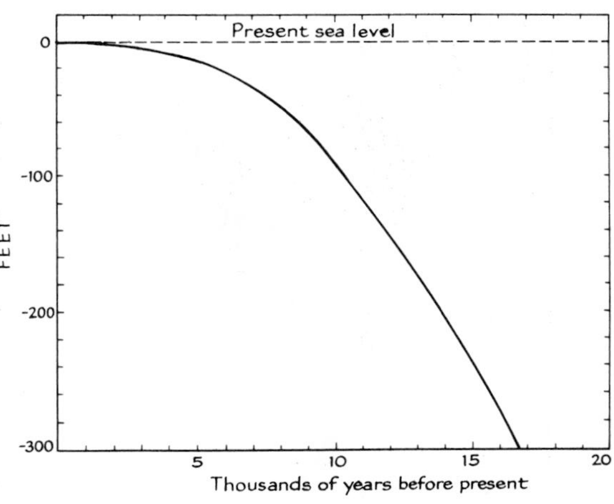

FIG. 13-33
Sea level has been rising for the last several thousand years. Here radiocarbon dates on samples of wood, shell, and peat originally deposited at sea level have been combined with archaeological data to produce this generalized curve of the rise of sea level. Redrawn from F. P. Shepard, Science, CXLIII (1964), 575.

During most of the glacial periods of the past, water impounded on the land in the form of ice was more extensive than it is at present. Consequently, sea level must have been lower than it is now. And during the interglacial periods, when glaciers were even less widespread than they are today, the sea level must have been higher. It is a difficult job to estimate how far the sea level fell during a great glacial advance. To begin with, we have to know the total volume of ice at the height of the advance. To calculate that we must know what part of the earth's area was covered by ice, and what the average thickness of the ice cover was. We can make a fairly good guess of the area that was covered by studying evidence that still exists. But to estimate the average thickness of the ice is extremely difficult. In any event, through a series of carefully controlled approximations, it has been estimated that during the maximum extent of Pleistocene glaciation the sea level was from 350 to 400 feet lower than it is now. Most geologists accept this estimate, although some feel that it is too conservative. During the height of the Wisconsin glaciation, the last of the four major ice advances, sea level is usually estimated as having been between 230 and 330 feet lower than at present.

Pluvial periods

During the Ice Age, when glaciers lay across Canada and northern United States and draped the flanks of most of the higher mountains of the West, the climate of the arid and semiarid areas of the western United States was quite different from what it is today. Glaciations produced *pluvial periods* (from the Latin *pluvia,* "rain") when the climate was undoubtedly not as lush and moist as that of the eastern United States today, but certainly more hospitable than we now find in this region. During any single pluvial period, rainfall was greater, evaporation less, and vegetation more extensive. At this time large sections of the southwestern states were dotted by lakes, known as *pluvial lakes* (Fig. 13-34).

What was responsible for this pluvial climate? The presence of continental glaciers in the north is thought to have modified the general wind circulation of the globe. The belt of

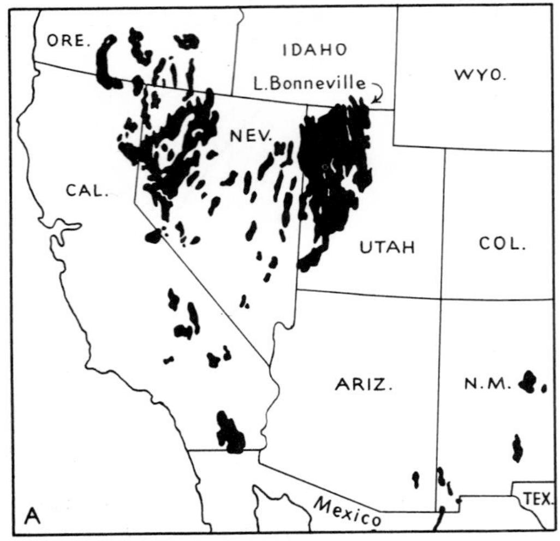

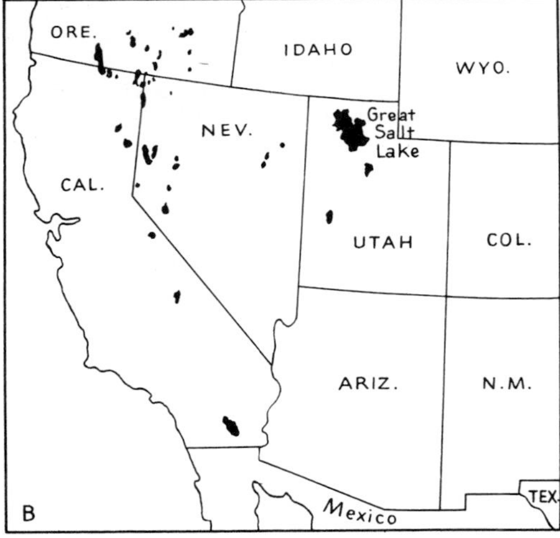

FIG. 13-34
During periods of glaciation, many basins of western United States held permanent lakes where there are only intermittent water bodies today. Modern saltwater lakes are mere remnants of other basins formerly filled with lakes. Relative number and size of modern lakes (B) *are compared with those existing during the glaciation of higher mountains and northern United States* (A). *Redrawn from O. E. Meinzer, "Map of the Pleistocene Lakes of the Basin-and-Range Province and Its Significance," Geol. Soc. Am. Bull., XXXIII (1922), 543, 545.*

rain-bearing winds was moved to the south and the temperatures were lowered. Consequently, the rates of evaporation decreased and at the same time the amount of precipitation increased. When the ice receded, the climate again became very much what it is today.

PRE-PLEISTOCENE GLACIATIONS

So far, we have talked only about the glaciers that exist today, and about those that moved within the past million years of the geologic time scale, the Pleistocene. But the Pleistocene, in which we are still living, is a mere moment in geologic time. Geologists have found evidence that glaciers appeared and disappeared in other periods during the ancient past. The record is fragmentary, as we would expect, for time tends to conceal, destroy, and jumble the effects of glaciation, but it seems certain that there was extensive glaciation during two periods before the Great Ice Age. One of these was near the end of the Paleozoic era, probably in the Permian, 230 million years ago. The other was in the late Precambrian, over 600 million years ago. A third period of widespread glaciation may have occurred in the earliest Paleozoic, almost 600 million years ago.

This glaciation timetable is based on evidence found in rocks that were formed from sediments characteristic of glacier activity. A rock formed from the lithification of till is a tillite. Late Paleozoic tillites have been discovered in Africa, India, South America, and Australia. Lying beneath the tillite in many areas is the striated and polished pavement marking the path of the ancient glaciers.

CAUSES OF GLACIATION

As Louis Agassiz did over a hundred years ago, we can travel about the world today and observe modern glaciers at work, and we can reason convincingly that glaciers were more extensive in the past than they are at present. We can even make out a good case for the belief that glacier ice advanced and receded many times in the immediate and more remote geologic past. But can we explain why glaciation takes place? The answer to that question is a simple "no." Still, we can examine the general problem and take stock of what we do know.

The geologic record has contributed some basic data that any theory of the causes of glaciation must take into account. Among these are the following:

(1) *Periods of extensive glaciation have coincided with periods of high and extensive continents.* During most of geologic time the continents have been lower than they are today, and shallow seas have flooded across their margins. Such conditions were unfavorable for glaciation. But for several million years the continents have been increasing in elevation, until now, in the Pleistocene, they stand on the average an estimated 1,500 feet higher than they did in the mid-Cenozoic. We have already found that the last Great Ice Age came with the Pleistocene. And we know, too, that the other great glaciations coincided with high continents.

(2) *Glaciation is not due to a slow, long-term cooling off of*

the earth. We have already found that extensive glaciation occurred several times during the geologic past. But these glacial periods are unusual, for during most of geologic history the climate has been nonglacial.

(3) *Advance and retreat of glaciers have probably been simultaneous throughout the world.* For instance, dating by means of radioactive carbon has demonstrated that geologically recent fluctuations of the continental glaciers in North America occurred at the same time as similar fluctuations in Europe. Furthermore, observations indicate that the general retreat of glaciers now recorded in North America and Europe is duplicated in South America.

The first of these three points—namely, that glaciation has coincided with high and extensive landmasses—tempts us to assign the cause of glaciation to the periodic growth of continents. Although most investigators do see a cause-and-effect relationship between glaciation and large landmasses, few of them accept this as a completely satisfactory explanation of glaciation. Their reason is very simple. The Pleistocene, as we discovered, was marked by at least four major glacier stages with intervening interglacial stages. If these fluctuations were caused solely by changes in the height and the extent of the landmasses of the world, then we would have to conclude that our continents have been bobbing up and down like corks throughout the Pleistocene. There is absolutely no evidence that this is true. We can say, however, that geologic processes operating slowly through millions of years may increase the size and elevation of the continents to the point at which climatic changes of shorter duration can bring about the glaciations and deglaciations of an ice age.

If this is true, then we must seek, in addition to a geologic cause, a climatic cause for glaciation. Because the immediate cause of glaciation is the persistence of winter snowfall through the summer months, the summers must have grown cooler and cloudier before each ice advance. The winters, on the other hand, may have been no colder than they are at present. In fact, excessive cold restricts snowfall. So for the onset of a glacial stage we need to postulate somewhat cooler and cloudier summers than we have now, and moderate winters.

But what caused the change in climate? Here we have many suggestions but little agreement. Among the reasons proposed for climatic changes are: (1) fluctuations in the amount of heat generated by the sun, (2) variations in the amount of solar energy that gets through the atmosphere to the earth's surface, (3) changes in the relationship of the earth to the sun, and (4) shifts in the patterns of oceanic circulation, which in turn affect the earth's climatic patterns. No single theory or combination of theories is completely satisfactory. In summary, we can say only that the riddle of glaciation is still with us and presents us with a major unsolved problem in geology.

IMPLICATIONS FOR THE FUTURE

If geology teaches us nothing else, it demonstrates that our globe is in constant change—that the face of the earth is

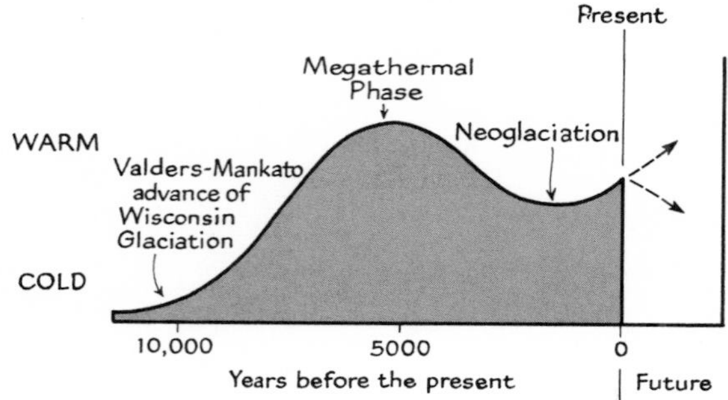

FIG. 13-35
The climate during the last few thousand years has not been constant. Rather, it has been marked by fluctuations, generalized in the graph below. We can assume that the climate of the future will vary from that of the present. On this basis, we are either part way out of one glaciation or part way into another.

mobile. Mountains rise, only to be laid low by erosion; seas lap over the continents; entire regions progress through various stages; and glaciers come and go. We still live in the Pleistocene Ice Age, a pinpoint in time that has been preceded by, and will be followed by, extensive climatic changes.

Since the height of the last glacial invasion of the northern United States some 10,000 years ago, the climate has sometimes been warmer, sometimes colder than that of the present. Thus at one point there was a worldwide rise in temperature that produced a climate warmer than we are used to. This period, known as the *Megathermal* or *Altithermal Phase* (that is, a period of great heat), reached its height about 6,000 years ago. Plants that are now found only in more southerly latitudes began to grow in northern areas, and sea levels around the world rose somewhat. Many small glaciers in our western mountains disappeared completely, the glaciers in the Alps retreated, and the Greenland icecap shrank.

The Megathermal Phase gave way to a period in which the climate grew cold again. Plant life was pushed southward, and extensive areas in the higher latitudes and altitudes were stripped of their forests. Today we are apparently beginning to emerge from the latter phase, which some have called the "Little Ice Age," or "Neoglaciation."

What will happen in the future? We can be sure that the climate will grow either hotter or colder and that glaciers will either recede or advance in the ages ahead, just as they have in the past. But just what the changes will be and when they will occur, we cannot tell with certainty. We can, though, predict what would happen at either of the two extremes: (1) complete deglaciation, and (2) a resurgence of glacier ice on a continental scale.

If modern glaciers continue to waste away until they eventually disappear altogether, our descendants will be confronted with a flooding of the lowlands bordering the modern seas. As we have seen, if all the ice melted, sea level would rise 70 to 200 feet. It is easy to foresee what would happen to our coastal cities. Furthermore, a climatic change that caused a complete deglaciation all over the world would alter the present pattern of our climatic belts. The northern United States would have a less rigorous climate, and there would be a general poleward expansion of the temperate and tropical zones. Such a development might affect the entire fabric of civilization.

If we dislike the thought of advancing seas and poleward shifts of warmer climate, we can contemplate the other alternative—a cooling of the climate, at least during the summer months. This shift would bring about the expansion of present glaciers, the birth of new ones, and a slow drainage of the harbors of the world.

We cannot say which way the world will go. At present, we are either part way out of one glaciation or part way into another. Whatever happens will have a profound effect on man's long-range future.

SUMMARY OUTLINE

Glacier ice
Snow → firn → ice

Types of glaciers
Valley glaciers, piedmont glaciers, ice sheets

Movement of glaciers
Advance when accumulation exceeds wastage
Retreat when wastage exceeds accumulation
Brittle zone of fracture above plastic zone of flow

Glacial erosion
Plucking and abrasion
Striations, polish, and grooves
Cirques and tarns
Horns, arêtes, and cols
U-shaped valleys, hanging valleys, and pater noster lakes
Fiords
Asymmetric rock knobs and hills

Glacial deposition
Till (unstratified drift) forms moraines, drumlins, boulder trains, and erratics
Outwash (stratified drift) is found in outwash plains, eskers, crevasse fillings, kames, and kame terraces

Glacial theory
Venetz, Charpentier, Agassiz
Proof based on "present is key to the past"

Multiple glaciation
Nebraskan, Kansan, Illinoian, Wisconsin

Indirect results of glaciation
Changing sea level
Pluvial periods

Causes of glaciation
Unknown at present
Geologic and climatic data

The future
Change is the forecast

SELECTED REFERENCES

Charlesworth, J. K., *The Quaternary Era* (2 vols.). London: Edward Arnold, 1957.

Flint, Richard Foster, *Glacial and Pleistocene Geology*. New York: John Wiley & Sons, Inc., 1957.

Thwaites, F. T., *Outline of Glacial Geology*. Madison, Wisconsin: Published by the author, 1956.

Zeuner, F. E., *The Pleistocene Period, Its Climate, Chronology, and Faunal Successions*. London: Hutchinson and Co., 1959.

14 Deserts

All living things, including human beings, need moisture to survive. So it is not strange that the dry regions of the earth are sparsely populated, and our knowledge of these regions is scanty at best. Still, deserts and near-deserts cover nearly a third of the land surface of the earth, and we cannot measure their importance solely in terms of population density.

DISTRIBUTION AND CAUSES

Although there is no generally accepted definition of a desert, we can at least say that a desert is characterized by a lack of moisture—leading to, among other things, a restriction of the number of living things that can exist there. There may be too little initial moisture, or the moisture that does occur may be evaporated by extremely high temperatures or locked up in ice by extreme cold. Since we are not concerned here with polar deserts, we shall consider only those in the hotter climates. Their distribution is shown in Fig. 14-1.

The deserts of the middle and low latitudes fall into two general groups. The first are the so-called *topographic deserts,* deficient in rainfall either because they are located toward the center of continents, far from the oceans, or more commonly because they are cut off from rain-bearing winds by high mountains. Takla Makan, north of Tibet and Kashmir in extreme western China, is an example of a desert located deep inside a continental landmass. The desert climate of large sections of Nevada, Utah, Arizona, and Colorado, on the other hand, is caused by the Sierra Nevada of California, which cut off the rain-bearing winds blowing in from the Pacific. A similar, though smaller, desert area in western Argentina has been created by the Andes mountains.

Much more extensive than the topographic deserts are the *tropical deserts,* lying in zones that range between 5 to 30 degrees north and south of the equator. We can best understand their origin by looking at the general circulation of the earth's atmosphere.

Imagine our earth as completely covered by water. In such

a situation we would find that the air moved in the manner depicted in Fig. 14-2. The equator, where the greatest heating by the sun takes place, would be a belt of warm, rising air marked by low pressure. At the poles, lower temperatures would cause the air to settle and create a high-pressure zone. Other high-pressure zones of descending air, the subtropical high-pressure zones (the so-called "horse latitudes"), would lie in belts at about 30 degrees north and south of the equator. And at about 60 degrees north and south would be two more belts of lower atmospheric pressure. At the surface of the earth, air would move away from zones of high pressure toward zones of low pressure. Thus from the equatorward sides of each of the horse-latitude belts, air would move toward the equator. From the poleward sides, wind would blow generally toward low-pressure belts at about 60 degress north and south.

If it were not for the rotation of the earth, these surface winds would blow either directly south or directly north. But the earth's rotation introduces a factor known as the *Coriolis effect,* named after G.G. Coriolis (core-ee-oh′-liss), a nineteenth-century French mathematician who made the first extensive analysis of this phenomenon. The Coriolis effect influences everything that moves across the face of the earth—the atmosphere, ocean currents, birds in flight, aircraft, flowing streams, even an automobile speeding along a straight road.

We shall not analyze the reason for the effect, but the results can be simply stated.

Because of the Coriolis effect, anything moving in the Northern Hemisphere tends to veer to the right. And in the Southern Hemisphere any moving object tends to veer to the left.

Now apply this principle to the movement of air. If we stand at 30 degrees north and face southward, in the direction

FIG. 14-1
Deserts and near-deserts cover nearly one-third of the land surface of the earth. Middle- and low-latitude deserts, but not polar deserts, are shown here.

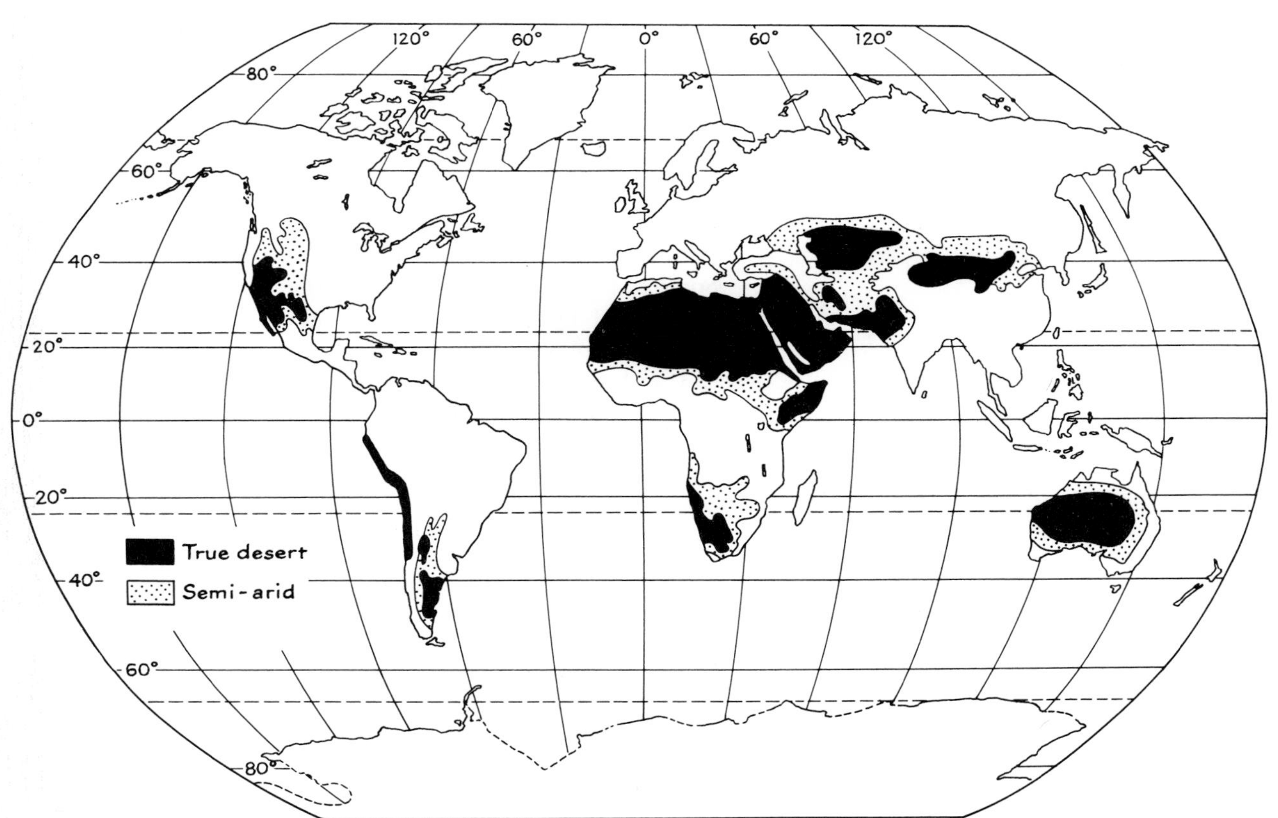

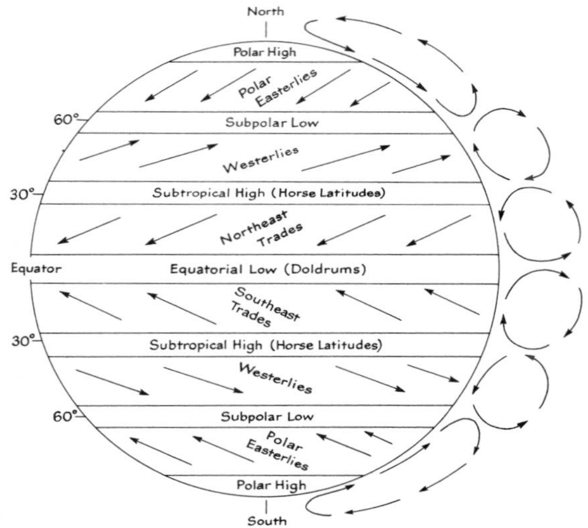

FIG. 14-2
Idealized circulation of air on an earth presumed to have no landmasses. See text for discussion.

toward which the air moves, the Coriolis effect will shift the air movement to our right—that is, to the west. These are the northeast trade winds. Standing at 30 degrees south and facing northward, we find that the winds blowing toward the low pressure near the equator will veer to the left, and are known as the southeast trades. Remember that to apply the Coriolis effect you must face in the direction *toward* which the air moves. In contrast, the wind is named for the direction *from* which it moves.

Now to return to the origin of tropical deserts. At about 30 degrees north and south of the equator, air descends in the subtropical high-pressure zones and spreads laterally across the surface toward both the equator and the poles. Under the influence of the Coriolis effect, the air currents moving toward the poles become the "prevailing westerly winds" of the middle latitudes, and those moving toward the equator become the trade winds of the low latitudes.

Now the warmer the air becomes, the more moisture it can hold, and the less likely it is to release moisture as precipitation. In the subtropical high-pressure belts, the air is heated as it descends over the warm land and tends to retain the moisture it contains. Consequently, the climate in these areas is relatively dry. The air that moves along in the trade winds continues to be heated as it enters warmer and warmer latitudes, and the dry belt is extended toward the equator. Finally, as the air approaches the equator itself, it becomes so heated that it rises to a higher altitude and is rapidly cooled. Then, unable to carry its great quantities of moisture, it releases the torrential rainfalls that are characteristic of the true tropics. This rising air eventually moves poleward, some of it descending again in the horse latitudes to begin its path all over again.

It is this continuing circulation of the air that creates the great deserts on either side of the equator. These include the Sahara Desert of North Africa, the Arabian Desert of the Middle East, the Victoria Desert of Australia, the Kalahari Desert of Bechuanaland in South Africa, the Sonora Desert of northwestern Mexico, southern Arizona, and California, the Atacama Desert of Peru and Chile, and the deserts of Afghanistan, Baluchistan, and northwestern India.

Some of the smaller deserts along the tropical coastlines have been created by the influence of oceanic currents bordering the continents. Winds blow in across the cool water of the ocean and suddenly strike the hot tropical landmass. There the air is heated, and its ability to retain moisture is increased. The resulting lack of precipitation gives rise to desert conditions, as along the coast of southern Peru and northern Chile, where the cool Humboldt Current flows north toward the equator.

CLIMATE

Rainfall

In the well-watered sections of the eastern United States and Canada, and of western Europe, 30 to 60 inches of rain fall annually. But most deserts receive only 10 to 15 inches of rainfall a year, and in some there is less. Over much of the Sahara Desert, for example, as well as over the Kalahari, Sonora, and Atacama deserts, the annual rainfall is usually less than 5 inches. At Lima, Peru, only 2 inches of rain fall during the average year, and Cairo, Egypt, does not receive even that much. Some parched areas often go for years without a single drop of rain. In fact, records at Calama, Chile, show a complete lack of rainfall for a 13-year period. Still there is probably no place in the world, even in the driest deserts, that does not receive some rain, even though years may pass between showers.

Rainfall in the deserts is both scanty and irregular; the scantier it is, the more erratic and unpredictable it is. Statistics on rainfall are therefore of little help in predicting when rain can be expected in a desert. Four years passed without rain in the town of Iquique, Chile, but in the fifth year there was a single rainfall of 0.6 inch. We can say that the five-year average rainfall was 0.12 inch, but the fact remains that the residents of this town enjoyed only one rain in five years.

Temperature

Temperatures in the desert swing from one extreme to the other in just a few hours. The air is heated rapidly during the day and cools rapidly at night, particularly in the tropical deserts. During a single 24-hour period in northern Tripoli, a daytime high of 99°F was followed by a nighttime low of 31°F, a variation of 68°F. The highest temperature in the shade officially recorded in an American desert was 134°F, in Death Valley, California.

In the tropical deserts on either side of the equator, winter and summer are very much alike. "Winter" temperatures are not quite so high as in summer—and the nighttime temperature occasionally drops below freezing—but once the sun begins to shine, the temperature quickly rises to 60°, 70°, or even 80°F. In topographic deserts, farther away from the equator, however, the winters are often very severe. Thus at Urga, Mongolia, the mean temperature in July is 63°F, but in January it falls to −16°F. In fact, the mean temperature there is below freezing during six months of the year.

Winds

To add to the unpleasantness of the desert climate, violent winds often sweep across the parched earth. Unchecked by vegetation, they carry large clouds of dust to great heights above the surface and drive particles of sand along the ground. Locally, the winds are probably helped along by the rapid heating of the air during the day, which causes swift upward movements and reinforces the general movement of the surface winds that account for the deserts themselves.

WEATHERING AND SOILS

Because of the lack of moisture in the desert, the rate of weathering, both chemical and mechanical, is extremely slow. Since most of the weathered material consists of unaltered

FIG. 14-3
Stone-littered surfaces are common in the desert. This is a close-up view of the slopes leading down into Death Valley, California. Photo by Sheldon Judson.

rock and mineral fragments, mechanical weathering probably predominates (see Fig. 14-3).

Some mechanical weathering is simply the result of gravity, as the shattering of rock material when it falls from a cliff. Wind-driven sand also brings about some degree of mechanical weathering. Sudden flooding of a desert by a cloudburst moves material to lower elevations, reducing the size of the rock fragments and scouring the bedrock surface in the process. In almost every desert in the world, temperatures fall low enough to permit frost action. But here again the deficiency of moisture slows the process. Finally, the wide temperature variations characteristic of deserts cause rock materials to expand and contract, and may produce some mechanical weathering.

This low rate of weathering is reflected in the soils of the desert. Seldom do we find extensive areas of residual soil, for the lack of protective vegetation permits the winds and occasional floods to strip away the soil-producing minerals before they can develop into true soils. Even so, soils do sometimes develop in local areas; but they lack the humus of the soils in moister climates, and they contain concentrations of such soluble substances as calcite, gypsum, and even halite because there is not enough water present to carry these minerals away in solution. In the deserts of Australia, rocklike concentrations of calcite, iron oxide, and even silica sometimes form a crust on the surface.

WATER

Although rainfall is extremely sparse in desert areas, there is is still enough water present to act as an important agent of erosion, transportation, and deposition. In fact, water is probably more effective than even the driving winds in molding desert landscape.

Running water

Very few streams flowing through desert regions ever find their way to the sea. And the few that do, such as the Colorado River in the United States and the Nile of Egypt, originate in well-watered areas where they receive enough water to sustain them through their long course across the desert. Most desert stream beds, however, are dry over long periods of time and flow only when an occasional flood comes along. Even then the flow is short-lived, for the water either evaporates rapidly or vanishes into the highly permeable rubble and debris of the desert. In some places, however, such as the western United States, broad desert plains slope down from the mountain ranges toward central basins, called *playas,* where surface runoff collects from time to time. But the *playa lakes* formed in these basins usually dry up in a short time or at best exist as shallow, salty lakes, of which Great Salt Lake is the best-known example.

Although the total rainfall in desert regions is scant and spottily distributed, the runoff from a single desert rain is often catastrophic. The very deficiency of rainfall is the main reason for the great effectiveness of water as a geologic agent in the desert. Since there is not enough water to support a protective cover of vegetation, the runoff from the rare desert rain sweeps unimpeded across the surface. Rapid and intense, the flood waters pick up the loose rubble of a desert slope or channel and carry it along until they either reach a desert basin, evaporate, or sink into the ground. The runoff sometimes concentrates in vertically walled channels in dry regions —the *washes* or *arroyos* of the American Southwest, and the wadies of North Africa and the Near East (Fig. 14-4). In other places, the water floods across the land in great sheets in a complex system of braided channels. In either case the water acts as an effective agent of erosion, transportation, and deposition.

Desert floods, then, are unlike the floods in humid areas. The typical desert flood, like the rain that produces it, is local in extent and of short duration. In moist regions, most floods arise from a general rain falling over a relatively long period of time; consequently, they affect large areas. Because of the widespread vegetative cover, these floods tend to rise and fall slowly. But on the bare ground of the desert, the runoff moves swiftly and floods rise and fall with great rapidity. These "flash" floods give little warning, and the experienced desert traveler has a healthy respect for them. He will never strike camp on a dry stream floor, even though the stream banks offer protection from the wind. He knows that at any moment a surging wall of debris-laden water may sweep down the stream bed, destroying everything in its path.

Rainsplash

Even the individual raindrops falling on a barren surface are remarkably effective agents of erosion, for each drop tends to throw particles of unconsolidated material into the air. Careful measurements have shown that a heavy rainstorm may move as much as 100 tons of material per acre simply by

FIG 14-4
Runoff from the rare desert rains may concentrate in vertically walled wadies or washes like this 80-year-old arroyo in Chaco Canyon, northwestern New Mexico. During the occasional periods of flow, erosion is rapid. Photo by Sheldon Judson.

means of rainsplash. On a level surface the particles are merely moved back and forth, but on an inclined surface they tend to move downslope.

Underground water

Since most underground water is derived from precipitation, it is not surprising that ground-water supplies are very meager and unreliable in desert areas. Even the water that does fall tends to evaporate before it can find its way down to underground reservoirs. If some of the surface water does manage to infiltrate into the zone of aeration, chances are that the capillary action of the rock particles will be strong enough to resist the influence of gravity. Consequently, the water is prevented from sinking down any deeper and is held in the zone of aeration as suspended water. Eventually, unless it is used by desert plants, this water is drawn back to the surface by evaporation and lost to the atmosphere.

And yet deserts are not completely devoid of ground water. Sometimes a relatively abundant supply is delivered by systems leading down from areas of higher rainfall. In the Sahara Desert, for example, the so-called Nubian sandstone brings artesian water to the oases of El Kharga and Dakhla, 650 miles north of where the sandstone cuts beneath the surface in the Sudan. But even a supply of this sort is limited in amount, and dissolved salts sometimes make it undrinkable.

In general, then, the very arid regions of the earth have extremely limited supplies of ground water; and if these areas are to be developed for human habitation, some other source of water will have to be devised. In the semiarid deserts, on the other hand, where the rainfall may reach 10 inches or more per year, ground-water supplies are more dependable. But even here the rate of withdrawal must be carefully balanced against the rate of natural recharge if these supplies are to be used over any prolonged period of time.

WORK OF THE WIND

Although wind is less effective than water as an agent of erosion, it does play an important role in transporting earth materials in arid and semiarid regions—and in more humid areas as well. Moreover, even in parts of the world where the action of the wind is negligible today, we find evidence that it has been more effective at certain times in the past.

Movement of material

Wind velocities increase rapidly with height above the ground surface, just as the velocity of running water increases at levels above the channel floor. Furthermore, like running water, most air moves in turbulent flow. But wind velocities increase at a greater rate than water velocities, and the maximum velocities attained are much higher.

The general movement of wind is forward, across the surface of the land. But within this general movement the air is moving upward, downward, and from side to side. In the zone a few feet above ground surface, the average velocity of upward motion in an air eddy is approximately one-fifth the average forward velocity of the wind. This upward movement greatly affects the wind's ability to transport small particles of earth material, as we shall see.

Right along the surface of the ground there is a thin but definite zone where the air moves very little or not at all. Field and laboratory studies have shown that the depth of this zone depends on the size of the particles that cover the surface. On the average, the depth of this "zone of no movement" is about one-thirtieth the average diameter of the surface grains (see Fig. 14-5). Thus over a surface of evenly distributed pebbles with an average diameter of 30 mm, the zone of no movement would be about 1 mm deep. This fact, too, has a bearing on the wind's ability to transport material.

DUST STORMS AND SANDSTORMS. Material blown along by the wind usually falls into two size groups. The diameter of wind-driven sand grains averages between 0.15 mm and 0.30 mm, with a few grains as fine as 0.06 mm. All particles smaller than 0.06 mm are classified as dust.

In a true *dust storm*, the wind picks up fine particles and sweeps them upward hundreds or even thousands of feet into the air, forming a great cloud that may blot out the sun and darken the sky. In contrast, a *sandstorm* is a low, moving blanket of wind-driven sand with an upper surface 3 feet or less above the ground. Actually, the greatest concentration of moving sand is usually just a few inches above the ground surface, and individual grains seldom rise even as high as 6 feet. Above the blanket of moving sand, the air is quite clear, and a man on the ground appears to be partially submerged, as though he were standing in a shallow pond.

Often, of course, the dust and sand are mixed together in a wind-driven storm. But the wind soon sweeps the finer particles off, and eventually the air above the blanket of moving sand becomes clear.

Apparently, then, the wind handles particles of different size in different ways. A dust-sized grain is swept high into the air, and a sand-sized grain is driven along closer to the ground. The difference arises from the strength of the wind and the terminal velocity of the grain.

We defined the terminal velocity of a grain as the constant rate of fall attained by the grain when the acceleration due to gravity is balanced by the resistance of the fluid—in this case, the air—through which the grain falls (see "Transportation" in Chapter 11). Terminal velocity varies only with the size of a particle when shape and density are constant. As the particle size increases, both the pull of gravity and the air resistance increase too. But the pull of gravity increases at a faster rate than the air resistance: a particle with a diameter of 0.01 mm has a terminal velocity in air of about 0.01 meter per second; a particle with a 0.2-mm diameter has a terminal velocity of about 1 meter per second; and a particle with a diameter of 1 mm has a terminal velocity of about 8 meters per second.

To be carried upward by an eddy of turbulent air, a particle must have a terminal velocity that is less than the upward velocity of the eddy. Close to the ground surface,

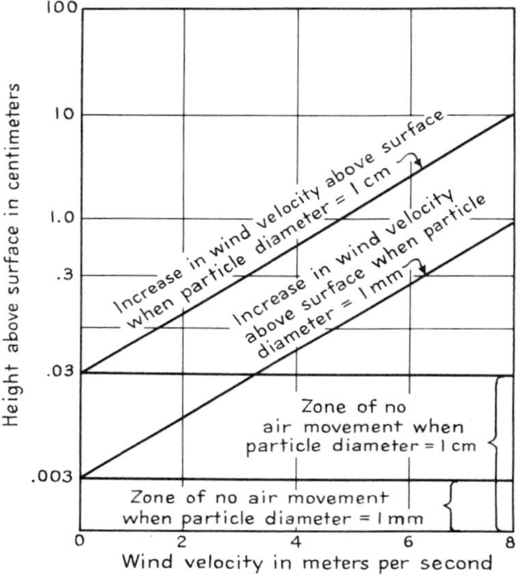

FIG. 14-5
In a thin zone close to the ground there is little or no air movement, regardless of the wind velocity immediately above. This zone is approximately one-thirtieth the average diameter of surface particles. Two zones are shown in the graph: one for surfaces on which the particles average 1 millimeter in diameter, and one for surfaces with 1-centimeter particles. Diagonal lines represent the increase in velocity of a wind of given intensity blowing over surfaces covered with particles of 1 millimeter and 1 centimeter average diameter, respectively. Reproduced by permission from R. A. Bagnold, The Physics of Blown Sand and Desert Dunes, (London: Methuen & Co., Ltd., 1941), p. 54.

where the upward currents are particularly strong, dust particles are swept up into the air and carried in supension. Sand grains, however, have terminal velocities greater than the velocity of the upward moving air; they are lifted for a moment and then fall back to the ground. But how does a sand grain get lifted into the air at all if the eddies of turbulent air are unable to support it?

Movement of sand grains. Careful observations, both in the laboratory and on open deserts, show sand grains moving forward in a series of jumps, in a process known as *saltation.* We used the same term to describe the motion of particles along a stream bed. But there is a difference: an eddy of water can actually lift individual particles into the main current whereas wind by itself cannot pick up sand particles from the ground.

Sand particles are thrown into the air only under the impact of other particles. When the wind reaches a critical velocity, grains of sand begin to roll forward along the surface. Suddenly, one rolling grain collides with another; the impact may either lift the second particle into the air or cause the first to fly up.

Once in the air, the sand grain is subjected to two forces. First, gravity tends to pull it down to earth again, and eventually it succeeds. But even as the grain falls, the horizontal velocity of the wind drives it forward. The resulting course of the sand grain is parabolic from the point where it was first thrown into the air to the point where it finally hits the ground. The angle of impact varies between 10° and 16° (see Fig. 14-7).

When the grain strikes the surface, it may either bounce off a large particle and be driven forward once again by the wind, or it may bury itself in the loose sand, perhaps throwing other grains into the air by its impact.

In any event, it is through the general process of saltation that a sand cloud is kept in motion. Countless grains are thrown into the air by impact and are driven along by the wind until they fall back to the ground. Then they either bounce back into the air again or else pop other grains upward by impact. The initial energy that lifts each grain into the air comes from the impact of another grain, and the wind contributes additional energy to keep it moving. When the wind dies, all the individual particles in the sand cloud settle to earth.

FIG. 14-6
A windstorm moving both sand and dust in central Wisconsin. The poorest visibility is just above the ground surface, where the bulk of the material being moved is sand. Photo by Elliott A. Riggs.

Some sand grains, particularly the large ones, never rise into the air at all, even under the impact of other grains. They simply roll forward along the ground, very much like the rolling and sliding of particles along the bed of a stream of water. It has been estimated that between one-fifth and one-quarter of the material carried along in a sandstorm travels by rolling, the rest by means of saltation.

Notice that once the wind has started the sand grains moving along the surface, initiating saltation, the wind no longer acts to keep them rolling. The cloud of saltating grains obstructs the wind and shields the ground surface from its force; thus, as soon as saltation begins, the velocity of near-surface winds drops rapidly. Saltation continues only because the impact of the grains continues. The stronger the winds blow during saltation, the heavier will be the blanket of sand, and the less the possibility that surface grains will be rolled by the wind.

Movement of dust particles. As we have seen, dust particles are small enough and have low enough terminal velocities to be lifted aloft by currents of turbulent air and to be carried along in suspension. But just how does the wind lift these tiny particles in the first place?

Laboratory experiments show that under ordinary conditions particles smaller than 0.03 mm in diameter cannot be swept up by the wind once they have settled to the ground. In dry country, for example, dust may lie undisturbed on the ground even though a brisk wind is blowing. But if a flock of sheep passes by and kicks loose some of the dust, a dust plume will rise into the air and move along with the wind.

The explanation for this seeming reluctance of dust particles to be disturbed lies in the nature of air movement. The small dust grains lie within the thin zone of negligible air-movement at the surface. They are so small that they do not create local eddies and disturbances in the air, and the wind passes them by. Or the dust particles may be shielded by larger particles against the action of the wind.

Some agent other than the wind must set dust particles in motion and lift them into a zone of turbulent air—perhaps the impact of larger particles, or sudden downdrafts in the air movement. Irregularities in a plowed field or in a recently exposed stream bed may help the wind to begin its work by creating local turbulence at the surface. Also, vertical downdrafts of chilled air during a thunderstorm sometimes strike the ground with velocities of 25 to 50 miles an hour and churn up great swaths of dust.

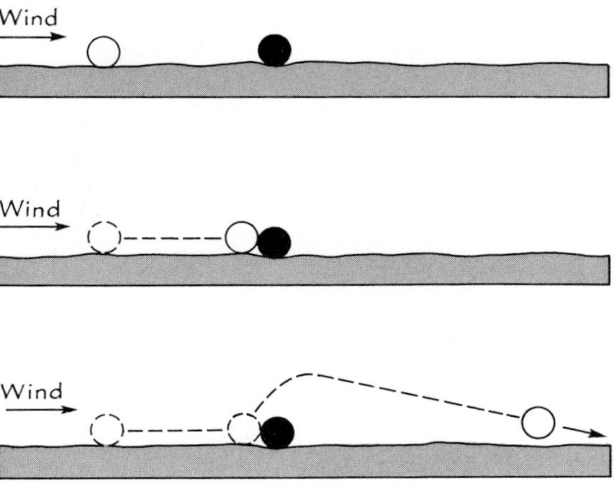

FIG. 14-7
A sand grain is too heavy to be picked up by the wind, but may be put into the air by saltation. Here a single grain is rolled forward by the wind until it bounces off a second grain. Once in the air, it is driven forward by the wind, then pulled to the ground by gravity. It follows a parabolic path, hitting the ground at an angle between 10° and 16°.

Erosion

Erosion by the wind is accomplished through two processes: *abrasion* and *deflation*.

ABRASION. Like the particles carried by a stream of running water, saltating grains of sand driven by the wind are highly effective abrasive agents in eroding rock surfaces. As we have seen, wind-driven sand seldom rises more than 3 feet above the surface of the earth, and measurements show that most of the grains are concentrated in the 18 inches closest to the ground. In this 18-inch layer the abrasive power of the moving grains is concentrated.

Although evidence of abrasion by sand grains is rather meager, there is enough to indicate that this erosive process does take place. For example, we sometimes find fence posts and telephone poles abraded at ground level and bedrock cliffs with a small notch along their base. In desert areas the evidence is more impressive, for here the wind-driven sand has in some places cut troughs or furrows in the softer rocks. The knife-edge ridges between these troughs are called *yardangs,* a term used in the deserts of Chinese Turkestan, where they were first described; the furrows themselves are called

FIG. 14-8
Ventifacts exhibit a variety of facets, pits, ridges, and grooves, as well as surface sheen. Scale is indicated by 2-inch squares. Photo by Walter R. Fleischer.

yardang troughs. The cross profile of one of these troughs is not unlike that of a glaciated mountain valley in miniature, the troughs ranging from a few inches to perhaps 25 feet in depth. They run in the usual direction of the wind, and their deepening by sand abrasion has actually been observed during sandstorms.

The most common products of abrasion are certain pebbles, cobbles, and even boulders that have been eroded in a particular way. These pieces of rock are called *ventifacts,* from the Latin for "wind" and "made." They are found not only on deserts, but also along modern beaches—in fact, wherever the wind blows sand grains against rock surfaces (see Figs. 14-8, 14-9, and 14-10).

The surface of ventifacts is characterized by a relatively high gloss or sheen and by a variety of facets, pits, gouges, and ridges.

The face of an individual ventifact may display only one facet or 20 facets—or more—sometimes flat, but more commonly they are curved. Where two facets meet, they often form a well-defined ridge, and the intersection of three or more facets gives the ventifact the appearance of a small pyramid. Apparently, the surface becomes pitted when it lies across the direction of wind movement at an angle of 55° or more; it becomes grooved when it lies at angles of less than 55°.

FIG. 14-9
A ventifact with 3 well-developed facets, on the floor of the Mojave Desert, California. Pocket knife to right of ventifact gives scale. Photo by Sheldon Judson.

But how is the wind able to cut more than one facet on a rock surface? If the original rock is somewhat angular and properly positioned in the wind's path, it may split the wind, so that two faces are cut simultaneously. Or if the wind changes its characteristic direction of movement, it may cut facets at various angles on the stone. Finally, underlying materials may be scoured away and the rock itself may shift position, or it may be moved by the force of very high winds, by the activities of animals, or by frost action. Whatever the cause, any shift in the position of the rock may expose a new surface to the abrasive action of wind-borne particles. Wind-splitting angles and variable winds probably create the multiple facets on large ventifacts, whereas movement of the rock itself is probably responsible for the variety of faces on ventifacts less than 10 or 12 inches in diameter.

DEFLATION. Deflation (from the Latin "to blow away") is the erosive process of the wind carrying off unconsolidated material. The process creates several recognizable features in the landscape. For example, it often scoops out basins in soft, unconsolidated deposits ranging from a few feet to several miles in diameter. These basins are known as *blowouts,* for obvious reasons (see Fig. 14-11). Even in relatively consolidated material, the wind will excavate sizable basins if some other agency is at work loosening the material. We find such depressions in the almost featureless High Plains of eastern New Mexico and western Texas, where the bedrock is loosely cemented by calcium carbonate. Several times during the Pleistocene, the climate in this area shifted back and forth between moist and dry. During the moist periods, water dissolved some of the calcium carbonate and left the sandstone particles lying on the surface. Then, during the dry periods, the wind came along and removed the loosened material. Today, we find the larger particles piled up in sand hills on the leeward side of the basin excavated by the wind. The smaller dust particles were carried farther along and spread in a blanket across the plains to the east (see Fig. 14-12).

In arid and semiarid country we sometimes see finely honeycombed rocks, and others called *pedestal rocks,* that have been fashioned into weird pillars resembling toadstools. Although wind has often been cited as the cause of these formations, differential weathering is primarily responsible. The wind has merely removed the loose products of weathering.

Deflation removes only the sand and dust particles from a deposit and leaves behind the larger particles of pebble or cobble size. As time passes, these stones form a surface cover, a *desert pavement* that cuts off further deflation.

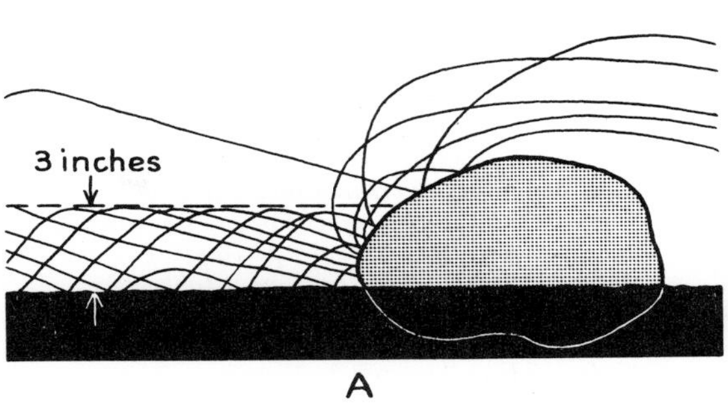

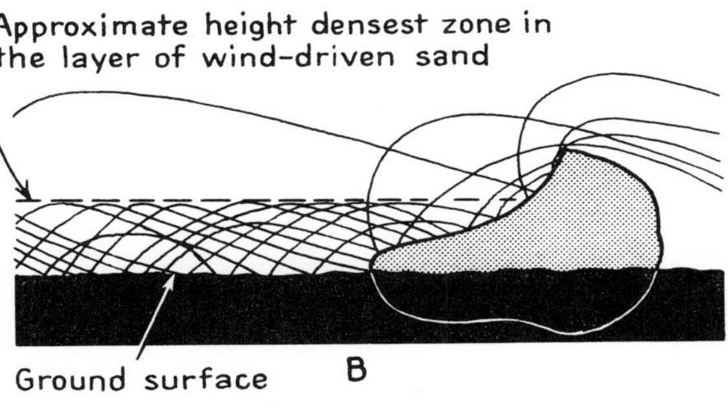

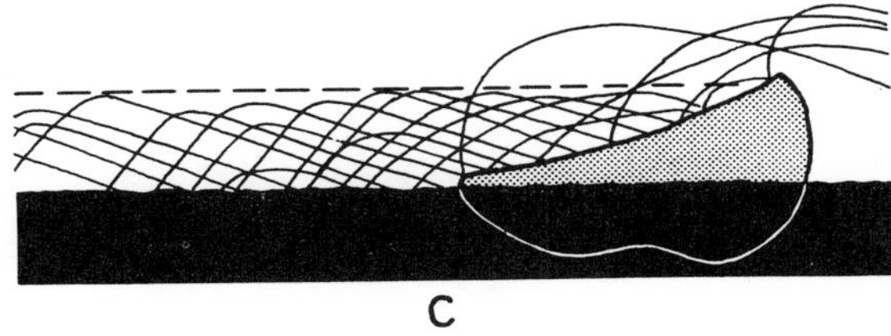

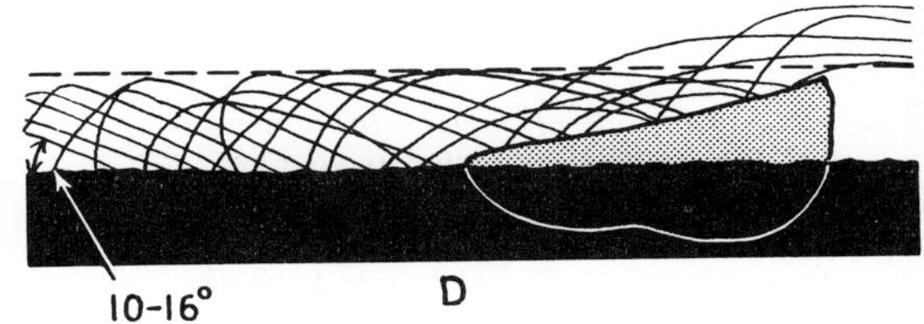

FIG. 14-10
A facet on a ventifact is cut by the impact of grains of wind-driven sand. Redrawn from Robert P. Sharp, "Pleistocene Ventifacts East of the Big Horn Mountains, Wyoming," J. Geol., LVII (1949), 182.

Deposition

Whenever the wind loses its velocity, and hence its ability to transport the sand and dust particles it has picked up from the surface, it drops them back to the ground. The landscape features formed by wind-deposited materials are of various types, depending on the size of particles, the presence or absence of vegetation, the constancy of wind direction, and the amount of material available for movement by the wind. We still have a great deal to learn about this sort of deposit, but there are certain observations and generalizations that seem quite valid.

LOESS. Loess is a buff-colored, unstratified deposit composed of small, angular mineral fragments. Loess deposits range in thickness from a few inches to 30 or more feet in the central United States, to several hundred feet in parts of China. A large part of the surface deposits across some 200,000 square miles of the Mississippi River basin is made up of loess,

FIG. 14-11
Wind has excavated this blowout in unconsolidated sand deposits of Terry Andrae State Park, near Lake Michigan in eastern Wisconsin. Photo by Wisconsin Conservation Department.

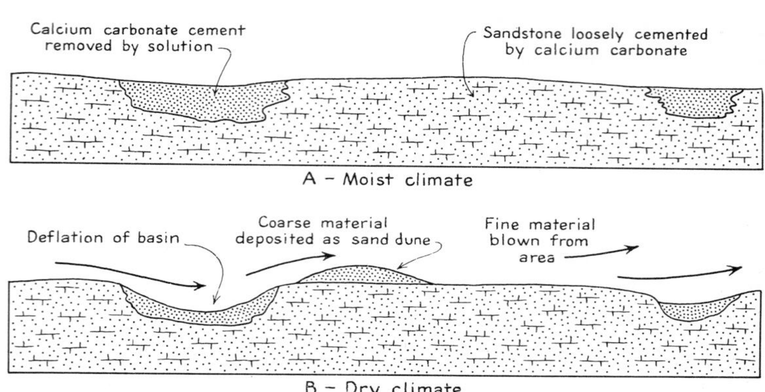

FIG. 14-12
The High Plains of eastern New Mexico and western Texas are pockmarked with broad, shallow depressions fashioned in loosely consolidated sandstone. In this instance, wind deflation has created blowouts, but only after the calcite cement of the sandstone was destroyed by downward-percolating waters. Destruction of the cement took place during moist periods in the Pleistocene, and deflation occurred in intervening dry periods. Redrawn from Sheldon Judson, Geology of the San Jon Site, Eastern New Mexico. Smithsonian Miscellaneous Collections, CXXI, No. 1 (1953), 13.

and this material has produced the modern fertile soils of several midwestern states, particularly Iowa, Illinois, and Missouri (see Fig. 14-13).

Most geologists, though not all, believe loess to be material originally deposited by the wind. They base their conclusion on several facts. The individual particles in a loess deposit are very small, strikingly like the particles of dust carried about by the wind today. Moreover, loess deposits stretch over hill slopes, valleys, and plains alike, an indication that the material has settled from the air. And the shells of air-breathing snails present in loess strongly impugn the possibility that the deposits were laid down by water.

Many exposures in the north-central United States reveal that loess deposits there are intimately associated with till and

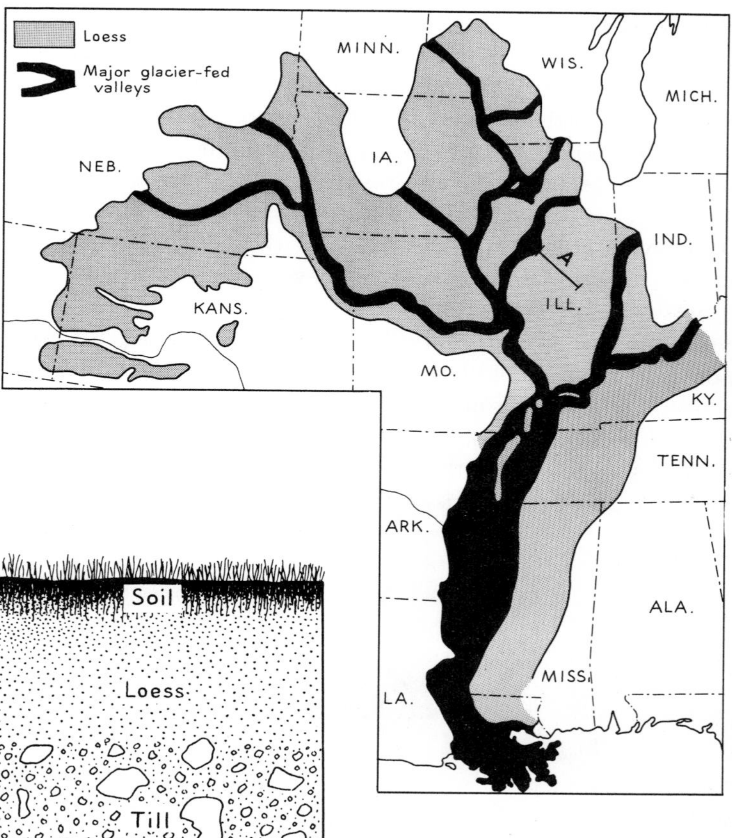

FIG. 14-13
The great bulk of the loess in the central United States is intimately related to the major glacier-fed valleys of the area and was probably derived from the flood plains of these valleys. In Kansas and parts of Nebraska, however, the loess is probably nonglacial in origin and has presumably been derived from local sources and the more arid regions to the west. The line of section marked A in Illinois refers to Fig. 14-15.

FIG. 14-14
In many places, unweathered till is overlain by loess on which a soil zone has developed. The lack of a weathering zone on the till beneath loess often indicates rapid deposition of the loess immediately after the disappearance of the glacier ice and before weathering processes could affect the till. Not until loess deposition has slowed or halted is there time available to allow weathering and organic activity capable of producing a soil.

outwash deposits built up during the Great Ice Age. Since the loess lies directly on top of the glacial deposits in many areas, it seems likely that it was deposited by the wind during periods when glaciation was at its height, rather than during interglacial intervals. Also, since there is no visible zone of weathering on the till and outwash deposits, the loess probably was laid down on the newly formed glacial deposits before any soil could develop on them (see Fig. 14-14).

Certain relationships between the loess deposits in the Midwest and the streams that drain the ancient glacial areas serve to strengthen the conclusion that there is a close connection between glaciation and the deposit of wind-borne materials. Figure 14-15, for example, shows that the major glacial streams cut across the loess belt and that the thickness of the loess decreases toward the east and away from the banks of the streams. Moreover, the mean size of the particles decreases away from the glacial streams. These facts can best be explained as follows. We know that loess is not forming in this area at the present, so we must look for more favorable conditions in the past. During the Great Ice Age of the Pleistocene, the rivers of the Midwest carried large amounts of debris-laden meltwater from the glaciers. Consequently, the flood plains of these rivers built up at a rapid rate and were broader than they are today. During periods of low water, the flood plains were wide expanses of gravel, sand, silt, and clay exposed to strong westerly winds. These winds whipped the dust-sized material from the flood plains, moved it eastward, and laid down the thickest and coarsest of it closest to the rivers.

Some geologists, however, have suggested that loess deposits, particularly those in the lower Mississippi Valley, were not laid down by the wind, but rather have been derived from fine-grained back-swamp deposits through a process called "loessification," the details of which we need not consider here. Suffice it to say that most investigators believe that the loess in the Mississippi Valley was built up by the action of wind blowing across glacial outwash deposits and then scattering the fine particles over the landscape. In fact, much the same explanation is generally accepted for the great belt of loess that extends across France into Germany north of the Alps, on into the Balkan countries, and eastward across the plains of Poland and western Russia.

All loess, however, is not derived from glacial deposits. In one of the earliest studies of loess, it was shown that the Gobi Desert has provided the source material for the vast stretches of yellow loess that blanket much of northern China, and that give the characteristic color to the Yellow River and the Yellow Sea. Much of the land used for cotton growing in the eastern Sudan of Africa is thought to be made up of particles blown from the Sahara Desert to the west. We have already seen that finely divided mineral fragments are swept up in suspension during desert sandstorms and are carried along by the wind far beyond the confines of the desert. Clearly, then, the large amounts of very fine material present in most deserts would make an excellent source of loess.

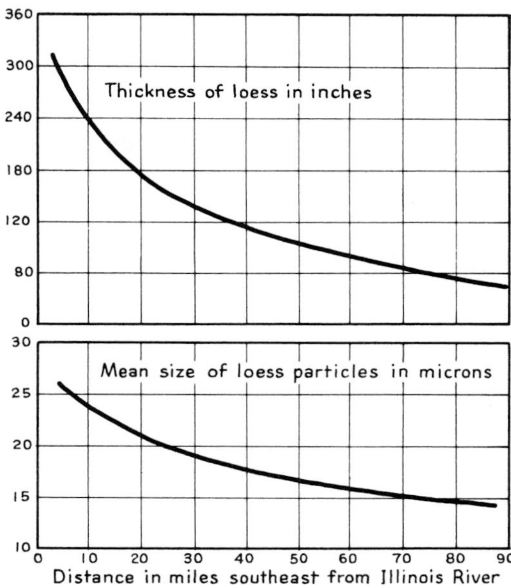

FIG. 14-15
Loess related to the major glacier-fed rivers in the Midwest shows a decrease in thickness away from the rivers and a decrease in the size of individual particles. An example is shown in this diagram, based on data gathered along the line A in Fig. 14-13. Redrawn from G. D. Smith, "Illinois Loess—Variations in Its Properties and Distributions," U. of Ill. Agricultural Experiment Station, Bull. 490 (1942), Figs. 5 and 6.

FIG. 14-16
The shaded area indicates the wind shadow created by an obstacle. The wind is diverted over and around the obstacle. Within the wind shadow, wind velocity is low and air movement is marked by eddies. A surface of discontinuity separates the air within the wind shadow from the air outside. Reproduced by permission from R. A. Bagnold, op. cit., p. 190.

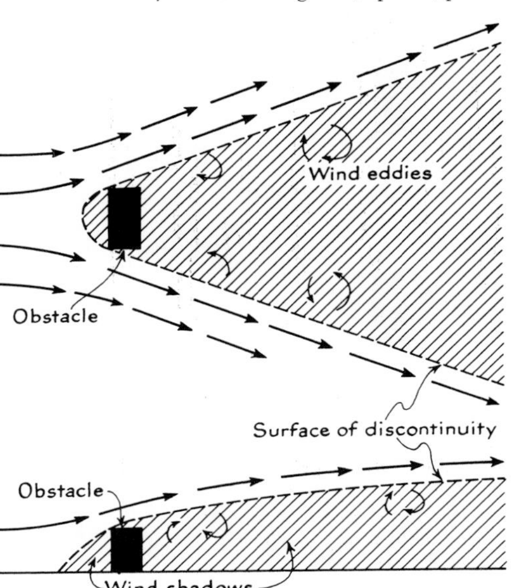

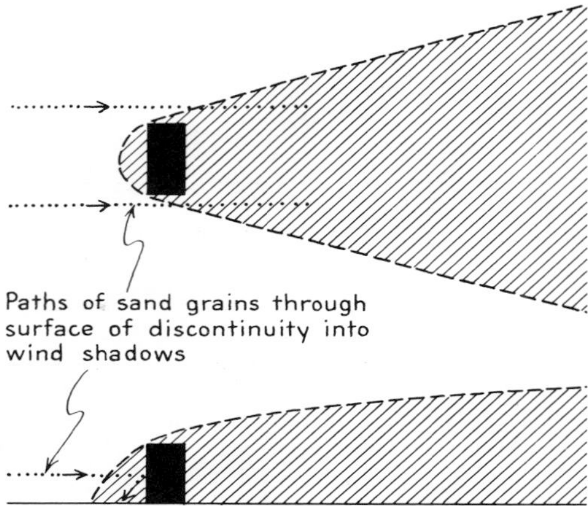

FIG. 14-17
Because of its momentum, the sand in the more rapidly moving air outside the wind shadow either passes through the surface of discontinuity to settle in the wind shadow behind the obstacle or strikes the obstacle and falls in the wind shadow in front of the obstacle. Reproduced by permission from R. A. Bagnold, op. cit., p. 190.

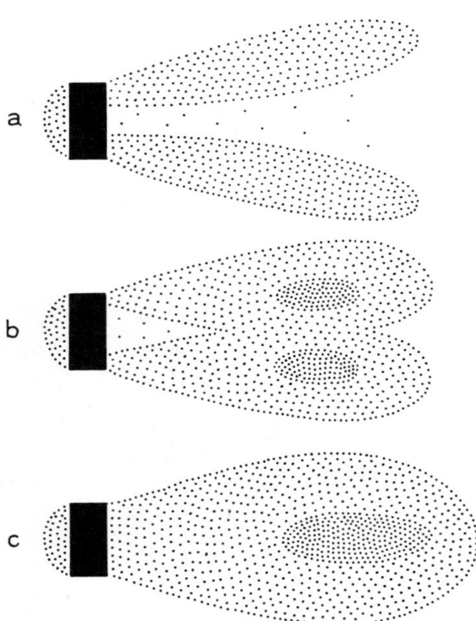

FIG. 14-18
Sand falling in the wind shadow tends to be gathered by wind eddies within the shadow to form a shadow dune, as shown in this sequence of diagrams. Reproduced by permission from R. A. Bagnold, op. cit., p. 190.

Sand deposits. Unlike deposits of loess, which blanket whole areas, sand deposits assume certain characteristic and recognizable shapes. Wind often heaps the sand particles into mounds and ridges called *dunes,* which sometimes move slowly along in the direction of the wind. Some dunes are only a few feet in height, but others reach tremendous sizes. In southern Iran, dunes have grown to 700 feet in height, with a base over 3,000 feet wide.

In Chapter 11 we found that as the velocity of a stream falls, so does the energy available for the transportation of material; consequently, deposition of material takes place. The same relation between decreasing energy and increasing deposition applies to the wind. But in dealing with wind-deposited sand we need to examine the relationship more closely and to explain why sand is deposited in the form of dunes rather than as a regular, continuous blanket.

The wind shadow. Any obstacle—large or small—across the path of the wind will divert moving air and create a "wind shadow" to the leeward, as well as a smaller shadow to the windward immediately in front of the obstacle. Within each wind shadow the air moves in eddies, with an average motion less than that of the wind sweeping by outside. The boundary between the two zones of air moving at different velocities is called the *surface of discontinuity* (see Fig. 14-16).

When sand particles driven along by the wind strike an obstacle, they settle in the wind shadow immediately in front of it. Because the wind velocity (hence energy) is low in this wind shadow, deposition takes place and gradually a small mound of sand builds up. Other particles move past the obstacle and cross through the surface of discontinuity into the leeward wind shadow behind the barrier. Here again the velocities are low, deposition takes place, and a mound of sand (a dune) builds up—a process aided by eddying air that tends to sweep the sand in toward the center of the wind shadow (see Figs. 14-17, 14-18).

Wind shadow of a dune. Actually, a sand dune itself acts as a barrier to the wind; and by disrupting the flow of air, it may cause the continued deposition of sand. A profile through a dune in the direction toward which the wind blows shows a gentle slope facing the wind and a steep slope to the leeward. A wind shadow exists in front of the steep leeward slope, and it is here that deposition is active. The wind drives the sand grains up the gentle windward slope to the dune crest and then drops them into the wind shadow. The steep leeward slope is called the *slip face* of the dune because of the small sand slides that take place there.

The slip face is necessary for the existence of a true wind shadow. Here is how the slip face is formed. A mound of sand affects the flow of air across it, as shown in the topmost diagram of Fig. 14-19. Notice that the wind flows over the mound in streamlined patterns. These lines of flow tend to converge toward the top of the mound and diverge to the leeward. In the zone of diverging air flow, velocities are less than in the zone of converging flow. Consequently, sand tends to be deposited on the leeward slope just over the top of the mound where the velocity begins to slacken. This slope steepens because of deposition, and eventually the sand slumps under the influence of gravity. The slump usually takes place at an angle of about 34° from the horizontal. A slip face is thus produced, steep enough to create a wind shadow in its lee. Within this shadow, sand grains fall like snow through quiet air. Continued deposition and periodic slumping along the slip face account for the slow growth or movement of the dune in the direction toward which the wind blows.

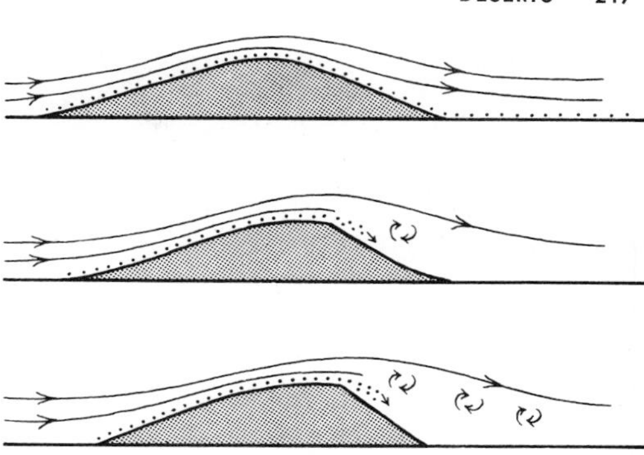

FIG. 14-19
The development of a slip face on a dune. Wind converges on the windward side of the dune and over its crest, and diverges to the lee of the dune. The eventual result is the creation of a wind shadow in the lee of the dune. In this wind shadow, sand falls until a critical angle of slope (about 34°) is reached. Then a small landslide occurs, and the slip face is formed. Reproduced by permission from R. A. Bagnold, op. cit., p. 202.

Shoreline dunes. Not all dunes are found in the deserts. Along the shores of the ocean and of large lakes, ridges of windblown sand called *fore dunes* are built up even in humid climates. They are well developed along the southern and western shores of Lake Michigan, along the Atlantic coast from Massachusetts southward, along the southern coast of California, and at various points along the coasts of Oregon and Washington (see Fig. 14-21).

These fore dunes are fashioned by the influence of strong onshore winds acting on the sand particles of the beach. On most coasts, the vegetation is dense enough to check the inland movement of the dunes, and they are concentrated in a narrow belt that parallels the shoreline. These dunes usually have an irregular surface, sometimes pock-marked by blowouts (see "Deflation," above).

Sometimes, however, in areas where vegetation is scanty, the sand moves inland in a series of ridges at right angles to the wind. These *transverse dunes* exhibit the gentle windward slope and the steep leeward slope characteristic of other dunes. Transverse dunes are also common in arid and semiarid country where sand is abundant and vegetation sparse.

Barchans. Barchans are sand dunes shaped like a crescent, with their horns pointing downwind. They move slowly with the wind, the smaller ones at a rate of about 50 feet a year, the larger ones about 25 feet a year. The maximum height obtained by barchans is about 100 feet, and their maximum spread from horn to horn is about 1,000 feet (see Figs. 14-22, 14-23).

Just what leads to the formation of a barchan is still a matter of dispute. Certain conditions do seem essential, however: a wind that blows from a fixed direction, a relatively flat surface of hard ground, a limited supply of sand, and a lack of vegetation.

Parabolic dunes. Long, scoop-shaped, parabolic dunes look rather like barchans in reverse—that is, their horns point upwind rather than downwind. They are usually covered with sparse vegetation that permits limited movement of the sand. Parabolic dunes are quite common in coastal areas and in various places throughout the southwestern states. Ancient parabolic dunes, no longer active, exist in the upper Mississippi Valley and in Central Europe.

FIG. 14-20
Trees buried by a moving sand dune near the Lake Michigan shore in Porter County, Indiana, have been resurrected as the dune migrates farther inland. Photo by David A. De Vries.

Longitudinal dunes. Longitudinal dunes are long ridges of sand running in the general direction of wind movement. The smaller types are less than 10 feet high and about 200 feet long. In the Libyan Desert, however, they commonly reach a height of 300 feet and may extend for 60 miles across the

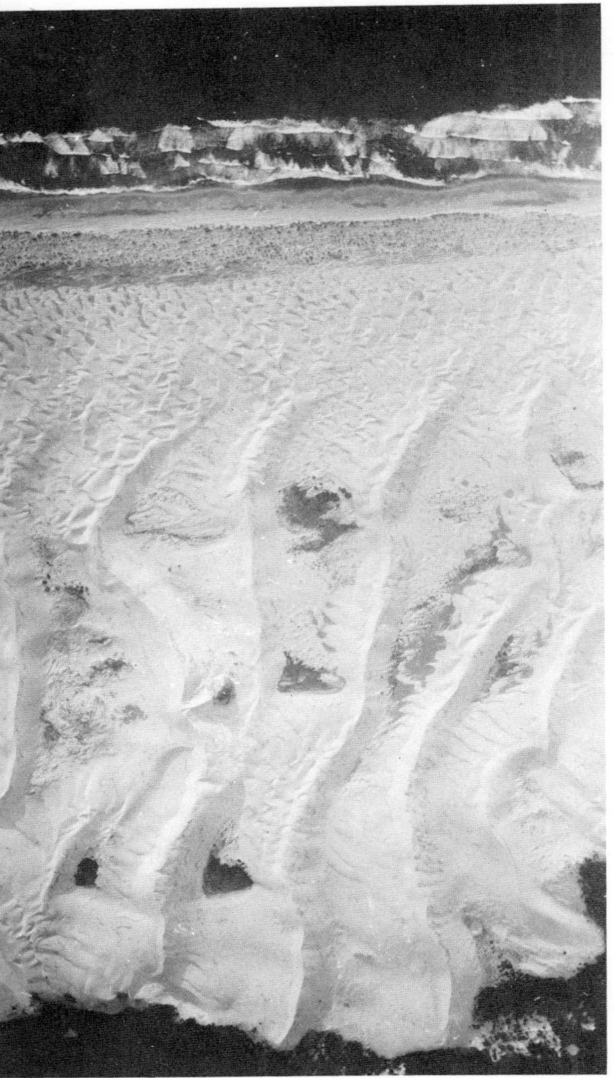

FIG. 14-21
These shoreline dunes form complex patterns behind the beach at Coos Bay, Oregon. The beach serves as a source of sand and this source is continuously renewed by longshore currents of ocean water. Onshore winds (from the left) drive the beach sand inland. Photo shows about 1,500 feet across.

FIG. 14-22
A barchan is a crescent-shaped dune with its horns pointed downwind and its slip face on the inside of the crescent.

country. There they are known as *seif dunes* (rhymes with "strife"), from the Arabic word for "sword."

Stratification in dunes. The layers of sand within a dune are usually inclined. The layers along the slip face have an angle of about 34°, whereas the layers along the windward slope are gentler.

Since the steeper beds along the slip face are analogous to the *foreset beds* in a delta (see Fig. 11-32), we can use the same term in referring to them. These beds develop if there is a continuous deposition of sand on the leeward side of the dune, as in barchans and actively moving transverse dunes.

Backset beds develop on the gentler slope to the windward. These beds constitute a large part of the total volume of a dune, especially if there is enough vegetation to trap most of the sand before it can cross over to the slip face. *Topset beds* are nearly horizontal beds laid down on top of the inclined foreset or backset beds.

DESERT LANDSCAPES

The sparse vegetative cover, the slow rate of weathering, and the skimpy soils of the desert produce a distinctive landscape. The vistas seem infinite, for no trees check the eye as it sweeps on to the distant horizon and up into the cloudless skies. There are occasional mountains and canyons, of course, but most of the country consists of open plains. Scattered over the plains are broad, wind-swept slopes of bare rock or rubble; flat floored, salt-rich playas covered with fine-grained sediments; slowly moving sand dunes; and valleys floored with the deposits of occasional floods or mudflows. The desert plains are sometimes cut by deep, steep-walled canyons, such as the canyon of the Colorado and its tributaries. And here and there ranges of rock mountains rise abruptly from the plains, bordered by the slopes of alluvial fans leading down from the mountain gorges. Often a series of individual fans coalesce to form a ramplike apron of rubbly debris along the mountain front.

In the desert, the nature of the bedrock has a much more striking effect on the appearance of the landscape than it does in humid areas. Where there is plenty of moisture, the lush vegetation, well-developed soils, and unconsolidated debris cloak the slopes and obscure irregularities in the solid bedrock. Graceful curves lead from the hill crest down to valley floors. But in the desert the structure of the earth's crust is far more apparent, and the landscape gives a more faithful reflection of the unadorned bedrock (see Fig. 14-25).

The arid cycle of erosion

In discussing the cycle of erosion back in Chapter 11, we chose our examples largely from humid climates. But in a broad sense the concept is valid in arid regions as well, for the desert landscape goes through an erosional sequence.

PEDIMENTS. We found that in a humid climate the end product of erosion is thought to be a gently rolling plain called a peneplain. In dealing with the arid and semiarid climates we are concerned with a somewhat different erosional form, the pediment. As soon as land is upraised, as in a mountain range or a high plateau, erosion begins to work. The steep faces of the upraised block are worn backward, and slopes are carved on the bedrock. These slopes are thinly veneered with gravel, and they grade downward toward desert streams or basins. These are the surfaces of erosion that we refer to as *pediments,* because in cross section they resemble the triangular unit at the front of Greek temples (Fig. 14-26).

The precise manner in which pediments form is still not clear. We can say, however, that a steep cliff is eroded backward at a constant angle. Important in the process are mechanical weathering, slope wash, and rill wash. Intermittent streams may erode the front locally as they swing first to one side and then to the other after issuing forth from the highlands behind the cliff. In any event, the eroded material is carried down over the ever widening pediment. With time, the mountain mass is destroyed or reduced to a low dome with perhaps a few projections of resistant rock rising from its surface.

During this process, there is a sequence of landforms. But the sequence differs somewhat from that in a humid climate. First, the pediment is present from the very beginning of the arid cycle, whereas the peneplain does not appear until old age in a humid climate. Desert areas progress through a series of stages as the cliff at the head of the pediment retreats at the expense of the landmass behind it. As the desert area becomes older, the pediments become more and more extensive in area, and the plateau or mountain zones more and more restricted. The slope of the scarp at the head of the pediment and even the pediment itself do not become appreciably gentler from the beginning of the cycle to the end. This is in contrast to the slopes that develop in more humid climates, for these slopes appear to become less steep with the passage of time (Fig. 14-27).

Another difference between the cycle of erosion in an arid climate and that in a humid climate is brought about by the presence of broad desert basins that have no outlet to the sea. These basins were created by earth movements that dropped local land areas downward relative to adjacent mountain masses, as in large sections of southwestern United States. The earth movements are *not* caused by the climate, but the basins do persist because there is insufficient rainfall to establish stream valleys leading to the sea. Consequently, the landscape is leveled by a combination of erosion and deposition. The mountains are attacked by expanding pediments that grade into the basins. But the products of erosion cannot be removed from the basins except by wind. As fine sediments are deposited in the basins, therefore, they bury the lower slopes of the pediments (Fig. 14-28). Eventually the basins are filled, and the upper portions of the pediments extend toward the divides, where a few small knobs or peaks mark the last vestiges of the mountains.

We must not infer that all arid lands are composed of mountains and intervening basins, however. In many deserts,

FIG. 14-23
These barchans are moving across the Pampa de Islay, Peru, in the direction in which their horns point. Photo by Aerial Explorations, Inc.

FIG. 14-24
Wind was an active agent in the geologic past, and some sandstone has been formed by the lithification of dune deposits. Note the inclined bedding in this cliff of ancient wind-blown sand in Zion Canyon, Utah. Photo by Raymond C. Murray.

FIG. 14-25
In the desert, as here in the Grand Canyon of the Colorado in Arizona, the structure of the earth's crust is unobscured by soils and vegetation. Photo by U.S. Geol. Survey.

drainage does reach the sea through continuous valley systems. And here pediments develop along the streams and move back into the landmass as the valley walls retreat.

SUMMARY OUTLINE

Deserts
  Cover one-third of earth's surface
Moisture deficiency
  Topographic position behind mountains or in interior of continents
  Relation to planetary wind circulation

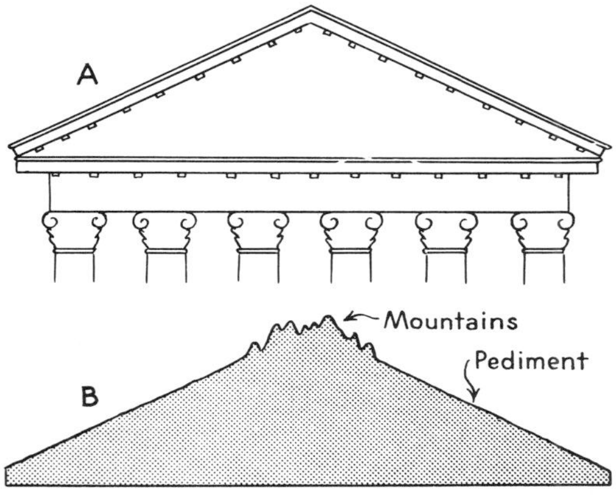

FIG. 14-26
Erosion carves a form similar in cross section to the pediment of a Greek temple, the triangular gable above the columns.

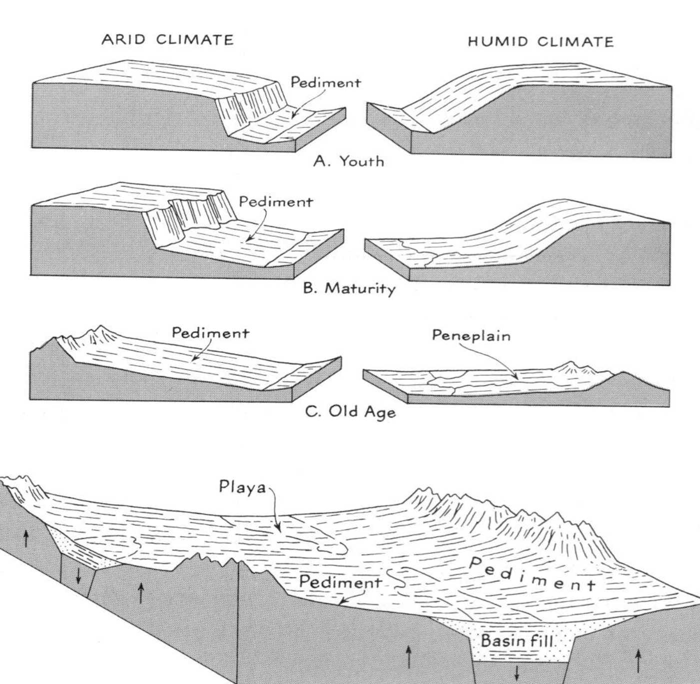

FIG. 14-27
Suggested comparison between the sequence of erosional stages in an arid climate and those in a humid climate. See text for discussion.

FIG. 14-28
In large sections of southwestern United States tectonic movements have produced great basins flanked by mountain ranges. Erosion has fashioned pediments around the flanks of the upthrown mountain blocks, and the products of this erosion have been dumped in the intervening basins. Intermittent lakes, or playas, often occupy the bottoms of these basins.

FIG. 14-29
South of Phoenix, Arizona, these desert mountains are girdled by the sloping surfaces of stream-eroded pediments. Photo by William C. Bradley.

Rainfall
- 10 to 15 inches per year or less
- Unpredictable

Temperatures
- Great daily fluctuation
- Annual temperature either hot or cold

Weathering
- Mechanical weathering predominates

Running water
- Usually intermittent
- Most important agent in desert erosion and transportation

Underground water
- Small, unreliable supplies

Wind motion
- Largely turbulent

Dust storms and *sandstorms*

Sand grains
- Moved by saltation and rolling

Dust grains
- Moved in suspension by turbulent air

Erosion
- Abrasion—ventifacts and yardangs
- Deflation—blowouts

Dust deposition
- Produces loess
- Loess related to deserts and to glacial outwash

Sand deposition
- Dunes
- Wind shadow—deposition of sand
- Slip face located on lee of dune, in zone of most active deposition

Dune types
- Fore dunes, transverse, barchan, parabolic, longitudinal

Arid cycle of erosion
- Progressive development of landforms
- Pediment, the erosional landform in an arid climate, counterpart of the peneplain in a humid climate

SELECTED REFERENCES

Bagnold, R. A., *The Physics of Blown Sand and Desert Dunes.* London: Methuen & Co., Ltd., 1941.

Blackwelder, Eliot, "Geomorphic Processes in the Desert," *Calif. Div. Mines Bull.* 170, Chap. 5 (1954), 11–20.

Bryan, Kirk, *Erosion and Sedimentation in the Papago Country, Arizona.* Washington, D.C.: U.S. Geol. Survey Bull. 730, 1922.

Gautier, E. F., *Sahara, The Great Desert,* trans. D. F. Mayhew. New York: Columbia Univ. Press, 1935.

Sharp, R. P., "Pleistocene Ventifacts East of the Big Horn Mountains, Wyoming," *J. Geol.,* LVII (1949), 175–95.

15

Oceans and shorelines

More than 70 per cent of the surface of the earth lies deep in mystery beneath the oceans, essentially unknown and unexplored, although they are of the utmost importance to the geologist. It was in the oceans of the past that most of the sedimentary rocks were formed—rocks that today cover three-quarters of the continental land masses—and the great ocean basins seem clearly linked to the origin of the continents.

We are only beginning to piece together the complex picture of the ocean floors—their topography, composition, and history, and the nature of the chemical and physical processes that operate across them. In this chapter we shall trace in briefest outline some of the facts that have been assembled and some of the problems that have arisen concerning the oceans and the ocean basins.

OCEAN WATER

The Northern Hemisphere is sometimes referred to as the "land hemisphere," because north of the equator the oceans and seas cover only about 60 per cent of the earth's surface, whereas in the Southern Hemisphere over 80 per cent is flooded by marine waters. Between 45°N. and 70°N., the ocean occupies only 38 per cent of the surface; in contrast, 98 per cent of the earth's surface is covered by the ocean between 35°S. and 65°S.

The greatest ocean depth so far recorded, at a spot in the Pacific Ocean midway between the islands of Guam and Yap, is 35,640 feet—6¾ miles—considerably greater than the height of Mt. Everest, the world's highest mountain, slightly more than 29,000 feet above sea level. The average ocean depth is about 12,400 feet; the mean elevation of the continents is only 2,700 feet (see Fig. 15-2).

It has been estimated that the globe would be covered with a layer of water about a mile and a half or two miles thick if all the irregularities of the surface were eliminated. Such a situation has probably never existed in the past, nor need we worry about its occurring in the future. Modern oceans are confined to great basins and, presumably, so were the oceans of the past. We shall discuss the characteristics of these basins in some detail later in the chapter.

The nature of sea water

About half of the known elements have been identified in sea water, and many others undoubtedly await discovery. Included among the materials known to be dissolved in the sea are the chlorides that give sea water its familiar saltiness, all the gases found in the atmosphere, and a large number of less abundant materials, including such rare elements as uranium, gold, and silver.

SALTS DISSOLVED IN SEA WATER. Through millions of years of geologic time, the rivers of the world have been slowly transporting tremendous quantities of dissolved material to the oceans. Some of this material, such as iron, silicon, and calcium, is used by plants and animals in their life processes and is in effect removed from the water. As a result, the amount of these elements present in solution is less than we would expect to find, judging from the rate at which rivers are currently supplying them to the oceans. On the other hand, we find a relatively high percentage of the "salt" ions, notably Cl^-, even though rivers are presently supplying these materials at a relatively low rate. Salt ions have continued to collect in the sea water because plants and animals do not concentrate them and because they are extremely soluble.

Since the proportions of the various salt ions are relatively constant throughout the oceans, a measurement of any one of them enables us to compute the abundance of the others. The total concentration of salt ions—that is, the salinity of the sea water—varies from place to place, however. At the equator, heavy precipitation dilutes the sea water, reducing its salinity. But in the subtropical belts to the north and south, low rainfall and high evaporation tend to increase salinity, as indicated in Fig. 15-3. In the arctic and antarctic areas, the melting of glacier ice serves to reduce the saltiness of the seas.

GASES DISSOLVED IN SEA WATER. Although all the gases found in the atmosphere are also present in water, probably the most important are oxygen and carbon dioxide. Near the surface of the oceans the water is saturated with both gases, but their concentration and relative proportions vary with depth. As the surface water circulates downward through the first few scores of feet, intense plant activity depletes the supply of carbon dioxide. At the same time, oxygen is given off by the plants. Consequently, this near-surface zone is deficient in carbon dioxide and tends to be oversaturated with oxygen.

Below the depth to which light can penetrate effectively, however, plant activity falls off and the amount of oxygen in solution decreases. Of the oxygen present, some is used by animals and some becomes involved in the oxidation of organic matter settling toward the bottom. At the same time, the relative amount of carbon dioxide increases, because there is no plant activity to deplete it. Thus with increasing

Land Hemisphere

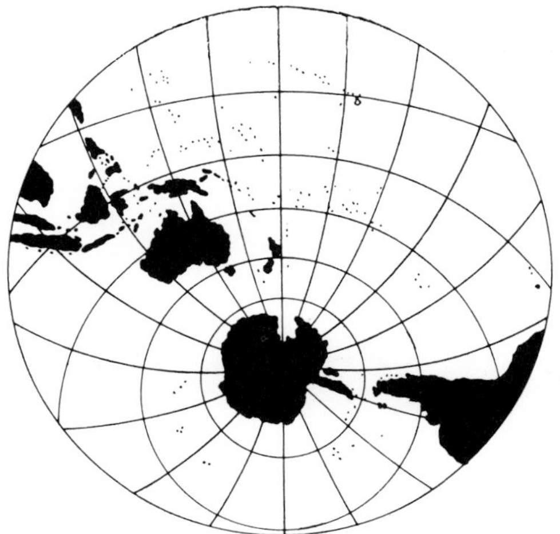

Water Hemisphere

FIG. 15-1
On the land hemisphere map, centered on western Europe, land and sea are about evenly divided. But an indisputable predominance of the seas is revealed on the water hemisphere map, centered on New Zealand.

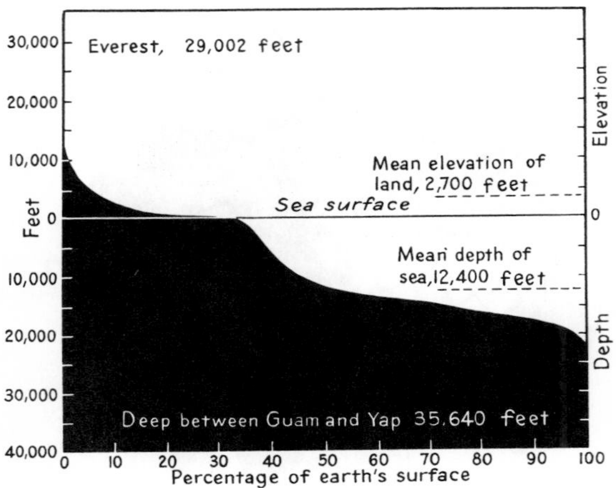

FIG. 15-2
The relative distribution of land and sea. Note that the mean ocean depth is 12,400 feet, whereas the mean elevation of the land is only 2,700 feet. Modified from H. U. Sverdrup and others, The Oceans (Englewood Cliffs, N.J.: Prentice-Hall, Inc., 1942), p. 19.

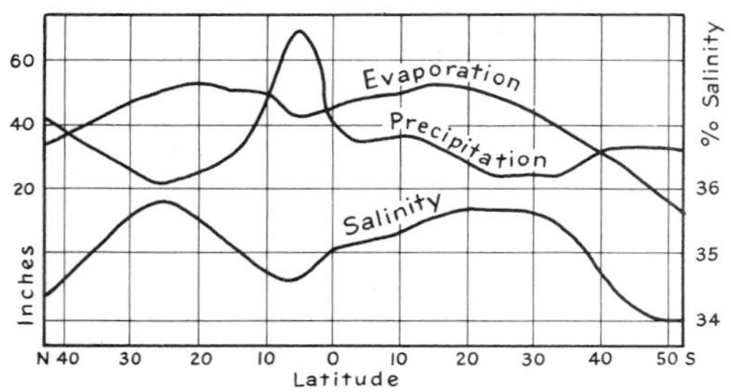

FIG. 15-3
Total salinity varies in the oceans from south to north across the equator. The low salinity of surface waters in the vicinity of the equator is attributed to the freshening effect of heavy tropical rains. North and south of this zone the rainfall decreases, and evaporation increases; as a result, the total salinity of the surface waters increases. Redrawn from R. H. Fleming and Roger Revelle, "Physical Processes in the Oceans," in Trask, Recent Marine Sediments—A Symposium (Tulsa: Am. Assoc. Petroleum Geol., 1939), p. 88.

depth, oxygen becomes relatively less abundant and carbon dioxide relatively more abundant.

Were it not for the slow circulation of sea water through the ocean basins, water at the greatest depths would be devoid of oxygen. Actually, at the bottom of some ocean basins, circulation of water is so slow that almost no oxygen is present, and the water has become stagnant. Here are high concentrations of hydrogen sulfide. This is true, for example, in the Black Sea below a depth of 450-500 feet, and in many of the Norwegian fiords whose glacially-deepened basins lie below the general level of the adjacent floor of the North Atlantic. Because of the almost complete absence of oxygen at the bottom of these basins, sediments lying there oxidize very slowly, if at all. Consequently, a high content of organic matter and the hydrogen sulfide compounds that are produced give them their characteristic black color. It is probable that petroleum was formed in some environment such as this in the ancient seas.

Movement of sea water

The movement of sea water is of two general types: (1) the movement of the average level of the surface either up or down relative to the land—called *changes of sea level,* and (2) the transfer of water from one place to another in ocean basins by movements generally referred to as *currents.*

Changes of sea level

The level of the sea in relation to dry land is constantly changing. The daily changes caused by tides are familiar enough; but much slower fluctuations are no less real or important; in fact, in the geologic past such changes have been very extensive and significant.

EUSTATIC AND TECTONIC CHANGES OF SEA LEVEL. It is easy enough to measure the daily changes in sea level caused by the rise and fall of tides along the coastline. But there are other movements so slow that they are revealed only by long-continued records of sea level, or so local and rare that they are not generally recognized.

A change in sea level relative to land can be caused by the upward or downward movement of either the ocean or the land, or by their combined movement. If the movement is confined to the ocean, change of level is *eustatic,* a term that refers to the static condition or continuing stability of the landmass. When the relative sea level changes because of land movement, the change is *tectonic* (from the Greek for "builder" or "architect"), reference to the movements that shape the earth's surface (see Chapter 16).

Often it is difficult, if not impossible, to distinguish between eustatic and tectonic movements of sea level by observing only a small section of the shore. Eustatic changes of level, however, are worldwide; and when recording stations over an extensive area report a long-continued movement of the sea, the movement can safely be termed eustatic. In contrast, tectonic movements tend to be local and spasmodic, controlled as they are by the forces that crumple and distort solid earth materials.

Eustatic movements may be caused in various ways. If the amount of water locked up in glaciers and lakes increases, the sea level falls; then, if the glaciers melt or if the lakes are drained, the sea level rises. Or sea level may rise or fall as a result of changes in the size of ocean basins, either because of continuing deposition of sediments on their floors or because of actual deformation by earth forces. Still another cause of eustatic change lies in the addition or removal of water from the earth's surface. Volcanoes are constantly adding new water to our atmosphere that eventually finds it way to the sea. And water is constantly being trapped in sedimentary deposits and incorporated in such minerals as clay, causing at least a temporary loss to the oceans.

Tectonic and eustatic changes are continuously taking place around the globe; mean sea level is endlessly rising and falling. Although recent changes in sea level are slight, we have ample evidence that they are actually occurring.

Recent changes in sea level. On the basis of tidal measurements made at various points around the world, observers have concluded that a eustatic rise in sea level is taking place at the present time. The flooding of many river mouths from New England southward indicates that the rise has a long history, substantiated by the discovery of submerged stumps of ancient trees and primitive artifacts. The invasion of the sea is attributed to the melting of mountain glaciers and to the depletion of the Greenland and Antarctic icecaps. But there is still enough water stored in modern glaciers to raise the sea another 70 to 200 feet if it were all to melt, as it probably will in time (see "Indirect effects of glaciation" in Chapter 13).

Modern changes in sea level caused by tectonic movements have been observed in localities where the crust of the earth is known to be undergoing deformation at the present day. A striking example of movement of this sort in Japan is described in Chapter 19.

TABLE 15-1

The major constituents dissolved in sea water

ION		PERCENTAGE OF ALL DISSOLVED MATERIAL
Chlorine	Cl^-	55.04
Sodium	Na^+	30.61
Sulfate	SO_4^{2-}	7.68
Magnesium	Mg^{2+}	3.69
Calcium	Ca^{2+}	1.16
Potassium	K^+	1.10
Bicarbonate	HCO_3^-	.41
		99.69

From H. U. Sverdrup, Martin W. Johnson, and Richard H. Fleming. *The Oceans* (Englewood Cliffs, N. J.: Prentice-Hall, Inc., 1942), p. 166.

FIG. 15-4
In the recent geologic past, ocean waves beveled this platform across tilted rocks on the California coast south of San Francisco. Today the platform stands slightly above sea level as evidence of a change in level between land and sea. In this instance, geologists believe that the motion has been tectonic and that the land has moved upward relative to the sea. Photo by William C. Bradley.

Changes of sea level in the geologic past. Recent changes in sea level seem quite insignificant, however, compared to those of the geologic past. Yet, the rate of sea-level change may never have been much more rapid than it is today; for when it is projected back over vast stretches of geological time, today's rate readily explains the presence of sea shells in lofty mountains and of shoreline terraces now submerged beneath the sea.

As we have seen, sedimentary rocks constitute some 75 per cent of all the rocks exposed at the earth's surface. Of these, the great majority are marine rocks formed from sediments laid down on the floors of ancient seas and now stranded above sea level. For over a century and a half, geologists the world over have studied the details recorded in these marine sedimentary rocks and have pieced together at least a part of the complex story of the advances and retreats of the ancient seas. The sequence of these events is a part of the story of historical geology. Suffice it to say here that the shape of the continents has been changing constantly through geologic time as the oceans spilled out of their basins, flooded slowly across the lands, and then withdrew—a process that has been repeated many times.

Many of the modern coastal lands are marked by terraces arranged like great steps in a giant stairway. Each terrace indicates that the sea stood at this general level long enough to create, by erosion and deposition, a relatively smooth surface sloping gently seaward. Their position today above sea level indicates that the sea has retreated because of eustatic or tectonic movements, or both.

Continental glaciation has caused one type of earth movement leading to shoreline changes. The weight of a continental glacier is great enough to cause a downward warping of the land it covers. When the glacier melts and the load of ice is removed, the land slowly recovers and achieves its original balance once again (see Fig. 15-5).

We have good evidence of the recoil of land following glacial retreat along the shores of the Gulf of Bothnia and the Baltic Sea. Accurate measurements show that from 1800 to

FIG. 15-5
Torghatten Island off the coast of Norway testifies to a 400-foot drop in sea level, the distance from the dotted line to the surface of the present-day ocean. Note the benches that were cut at the time of higher sea level. A tunnel was cut by wave action when the sea stood at the higher level. Here the earth's crust has moved upward after being warped down by the weight of the now vanished Scandinavian ice sheet. Photo by C. A. Ericksen.

1918, the land rose at rates ranging from 0.0 inch per year at the southern end to 0.44 inch per year at the northern end. Studies indicate further that the land has been rising at a comparable rate for 5,000 years. Areas that were obviously sea beaches until recent times are now elevated from a few feet to more than 800 feet above sea level. A comparison of precise measurements along railroads and highways in Finland made from 1892 to 1908, with measurements made from 1935 to 1950, shows that uplift there has proceeded at the rate of from one to three feet per century. The greatest change has been on the Gulf of Bothnia, at about 64°N. Most of this movement has been caused by the recoil of the land following the retreat of the Scandinavian icecap.

Similar histories of warping and recoil have been established in other regions, including the Great Lakes area in the United States. At one stage in the final retreat of the North American ice sheet, the present lakes Superior, Michigan, and Huron had higher water levels than they do now and were joined together to form Lake Algonquin. Beaches around the borders of Lake Algonquin were horizontal at the time of their formation; today they are still horizontal south of Green Bay, Wisconsin, and Manistee, Michigan. But 180 miles north, at Sault Sainte Marie, Michigan, the oldest Algonquin beach is 360 feet higher than it is at Manistee.

Another example of land that has risen hundreds of feet following the retreat of a glacier is found in raised beaches along the Atlantic coast and in the effects left by an arm of the sea that penetrated beyond Montreal and Ottawa. Geologists predict that the ocean will be completely driven from 500-foot-deep Hudson Bay by the time the landmass has recovered from the depression it was subjected to during the Great Ice Age.

It is obviously a more difficult task to establish that sea levels were once lower than at present, since the evidence lies deep beneath the modern seas. But recent investigations of the sea bottom have revealed hints that the sea level has not always been as high as it is at present. These features include flat-topped submarine mountains, great submarine valleys and submerged terraces.

FIG. 15-6
Twice a day the tides cause the withdrawal of ocean water and the exposure of this muddy bottom along a Maine inlet. Photo by Sheldon Judson.

CURRENTS

Sea water is in constant movement, in some places horizontally, in others downward, and in still others upward. Its rate of movement varies from spot to spot, but it has been estimated that there is a complete mixing of all the water of the oceans about once every 1,800 years. We must assume that movements similar to those of the present have been going on throughout the long history of the earth. By studying modern seas, we can gain an insight into the history recorded in sedimentary rocks that were once muds and sands on the floors of ancient seas.

Although we still cannot explain completely the movements of the modern oceans, we do know that they are caused chiefly by tides, by the changing density of sea water, by wind, and by the rotation of the earth.

FIG. 15-7
In some restricted arms of the sea, the incoming tide may have a steepened front called a tidal bore that surges forward at 10 to 15 miles per hour. Tidal bores are well developed in a number of rivers, including the Amazon, the Severn, the Yangtze, and the Elbe. This one is seen near Moncton, New Brunswick, along the Petitcodiac River off the Bay of Fundy. Photo by Sheldon Judson.

Tidal currents

The attractive forces that operate between the sun, the moon, and the earth set the waters of the ocean in horizontal motion to produce *tidal currents.* The speed of these currents may reach several miles per hour if local conditions are favorable. Velocities in excess of 12 miles per hour develop during the spring tides in Seymour Narrows, between Vancouver and British Columbia, and tidal currents of half this velocity are not uncommon. The swiftest currents usually build up where a body of sea water has access to the open ocean only through a narrow and restricted passage. Such currents are capable of moving particles up to, and including, those of sand size, and they may be strong enough to scour the sea floor.

Density currents

The density of sea water varies from place to place with changes in temperature, salinity, and the amount of material held in suspension. Thus cold, heavy water sinks below warmer and lighter water; water of high salinity is heavier than water of low salinity and sinks beneath it; and heavy muddy water sinks beneath light, clear water.

In the Straits of Gibraltar, the water passage between the Atlantic and the Mediterranean, differences in density are partially responsible for a pair of currents flowing one above the other. The Mediterranean, lying in a warm, dry climatic belt, loses about five feet of water every year through evaporation. Consequently, the saltier, heavier water of the Mediterranean moves outward along the bottom of the Straits and sinks downward into the less salty, lighter water of the Atlantic. At the same time, the lighter surface water of the Atlantic moves into the Mediterranean basin. The water flowing from the Mediterranean settles to a depth of a little over 3,000 feet in the Atlantic and then spreads slowly outward beyond the equator on the south, the Azores on the west, and Ireland on the north. It has been estimated that as a result of this activity the water of the Mediterranean basin is changed once every 75 years (see Fig. 15-8).

The density of water is also affected by variations in temperature. As a result of such variations, water from the cold arctic and antarctic regions creeps slowly toward the warmer environment near the equator. The cold, relatively dense water from the arctic sinks near Greenland in the North Atlantic and can be traced to the equator and beyond as far as

FIG. 15-8
A density current flows from the Mediterranean Sea through the Straits of Gibraltar and spreads out into the Atlantic Ocean. High evaporation and low rainfall in the Mediterranean area produce a more saline and hence heavier water than the water of the neighboring Atlantic Ocean. As a result, Mediterranean water flows out through the lower portion of the Straits, and lighter Atlantic water moves above it and in the opposite direction to replace it. The higher temperature of the Mediterranean water is more than counteracted by its greater salinity, and the water sinks to a level in the Atlantic somewhat lower than 3,000 feet below the surface.

FIG. 15-9
This photograph shows a muddy Alaskan stream entering the clearer waters of the Gulf of Alaska. Although turbid, the stream water does not sink, because it is still lighter than the salt water of the ocean.

60°S. Denser and colder water moves downward to the sea floor off Antarctica and creeps northward, pushing beneath the North Atlantic water. In fact, the antarctic water reaches well north of the equator before it loses its identity. The speed of these currents has yet to be measured accurately, but estimates put the speed of antarctic water along the sea floor at a mile or more per day.

A third type of density current, known as a *turbidity current,* is caused by the fact that turbid or muddy water has a greater density than clear water and therefore sinks beneath it. Evidence that marine turbidity currents exist in the ocean is largely indirect. We can demonstrate how these currents operate on a small scale in the laboratory, and they have actually been observed in fresh-water lakes and reservoirs, so it seems safe enough to assume that they also exist in the oceans.

Moreover, turbidity currents seem to offer the most plausible explanation of certain deposits that have been studied from the deep ocean basins. Samples of sediments from these basins contain thin layers of sand that could not have been carried so far from shore by the slow drift of water along the ocean floor. But rapidly moving turbidity currents would be quite capable of moving the sand down the slopes of the ocean basins to the deep floors.

Analysis of other samples from the ocean floor reveals that particles become progressively finer from bottom to top of the deposit. The best explanation of this *graded bedding* is that the deposit was laid down by a turbidity current carrying particles of many different sizes, and that the larger particles were the first to be dropped on the ocean floor. Such deposits are called *turbidites.*

Turbidity currents may be set in motion by the slumping and sliding of material along the slopes of the ocean basin under the influence of gravity, either by itself or aided by the jarring of an earthquake. Or the currents may be created by the churning up of bottom sediments under the influence of violent storms.

Major surface currents

The major movements of water near the ocean's surface occur in such currents as the Gulf Stream, the Japanese Current, and the Equatorial Currents. These great currents are caused by a variety of factors, including the prevailing winds, the rotation of the earth, variations in the density of sea water, and the shape of ocean basins. Let us examine, by way of illustration, the surface currents of the Atlantic Ocean in both the Northern and Southern hemispheres, as shown in Fig. 15-10.

The Equatorial Currents lie on each side of the equator, and they move almost due west. They derive their energy largely from the trade winds that blow constantly toward the equator, from the northeast in the Northern Hemisphere and from the southeast in the Southern Hemisphere. The westerly direction of the currents is explained by the Coriolis effect, discussed in Chapter 14. You will remember that this effect is produced by the rotation of the earth and that it causes moving objects to veer to the right in the Northern Hemisphere and to the left in the Southern Hemisphere. As the water driven by the trade winds moves toward the equator, it is deflected to the right (toward the west) in the Northern Hemisphere and to the left (also toward the west) in the Southern. As a result, the North and South Equatorial Currents are formed. As these currents approach South America, one is deflected north and the other south. This deflection is caused largely by the shape of the ocean basins, but it is aided by the Coriolis effect and by the slightly higher level of the oceans along the equator where rainfall is heavier than elsewhere.

The North Equatorial Current moves into the Caribbean waters and then northeastward, first as the Florida Current and then as the Gulf Stream. The Gulf Stream, in turn, is deflected to the east (to the right) by the Coriolis effect. This easterly movement is strengthened by prevailing westerly winds between 35°N. and 45°N., where it becomes the North Atlantic Current. As it approaches Europe, the North Atlantic Current splits. Part of it moves northward as a warm current past the British Isles and parallel to the Norwegian coast. The other part is deflected southward as the cool Canaries Current, and eventually is caught up against the Northeast Trade Winds, which drive it into the North Equatorial Current.

In the South Atlantic, the picture is very much the same—a kind of mirror image of the currents in the North Atlantic. After the South Equatorial Current is deflected southward, it travels parallel to the eastern coast of South America as the Brazil Current. Then it is bent back to the east (toward the left) by the Coriolis effect and is driven by prevailing westerly winds toward Africa. This easterly moving current veers more and more to the left until finally, off Africa, it is moving northward. There it is known as the Buenguela Current, which in turn is caught up by the trade winds and is turned back into the South Equatorial Current.

The cold surface water from the antarctic regions moves along a fairly simple course, uncomplicated by large land-

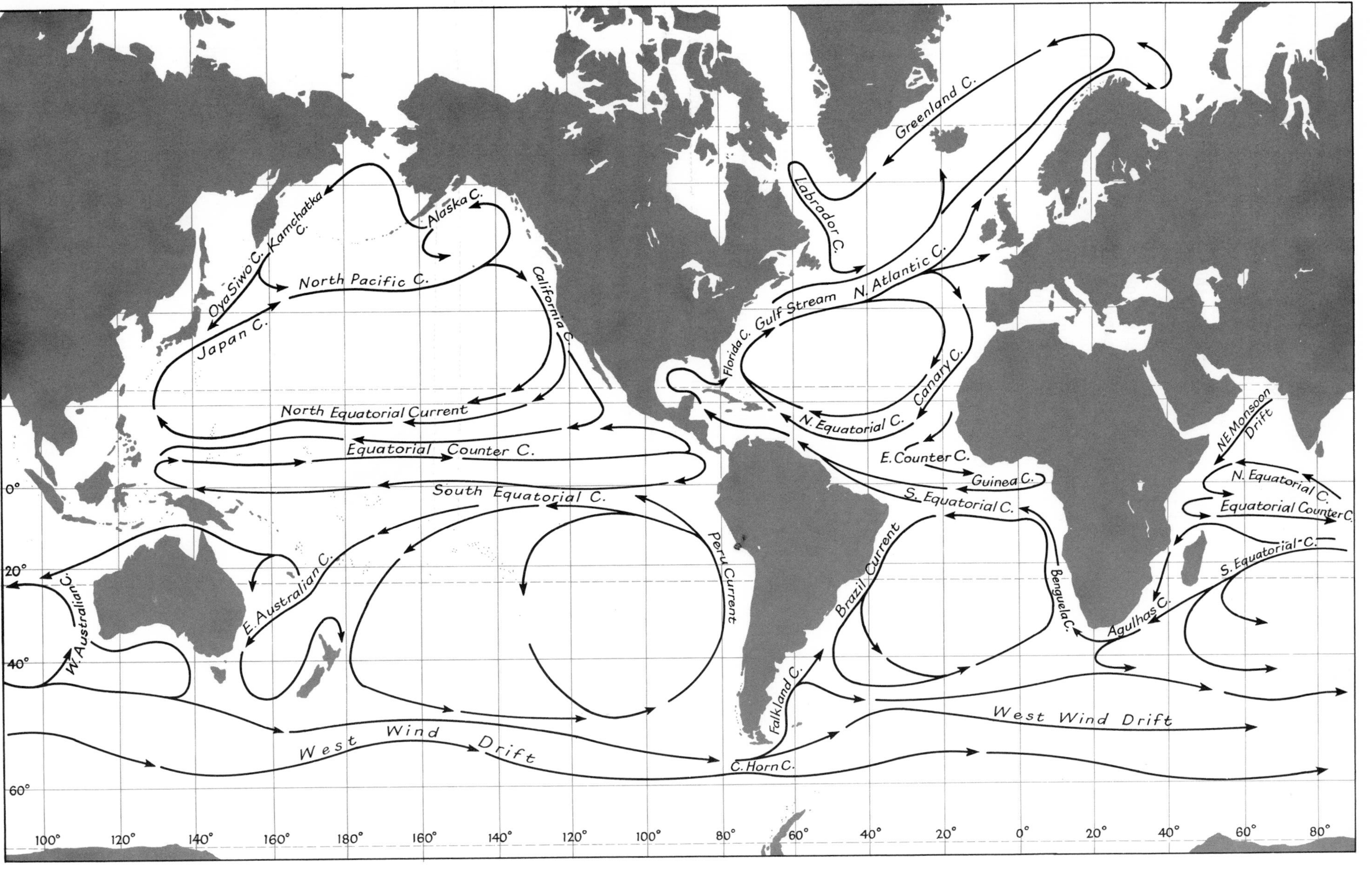

FIG. 15-10
Major surface currents of the oceans of the world.

masses. It is driven in an easterly direction by the prevailing winds from the west. In the Northern Hemisphere, however, the picture is complicated by continental masses. Arctic water emerges from the polar seas through the straits on either side of Greenland, to form the Labrador Current on the west and the Greenland Current on the east. Both currents subsequently join the North Atlantic Current and are deflected easterly and northeasterly.

We need not examine in detail the surface currents of the Pacific and Indian oceans. We can note, however, that the surface currents of the Pacific follow the same general patterns as those of the Atlantic. Furthermore, the surface currents of the Indian Ocean differ only in detail from those of the South Atlantic (see Fig. 15-10).

THE OCEAN BASINS

Most geologists now agree that the continents of the world are composed largely of sialic rock overlying a layer of heavier, crystalline simatic rock. (For a discussion of the terms *sial* and *sima,* see "Types of igneous rocks" in Chapter 6.) The sialic layer seems to be missing from the deep ocean basins, however, for the ocean floor is apparently made up of simatic rock with a covering of sediments that reaches a thickness of 5,000 to 6,000 feet in places but that probably averages about 3,000 feet. We may think of the continents, then, as great blocks of relatively light material buoyed up on masses of denser material.

Most of the sea water surrounding the continents is held in one great basin that girdles the Southern Hemisphere and branches northward under the Atlantic, Pacific, and Indian oceans. The Atlantic and Pacific oceans in turn are connected with the Arctic Ocean through narrow straits. But the oceans still flood over the margins of the continents, for even this great, fingered basin cannot contain all the water of the seas.

TOPOGRAPHY OF THE SEA FLOOR

Continental shelves, slopes, and ocean deeps

The margins of the continents that lie flooded beneath the seas are referred to as *continental shelves.* The average width of these shelves is a little over 40 miles, but there are many local variations. Along the western coast of South America, for example, the shelf is altogether missing, or at best but a few miles in width. In contrast, the shelf reaches out 150 miles off Florida, about 350 miles off the coast of South America south of the Rio de la Plata, and from 750 to 800 miles off the arctic coasts of Europe and Russia.

The seaward edge of the continental shelves has an average depth of about 430 feet, but it is commonly as deep as 600 feet (100 fathoms) or as shallow as 300 feet. Soundings indicate that the topography of the shelves changes somewhat from one place to another, but there seems to be a general lack of spectacular features. Some shelves, such as those off Labrador, Nova Scotia, and New England, show the marks of vanished continental glaciers, the material they deposited in some places and eroded away in others. The surface of almost all the shelves is irregularly marked by hills, valleys, and depressions of low to moderate relief. Furthermore, soundings along the shelf bordering the eastern coast of North America show the presence of submarine terraces that record former lower levels of the ocean, just as higher levels are recorded by terraces stranded above sea level.

Generally, the shelves slope gently toward the ocean basins until they are abruptly terminated by the steeper *continental slopes* that descend thousands of feet into the ocean deeps. Continental slopes are steepest in their upper portion, and commonly extend more than 12,000 feet downward. In certain places where earth movements have created deep trenches in the ocean floor, the continental slopes reach to much greater depths. Off the island of Mindanao, in the Philippines, the slope drops down for some 30,000 feet. Scarring the face of the continental slopes at various places around the world are deep submarine canyons; but the floor of the great world-encircling basin that contains the oceans is far more irregular than the surface of the continental shelves and slopes. The more soundings that are made, the more complex and spectacular the topography appears (see Fig. 15-11). The ocean floor is divided into innumerable smaller basins and is marked by plains, plateaus, valleys, towering peaks, and mountain ranges.

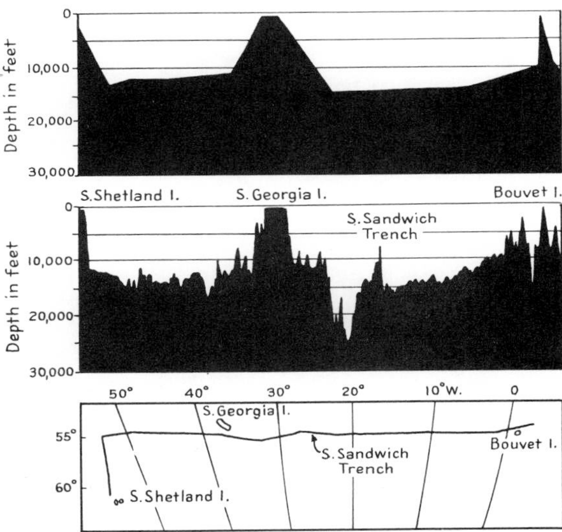

FIG. 15-11
The more depth determinations we have, the more complex our picture of the ocean floor becomes. The location of a line of profile is shown in the lowest of the three diagrams. The upper diagram is a section along this line of profile and is based on very few depth determinations. The middle diagram, a section along the same line of profile, is based on more extensive soundings of the ocean floor than the first profile. Redrawn from H. U. Sverdrup and others, op. cit., p. 18.

SUBMARINE VALLEYS. The surfaces of the continental shelves, slopes, and ocean deeps are all furrowed by submarine valleys of varying width, depth, and length, rather like the valleys of the continents. The origin of the deep, spectacular valleys, the *submarine canyons* that crease the continental slopes, is still in dispute, but the origin of the lesser valleys along the shallow continental shelves is fairly well understood.

Some of the valleys that cut across the continental shelves seem to be seaward extensions of large valleys on the adjoining land. One of the best-known submarine valleys is the submerged extension of the Hudson Valley off the eastern coast of the United States. This valley extension is relatively straight, cuts down about 200 feet into the continental shelf, and widens from about three miles at the coastline to approximately 15 miles at its seaward end. It is speculated that this and similar valleys, such as those in the China Sea, were cut during periods of Pleistocene glaciation, when sea level was perhaps 300 feet lower than it is at present, and when large portions of the continental shelves were exposed to erosion by land streams.

In addition to these larger stream valleys, there are smaller troughs in the continental shelves that are presumed to have been cut by tidal scouring. Several troughs of this sort occur off the northeastern coast of the United States. Other valleys were apparently cut on the continental shelves by glacier ice that may simply have deepened already-existing valleys.

More difficult to explain are the deep submarine canyons along the continental slopes and along the floor of the deep ocean basins. The canyons on the continental slopes have been known since the latter part of the nineteenth century. Today, even though soundings are scattered and incomplete, it seems certain that submarine canyons are characteristic of the continental slopes all around the world. Some canyons, such as those on the slopes off the Hudson and Congo rivers, appear to be extensions of valleys on the land or on the continental shelves. Others seem to have no association with such valleys. In any event, these canyons have V-shaped cross profiles and gradients that decrease along the lower sections of the continental slopes. Their slightly winding courses may extend out to sea as far as 145 miles, as does the Congo canyon. Some canyons cut down more than a mile beneath the surface of the continental slope.

Many theories have been advanced to explain the origin of these submarine canyons. Some investigators think that they were formed by earth movements, others conclude that they were carved out by turbidity currents, and still others believe erosion by tidal scour to be the cause. Then there are those who speculate that the canyons were cut during a vast lowering of the sea in the recent geologic past, or were fashioned by the emergence of submarine springs along the slopes, or by submarine mudflows and landslides. Suffice it to say that no single explanation has yet proved satisfactory to a majority of investigators, and the origin of these canyons is still being debated.

Sonic depth measurements have revealed that other submarine valleys, some as deep as 12,000 feet or more, run for great distances across the floors of the ocean out beyond the continental slopes. Valleys of this sort are known in both the Atlantic and the Pacific, but data on them are too meager to permit exact descriptions, much less explanations of their origin.

Running generally from north to south along the center of the Atlantic Ocean is a broad zone, known as the Mid-Atlantic Ridge, that rises above the general elevation of the deep ocean basin. A submarine valley 25 to 50 miles wide and hundreds of feet deep follows along the crest of this ridge in the North Atlantic and probably also in the South Atlantic.

FIG. 15-12
Soundings in the Pacific Ocean during World War II revealed the presence of many flat-topped submarine mountains called guyots. The guyot in this profile is located at 8.8°N., 163.1°E. Redrawn from H. H. Hess, "Drowned Ancient Islands of the Pacific Basin," Am. J. Sci., CCXLIV (1946), 777.

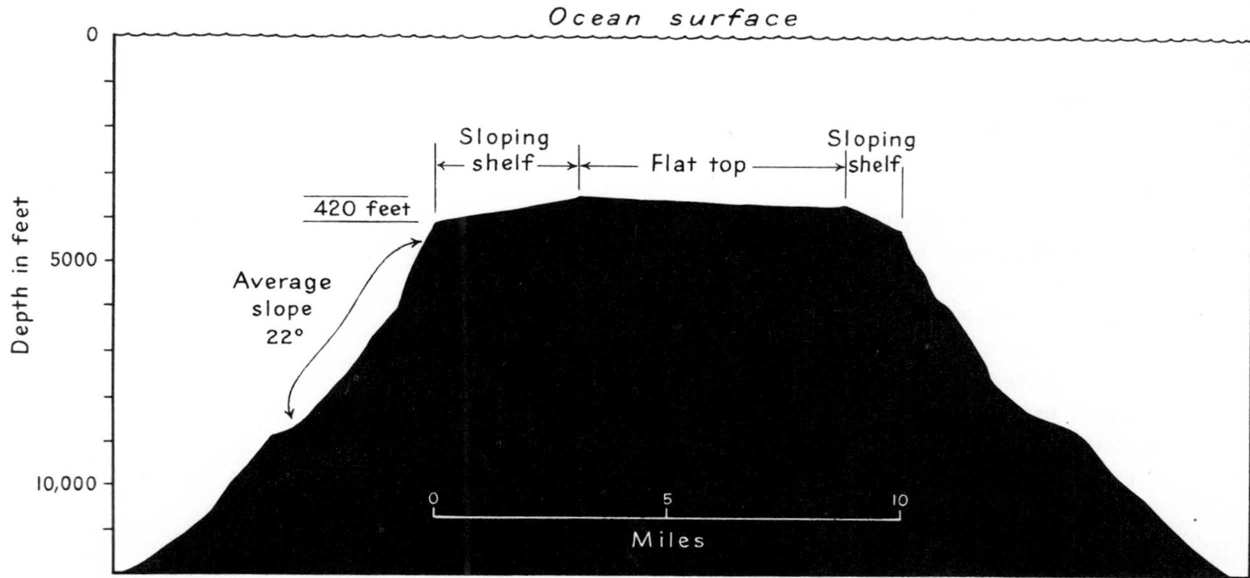

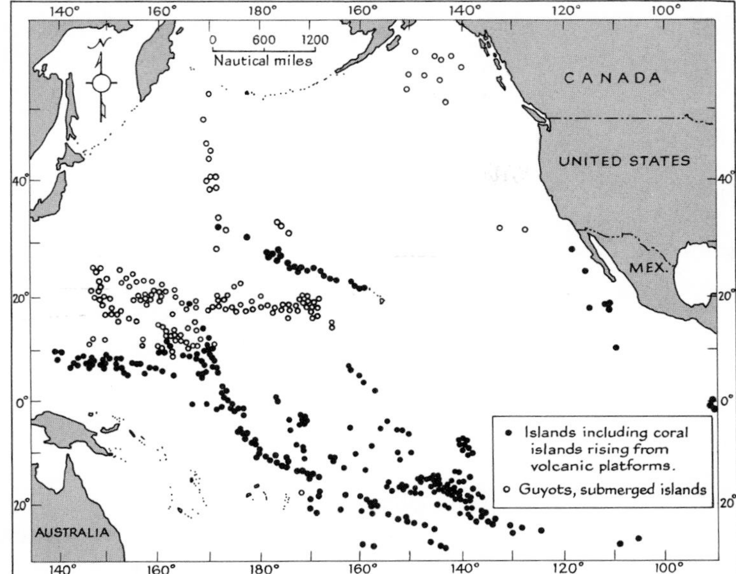

FIG. 15-13
Guyots of the Pacific Ocean basin occur in groups, as do the chains of present-day volcanic-based islands. Redrawn from H. W. Menard, "Geology of the Pacific Floor," Experientia, XV, No. 6 (1959), 210, 212.

Oceanographers have suggested that this submarine valley is similar to the Valley of the Dead Sea in the Near East and to the so-called Rift Valley of Africa, which contains such lakes as Tanganyika and Nyassa. These land valleys have been caused by the down-dropping of sections of the earth's crust. The submarine valley on the crest of the Mid-Atlantic Ridge may have been formed in the same way.

SEAMOUNTS. Dotting the ocean floors are drowned, isolated steep-sloped peaks called *seamounts.* They stand at least 3,000 feet above the surrounding ocean floor, their crests covered by depths of water measured in thousands of feet. Seamounts have been identified in all the oceans, but the greatest number by far are reported from the Pacific Ocean. There, by the mid-1960's, some 1,500 such peaks had been mapped; it is estimated that ten times this number remain to be discovered.

Most seamounts have sharp peaks, and, insofar as we can tell, they are all of volcanic origin. Some of the peaks have flat tops called *tablemounts* or *guyots* (pronounced *gee*—hard "g" as in geese—*yoz*) in honor of Arnold Guyot, a Swiss-American geologist of the mid-nineteenth century. Guyots are thought to be volcanic cones whose tops have been cut off by the action of surface waves. Most evidence suggests that the guyots then sank beneath the sea, but it is also possible that they were drowned by a rise in sea level (see Figs. 15-12, 15-13).

SUBMARINE RIDGES, RISES, AND FRACTURES. Among the major features of the deep ocean basins are long, submerged ridges and rises. In general, ridges have steep sides and irregular topography. The rises differ in being broader and gentler in form. They rise thousands of feet above the deep ocean floor and in some places actually appear above the surface to form islands. These ridges and rises form a more or less integrated system of high topography that segments the deep oceans into smaller basins (see Fig. 15-14).

In addition to these two forms, long towering escarpments caused by earth movements scar some sections of the ocean floor. Thus the Mendocino, Murray, Clipperton, and Clarion

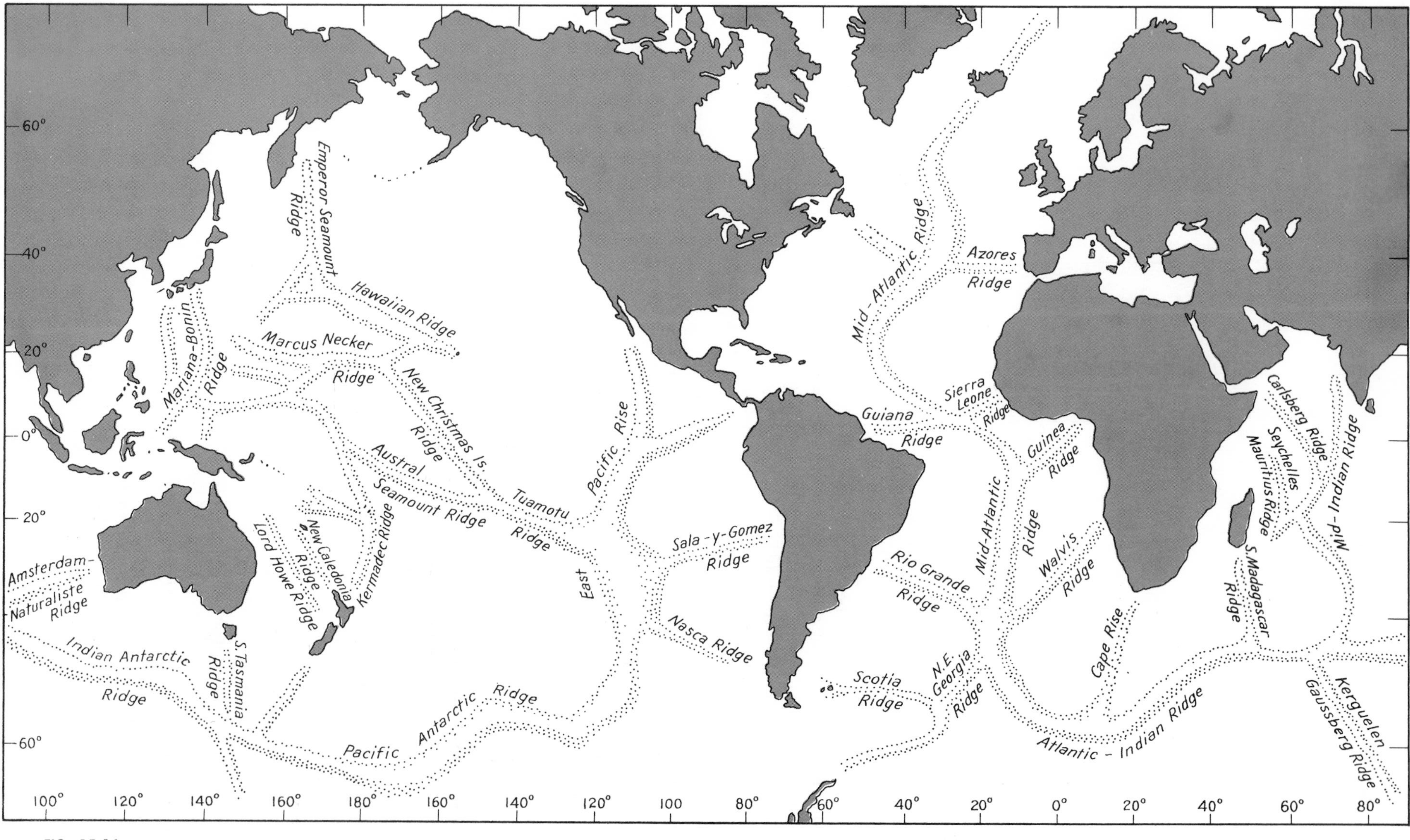

FIG. 15-14
A system of ridges and rises of topography segment the ocean basins into smaller units.

fracture zones stretch westward into the Pacific from the coasts of the United States and Central America (see Fig. 15-15). The vast Mendocino Escarpment reaches heights of 8,000 feet and extends 2,000 miles into the central Pacific. Less well-known but similar fractures and related escarpments lie to the south of this system. And fracture systems of similar magnitude may offset the Mid-Atlantic Ridge just north of the equator.

DEEP-SEA TRENCHES. The greatest ocean depths occur in great arcuate or bow-shaped *trenches* on the sea floor bordering some of the continents. Several of these trenches dip to more than 30,000 feet below the ocean surface, and they may reach 125 miles in breadth and 1,500 or more miles in length. Since arcuate chains of islands are often located near these deep trenches, they are sometimes known as *island arc deeps.* So far as we know, most of them occur in the Pacific Ocean, particularly beneath the western Pacific and the Indonesian waters (see Fig. 15-16).

These deep-sea trenches were formed by tectonic movements of the earth's crust, but the exact mechanism involved has not yet been satisfactorily explained.

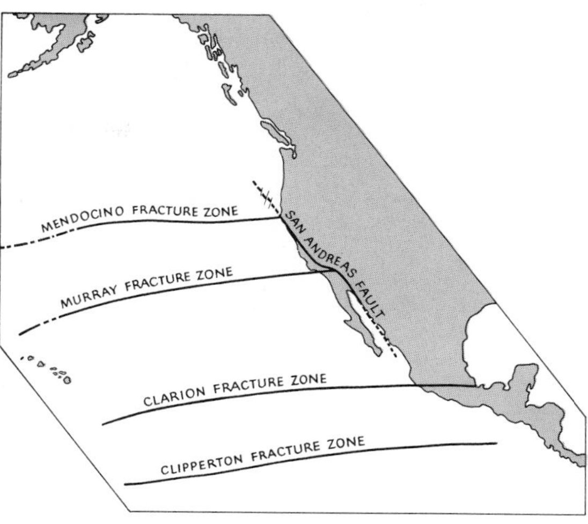

FIG. 15-15
Long fracture zones in the sea floor reach westward into the Pacific from western North America and Central America. See text for discussion. Redrawn from H. W. Menard, "Deformation of the Northeastern Pacific Basin and the West Coast of North America," Geol. Soc. Am. Bull., LXVI (1955).

SEDIMENTS OF THE OCEAN

In earlier chapters, we have spoken from time to time of the processes by which earth materials are weathered, eroded, transported, and finally deposited to be transformed into sedimentary rocks. The great ocean basins of the world constitute the ultimate collection area for the sediments and dissolved material that are carried from the land. And the great bulk of the sedimentary rocks found on our modern landmasses were once deposits on the ocean floors of the past. In this section we shall speak briefly of the sediments being laid down in the modern oceans—the sediments destined to become the sedimentary rocks of the future.

Deposits on the continental shelves

Theoretically, when particles of solid material are carried out and deposited in a body of water, the largest particles should fall out nearest the shore and the finest particles farthest away from the shore, in a neatly graduated pattern. But there are a great many exceptions to this generalization. Many deposits on the continental shelves show little tendency to grade from coarse to fine away from the shoreline. We would expect to find sand close to shore only—actually it shows up from place to place all along the typical continental shelf right up to the lip of the continental slope. It is particularly common in areas of low relief on the shelf. In fact, on glaciated continental shelves, sand mixed with gravel and cobbles comprises a large part of the total amount of deposited material.

Also common on the continental shelves are deposits of mud, especially off the mouths of large rivers and along the course of ocean currents that sweep across the river-laid deposits. Mud also tends to collect in shallow depressions across the surface of the shelves, in lagoons, sheltered bays, and gulfs.

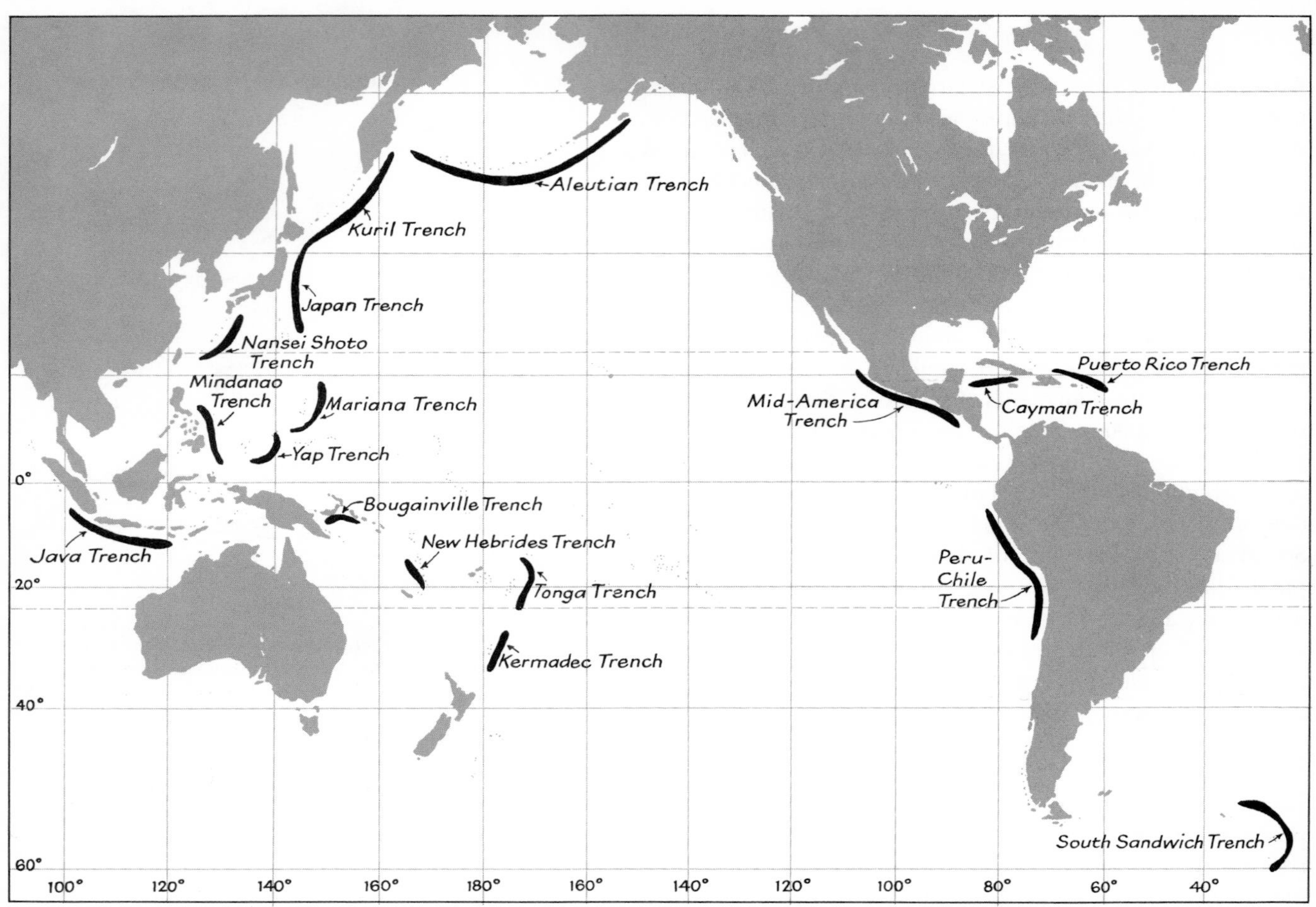

FIG. 15-16
Deep-sea trenches outline the Pacific Ocean.

Where neither sand nor mud collects on the shelves, the surface is often covered with fragments of rock and gravel. This is commonly the case on open stretches of a shelf, where strong ocean currents can winnow out the finer material, and off rocky points and exposed stretches of rocky shoreline. In narrow straits running between islands or giving access to bays, the energy of tidal and current movements is often so effectively concentrated that the bottom is scoured clean and the underlying solid rock is exposed.

Strangely, although the geologic record indicates many calcareous deposits laid down in the ancient seas, eventually to give rise to the rock we call limestone, only a few calcareous deposits are being built up on the continental shelves of modern seas. And most of these limy mud deposits are being built up in warmer waters, particularly near coral reefs. No satisfactory explanation accounts for the apparent deficiency.

Deposits on the continental slopes

Although we have less information about the deposits being laid down on the continental slopes than we have about the shelf deposits, evidence indicates that here, too, gravel, sand, mud, and bedrock are all found on the bottom. And deposition, it seems, is taking place even more rapidly on the slopes than on the shelves.

Deposits on the deep-sea floor

The deposits that spread across the floors of the deep sea are generally much finer than those on the slopes and shelves lying off the continents, although occasional beds of sand have been found even in the deeps.

Deep-sea deposits of material derived from the continents are referred to as *terrigenous* ("produced on the earth") *deposits.* Those formed of material derived from the ocean itself are *pelagic* ("pertaining to the ocean") *deposits.*

Among the terrigenous deposits are beds of wind-borne volcanic ash that has fallen over the ocean and has settled through thousands of feet of water to the sea bottom. In the polar regions, silts and sands from glacier ice make up much of the bottom deposit, and around the margins of the continents we often find deep-sea mud deposits of silt and clay washed down from the landmasses. Much of the ocean bottom, especially in the Pacific, is covered by an extremely fine-grained deposit known as *brown clay,* which may have originated on the continents and then drifted out into the open ocean.

In the Antarctic and Arctic oceans some of the deep ocean sediments are believed to have been ice-rafted from the land to the oceans by icebergs. These *glacial marine* deposits are chiefly silt containing coarse fragments. Near the landmasses are extensive layers of sand and coarse silt deposited by turbidity currents, the *turbidites,* discussed previously.

Most of the pelagic deep-sea deposits consist of *oozes,* sediments of which at least 30 per cent by volume is made up of the hard parts of very small, sometimes microscopic, organisms. These hard parts are constructed of mineral matter extracted from the sea water by tiny plants and animals. With the death of the organism, the remains sink slowly to the sea floor. In composition, the oozes are either calcareous or siliceous.

Two calcareous oozes are common in the deep seas. In one—*globigerina ooze*—the limy shells of minute one-celled animals called *Globigerina* abound; in the other—*pteropod ooze*—the shells of tiny marine molluscs predominate. Globigerina oozes cover large portions of the floors of the Atlantic, Pacific, and Indian oceans, while the greatest known concentration of pteropod ooze is in a long belt running from north to south in the Atlantic Ocean midway between South America and Africa.

Siliceous oozes include *radiolarian ooze,* made up largely of the delicate and complex hard parts of minute marine protozoa called *Radiolaria,* and by *diatomaceous ooze,* made up of the siliceous cell walls of one-celled marine algae known as *diatoms.* Radiolarian ooze predominates in a long east-west belt in the Pacific Ocean just north of the equator; while the greatest concentration of diatomaceous ooze occurs in the North Pacific and in the Antarctic Ocean.

Some of the pelagic deposits of the sea floor have apparently crystallized directly from sea water, and these we refer to as *authigenic* (from the Greek, "born on the spot"). In large areas of the southern Pacific Ocean, the silicate mineral *phillipsite* constitutes the great bulk of the sediments, but the mineral grains are too large to have been transported by the currents in the area of their present location; thus, they are thought to have crystallized directly from sea water.

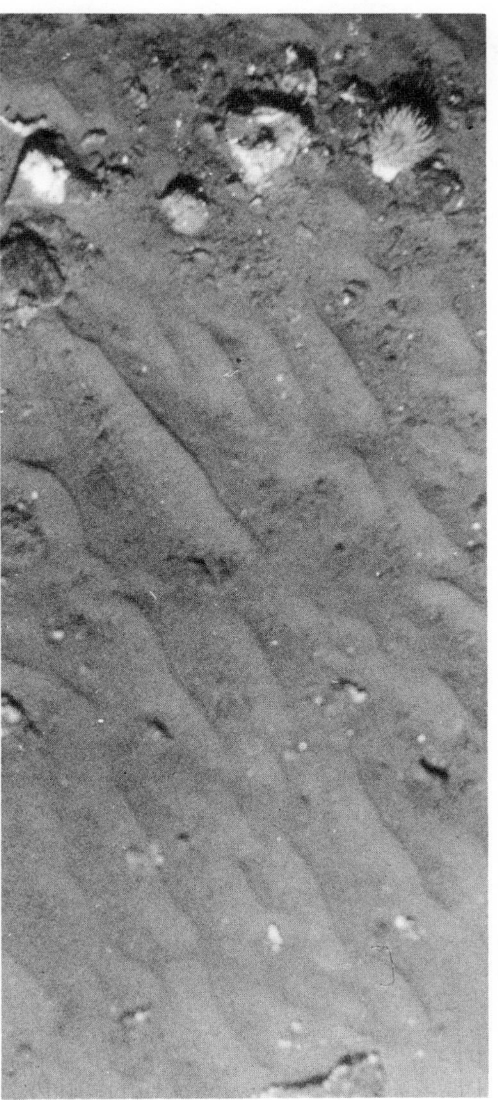

FIG. 15-17
Ripple-marked sand on the continental shelf between George's and Brown's Banks, off the New England coast. The ripple marks indicate currents moving diagonally from the upper right toward the lower left. The "sand dollar" in the lower left is 2 to 3 inches in diameter. Photo by D. M. Owen, Woods Hole Oceanographic Institution.

More spectacular authigenic deposits are the *manganese nodules* (see Fig. 15-19). These average 10 inches in diameter and when cut open exhibit the patterns of concentric growth. Composed largely of oxides of manganese and iron, they contain in addition the oxides of many of the rarer elements. It is estimated that they cover some 20 per cent of the floor of the Pacific. Their composition and abundance has suggested a potential commercial use as an ore not only of manganese but also of such rarer elements as cobalt, titanium, and zirconium.

Most sediments are deposited in the shallow waters of the continental shelves or on the slopes leading down to the deep sea. Very few sediments get to the deep sea floor, where the rate of sedimentation on average seems to be 0.5 inches per 1,000 years or less. In contrast, on shelves and slopes the rate appears to be 10 to 20 times this rate.

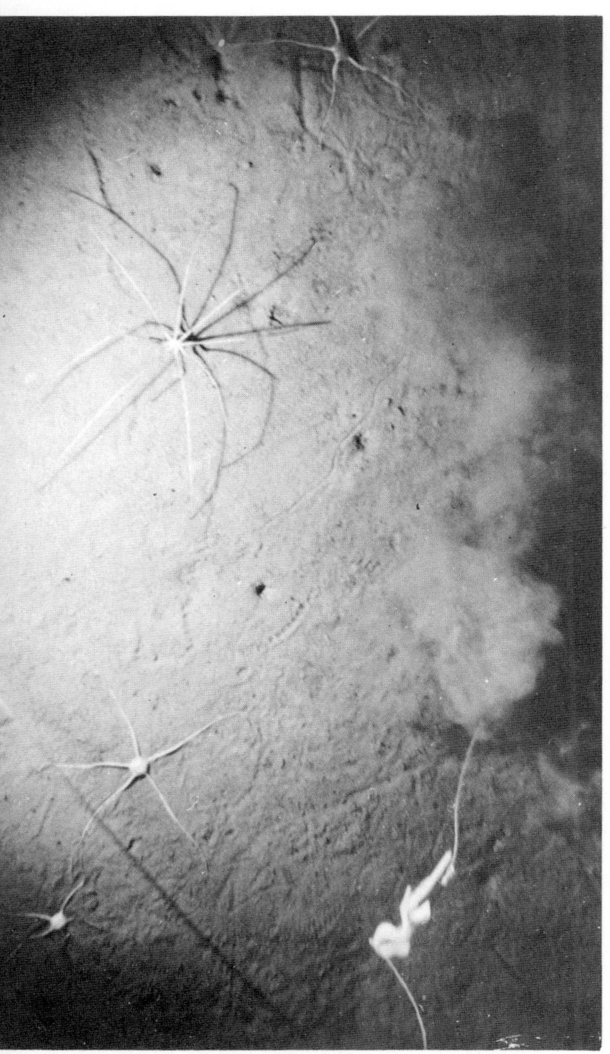

FIG. 15-18
This muddy sea floor is south of Cape Cod, Massachusetts, at a depth of 6,000 feet. The cloud of sediment was raised by a fishing line and sinker. The larger animal is a sea spider measuring 28 inches. The smaller, five-armed animals are brittle stars. Pohto by D. M. Owen, Woods Hole Oceanographic Institution.

SHORELINES

Few people have occasion to make a detailed study of the ocean currents or of the topography of the ocean floor; but most of us have many opportunities to observe the activity of water along the shorelines of oceans or lakes. The nature and results of wave action along such shorelines can be a drama of power and persistence.

The processes

The energy that works upon and modifies a shoreline comes largely from the movement of water produced by tides, by wind-formed waves, and, to a lesser extent, by tsunami (see Chapter 19). Since we have already discussed tidal currents, we may now turn to the nature and behavior of wind-formed waves as they advance against a shoreline.

WIND-FORMED WAVES. Most water waves are produced by the friction of air as it moves across a water surface. The harder the wind blows, the higher the water is piled up into long *wave crests* with intervening troughs, both crests and troughs at right angles to the wind. The distance between two successive wave crests is the *wave length,* and the vertical distance between the wave crest and the bottom of an adjacent trough is the *wave height* (Fig. 15-21). When the wind is blowing, the waves it generates are called a *sea.* But wind-formed waves persist even after the wind that formed them dies. These waves, or *swells,* may travel for hundreds or even thousands of miles from their zone of origin.

We are concerned with both the movement of the wave form and the motion of water particles in the path of the wave. Obviously the wave form itself moves forward at a measurable rate. But in deep water, the water particles in the path of the wave describe a circular orbit: any given particle moves forward on the crest of the wave, sinks as the following trough approaches, moves backward under the trough, and rises as the next crest advances. Such a motion can best be visualized by imagining a cork bobbing up and down on the water surface as successive wave crests and troughs pass by.

The cork itself makes only very slight forward progress under the influence of the wind. Wave motion extends downward, until at a depth equal to about one-half the wave length it is virtually negligible. But between this level and the surface, water particles move forward under the crest and backward under the trough of each wave, in orbits that decrease in diameter with depth (Fig. 15-22).

As the wave approaches a shoreline and the water becomes more shallow, definite changes take place in the motion of the particles and in the form of the wave itself. When the depth of water is about half the wave length, the bottom begins to interfere with the motion of water particles in the path of the wave and their orbits become increasingly elliptical. As a result, the length and velocity of the wave decrease and its front becomes steeper. When the water becomes shallow enough and the front of the wave steep enough, the wave crest falls forward as a breaker, producing what we call *surf*. At this moment, the water particles within the wave are thrown forward against the shoreline. The energy thus developed is then available to erode the shoreline or to set up currents along the shore that can transport the sediments produced by erosion.

WAVE REFRACTION AND COASTAL CURRENTS. Although most waves advance obliquely toward a shoreline, the influence of the sea floor tends to bend or refract them until they approach the shore nearly head-on.

Let us assume that we have a relatively straight stretch of shoreline with waves approaching it obliquely over an even bottom that grows shallow at a constant rate. As a wave crest nears the shore, the section closest to land feels the effect of the shelving bottom first and is retarded, while the seaward part continues along at its original speed. The effect is to swing the wave around and to change the direction of its approach to the shore, as shown in Fig. 15-23.

As a wave breaks, not all its energy is expended on the erosion of the shoreline. Some of the water thrown forward is deflected and moves laterally, parallel to the shore. The energy of this water movement is partly used up by friction along the bottom, and partly by the transportation of material.

Refraction also helps explain why, on an irregular shoreline, the greatest energy is usually concentrated on the headland and the least along the bays. Figure 15-24 shows a bay separating two promontories, and a series of wave crests sweeping in to the shore across a bottom that is shallow off the headland and deep off the mouth of the bay.

Where the depth of the water is greater than one-half the wave length, the crest of the advancing wave is relatively straight. Closer to shore, off the headlands, however, the depth becomes less than half the wave length, and the wave begins to slow down. In the deeper water of the bay it continues to move rapidly shoreward until there, too, the water grows shallow and the wave crest slows. This differential bending of the wave tends to make it conform in a general way to the shoreline. In so doing, the wave energy is concentrated on the

FIG. 15-19
This photograph of the deep-sea floor was taken in the Atlantic Ocean at a depth of 18,000 feet, where water pressure is about 9,000 lbs/sq in. The spherical objects are probably iron-manganese nodules; the largest measure about 5 inches in diameter. These are partially buried by fine sediments. Photo by D. M. Owen, Woods Hole Oceanographic Institution.

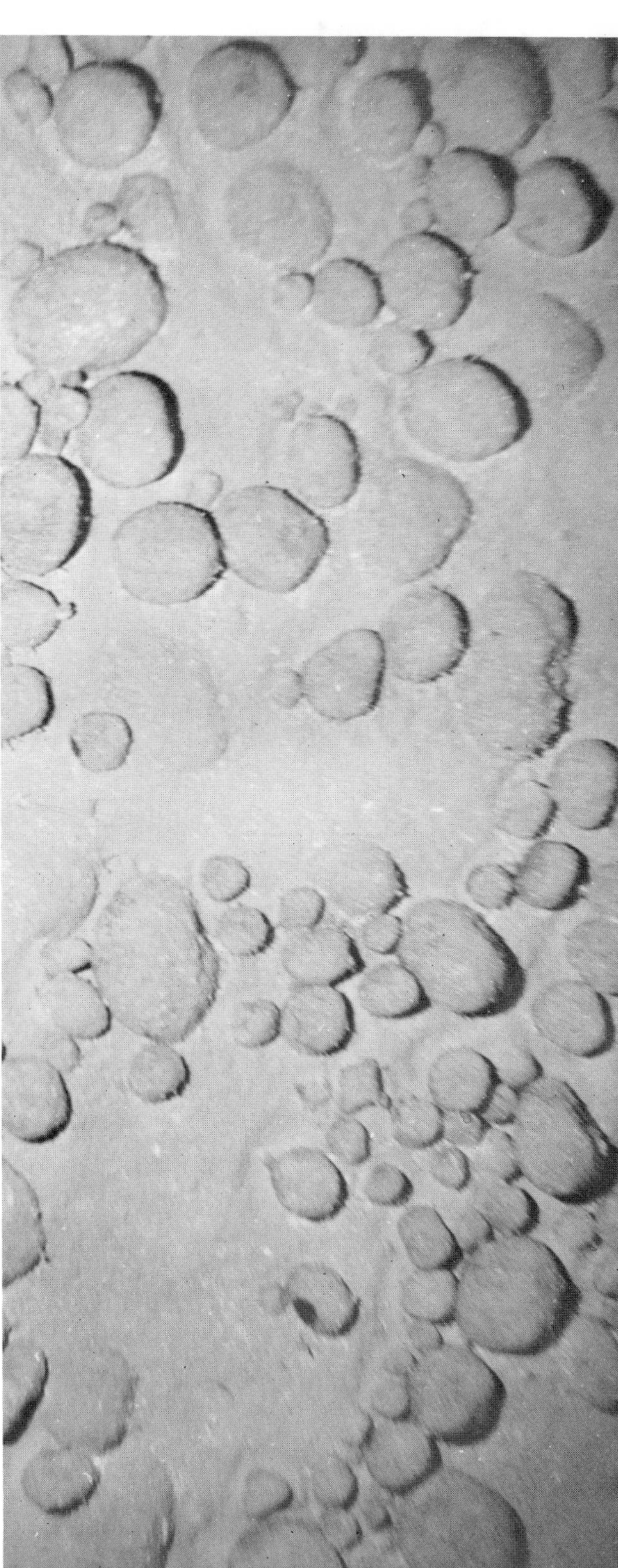

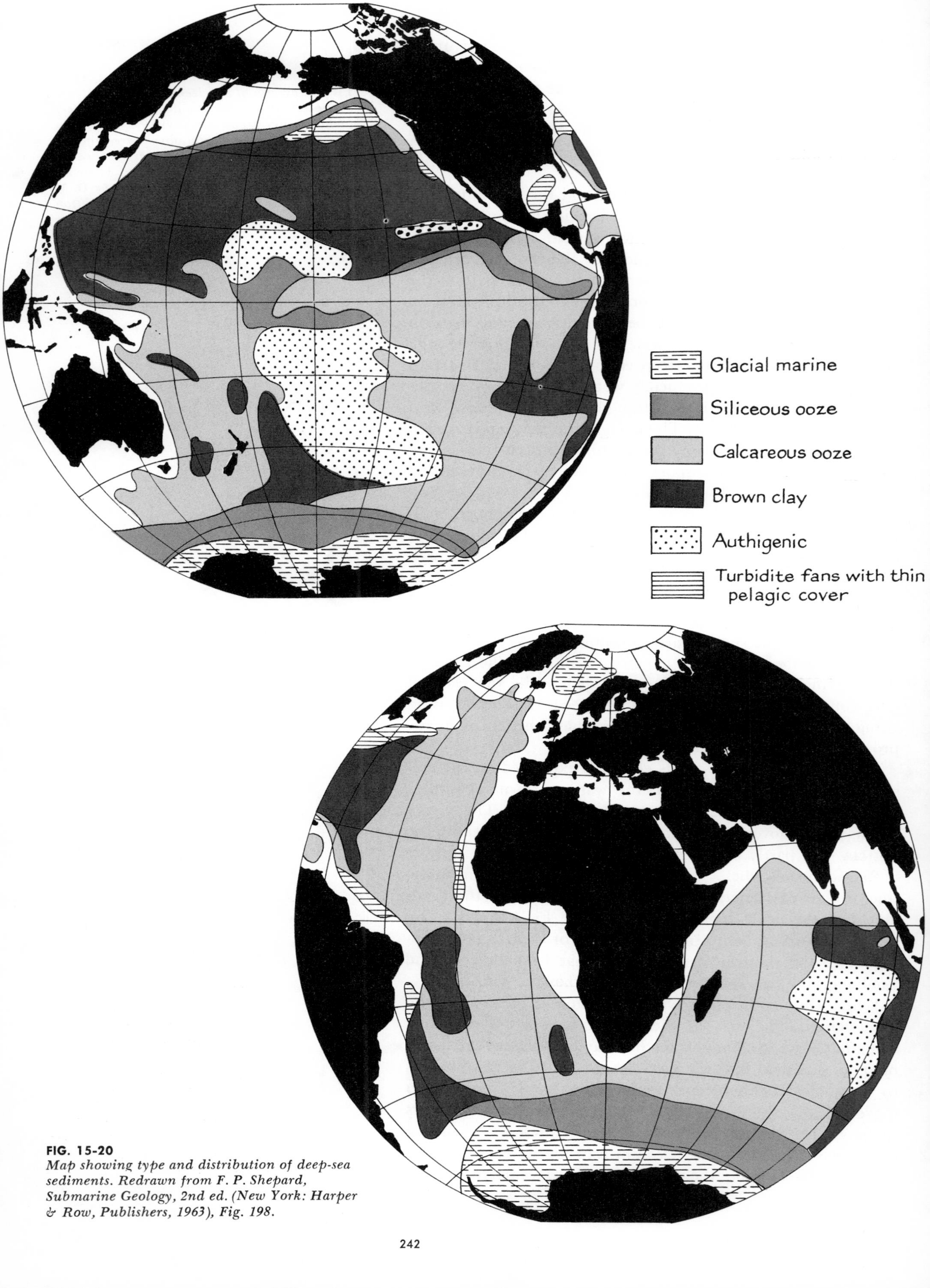

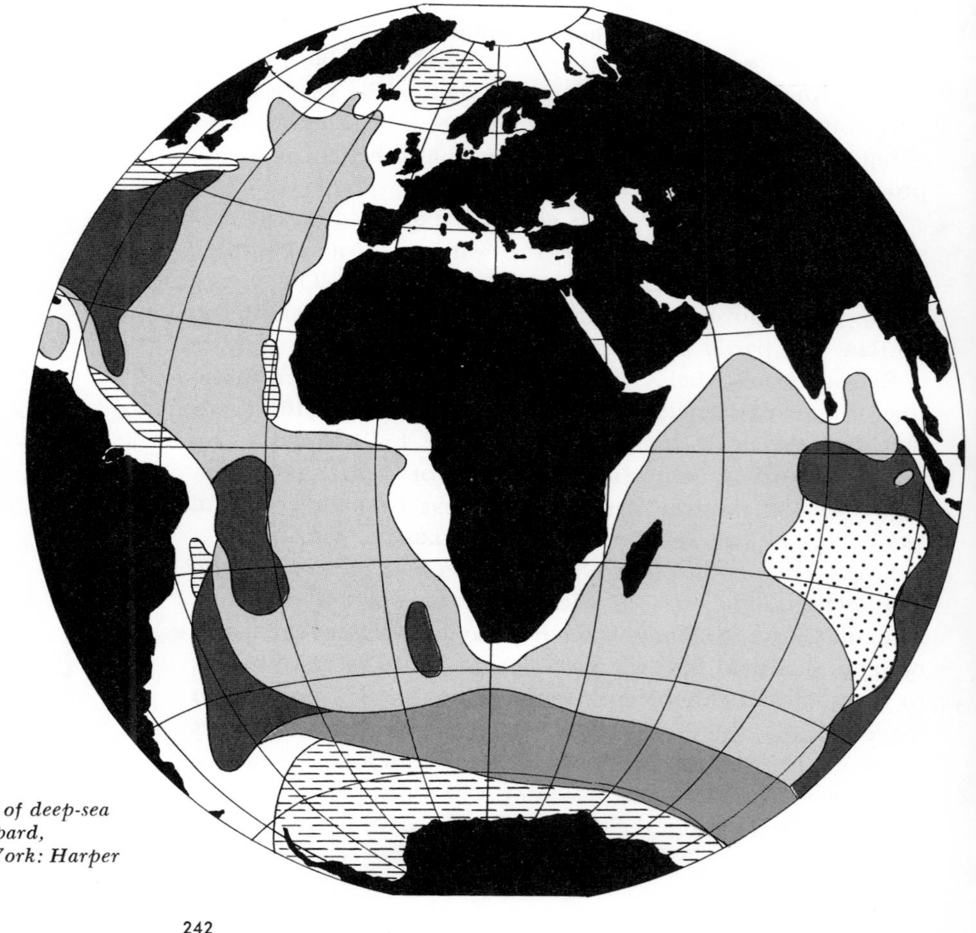

FIG. 15-20
Map showing type and distribution of deep-sea sediments. Redrawn from F. P. Shepard, Submarine Geology, 2nd ed. (New York: Harper & Row, Publishers, 1963), Fig. 198.

headland and dispersed around the bay, as suggested in Fig. 15-24.

A composite profile of a shoreline from a point above high tide seaward to some point below low tide reveals features that change constantly as they are influenced by the nature of waves and currents along the shore. All features are not present on all shorelines, but several are present in most shore profiles. The *offshore* section extends seaward from low tide. The *shore* or *beach* section reaches from low tide to the foot of the *sea cliff* and is divided into two segments. In front of the sea cliff is the *backshore,* characterized by one or more *berms,* resembling small terraces with low ridges on their seaward edges built up by storm waves. Seaward from the berms to low tide is the *foreshore.* Inland from the shore lies the *coast.* Deposits of the shore may veneer a surface cut by the waves on bedrock and known as the *wave-cut terrace.* In the offshore section, too, there may be an accumulation of unconsolidated deposits comprising a *wave-built terrace* (Fig. 15-25).

The shoreline profile is ever changing. During great storms the surf may pound in directly against the sea cliff, eroding it back and at the same time scouring down through the beach deposits to abrade the wave-cut terrace. As the storm (and hence the available energy) subsides, new beach deposits build up out in front of the sea cliff. The profile of a shoreline at any one time, then, is an expression of the available energy: it changes as the energy varies. This relation between profile and available energy is similar to the changing of a stream's gradient and channel as the discharge (and therefore the energy) of the stream varies (see Chapter 11).

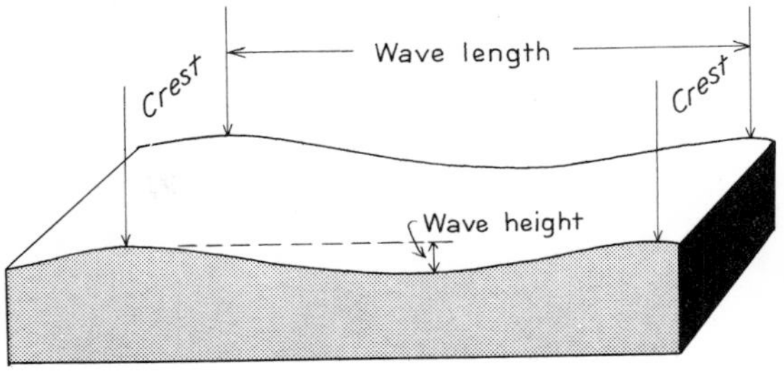

FIG. 15-21
Diagrammatic explanation of terms used in describing waves of water.

Shoreline features

Not even shorelines have escaped man's constant desire for classification into neat pigeonholes. But to date no completely acceptable system of classification has been devised. For many years it was common practice to group shorelines as *emergent* or *submergent,* depending upon whether the sea had gone down or had come up in relation to the landmass. Thus large sections of the California coast, having emerged from the sea during geologically recent times, would be termed emergent. Across the continent, the shoreline of New England indicates that it has been drowned by a slowly rising sea and would be referred to as submergent. The system has been criticized because some of the features that were thought to represent emergence of the land actually form where the land is being submerged. Conversely, along shorelines of submergence, features thought to characterize emergence may also develop.

Another attempt at a classification is based on the processes that form shorelines. Some have major features traceable to glacial erosion, others to glacial deposition. The system divided along these lines has much to recommend it. Nevertheless, we shall examine some of the individual shoreline features without attempting to fit them into an all-inclusive system.

Erosion and deposition work hand in hand to produce most

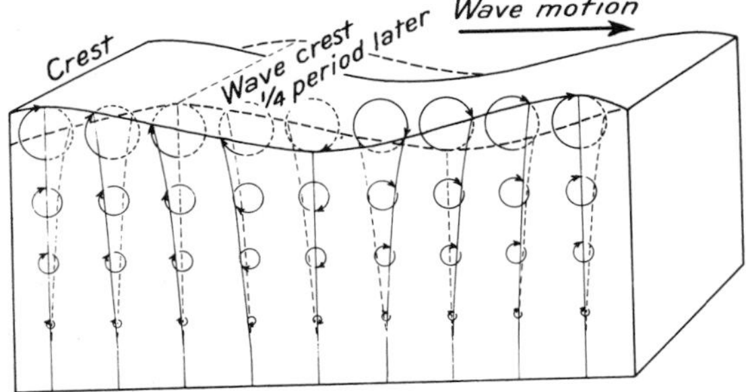

FIG. 15-22
The motion of water particles relative to wave motion in deep water. Water particles move forward under the crest and backward under the trough, in orbits that decrease in diameter with depth. Such motion extends downward to a distance of about one-half the wave length. Redrawn from U.S. Hydrographic Office Publication 604 (1951), Fig. 1-2.

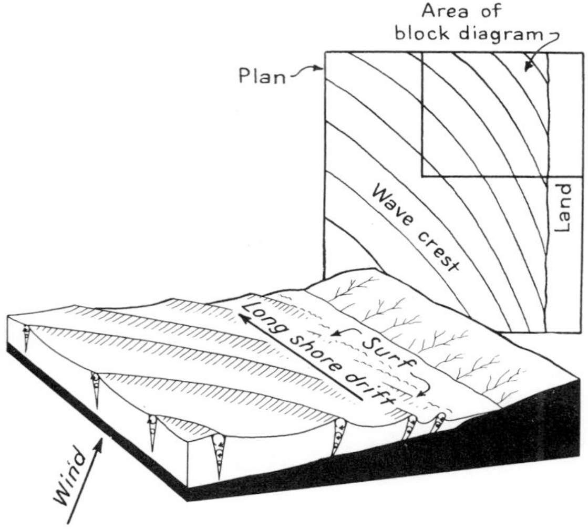

FIG. 15-23
Wave crests that advance at an angle on a straight shoreline and across a bottom that shallows at a uniform rate are bent shoreward, as suggested in this diagram. Refraction is caused by the increasing interference of the bottom with the orbits of water-particle motion within the wave.

FIG. 15-24
Refraction of waves on an irregular shoreline. It is assumed that the water is deeper off the bay than off the headlands. Consider that the original wave is divided into three equal segments, A-B, B-C, and C-D. Each segment has the same potential energy. But observe that by the time the wave reaches the shore, the energy of A-B and C-D has been concentrated along the short shoreline of headlands A′-B′ and C′-D′, whereas the energy of B-C has been dispersed over a greater front (B′-C′) around the bay. Energy for erosion per unit of shoreline is therefore greater on the headlands than along the bay.

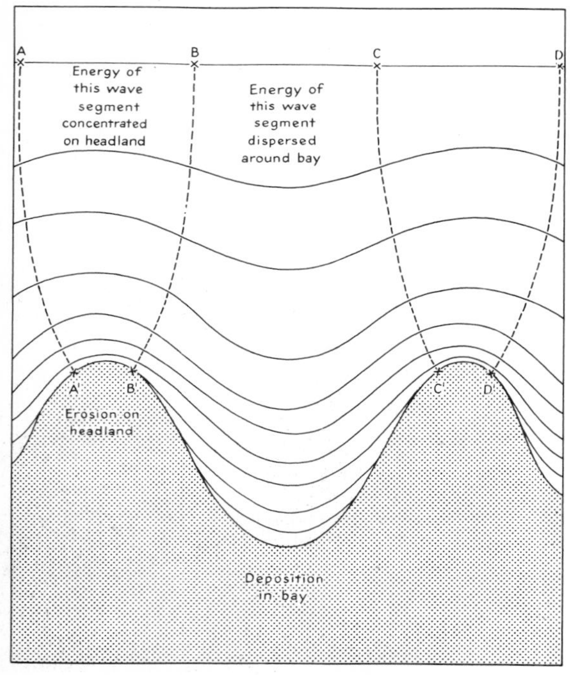

of the features of the shoreline. An exception to this generalization is an offshore island that is merely the top of a hill or a ridge that was completely surrounded by water as the sea rose in relation to the land. But even islands formed in this way are modified by erosion and deposition.

FEATURES CAUSED BY EROSION. *Wave-cut cliffs* are common erosional features along a shore, particularly where it slopes steeply down beneath the sea (see Figs. 15-26, 15-27). Here waves can break directly on the shoreline, and thus expend the greatest part of their energy in eroding the land. Wave erosion pushes the wave-cut cliff steadily back, producing a wave-cut terrace or platform at its foot. Since the surging water of the breaking waves must cross this terrace before reaching the cliff, it loses a certain amount of energy through turbulence and friction. So the farther the cliff retreats, and the wider the terrace becomes, the less effective are the waves in eroding the cliff. If sea level remains constant, the retreat of the cliffs becomes slower and slower.

Waves pounding against a wave-cut cliff produce various features, as a result of the differential erosion of the weaker sections of the rock. Wave action may hollow out cavities or *sea caves* in the cliff, and if this erosion should cut through a headland, a *sea arch* is formed. The collapse of the roof of a sea arch leaves a mass of rock, a *stack,* isolated in front of the cliff (see Fig. 15-28).

FEATURES CAUSED BY DEPOSITION. Features of deposition along a shore are built of material eroded by the waves from the headlands, and of material brought down by the rivers that carry the products of weathering and erosion from the land masses. For example, part of the material eroded from a headland may be drifted by currents into the protection of a neighboring bay, where it is deposited to form a sandy beach.

The coastline of northeastern New Jersey (Fig. 15-29) illustrates some of the features caused by deposition. Notice that the Asbury Park-Long Branch section of the coastline is a zone of erosion that has been formed by the destruction of a broad headland area. Erosion still goes on along this part of the coast, where the soft sedimentary rocks are easily cut by the waves of the Atlantic. The material eroded from this section is moved both north and south along the coastline. Sand swept northward is deposited in Raritan Bay and forms a long, sandy beach projecting northward, a *spit* known as Sandy Hook.

Just south of Sandy Hook, the flooded valleys of the Navesink River and of the Shrewsbury River are bays that have been almost completely cut off from the open ocean by sandy beaches built up across their mouths. These beaches are called *bay barriers.*

Sand moved southward from the zone of erosion has built up another sand spit. Behind it lies a shallow lagoon, Barnegat Bay, that receives water from the sea through a *tidal inlet,* Barnegat Inlet. This passage through the spit was probably first opened by a violent storm, presumably of hurricane force. Just inside the inlet a delta has been formed

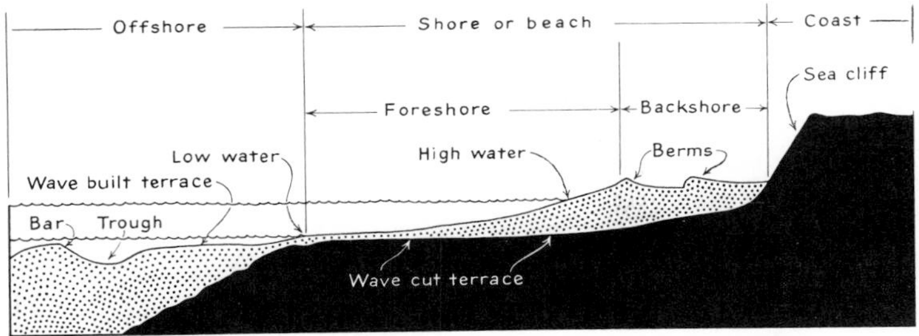

FIG. 15-25
Some of the features along a shoreline, and the nomenclature used in referring to them. In part, after Shepard, op. cit., p. 168.

of material partly deposited by the original breakthrough of the bar and partly by continued tidal currents entering the lagoon.

Long stretches of the shoreline from Long Island to Florida, and from Florida westward around the Gulf Coast, are marked by shallow, often marshy lagoons separated from the open sea by narrow sandy beaches. Many of these beaches are similar to those that enclose Barnegat Bay, apparently elongated spits attached to broad headlands. Others, such as those that enclose Pamlico Sound at Cape Hatteras, North Carolina, have no connection with the mainland. These sandy beaches are best termed *barrier islands.* It has been suggested that these islands originated from spits detached from the mainland as large storms breached them at various points. Some geologists think that they may represent spits isolated from the mainland by a slowly rising sea level. Still a third possibility is that over a long period of time wave action has eroded sand from the shallow sea floor and has heaped it up in ridges that lie just above sea level.

Another depositional feature, a *tombolo,* is a beach of sand or gravel that connects two islands, or connects an island with the mainland. Numerous examples exist along the New England coastline, fewer off the west coast, although Morro Rock, a small, steep-sided island, is tied to the California mainland by a tombolo.

CORAL REEF SHORELINES. In tropical and semitropical waters lying within a belt between about 30°N. and 25°S., many shorelines are characterized by coral reefs of varying sizes and types. These reefs are built up by individual corals with calcareous skeletons, as well as by other lime-secreting animals and plants. The coral-reef shorelines are of three types: the *fringing reef,* the *barrier reef,* and the *atoll.* A fringing reef grows out directly from a landmass, whereas a barrier reef is separated from the main body of land by a lagoon of varying width and depth opening to the sea through passes in the reef. An atoll is a ring of low, coral islands arranged around a central lagoon.

The origin of atolls has been debated for well over a century, ever since Charles Darwin first advanced his explanation in 1842. Darwin postulated that an atoll begins as a fringing reef around a volcanic island. Since the island rests as a dead load on the supporting material, it begins to subside, but at a rate slow enough for the coral to maintain a reef. With continued subsidence, the island becomes smaller and

FIG. 15-26
Waves beating directly on this New England shore provide the energy that erodes the headlands. Photo by Edward A. Schmitz.

smaller, and the actively growing section of the reef becomes a barrier reef. Then, with the final disappearance of the island below the sea, the upward-growing reef encloses only a lagoon and becomes a true atoll. In support of this theory are many volcanic islands in the Pacific now surrounded by barrier reefs. Furthermore, investigations on Bikini Island (an atoll) indicate that the volcanic rock core is surmounted by several thousand feet of coral rock. Finally, geophysical evidence suggests that there actually has been a subsidence of some of the volcanic islands of the Pacific.

The subsidence theory originally advanced by Darwin, however, does not explain the nearly constant depth of countless modern lagoons within atolls. In part to overcome this difficulty, the so-called "glacial control theory" has been advanced. Proponents of this explanation of atoll formation have postulated that volcanic islands were truncated at a lower sea level during one or more of the Pleistocene ice advances. Around the edges of such wave-planed platforms the coral reefs began to grow as the continental glaciers melted and sea level rose. The coral islands around the edge of the platforms would then ring lagoons of more or less constant depth. In summary, there is evidence in support of each theory. When the final answer is known, both may be applicable.

FIG. 15-27
Waves have cut into volcanic rocks to produce these cliffs along the shore of Attu Island in the Aleutians. Official U.S. Navy Photo.

FIG. 15-28
The sea has cut arches through this promontory. To the far right is a stack, a rock mass that erosion has cut off from the mainland. Arches State Park, California. Photo by Sheldon Judson.

SUMMARY OUTLINE

Extent of oceans
More than 70 per cent of earth's surface

Dissolved material
Gives sea water its familiar "saltiness"
Introduced into oceans by "fresh-water" streams

Sea level
Rises and falls with time
Eustatic and tectonic movements

Circulation of ocean water
Tidal currents—local, but often swift
Density currents account for movement at depth
Surface currents, wind-driven

Ocean water
Contained in one large basin that branches northward as the Pacific, Atlantic, and Arctic oceans

Topography of ocean basins
Shelves, slopes, ocean deeps
Submarine valleys, seamounts; ridges, rises, and fractures; deep-sea trenches

Sediments
Thickest on shelves and slopes
Thinnest on deep-sea floor

Shorelines
Modified by energy derived from wind-driven waves

Profile of shoreline
Changes with amount of energy available

Shoreline features
Erosion: cliffs, stacks, caves, arches, tidal inlets
Deposition: spits, beaches, bay barriers, barrier islands, tombolos

Coral reef shorelines
Tropical and subtropical waters
Reef shorelines of atolls related to changing sea level

SELECTED REFERENCES

Carson, Rachel, *The Sea Around Us* (rev. ed.). New York: Oxford University Press, 1961.

Menard, H. W., *Marine Geology of the Pacific*. New York: McGraw-Hill Book Company, 1964.

Pickard, George L., *Descriptive Physical Oceanography*. New York: The Macmillan Company, 1964.

Russell, R. J., "Instability of Sea Level," *Am. Sci.,* XLV, No. 5 (1957), 414–30.

Shepard, F. P., *Submarine Geology* (2nd ed.). New York: Harper and Row, Publishers, 1963.

Sverdrup, H. U., Martin W. Johnson, and Richard H. Fleming, *The Oceans*. Englewood Cliffs, N.J.: Prentice-Hall, Inc., 1942.

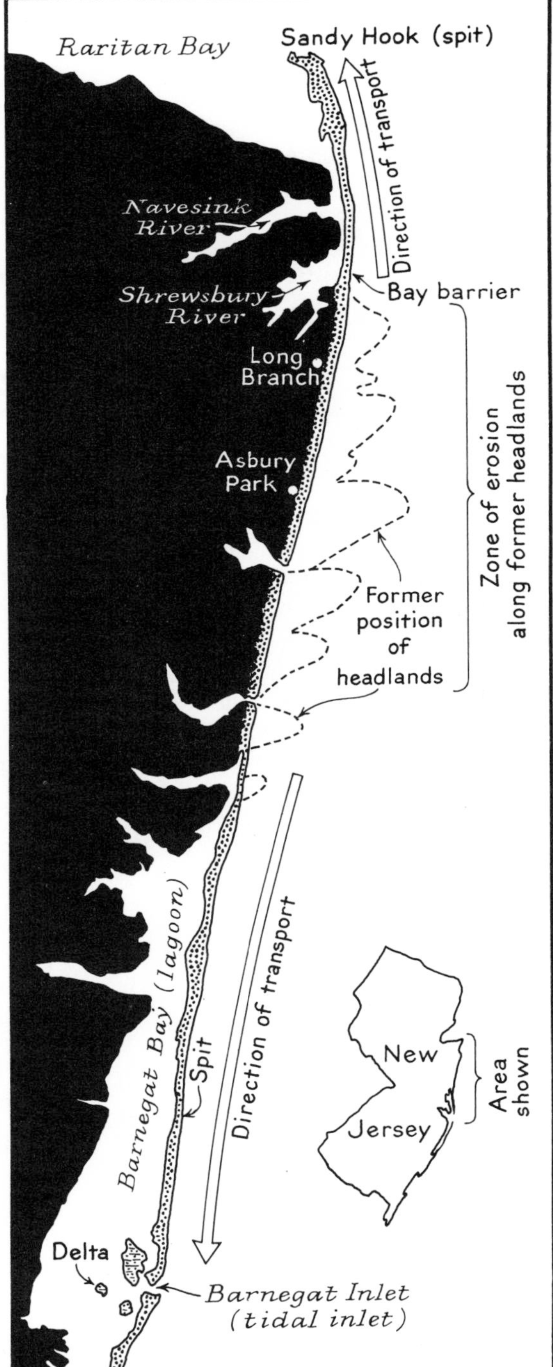

FIG. 15-29
Erosion by the sea has pushed back the New Jersey coastline as indicated on this map. Some of the material eroded from the headlands has been moved northward along the coast to form Sandy Hook, a spit. To the south, a similar but longer feature encloses Barnegat Bay, a lagoon with access to the open ocean through a tidal inlet. After an unpublished map by Paul MacClintock.

16 Deformation of the earth's crust

The crust of the earth is continuously changing. We have discussed the effects of erosion and of igneous activity, but land removed by erosion has been replaced on a much broader scale by deformation than by deposition during volcanic or fissure eruptions.

EVIDENCE OF CRUSTAL DEFORMATION

Evidence of ceaseless deformation is present in all rocks, no matter how young or old, in the earth's crust: some have been tilted (see Fig. 16-1), some ruptured; others have been depressed or elevated to thousands of feet.

In addition to this evidence of past movement recorded in the rocks themselves, other lines of evidence point to the same conclusion: the crust is being deformed. Abrupt movements, for instance, have occurred at the times of certain historic earthquakes, and slow movements are being measured by repeated land surveys and other means.

Abrupt movements

One movement of the earth's crust occurred on August 17, 1959, during a severe earthquake near Hebgen Reservoir, Montana. A section of Red Canyon dropped 20 feet, and the reservoir tilted. Were people not present to take pictures of the scarp left by this movement, we might never have known of its existence (see Fig. 16-2), because erosion soon smoothed out the evidence. Still visible in Tennessee, however, is a large section of ground that dropped vertically in the 1811 earthquake near New Madrid, Missouri. The depression formed in the earth's crust is now filled by Reelfoot Lake, under whose waters drowned trees can be seen.

At times the ground has moved upward. On a shore of Sagami Bay, Japan, not far from Yokohama, a cliff reared up during an earthquake in 1923. The amount of movement was measured by using some marine bivalves called Lithophaga ("rock eaters") as a reference. These little animals scoop out small caves for their 2-inch shells at mean sea level and spend their lives waiting for the sea to bring food at each rise of the tide. After the 1923 earthquake, rows of Lithophaga were found starved to death 15 feet above the waters that used to feed them.

Movements of the earth's crust during earthquakes have not been just up or down. In the provinces of Mino and Owari, Japan, in 1891, a great chunk of the earth's crust moved upward 10 feet and sideward 20 feet. In California in 1906, the movement was almost enitrely horizontal, about 20 feet at the maximum.

During the summer of 1954, a topographic survey was made of Fairview and Dixie valleys in Nevada. Then on December 16 there were two earthquakes centered in that area. A survey, rerun in 1955, showed the valleys twisted from 5 to 10 feet out of their former positions, and the crust was warped for miles around.

Slow movements

All the above cases of crustal deformation involved clearly visible displacements of several feet that occurred almost instantaneously. Other movements of the crust, however, are going on slowly and more or less continuously. The coast of California is moving northwestward an average of about 2 inches a year. In one place this slow creep has been noticeable without surveys: in Tres Pinos, California, a winery happened to construct one of its buildings straddling the two portions of the crust that are moving relative to each other. The building is gradually being twisted apart. In Japan, surveys have shown the crust to be composed of a mosaic of blocks, tens of miles across, that are milling about and tilting one way or another like ice cakes on a stormy sea. The amount of movement in a year is miniscule; but it is there, and it involves the entire thickness of the crust. Undeniably potent forces are at work, and these changes in the earth's crust are no superficial business.

FIG. 16-1
Rocks tilted almost vertically. Quartzite in the Great Smoky Mountains. Photo by L. B. Gillett.

Geologic evidence

We are not limited to recent events, however, for evidence that the earth's crust has been deformed. In Japan, for example, the same cliff that was thrust up in the 1923 earthquake contains other rows of Lithophaga holes. Japanese seismologists have correlated these with earthquakes in 33, 818, 1703, as well as 1923 (see Fig. 16-3). The total uplift has been 45 feet in nearly 2,000 years. This may seem unspectacular, but a little arithmetic will show that if uplift continued at this rate for two million years, not long in geologic time, the total rise would be 45,000 feet.

Rocks have been carefully studied along the section of the crust that broke along the San Andreas fault in the 1906 California quake. The studies indicate that some rocks now 350 miles apart on opposite sides of the fault were joined as a single unit seventy million years ago (see Fig. 16-4).

Another type of evidence of crustal deformation is found in mines, where coal is in the shape of the tree trunks from which it was formed. These have been found at various depths

FIG. 16-2
This 20-foot vertical scarp is in Red Canyon, Montana. It appeared during the Hebgen Lake earthquake of August 17, 1959. Photo by Gordon Oakeshott.

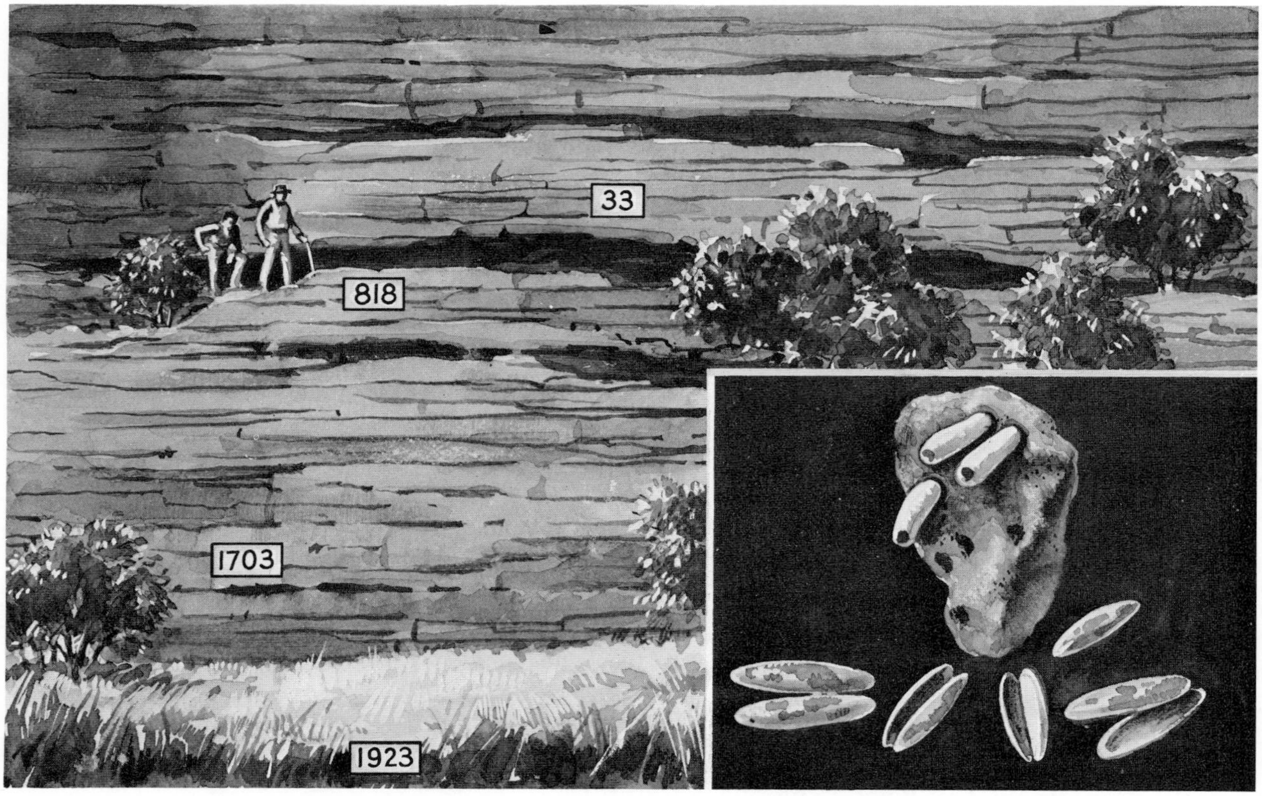

FIG. 16-3
Drawing showing elevated cliff on Sagami Bay, Japan. Lower right, Lithophaga shells.

—sometimes hundreds of feet—below the level of the swamps where the trees grew. Elsewhere, coral reefs that were living animals in ancient seas are found entombed in rocks formed from sediments that gradually buried them when the crust sank. These reefs are found at and below the present surface.

BROAD SURFACE FEATURES

Extensive movements of the crust have provided us with continents, and deformation of these continental portions of the crust has been going on continuously throughout geologic time, according to the story we read from their rocks. Deformation has produced the continental land features we find today: the plains, the plateaus, and the mountains.

On the North American continent, radioactive age determinations show that the basement complex, the oldest rocks

FIG. 16-4
A section of the San Andreas fault in the Indio Hills, California; view looks northwest. Total horizontal displacements along this fault have been estimated at 350 miles. An abrupt movement of 20 feet along this same fault caused the San Francisco earthquake of 1906. Spence Air Photos.

FIG. 16-5
Map of the broad surface features of North America.

underlying all other rocks of the continent, were formed 2.5 billion years ago. They consist of sedimentary rocks formed under the ocean and later deformed by heat and pressure. Today they are exposed in various parts of the continent, the largest exposure in the part of Canada called the *Canadian Shield,* an appreciable part of the northeastern portion of North America. It covers more than two million square miles and includes all of Labrador, much of Quebec, of Ontario and of the Northwest Territories; the northeastern parts of Manitoba and Saskatchewan and part of the Arctic Islands. Exposure at the surface could not have taken place without elevation—in this case brought about by a broad warping of the basement complex. Additional sediments were deposited on lower parts of elevated rocks, and these sediments now form the land to the south and west of the shield (see Fig. 16-5).

Bordering the shield are the interior lowlands, extending to eastern Ohio on the east, the Ouachita Mountains on the south, and the Arctic Ocean on the north. They are composed of sedimentary rocks, the oldest having been deposited in seas lapping up onto the shield during Cambrian time. On fourteen different occasions, portions of this continental lowland sank beneath the ocean and later rose above the water. So it was a restless area during this building of the continent, and the rocks bear the traces of unsettled times. Gently tilted in places, folded into small domes and basins in others, their thickness varies to more than 10,000 feet in areas of exceptional subsidence and deposition, still, they lie relatively low and flat and form plains.

FIG. 16-6
Measuring dip with Brunton compass.

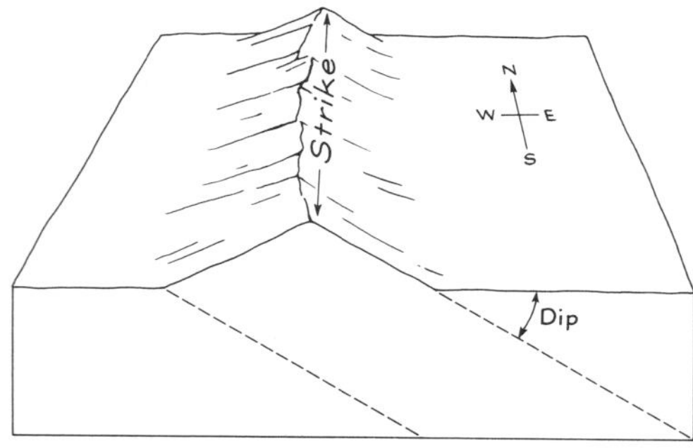

FIG. 16-7
Dip and strike. TOP: *Photo showing outcropping edges of tilted beds in southwestern Colorado, a few miles east of Durango.* BOTTOM: *Sketch illustrating terms used to describe the attitude of these beds. The beds strike north and dip 30° east. Photo by Soil Conservation Service, U.S. Dept. Agriculture.*

The sedimentary rocks surrounding the interior lowland plains have been broadly up-warped into plateaus, although the rocks still lie nearly flat. Still farther from the shield the plateaus merge into mountain ranges, which represent deformation at its greatest. As much as 50,000 feet of sediments accumulated here through the formation of basining in the basement complex; they then consolidated into sedimentary rock. Intense folding, rupture, and elevation of the entire region resulted in mountain ranges such as the Appalachians, the Basin and Range mountains, and the Rockies.

STRUCTURAL FEATURES

Plains, plateaus, and mountain ranges are broad features of the earth's surface produced by deformation of the earth's crust. The rocks that comprise them have certain structural features called *folds, faults, joints,* and *unconformities.*

In describing the attitudes of structural features, geologists have found it convenient to use two special terms: *dip* and *strike*. These are more easily described with reference to layered rocks. If a rock layer is not horizontal, the amount of its slope is called its *dip* (see Fig. 16-6), measured by specifying the acute angle that the layer makes with the horizontal. The dip is measured in the direction of the greatest amount of inclination. Its *strike* is the course or bearing of the outcrop of an inclined bed or structure on a level surface. If the rock layer is tilted so that it disappears below the surface but protrudes somewhat because of resistance to weathering, as in Fig. 16-7, strike is the direction in which the resulting ridge runs. A bed that has an east-west dip has a north-south strike, usually designated simply as north. A bed that dips either to the north or to the south has an east-west strike.

Folds

Folds are simply wrinkles produced in rocks while they are in a plastic state. They may range from a few feet to hundreds of miles across.

In the lowlands and plateaus, the sedimentary rock layers have been slightly bent over distances of hundreds of miles,

FIG. 16-8
An anticline in sandstones and shales along the C. & O. Canal, 3 miles west of Hancock, Maryland. Photo by Walcott.

FIG. 16-9
Anticline in beds of sandstone along Road 602, near Newport, Virginia. Photo by T. M. Gathright, II.

FIG. 16-10
Syncline and adjacent anticline in sandstone beds of the Moccasin formation along the river road to Goodwin's Ferry, Giles County, Virginia. Photo by T. M. Gathright, II.

forming monoclines. In a *monocline,* the strata dip for an indefinite or unknown length in one direction. Such folds cannot be readily identified because the amount of deformation is so widely distributed. Bore holes in the crust must be used to trace the bed in regions where it is not exposed at the surface.

Folds are seldom isolated structures; generally they occur in closely related groups. When the beds in a fold are arched so that they incline away from a ridge, or axis—as the roof of a house slopes away from the ridgepole—the fold is an *anticline* (see Figs. 16-8 and 16-9). An anticline's opposite is a *syncline,* its beds dipping inward from both sides toward the axis (see Fig. 16-10). Sometimes, these folds are very broad, sometimes tight and narrow. Sometimes they are tilted to one side, sometimes to one end (see Fig. 16-11). But all are anticlines

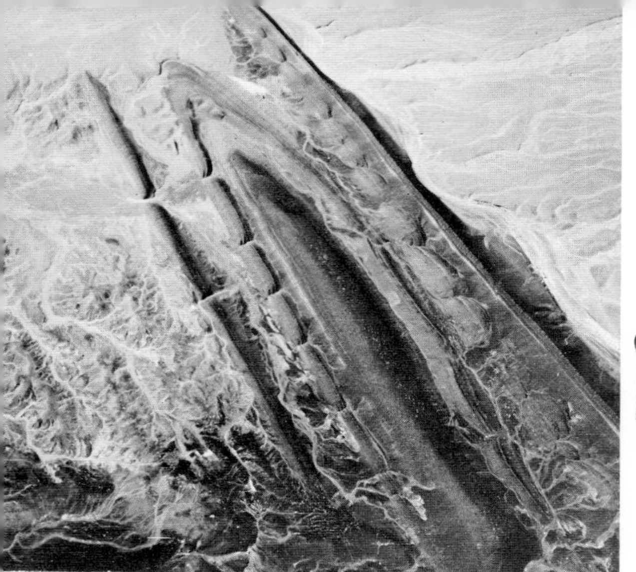

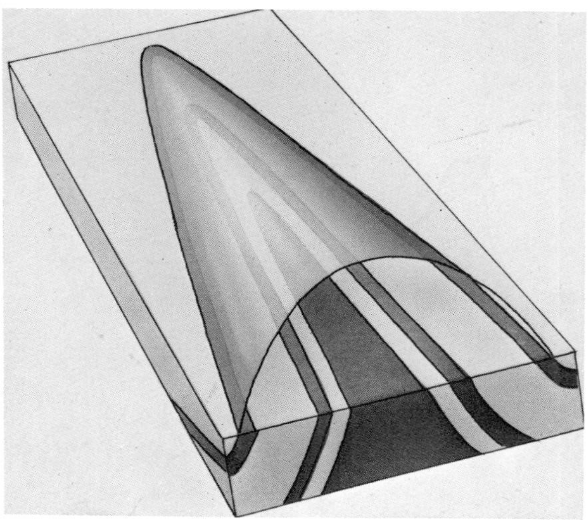

FIG. 16-11
Aerial photo showing resistant beds of an eroded plunging anticline. Sketch illustrates relationship of outcrops to fold. Spanish Sahara, Africa. Photo by U.S. Army Air Force.

FIG. 16-12
Nomenclature of a fold, shown on a plunging anticline, but applicable to a syncline, also. Axis is line joining places of sharpest folding. Axial plane includes axis and divides fold as symmetrically as possible. If axis is not horizontal, fold is said to be plunging, and angle between axis and horizonal is angle of plunge. Sides of a fold are called the limbs.

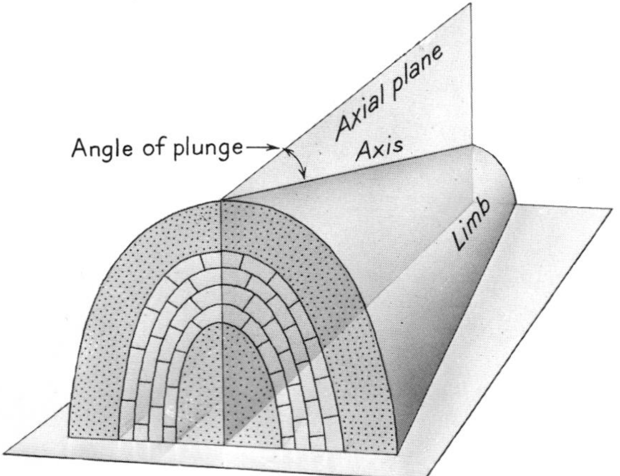

and synclines of one kind or another. The nomenclature of a fold is shown in Fig. 16-12 and some special types are illustrated in Fig. 16-13.

Faults

Crustal movements creating folds are so slow that rock masses can adjust to them without breaking. But when movements in the earth's crust are of such a nature that they fracture a rock mass and displace the separated sections, they produce a structural feature called a *fault*. The 1906 earthquake in California was caused by sudden movement along the San Andreas fault. There had been breaks along this fault before that earthquake, and there have been others since.

The displacement that takes place along most faults is not seen at the surface. In thousands of earthquakes each year, rupture of rock masses occurs without visibly disturbing the surface. And even when the surface has been displaced during an earthquake, erosion very often wears away the evidence. Records of movement, preserved in rock layers below the surface, are often encountered in mines. A seam of coal, for example, may run for miles, then be abruptly cut off by faulting of the beds.

Sometimes faults separate large masses of rock from the surrounding crust, to form *fault-block* mountains. The Sierra Nevada is actually a westward-tilted fault block: its eastern side stands nearly 10,000 feet above the abutting section of the crust. Erosion keeps modifying many of the block's details, but it is still an impressive sight, rising abruptly from the flat floor of Owens Valley. The fault block slopes gently westward until it disappears under the silts of the Great Valley of California. The highest protrusion on the Sierra Nevada is Mt. Whitney, 14,500 feet above sea level. Recurrent earthquakes in this region provide evidence that deformation is still going on. An earthquake on March 26, 1872, for example, elevated the eastern side of the Sierra Nevada by as much as 25 feet.

TYPES OF FAULTS. A fault along which the movement has been horizontal is called a *strike-slip fault*, because the slipping has been parallel to the strike of the fault. Strike-slip faults can be further designated *right-hand* or *left-hand*. The one sketched in Fig. 16-14 is right-hand: if you were walking along the road shown and came to the offset caused by the fault, you would have to go to the right to get onto the other section.

Faults have been classified in several other ways, but one of the most useful is based on the relative movement of the two rock masses affected by the fracture. The names of these masses were first devised by miners when they found themselves standing in a tunnel that cut across a fault. For obvious reasons, they called the mass of rock above the fault the *hanging wall,* and the one beneath it the *footwall.* A fault in which the hanging wall seems to have moved downward in relation to the footwall is a *normal fault*. A fault in which the hanging wall seems to have moved upward in relation to the footwall is a *thrust fault* (see Fig. 16-15).

Joints

The most common feature of rocks exposed at the surface, a *joint* is simply a break in a rock mass that shows no relative movement of the fractured rock along the break.

Joints occur in sets, the spacing between them ranging from just a few inches to a few yards. Usually the joints in any given set are almost parallel to one another, but the whole set may run in any direction—vertically, horizontally, or at some angle (see Fig. 16-16). Most rock masses are traversed by more than one set of joints, often with two sets intersecting at approximately right angles.

A pattern of essentially horizontal joints is called *sheeting* (see Fig. 16-17). Here the joints occur fairly close together near the surface, but less and less frequently the deeper we follow them down, until they seem to disappear altogether a few tens of feet below the surface. But even at some depth the rock shows a tendency to break along surfaces parallel to the surfaces of sheeting above. This type of jointing is especially common in masses of granite, and engineers often put it to good use in planning blasting operations.

Geologists have tried for years to work out a satisfactory explanation for jointing. The best theory so far suggests that jointing is the result of a *release of pressure*.[1] All rock masses that now show jointing have at some time in their past been buried beneath other rocks, where they were subjected to pressures great enough to make them flow plastically. So great was the distortion that the ions in some of the minerals comprising the rocks were twisted out of their normal positions in the crystalline structures (see Chapter 4). Then, as time passed, erosion stripped away the material under which the rocks had been buried and exposed them at the surface. Even though the pressure that had caused the plastic deformation no longer existed, the atomic distortions were permanent. In some zones, ions with the same electrical charge now found themselves side by side, but since there was no longer any confining pressure to hold them in these unnatural positions, the rocks broke apart.

Unconformities

We have mentioned examples of the complicated series of events that contributed to the building of a continent. Rock masses have been raised out of the seas in which they formed, subjected to erosion, then lowered sometimes to a level where sedimentation could be renewed. Activity of this sort produces a buried erosion surface. Some surfaces of this kind can be seen today because of another cycle of uplift. A buried surface of erosion or nondeposition that separates younger rocks from older rocks is called an *unconformity*.

The time represented by an unconformity is important geologic evidence of the history of a region, marking an interval when the surface was above the sea and sediments were not being deposited. Some unconformities represent gaps of a few thousand years; others, as many as 400 million years.

[1] P. W. Bridgman, "Reflections on Rupture," *J. Applied Physics*, IX, No. 8 (Aug., 1938), 517-28.

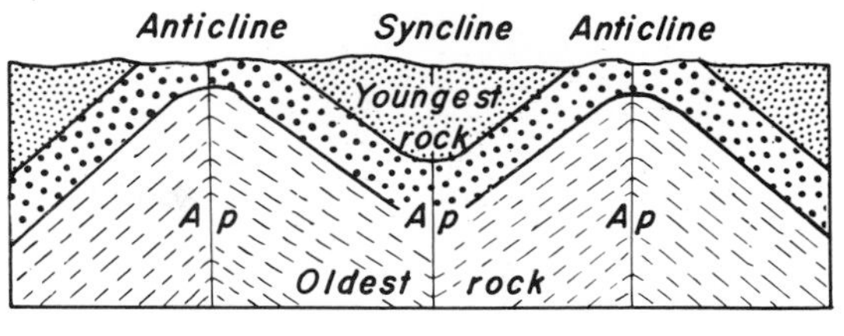

A.

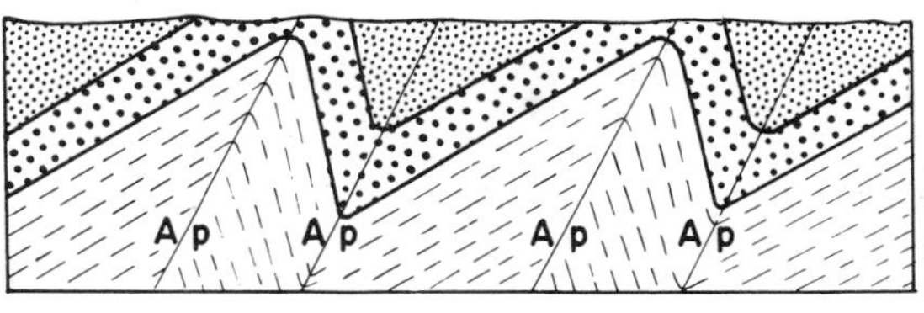

B.

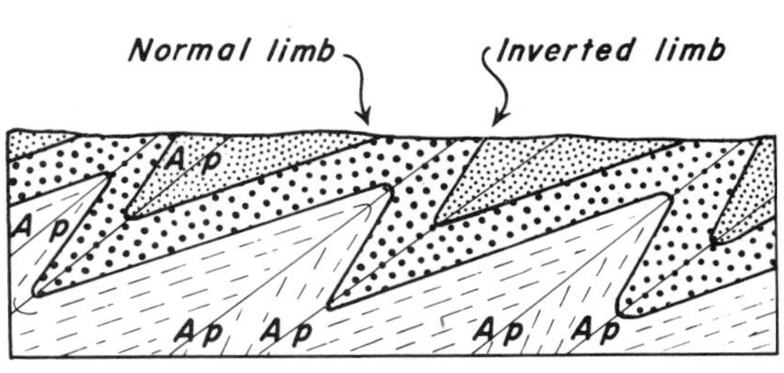

C.

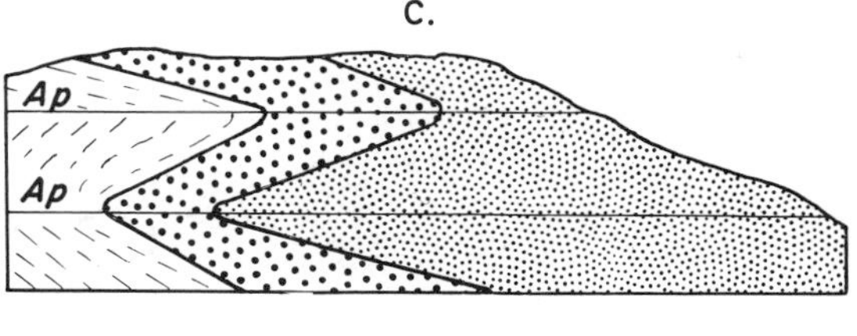

D.

FIG. 16-13
Types of folds. A: *Symmetrical fold. Axial plane (Ap) vertical, limbs dip in opposite directions at same angles.* B: *Asymmetrical fold. Axial plane inclined, limbs dip in opposite directions at different angles.* C: *Overturned fold. Axial plane inclined, limbs dip in same direction, usually at different angles.* D: *Recumbent fold. Axial plane horizontal. After Marland P. Billings, Structural Geology, 2nd ed. (Englewood Cliffs, N.J.: Prentice-Hall, Inc., 1954).*

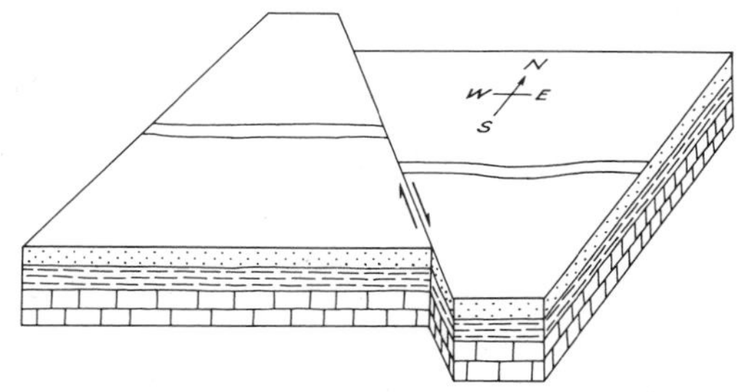

FIG. 16-14
Sketch of right-hand strike-slip fault depicting movement along San Andreas fault, California, in 1906.

FIG. 16-15
Thrust fault, 25 miles northwest of San Salvador on the Pan American Highway. Photo by Thos. F. Thompson.

FIG. 16-16
When this mass of distorted metamorphic rock with many igneous intrusions was blasted for a road cut, it broke in such a way that a set of nearly parallel major joints stood clearly revealed. They are seen here in shadows, nearly edge-on and inclined slightly from the vertical. They cut indiscriminately through the twisted metamorphic rock and massive igneous rock. Highway 2, near West Acton, Massachusetts. Photo by L. Don Leet.

There are three principal types of unconformities: angular unconformity, disconformity, and nonconformity.

ANGULAR UNCONFORMITY. An unconformity in which the older strata dip at an angle different from that of the younger strata is called an *angular unconformity*. On a wall of Box Canyon near Ouray, Colorado, can be seen some layers of Precambrian sedimentary rocks dipping at nearly 90°. Above them are some nearly-horizontal Devonian sedimentary rocks. The older rocks were deposited under the waters of the ocean and were then folded and uplifted above the water. While exposed at the surface, the tilted beds were beveled by erosion. Then, as time passed, these tilted and eroded rocks sank again beneath the ocean, where they were covered by new layers of sediments. Both were later elevated and exposed to view (see Fig. 16-18). On the basis of fossil evidence, we know that the second sedimentation began during the Devonian, indicating that more than 180 million years elapsed between the two periods of sedimentation. The Precambrian rocks meet the younger Devonian rocks at an angle, so this unconformity is an angular unconformity.

DISCONFORMITY. An unconformity with parallel beds on opposite sides is called a *disconformity*. It is formed when layered rocks are elevated and exposed to erosion, then lowered to undergo further deposition without being folded. Careful study and long experience are required to recognize a disconformity, because the younger beds are parallel to the older ones. Even geologists, who rely heavily on fossils to correlate the times of deposition of beds above and below a disconformity, have trouble identifying them. Much time and effort went into identifying three disconformities in the great pile of sedimentary rocks that form the upper walls of the Grand Canyon. Here the longest interruption in sedimentation lasted for about 80 million years, and it is represented by what is known as the "great unconformity."

NONCONFORMITY. An unconformity between igneous or metamorphic rocks that are exposed to erosion and then covered by sedimentary rocks is called a *nonconformity*. A structure of this sort is illustrated in Fig. 16-19. This shows a sandstone deposit lying on top of an eroded surface of granite. Field studies have revealed that pieces of weathered granite occur in the bottom layers of the sandstone, and also that cracks in the granite are filled with sandstone. Evidence of this type supports the conclusion that the sandstone was deposited on a weathered surface of granite; the granite did not come into its present position as an intrusion after the sandstone was formed.

FIG. 16-18
A striking angular unconformity between Precambrian sedimentary rocks that were twisted from their original horizontal attitude into a vertical position before deposition of overlying Devonian beds. In Box Canyon, near Ouray, Colorado. Photo by Kirtley F. Mather.

FIG. 16-17
Sheeting in granite. Photo by Dale.

SUMMARY OUTLINE

Deformation of the earth's crust
  Produced continents
  Worldwide

Evidence of deformation
  Abrupt movements at time of earthquakes
  Slow movements: creeping crust and tilting crustal blocks
  Recorded in rocks of all ages

Broad surface features produced by deformation
  Plains, plateaus, and mountain ranges

Structural features
  Folds, faults, joints, and unconformities
  Attitudes: dip and strike

Folds
  Wrinkles in rocks produced by folding of crust

Types of folds
  Monocline
  Anticlines and synclines

Faults
  Breaks in a rock mass with displacement of separated sections

Types of faults
  Strike-slip fault, normal fault, and thrust fault

Joints
  Breaks in rock masses that show no relative movement of fractured parts
  Occur in sets
  Produced by release of pressure

Unconformities
  Buried surfaces of erosion that separate younger rock from older rock

Types of unconformities
  Angular unconformity, nonconformity, and disconformity

FIG. 16-19
A nonconformity between light-colored granite and dark overlying Table Mountain sandstone on the Cape of Good Hope, South Africa. The cave, about 20 feet above sea level, was cut when sea level was higher than it is now. Photo by R. A. Daly.

SELECTED REFERENCES

Billings, Marland P., *Structural Geology* (2nd ed.). Englewood Cliffs, N.J.: Prentice-Hall, Inc., 1954.

De Sitter, L. U., *Structural Geology*. New York: McGraw-Hill Book Company, 1956.

Goguel, Jean, *Tectonics,* English translation from French edition of 1952, by Hans E. Thalmann. San Francisco: W. H. Freeman & Co., Publisher, 1962.

King, Philip B., *The Evolution of North America.* Princeton, N.J.: Princeton Univ. Press, 1959.

Mountains and mountain-building

17

Mountains are spectacular products of deforming forces acting on the earth's crust (see Fig. 17-1). They are called *mountains* because their peaks stand from a few hundred to a few thousand feet above the surrounding terrane. So one thing they all have in common is elevation above their immediate surroundings.

The oldest known rocks on the earth's surface today were a part of some ancient mountain range. In North America, the oldest ranges are found north of Lake Superior—"old" in rocks formed over 2,500 million years ago, "old" in deformation, "old" in topography. Throughout geologic history, mountains have been formed at various places. There is no place on the land where there have not been mountains at one time or another.

Looking around us today, we see many high mountains still withstanding weathering, mass movements, and the work of running water, wind, and glaciers. These *external* processes have been continually at work leveling the land for millions of years. We might expect that they would have reduced all the land surfaces of the earth to great plains long ago, yet we see many high mountains still standing. We must conclude, therefore, that there are *internal* forces at work that counteract the effects of the leveling processes by continually renewing the height of the land.

DISTRIBUTION OF MOUNTAINS

Mountains are the dominant surface features of the continents of the world: North America, South America, Eurasia, Africa, Australia, and Antarctica (see Fig. 17-2). Each continent has a core of old land that has been relatively stable for the past half-billion years, but the margins of the continents have been the scenes of active mountain-building.

In a general way, the major landmasses of the earth, except for about one-twentieth of the total land surface, are situated on the side of the globe opposite from water-covered areas. But this pattern becomes less striking when we realize that some mountains are actually submerged beneath the waters.

FIG. 17-1
Distorted rocks 12,000 feet high in the Bernese Alps, Switzerland. Photo by Bradford Washburn.

The Aleutian Islands, for example, are the peaks of volcanic mountains stretching out along 1,450 miles of the circumference of a circle centered at 62°40′N., 178°20′W. Other arcs of islands, including the Netherlands East Indies, festoon the western borders of the Pacific Ocean. On the outside curve of some of these island arcs there are great ocean deeps. Some of the major mountains of the continents are also arranged in arcs—the Himalayas, for example, and the mountains of Burma and Baluchistan.

The protruding peaks of the volcanic Hawaiian Islands are strung out along a nearly straight line 1,500 miles long, running to the northwest. Parallel to this line are other island chains of the Pacific: the Marquesas, Society, Tuamotu, Tubuai, and Samoa.

Under the Atlantic Ocean, from Iceland to the Antarctic, is a belt of mountains called the *Atlantic Ridge,* or *Mid-Atlantic Ridge,* which roughly parallels the outlines of the continents and is nearly midway between them. It stands as much as 6,000 feet above the ocean bottom and is covered in places by 9,000 feet of water. In a few places, its peaks protrude above the water to form islands such as the Azores, St. Helena, and Tristan da Cunha. There are similar ridges under the Indian Ocean. The *Kerguelen-Gaussberg Ridge* runs between India and Antarctica, and the *Carlsberg Ridge* runs from the Gulf of Aden south of Arabia to join Kerguelen-Gaussberg near the Maldive Islands southwest of India.

All these ridges and arcs are mountains of one kind or

FIG. 17-2
Areas more than 3,000 feet above sea level.

FIG. 17-3
Mountain ranges near Sion, Switzerland; view southwest down the Rhône Valley.
Photo by Bradford Washburn.

another, in the same way that the Himalayas, Alps, and Rockies are mountains.

DEVELOPMENT OF A MOUNTAIN RANGE

Mountains may occur as single isolated peaks, or in lines or groups, as in a mountain range (see Fig. 17-3). The development of a mountain range is called *orogeny* (oh-rah′-jenny) from the Greek *oros,* "mountain" and *genesis,* "to come into being." Orogenic forces determine where and when surface irregularities will appear in the earth's crust.

The production of a mountain range takes millions of years—years during which the internal forces of the earth are waging a constant battle against erosion. In order to produce the elevation of a Mt. Everest, for example, internal forces must push the land up faster than erosion can wear it away. But even if these forces succeed in elevating a mountain range, it is only a passing triumph, for external forces continually attack the elevated mass and in time will manage to reduce it nearly to sea level once again. But this, too, may be a passing triumph.

At the present time, the Appalachian Mountains are undergoing a new phase in their cycle of growth and decay. About 200 million years ago, according to one reconstruction of past events, sedimentary rocks were folded and elevated to heights as great as those of the modern Rockies. But by 80 million years ago, they had been eroded down to the level of flat plains. Then, 20 million years later, the region began to rise slowly once more, and now it has attained the form of a broad arch, with ridges and peaks standing out as the present Appalachian Mountains. Clearly, the forces in the earth's crust that work to create mountains are still active.

KINDS OF MOUNTAINS

It is very difficult to set up a clear-cut classification of mountains. Most mountains show all features that might be used to distinguish different types. But it is helpful to do the best we can by grouping certain types that are dominated at the present time by one characteristic. On this basis, there are four kinds of mountains: fold, fault-block, volcanic, and broadly upwarped (see Fig. 17-4). Mountain ranges consisting primarily of elevated folded sedimentary rocks are called *fold mountains.* Where faulting is dominant and has produced large elevated crustal blocks bounded by high-angle normal faults, these are called *fault-block mountains.* The rocks com-

I. Plateau

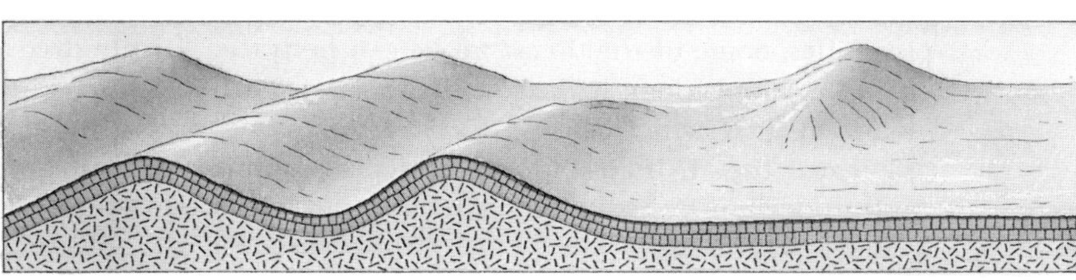

II Fold mountains – before erosion

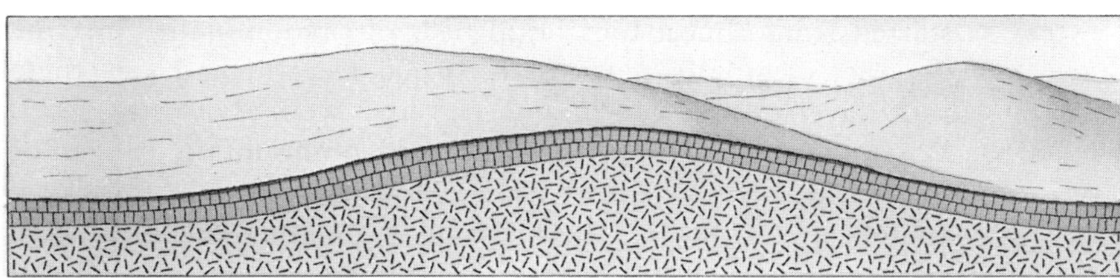

III Upwarped mountains – before erosion

IV Fault-block mountains – before erosion

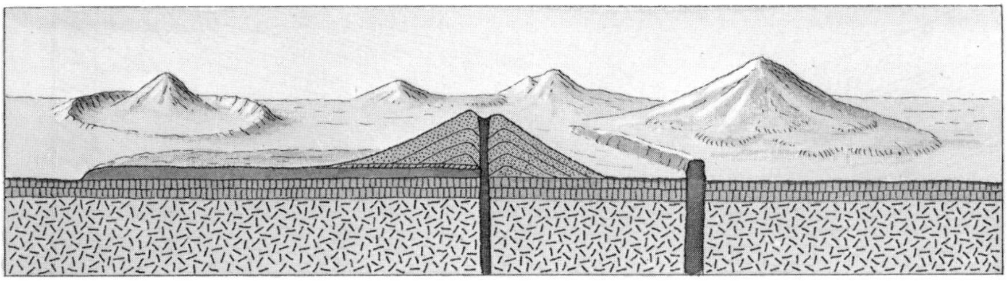

V Volcanic mountains

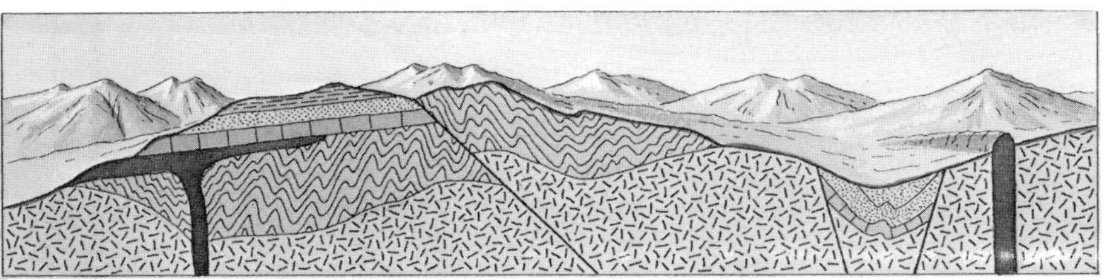

VI Complex mountains – much eroded

FIG. 17-4
Plateau and kinds of mountains. After A. K. Lobeck.

posing the fault blocks may be either flat-lying or folded. Mountains built up by the extrusion of lava and pyroclastic debris are called *volcanic mountains* (see Chapter 5). When broad upwarping of the crust has elevated and exposed rocks to erosion that produced mountainous relief, the resulting landforms are *broadly upwarped mountains.* The rocks thus broadly upwarped may be flat-lying, or folded during some previous cycle in their history, or both.

FIG. 17-5
Folded and elevated sediments form these mountains in the Rockies. Photo by D. B. Dowling.

Fold mountains

The Rockies, Alps, Andes, Himalayas, Juras, and Carpathians are fold mountains, the most numerous of the ranges. Fold mountains provide us with spectacular examples of deformed rocks: folds are conspicuous (see Fig. 17-5); anticlines and synclines are numerous and have been sliced open to view by streams cutting into them as the land moved upward during elevation. Along the borders of these mountains, faults become more numerous, and there are few unbroken folds. Some of the faults are normal faults on the flanks of anticlines. Many are low-angle thrust faults that have pushed masses of rock over other portions of the crust for miles. Some of the thrust faults can be traced for hundreds of miles along their strike, until they eventually die out. The lands against which these rocks were pushing now stand as plateaus—broad, high-standing regions deeply cut by streams and underlain by sedimentary rocks relatively little deformed.

Fold mountains were formed from thick deposits of sedimentary rock. The first Appalachian Mountains, for example, started from almost horizontal beds of predominantly marine deposits originally more than 40,000 feet thick. Later these rock layers were folded and elevated well above sea level. We find similar rocks in other folded mountain ranges of the world. In the Central Rocky Mountains and in the Coast Ranges of California, the original sedimentary deposits were approximately 30,000 feet thick. And marine deposits in the Himalayas may have been even thicker than that before elevation.

The major mountain ranges of the world have developed from thick deposits of sediments that accumulated in geosynclines. *Geosynclines* are huge sediment-filled troughs that

FIG. 17-6
A geosyncline underlying a part of the southern peninsula of Michigan. After A. C. Lane.

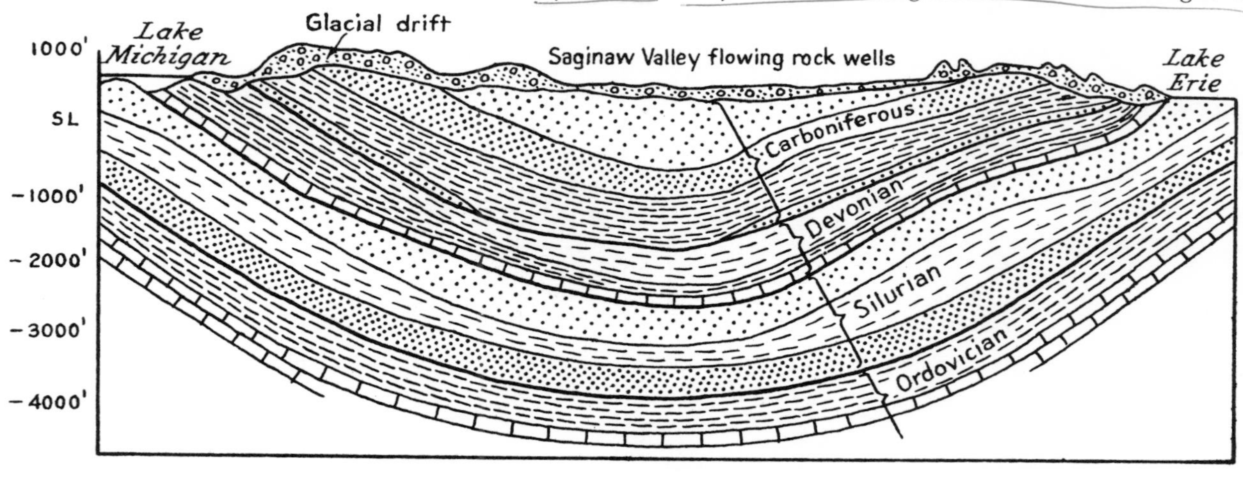

formed, in certain areas, from deformation of the earth's crust. Geosyncline means, literally "earth syncline" (see Fig. 17-6). Usually scores of miles wide and hundreds of miles long, many geosynclines have accumulated sediments 50,000 feet or more in thickness, their fossils, texture, ripple marks, and other features indicating that the water in which they accumulated was not deep—around 1,000 feet at most, it is estimated. So there must have been a slow sinking of the crust, as deposition of sediments more or less kept pace.

FORMATION OF A GEOSYNCLINE. We know that the development of fold mountain ranges is always preceded by the formation of geosynclines. But this is not a simple process that takes place all at once—a huge trough on the earth's surface does not suddenly develop into which the sediments pour until it is filled up. Rather, the formation of a geosyncline involves a slow, continuous downwarping of the earth's crust, with the deposition of sediments going on at the same time. The growing weight of the sediments tends to deepen the trough, but not enough to make room for the thicknesses known to have accumulated.

As a corollary to the problem of how the geosyncline sinks, there is the necessity for elevation of adjacent land to supply the staggering quantities of sediments to fill the geosyncline. Then, the geosyncline must also be elevated if it is to become a mountain range. There seems to have been continuous movement of the crust, sometimes down, sometimes up, in the making of mountains.

The sediments in a geosyncline eventually sink to levels where they become surrounded by denser rock, and their own buoyancy sets a limit to the depth to which they can sink under their own weight. For example, assume that we begin with a trough 1,000 feet deep and that we pour sediments into it. The sediments will push the bottom of the trough down into the denser substratum until it is 2,500 feet below sea level. But by that time, the sediments will have filled the trough to sea level, and there is no room to add any more. The whole system has become isostatic, or in balance, and the thickness of the sediments cannot be increased just by load.

The geosynclines that eventually became the first Appalachians had certain features that are common to all geosynclines. Sediments were delivered to them from bordering lands. Rocks that formed in the geosynclines were composed of types of sediment that accumulate only in shallow water—probably not deeper than 1,000 feet. Sometimes the sediments actually piled up above sea level—in south-central Pennsylvania, for example, an 8,000-foot layer of rock, originally deposited over a great delta plain, grades northwestward into limestone that was formed in a shallow sea. These rocks constitute only part of a deposit that was originally 40,000 feet thick. Such a thick deposit of shallow-water sediments could have accumulated only if deforming forces slowly deepened the geosyncline while sedimentation kept pace with the deepening.

Modern geosynclines are developing too slowly for us to

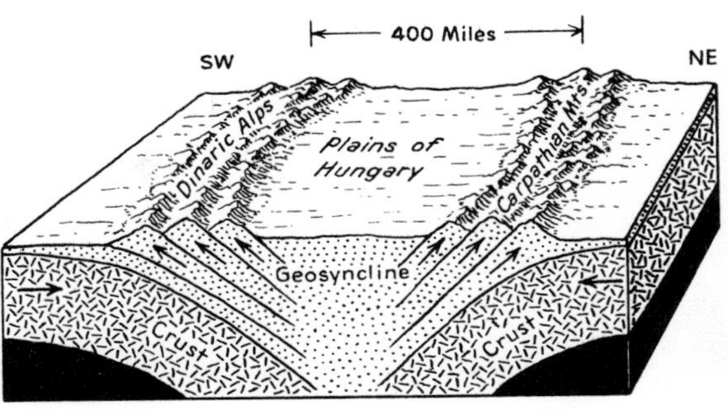

FIG. 17-7
Hypothetical section to illustrate a theory of the connection between geosyncline and the mountains formed from it. After Leopold Kober.

measure them directly. But by assuming that the rate of sedimentation in past eras was similar to the present rate, geologists have computed that the geosynclines of the past may have grown from 500 to 1,000 feet deeper every million years. Possibly, however, the modern rate of sedimentation is greater than in the past, because of the greater average height of the land today.

DEFORMATION OF GEOSYNCLINES. At some stage in the deepening and filling of a geosyncline, forces act to fold and elevate it. When its sedimentary rocks become so deeply buried that their strength is reduced by heat and pressure, they become folded instead of being forced more and more deeply into the substratum, and the elevation of fold mountain ranges begins (see Fig. 17-7).

Rocks at the surface are brittle, and they break before they flow. But under the heat and deep burial of the geosyncline they become plastic and change their shape and volume by folding and slow flow. It is at this stage in the process that bodies of molten rock are formed. Exactly how or why this happens, we still do not know. Clearly, however, igneous activity is prominent during the elevation of geosynclines.

The expansion of deeply buried rocks as they are heated or melted causes the whole overlying mass to rise. Near the edges of the geosyncline the rocks are squeezed upward and outward along great thrust faults; in the central area, they are pushed upward to form an intermountain plateau (see Fig. 17-8).

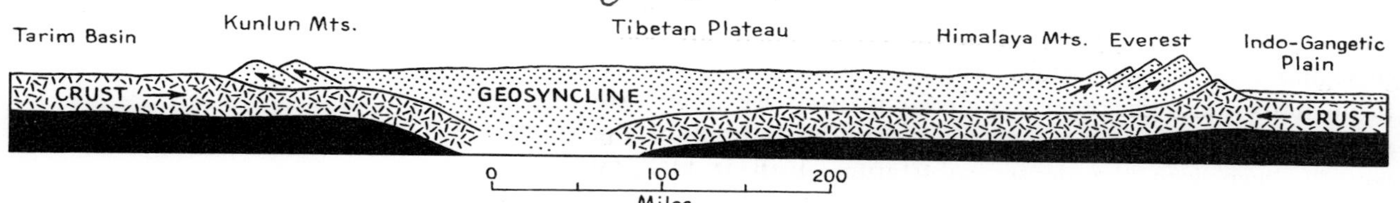

FIG. 17-8
Diagrammatic section illustrating a theory of the geosynclinal origin of the Himalaya Mountains, Tibetan Plateau, and Kunlun Mountains. After Arthur Holmes.

ZONES OF GEOSYNCLINES. Mountain ranges such as the first Appalachians were not formed by the deformation of *one* geosyncline, but rather by the deformation of many. Two great belts of roughly parallel geosynclines once occupied the region where the Appalachians now stand. Strung out along the Atlantic side of the continent from Newfoundland to Alabama, they extended 1,500 miles in length and 350 to 400 miles in width. They were supplied with sediments from elevated landmasses in what is now the central part of the United States, and with volcanic landmasses in what is now the Atlantic Ocean.

One zone of geosynclines bordered the continent itself and contained deposits of lime and sandstone. This zone was nonvolcanic. The other zone was offshore and was supplied by clay sediments from volcanic island arcs. This zone was marked by igneous activity (see Fig. 17-9). Moreover, the detailed history of each individual geosyncline within these zones was independent of the histories of its neighbors. But we can say that mountain-building in the entire area began

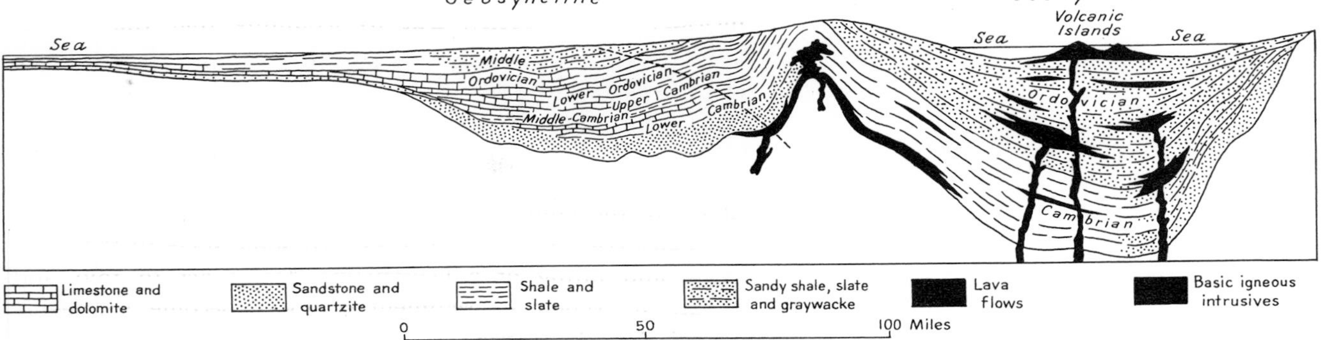

FIG. 17-9
Possible conditions in Appalachian geosynclines across New York, Vermont, and New Hampshire at the close of Ordovician time. After reconstruction by Kay.

in the early Paleozoic and reached its climax at the end of the Paleozoic.

Along the western border of North America two other geosynclinal zones similar to those in the east were also being filled with sediments during the Paleozoic. They extended more than 3,000 miles from Alaska to Mexico, and their combined width reached a maximum of 1,000 miles. Deformation and elevation began in these geosynclines at least as early as it did in the Appalachian belts, but it was more extensive, and it is continuing at the present time.

Modern counterparts of these ancient geosynclinal zones are thought to exist between the Pacific border of Asia and the arcs of volcanic islands off its coast.

CRUSTAL SHORTENING. For many years it has been generally thought that folded and thrust-faulted mountains have involved shrinking of the earth's crust. Some believe the shrinking occurred in the entire crust of the earth, others that it was limited to the upper part of the crust. There are some geologists who see the folding and thrusting as a result of sedimentary rocks sliding along an unyielding basement complex. But Billings concluded that "field geology indicates that the basement rock often participates in the folding."[1]

To estimate the amount of crustal shortening that appears to have resulted from folding of sedimentary beds, we determine the length of the beds before and after folding. Across a section of the Appalachians in Pennsylvania, for example, points originally 81 miles apart are now only 66 miles apart. They have been folded 15 miles closer to each other. This shortening is 18 per cent of the original distance between the points. In the Alps, points originally 390 miles apart are now separated by only 93 miles—a shortening of 77 per cent.

Intermountain plateaus

Bordering fold mountain ranges, and also enclosed within them, are high-standing plateaus underlain by relatively flat-lying rocks. A well-known example is the Colorado Plateau, a mile or more high, into which rivers have cut the Grand Canyon and a series of related gorges of truly mountainous relief (see Fig. 17-10). The plateau of Tibet, 14,000 feet high, is ringed by the folded mountains of the Himalayas, Kara-

[1] Marland P. Billings, "Diastrophism and Mountain Building," *Geol. Soc. Am. Bull.* LXXI (1960), 369.

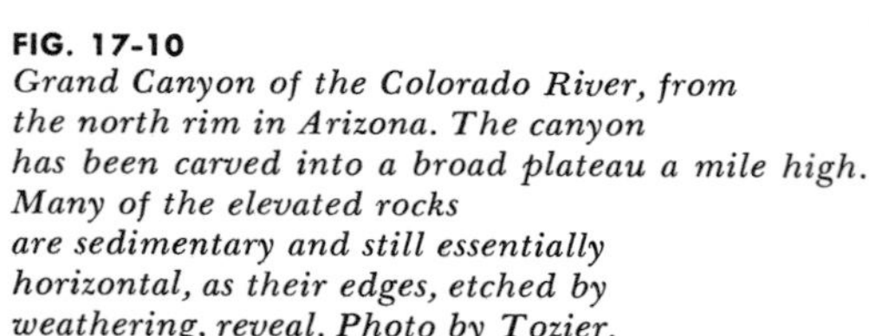

FIG. 17-10
Grand Canyon of the Colorado River, from the north rim in Arizona. The canyon has been carved into a broad plateau a mile high. Many of the elevated rocks are sedimentary and still essentially horizontal, as their edges, etched by weathering, reveal. Photo by Tozier.

korum, Kunlun, and Tien Shan; the Iranian Plateau by the Zagros Mountains and Northeast Border Ranges; the Plains of Hungary by the Dinaric Alps and Carpathian Mountains.

Broad vertical movements are required to elevate these thousands of square miles of nearly horizontal rocks to thousands of feet above sea level.

Fault-block mountains

Mountains formed from large uplifted sections of the earth's crust bounded by faults are classified as *fault-block mountains.* Their rocks, originally deposited in geosynclines, have sometimes been folded during an earlier cycle of deformation before they were uplifted; at other times their rocks are nearly flat-lying. Fault-block mountains were elevated at about the same time as their neighboring fold and broadly upwarped plateaus.

Fault-block mountains are bounded on at least two opposite sides by high-angle faults, usually normal ones. These mountains are often slightly tilted, causing elevation of one side and depression of the other.

There are classic examples of fault-block mountains in the Basin and Range country of Nevada: Oquirrh Range, Wasatch Range, Ruby-East Humboldt Range, Stillwater Range; and in California, the Inyo Mountains and Sierra Nevada (see Fig. 17-11). Fault-block mountains occur in other parts of the world, frequently adjacent to fold mountains. Although produced by the same regional deformation that elevates all mountain ranges, they are a special type.

Upwarped mountains

Many mountains today owe their present height and appearance to the broad upwarping and erosion that carved their elevated rocks. Mountains formed in this manner include the present Adirondacks, Appalachians, Black Hills, highlands of Labrador, and many other mountains in other parts of the world.

It is believed that most upwarped mountains had an earlier history similar to our present fold mountains. Then they were worn down and later re-elevated. The Adirondack Mountains, for example, were completely eroded by the time of the Cambrian period. They were then covered by a relatively thin veneer of sediments. Eventually, broad upwarping re-elevated the Adirondack region and brought it into the influence of erosional processes once again. The present Adirondack mountains were carved from the ancient Precambrian rocks after the thin covering of Paleozoic sediments had been removed.

While a thin layer of sediments was being deposited in the Adirondack region, thick sedimentary deposits were accumulating in the Appalachian geosynclines. It is believed that the first Appalachians were fold mountains, as has been pointed out. But the present ones owe their elevation to broad upwarping. In fact, most existing mountains that were initially folded and elevated prior to Tertiary time were reduced to low elevations and have been re-elevated by broad upwarping since Tertiary time.

Crust-deforming forces appear to be active the world over, but the effects they produce are governed by local crustal conditions and hence can be quite variable. At one time and place there may be warping to form a geosyncline. At the same place but a later time, the same portion of the earth's crust may undergo broad upwarping. The oldest known rocks on the globe are still not free from operation of these deforming forces.

ISOSTASY

The end products of mountain-building are great masses of rocks standing high above adjacent rocks, and one of the problems of geology is to explain why such masses do not sink back to their original levels.

Three possible explanations have been suggested. One is that the crust underlying mountains is strong enough to support them as dead loads. Laboratory experiments, however, have shown that no rocks are strong enough to support the weight of even comparatively low hills. Consequently, we must conclude that the crust beneath the mountains is not by itself capable of supporting the dead weight of mountains.

Another possible explanation is that mountains retain their elevation only because the forces that originally formed them are still active. Certainly in areas where mountain-building

FIG. 17-11
Section across the Basin and Range country of Nevada, Colorado Pleateau, and Colorado Piedmont. After A. K. Lobeck.

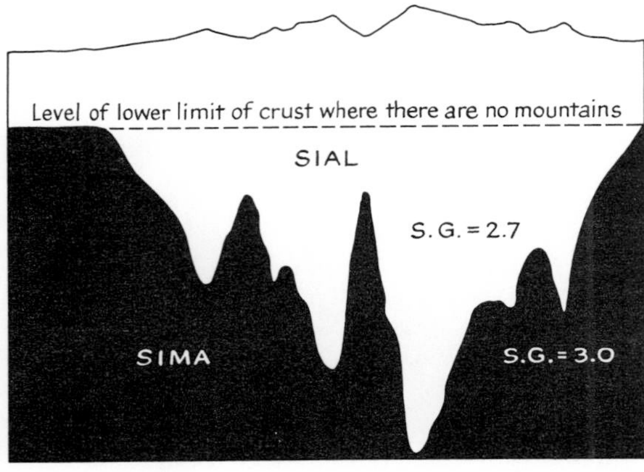

FIG. 17-12
Schematic representation of mountain roots. After Daly.

forces still make their presence known through earthquakes and changes of level it is quite reasonable to assume that they are contributing to the continued elevation of mountains. In fact, it would be difficult to point with assurance to any region on the globe that lacks at least some kind of active internal force.

A third explanation for the continued elevation of mountains is that they are isostatic in relationship to surrounding portions of the crust. That is, mountains are merely the tops of great masses of rock floating in a substratum, as icebergs float in water (see Fig. 17-12). Such a situation requires a substratum of rock, at not too great a depth, that will flow to adjust itself to an excess load. This rock, however, need not be a liquid in the ordinary sense of the word. It could be rock in a state not unlike that of silicone putty, which can be shaped into a ball that bounces but which under a very slight load—even under its own weight—gradually loses its shape entirely. Hence this rock would be rigid enough for stresses of short duration, but would have very little real strength over a long period of time. A small piece of art gum nine-tenths as dense as silicone putty would, in time, sink into the putty until it was floating with only a tenth of its volume above the surface. Likewise, a mountain range with an average specific gravity of 2.7 (that of granite) can sink into a layer of plastic simatic rock with a specific gravity of 3.0 until the range is floating with a "root" of about nine-tenths and a mountain of one-tenth its total volume.

If gravity were the only force acting on the earth's surface, all masses of surface rocks would be standing today at heights governed by their thickness and the ratio of their specific gravity to that of the rocks supporting them. This principle, that different portions of the earth's crust should balance out, depending on differences in their mass and specific gravity, is called *isostasy.* Isostasy (eye-sauce′-ta-see), from the Greek *iso,* "equal, alike, the same," and *stasis,* "standing," means "in equal balance."

Tests for isostasy

Geologists the world over are trying to determine how nearly the surface of the earth approaches isostasy.[2] One test for determining how near an area has progressed toward isostasy makes use of a plumb bob suspended on a plumb line. Originally, this device was simply a lead bob on a string—hence the term "plumb," from the Latin *plumbum,* "lead." Like every other object on the globe, the suspended bob is pulled by gravity. On the surface of a perfect sphere with uniform density, the bob would be pulled straight down, and the plumb line would point directly toward the center of the sphere. But if there is any variation from these ideal conditions—that is, if there are surface irregularities on the sphere, or if its density is not uniform—the plumb line will be deflected as the bob is attracted by the greatest concentrations of density.

[2] Phrases like "isostatic equilibrium" and "isostatic balance" are widely used in geological literature, but they are redundant.

Because the earth is not a perfect sphere, we would expect the plumb line to be affected by local variations. Assume that we are using the device over an area of uniform density, but near a high mountain with the same average density. Our plumb bob would be attracted by the mountain, and the plumb line would not point directly toward the center of the earth. Or suppose that we were on a smooth stretch of land but that small variations of density occurred at shallow depths (or large variations at great depths). The bob would be pulled toward the region of greatest density and again the plumb line would not point directly toward the center of the earth.

In the middle of the nineteenth century, British surveyors were using the plumb line to sight stars, in an attempt to fix the latitude of Kaliana, near Delhi in northern India, and of Kalianpur, about 375 miles due south. They observed that the difference in latitude between these two stations was 5° 23′ 37.06″. Then they checked the difference directly by standard surveying methods. The difference computed from these measurements was 5° 23′ 42.29″. There was a discrepancy of 5.23″, or about 500 feet, between the measurements. That may not seem very much over a distance of 375 miles, but it was too large to be explained by errors of observation. Scientists then concluded that the plumb line at Kaliana had been deflected more by the attraction of the Himalaya Range than it had been at Kalianpur farther south. Actually, however, the discrepancy should have been three time as large, assuming that the mountains were of the same average density as the surrounding terrane and that they were resting as a dead load on the surface.

The discrepancy first of all points to the conclusion that the Himalayas are *not* as dense as the surrounding terrane. Moreover, since the earth's crust cannot carry a dead weight such as the Himalayas, part of the lighter Himalayan rock must have sunk into the denser plastic substratum. Thus, the Himalayas and also the earth beneath them were attracting the plumb bob much less than expected. This theory fitted the measurements. And since it implied that "the higher the mountain, the deeper the root," it was evidence in support of isostasy.

Another test for isostasy is the direct measurement of the intensity of gravity. Since "weight" is simply a measure of the force that gravity exerts upon a mass, we can test variations in gravity by accurately measuring the weight of a mass at different places on the earth's surface. An object weighing one pound at sea level will, on the same scale at 10,000 feet above sea level, produce a smaller reading, reflecting the decrease in gravitational pull that accompanies increase in distance between the earth and the object. Accordingly, changes in the force of gravity are reflected in changes in the weight of the mass. An instrument used for measuring variations in the weight of a mass is called a *gravity meter*.

Gravity is usually defined in terms of the acceleration it produces on a body falling freely in a vacuum. This acceleration may be measured in feet per second per second, but it is more commonly expressed in centimeters per second per second. An acceleration of one centimeter per second during each second of free fall is a unit called the *gal,* after Galileo, who was a pioneer in the study of gravity. The acceleration of gravity at sea level is around 980 gals, but changes as small as a ten-millionth of this may be significant. Consequently, the common unit in which gravity differences are expressed is the *milligal,* or one-thousandth of a gal. A salt dome 2,000 feet in radius with its center 4,000 feet below the surface, and surrounded by sedimentary rock about 10 per cent denser, causes gravity directly above it to be about 1 milligal less than gravity at nearby points beyond the effect of the salt dome.

Now, the force of gravity at a given point is governed by (1) the distance of that point from the center of the earth—the farther it is from the center of the earth, the less an object will weigh; (2) the latitude of the point, and (3) the density of the materials in the immediate vicinity of the point. Factors 1 and 2, which can be computed for any point, enable us to establish a so-called theoretical value of gravity for a point. If a gravity meter shows the actual value to be different from this theoretical value, the difference is called a *gravity anomaly*. Thus, the force of gravity on top of a mountain should be less than that on the adjacent plain, but measurements show that no such simple relationship exists. This gravity anomaly and others result from irregularities in factor 3; actually, they supply evidence on how nearly the earth's surface does approach isostasy. If the earth were completely isostatic, of course, there would be no anomalies.

Many places on the earth's surface depart from isostasy. In the western mountains of the United States a belt of negative anomalies exists where actual gravity is less than theoretical gravity, indicating that these mountains have extensive sialic rocks under them. There is a negative anomaly of 338 milligals along the ocean trench bordering Puerto Rico, proof that the trench results from forceful depression of the crust and represents a radical departure from isostasy.

Positive anomalies on parts of the Island of Cyprus are as great as 280 milligals. On the other hand, parallel to, and south of, the island of Java, there is a belt of negative anomalies up to 165 milligals, suggesting that here a mass of lighter rocks is imbedded in a denser simatic substratum. A negative anomaly that has been attributed to a deep granitic root exists over the axis of the Karakorum Range of the Himalayas. In fact, few, if any, regions have been measured that are completely isostatic. One interpretation of this would be that internal forces are still at work everywhere deforming the earth's crust and preventing it from settling down into equilibrium.

CAUSE OF MOUNTAIN-BUILDING

Geologists have not yet agreed on a theory to explain the forces that deform the earth's crust and elevate mountain ranges. In fact, they differ as to whether the forces are dominantly horizontal, dominantly vertical, or combinations of both in different proportions. Adding to the problem, deformation and elevation seem to have been simultaneous in some mountain ranges, but at different times in others.

A valid theory must account for all the kinds of deformation found in all mountain ranges: the formation of geosynclines; folding, faulting, and elevation; and the generation of magma that accompanies the development of some mountain ranges.

Not very long ago, many geologists believed that mountain-building had been confined to certain epochs in earth history—the close of the Paleozoic, for example. But as more and more information became available it became clear that throughout the history of the earth, mountain-building has always been in process somewhere on the globe. The oldest rocks that have been studied are 3,370 million years old, and even these are probably remnants of an ancient mountain system. So in our attempts to explain mountain-building, we must keep in mind that this activity has persisted from the beginning of geologic time.

Several facts have been accepted by most geologists. One is that during the formation of fold mountain ranges there is a reduction in surface area—a shortening of the distance between points on the surface. This involves squeezing forces, such as result from horizontal compression. Then, it is generally agreed that in order to have mountains there must be vertical uplift, as in the elevation of fold mountains, in the elevation of many flat-lying rocks, and also in the re-elevation of older deformed rocks, such as the Appalachians. But on what causes these horizontal and vertical forces, there is no general agreement.

Colossal amounts of energy are required to deform and elevate large portions of the earth's crust into mountain ranges. To explain mountain-building, we must account for the source of this energy. The best we can do here is to outline three of the more prominent theories: (1) the thermal contraction theory, (2) the convection current theory, and (3) the continental migration theory.

Thermal contraction theory

The thermal contraction theory is based on the idea that heat is lost during the cooling of the earth. The loss of heat causes a decrease in the volume of the earth, and the crust yields to adjust itself to the earth's shrinking interior.

Regardless of the details of the earth's origin, there is strong evidence that at one stage it was a molten sphere. As it cooled, its radius decreased and its surface area shrunk. The thermal contraction theory states that the original heat energy present in the earth at its formation has provided the source of energy for mountain-building.

Harold Jeffreys, a world-renowned British geophysicist, supports this theory with computations based on seismological evidence and on the behavior of rocks subjected to heat and pressure in the laboratory. He has come to certain conclusions on the history of the earth's cooling: the earth is solid to a depth of 1,800 miles, but the temperature of this solid material varies. Near the surface, the rocks are undergoing no further cooling; but from a depth of a few miles to about 400 miles, the rocks are still cooling. Below 400 miles, the rocks are still as hot as they were when first solidified.

On the basis of these temperature conditions, we can picture three zones. The inner and outer zones are fixed in volume because they are not losing heat. But the middle zone is cooling, shrinking as it cools. The outer zone attempts to adjust itself to the shrinking zone below, and in this process becomes squeezed. The squeezing buckles it into low basins where sediments may accumulate and high places to provide the sedimentary materials. When the buckling of the crust pushes the sediments in the geosyncline to a depth at which the temperatures melt them, the melted sediments expand and produce the elevation of the geosyncline to form mountains.[3]

Some geologists have criticized the thermal contraction theory on the grounds that it fails to provide for enough shrinkage of the crust. Relying on seismological data that show the outer 400 miles of the mantle to be solid, some geologists conclude that the earth cannot have lost significant amounts of heat in the last 2 billion years—at least not enough heat to counterbalance the great volume of material we find in mountains. Another criticism involves the distribution of mountain ranges in time, in direction, and in place. Some feel that a contracting crust would shorten every great circle the same amount, and that mountains should therefore be more evenly distributed than they are. Underlying this objection is the assumption that heat is lost uniformly through the earth's crust; not taken into account is the localized heat and material loss due to volcanic eruptions.

Convection-current theory

Convection currents within the earth have also been suggested as an explanation of mountain-building. Convection is a mechanism by which heat is transferred from one place to another by the movement of particles. Its operation is illustrated in heating a pan of water on a stove: the water at the bottom heats fastest, rises (because it is lighter), and is replaced by cooler water sinking to the bottom. Under proper conditions, a pattern of circulation called a *convection current* is established. Convection currents normally occur in pairs, each called a *convection cell.*

It has been proposed that convection currents originating at the core may be circulating in the mantle of the earth (see Fig. 17-13). The materials of the mantle do not behave like water, but they do flow plastically if subjected to enough force. They have some strength, even though it may not be great. So to establish convection currents, the heat and

[3] Harold Jeffreys, *The Earth,* 4th ed. (New York: Cambridge Univ. Press, 1959), pp. 303-10.

expansion at the core must build up until the push to get out is greater than the strength of the overlying mantle. It has been computed that if we assume the mantle to be in equilibrium at a given time, then heating at the core has finally expanded the nearby mantle material until it starts to move upward, for about 25 million years it would gradually "speed up" until it was moving upward 5 inches a year. After currents reached the base of the crust, they would be deflected horizontally, move along the base of the crust, and eventually plunge back toward the core again. They are supposed to drag the crust downward, forming geosynclines. After the geosynclines have deepened to 50,000 feet, it is proposed that the currents crumpled and folded the sediments that were by now softened by immersion in hot mantle rocks. Then the convection currents lost their drive and slowed to a stop. Meanwhile, melting in the geosynclines caused local expansion and produced the uplift to form mountains. A quiescent period followed while heat at the core again built up where the strength of the overlying rocks was exceeded and another cycle could start.

This theory uses heat as the source of the energy. In its support are offered calculations that the temperature of the earth's core must be enormously high to keep the material liquid (see Chapter 20) under pressures of 25 to 50 million pounds per square inch. So heat in ample supply is presumably available for driving the convection mechanism. Also, folded and deformed rocks show that they yield plastically under the right conditions of heat and pressure, so it requires no great extrapolation from laboratory and field data to picture the materials of the mantle as capable of plastic movement assumed by the convection theory.

On the other hand, seismological evidence shows that the entire mantle has not been stirred by convection currents, regardless of the plausibility of arguments that it could be. Increasingly precise data on the travel times of waves in the mantle are becoming available through studies of earth waves generated by earthquakes and nuclear explosions. These data now clearly establish that there are zones in the mantle structure. There could be no such layering in the mantle if convection currents had stirred it, mixing the materials between the core and the top.

There are geologists who believe that the convection theory also fails to account for the geographical distribution of mountains, or for their dates of formation, in even a rough approximation.

FIG. 17-13
Convection currents and cells.

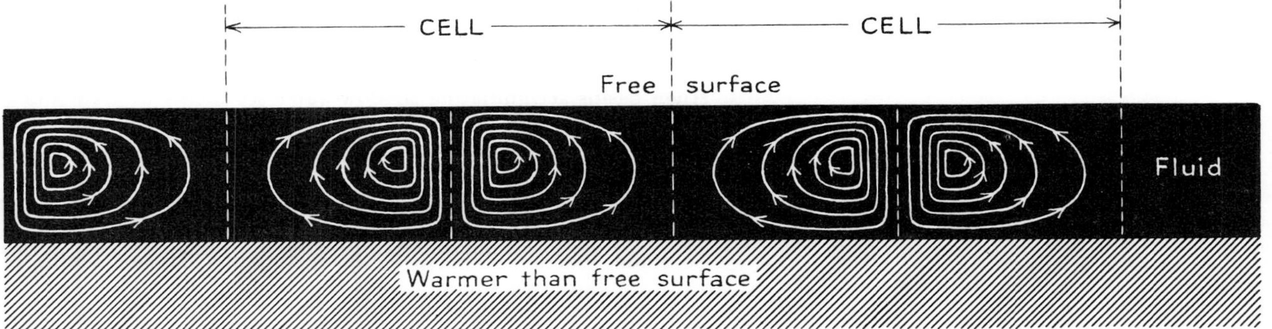

Continental drift theory

About a century ago, Antonio Snider proposed the continental drift theory in an attempt to explain the apparent matching of shorelines along the borders of the Atlantic Ocean, as well as structures on both sides of the Atlantic that trend in similar directions and resemble each other lithologically. Alfred Wegener revived the theory early in this century.

The theory of continental drift is examined in some detail in Chapter 21. Suffice it to say here that the theory calls for the splitting of a single large continent into smaller fragments now represented in our present continents, and that these "fragments" drifted laterally to their present positions.

It has been suggested that some mountains such as the Andes in South America and the Rockies in North America represent the crumpling up of earth material on the front edge of the drifting continents. Furthermore, some proponents of continental drift hold that the Alpine-Himalayas formed when Eurasia collided with Africa and India.

Time may prove some relation between these mountain systems and continental drift. But it is harder to see how mountains such as the Appalachians are to be explained by continental drift. Nor does it seem likely that the theory will be able to explain the formation of much older mountain ranges believed to have existed in the central regions of the present continents long before the "original continent" split up.

STATUS OF THE PROBLEM. In spite of the impressive lists of data being assembled about mountains, no theory proposed for the cause of mountain-building has been generally accepted. More data or better analyses of present data will apparently be needed before an ultimate solution is reached.

SUMMARY OUTLINE

Mountains
- Elevated landmasses
- Products of internal forces acting on the earth's crust

Distribution of mountains
- Dominant surface features of continents
- Occur in ocean basins

Development of a mountain range
- A process lasting millions of years

Kinds of mountains
- Difficult to classify
- Fold, fault-block, volcanic, upwarped

Fold mountains
- Composed of deformed rocks from thick sedimentary deposits in zones of geosynclines
- Rockies, Andes, Alps, Himalayas, Juras, Carpathians, ancient Appalachians

Geosynclines
- Huge basins accumulating shallow-water sediments in great thicknesses
- Deformed and elevated to become fold mountains—a process that involves crustal shrinking

Intermountain plateaus
- Produced by broad vertical uplift
- Colorado Plateau, Tibetan Plateau, Iranian Plateau, Plains of Hungary

Fault-block mountains
- Produced by faulting of large sections of the earth's crust
- Basin and Range, Inyo Mountains, Sierra Nevada

Upwarped mountains
- Produced by broad upwarping and erosion carving their rocks
- Adirondacks, present Appalachians, Black Hills, highland of Labrador

Isostasy
- Mountains float in a plastic substratum

Tests for isostasy
- Plumb line
- Gravity meter

Gravity measurements
- Reveal mountains have deep granitic roots
- Belts of negative anomalies
  - Evidence that deforming forces are still acting on earth's crust

Cause of mountain-building
- Three theories: thermal contraction, convection currents, drifting continents
- No theory generally accepted

SELECTED REFERENCES

Billings, Marland P., *Structural Geology* (2nd ed.). Englewood Cliffs, N.J.: Prentice-Hall, Inc., 1954.

Eardley, A. J., *Structural Geology of North America.* New York: Harper & Row, Publishers, 1951.

Goguel, Jean, *Tectonics,* trans. Hans E. Thalmann. San Francisco and London: W. H. Freeman & Company, Publishers, 1962.

Jeffreys, Harold, *The Earth* (4th ed.). New York: Cambridge Univ. Press, 1959.

King, Philip B., *The Evolution of North America.* Princeton: Princeton Univ. Press, 1959.

18 Metamorphism and metamorphic rocks

Most rocks exposed in mountainous regions of the earth today show evidence of change. At first glance, some of these seem to resemble familiar igneous rocks, but then we discover that their mineral grains are arranged in a peculiar manner (see Fig. 18-1). Other rocks have the same composition as limestone, but they seem to have developed larger mineral grains. Still others are strikingly different from both igneous rocks and sedimentary rocks. All these are metamorphic ("changed-form") rocks.

FORMATION OF METAMORPHIC ROCKS

Metamorphic rocks have been changed in the solid state in response to pronounced alterations in temperature, pressure, and chemical environment—all brought about by the same forces that fold, fault, inject magma into, and elevate or depress masses of rock. These forces bring about modifications *within* the rocks themselves, through the process called *metamorphism* (from the Greek *meta,* "beyond, over" and *morphē,* "form," hence *metamorphōsis,* ("change of form"). Metamorphism occurs within the earth's crust, below the zone of weathering and cementation and outside the zone of remelting. In this environment, rocks undergo chemical and structural changes in order to adjust to conditions that differ from those under which they were originally formed.

Under the influence of pressure, changes take place to reduce the space occupied by a rock mass. These changes, including recrystallization and formation of new minerals with closer atomic packing, are fundamental to metamorphism.

Fine-grained rocks are more readily changed than others because they expose greater areas of grain surface to chemically active fluids. On the other hand, some rocks that already include minerals formed at high temperatures are not again changed by being exposed to the high temperatures of metamorphism.

When rocks are buried to depths of several miles, they gradually become plastic and responsive to the heat and deforming forces that are active in the earth's crust and mantle (see Fig. 18-2). The type of the original rock, again, has an important effect on the results achieved by burial and deformation.

AGENTS OF METAMORPHISM

The term *metamorphism* is limited to changes that take place in the texture or composition of solid rocks. Metamorphism can occur only while a rock is solid[1] because once the rock's melting point has been reached, a magma is formed, and we are in the realm of igneous activity again.

Agents of metamorphism are heat, deforming pressures, and chemically active fluids.

Heat

An essential agent of metamorphism, heat may even be *the* essential agent. Turner and Verhoogen question whether pressure alone could produce changes in rocks, without a simultaneous increase in temperature. In fact, they say that metamorphism appears invariably to be controlled by temperature.

Pressure

The pressures produced by 20,000 to 30,000 feet of overlying rock material are not sufficient to bring about the metamorphism of most rocks. But between depths of about 30,000 to 40,000 feet, pressures of from 40,000 to 60,000 lbs/sq in. are produced, and these are great enough to cause most rocks to flow plastically. Such flow results in intergranular motion, the formation of minute shear planes within the rock, changes in texture, reorientation of grains, and crystal growth (see Fig. 18-3).

Pressures produced by the load of overlying materials combine with squeezing pressures that operate during the deformation of geosynclines. The squeezing pressures determine the ultimate extent of metamorphism in a particular region. For example, in certain areas of the Alps, deformation was so extensive that great folds were actually formed, and then overturned. There the original rocks have been metamorphosed to a greater degree than in areas where only slight folding occurred. The rocks in the upper portion of a geosyncline do not become involved in the deformation that produces metamorphism.

Chemically active fluids

Hydrothermal solutions released late in the solidification of magma often percolate beyond the margins of the magma reservoir and react on surrounding rocks. Sometimes they remove ions and substitute others. Or they may add ions to the rocks' minerals to produce new minerals. When chemical reactions within the rock or the introduction of ions from an external source cause one mineral to grow or change into another of different composition the process is called *metasomatism*. The term describes all ionic transfers, not just those that involve gases or solutions from a magma.

[1] Remember, though, that solid rock may exist in the plastic state.

FIG. 18-1
Contorted gneiss. Dark bands of ferromagnesian minerals trace out the pattern of distortion to which this rock was subjected by the processes of metamorphism. Two-inch squares form the background reference grid to give scale. From Bedford, Westchester County, New York. Photo by Walter R. Fleischer.

FIG. 18-2
Deformed beds of limestone. Photo from Gardner Collection, Harvard University.

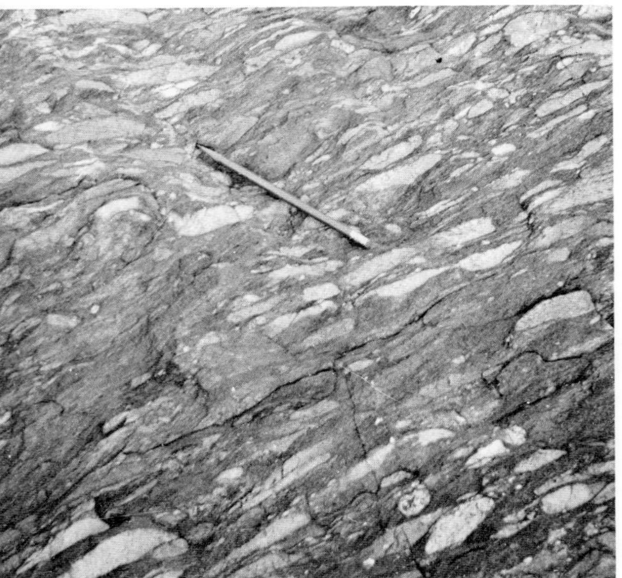

FIG. 18-3
Metamorphosed conglomerate showing stretched pebbles. Photo from Gardner Collection, Harvard University.

Some of the chemically active fluid of metamorphism is already liquid in the pores of a rock subjected to agents of metamorphism. It is believed that such pore liquid may often act as a catalyst; that is, it expedites changes without itself undergoing change.

TYPES OF METAMORPHISM

Several types of metamorphism occur, but we shall concern ourselves here with the two basic ones: contact metamorphism and regional metamorphism.

Contact metamorphism

The alteration of rocks by ionic transfer brought about by high temperatures and by the introduction of magmatic solutions at or near their contact with a body of magma is called *contact metamorphism*. At the actual surface of contact all the elements of a rock may be replaced by other elements introduced by hot gases and solutions escaping from the magma. Farther away, the replacement may be only partial.

Contact metamorphism occurs in restricted zones called *aureoles* ("halos"), which seldom measure more than a few hundred feet in width and may be only a fraction of an inch wide. Aureoles are found bordering laccoliths, stocks, and batholiths. During contact metamorphism, temperatures range from 570°F to 1470°F (300°C to 800°C) and load pressures from 100 to 3,000 atmospheres.

Contact metamorphism develops late in the mountain-building sequence and at relatively shallow depths. It is only late in the cooling of a magma that large quantities of hydrothermal solutions are released. And these are only released as the body of magma approaches the surface.

CONTACT METAMORPHIC MINERALS. A great deal of recrystallization is caused by the heat of contact metamorphism. Contact metamorphic minerals include diopside and tremolite, which are silicates of calcium and magnesium. The most important material brought in by hydrothermal solutions forms oxides and sulfides constituting ore minerals.

Regional metamorphism

Regional metamorphism is developed over extensive areas, often involving thousands of square miles of rock thousands of feet thick. Though it is believed that regional metamorphism is related to the existence of huge reservoirs of melted rock during the formation of some mountain ranges, this has not been proved. Its effects are best seen, however, in the root regions of old fold mountains and in the Precambrian continental shields. Thousands of feet of rock have had to be eroded in order to expose these metamorphic rocks to view.

REGIONAL METAMORPHIC MINERALS. During regional metamorphism, many new minerals are developed as rocks respond to increases in temperature and pressure. These include some new silicate minerals not found in igneous and sedimentary rocks, such as sillimanite, kyanite, andalusite, staurolite, almandite, garnet, brown biotite, epidote, and chlorite.

The first three of these are silicates with the formula Al_2SiO_5. Their independent SiO_4 tetrahedra are bound together by positive ions of aluminum. *Sillimanite* (in honor of Benjamin Silliman, professor of chemistry at Yale) develops in long, slender crystals that are brown, green, or white in color. *Kyanite* (from the Greek *kyanos,* "blue") forms blade-like blue crystals. *Andalusite* (from *Andalusia,* a province of Spain) forms coarse, nearly square prisms.

Staurolite (from the Greek *stauros,* "cross") is a silicate composed of independent tetrahedra bound together by positive ions of iron and aluminum. Staurolite has a unique crystal habit that is striking and easy to recognize: it develops six-sided prisms that intersect either at 90°, forming a cross (see Fig. 18-4), or at 60°, forming an X.

Garnets (from the Latin *granatus,* "a grain") are a group of metamorphic silicate minerals. All have the same atomic structure of independent SiO_4 tetrahedra, but a wide variety of chemical compositions is produced by the many positive ions that bind the tetrahedra together. These ions may be iron, magnesium, aluminum, calcium, manganese, or chronium. But whatever the chemical composition, garnets appear as distinctive 12-sided or 24-sided fully developed crystals (see Fig. 18-5). Actually, it is difficult to distinguish one kind of garnet from another without resorting to chemical analysis. A common deep red garnet of iron and aluminum is called *almandite.*

Epidote is a silicate of calcium, aluminum, and iron in which the tetrahedra are in pairs and these pairs are in-

FIG. 18-4
Crystals of staurolite from Farmington, Georgia. Photo by Benjamin M. Shaub.

FIG. 18-5
Garnet crystal in mica schist. The mold once occupied by another crystal can also be seen. Ruled 2-inch squares give scale for size. Photo by Walter R. Fleischer.

dependent of each other. On a freshly broken surface, this mineral is pistachio green in color; otherwise it is black or blackish-green.

Chlorite is a sheet-structure silicate of calcium, magnesium, aluminum, and iron. The characteristic green color of chlorite was the basis for its name, from the Greek *chlōros,* "green" (as in chlorophyll). Chloride exhibits a cleavage similar to that of mica, but the small scales produced by the cleavage are not elastic, like those of mica. Chlorite occurs either as aggregates of minute scales or as individual scales scattered throughout a rock.

Regional metamorphic zones. Regional metamorphism may be divided into zones: high-grade, middle-grade, and low-grade. Each grade is related to the temperature and pressure reached during metamorphism. High-grade metamorphism occurs in rocks nearest the magma reservoir, outside the zone of contact metamorphism. Low-grade metamorphism is found farthest away from the reservoir and blends into unchanged sedimentary rock.

Metamorphic zones are identified by using certain diagnostic metamorphic minerals called *index minerals.* Zones of regional metamorphism reflect the varied mineralogical response of chemically similar rocks to different physical conditions, especially temperatures. And each index mineral gives an indication of the conditions at the time of its formation.

The first appearance of chlorite, for example, tells us that we are at the beginning of a low-grade metamorphic zone. The first appearance of almandite is evidence of the beginning of a middle-grade metamorphic zone. And the the first appearance of sillimanite marks a high-grade zone. Other minerals sometimes occur in association with each of these index minerals, but they are usually of little help in determining the degree of metamorphism of a given zone.

By noting the appearance of the minerals that are characteristic of each metamorphic zone, it is possible to draw a map of the regional metamorphism of an entire area. Of course, the rocks must have the proper chemical composition to allow these minerals to form.

REGIONAL METAMORPHIC ROCKS

Contact and regional metamorphic rocks are found in mountain ranges and on continental shields. The regional metamorphic rocks are by far the most widespread. They vary greatly in appearance, texture, and composition.

Even when different regional metamorphic rocks have all

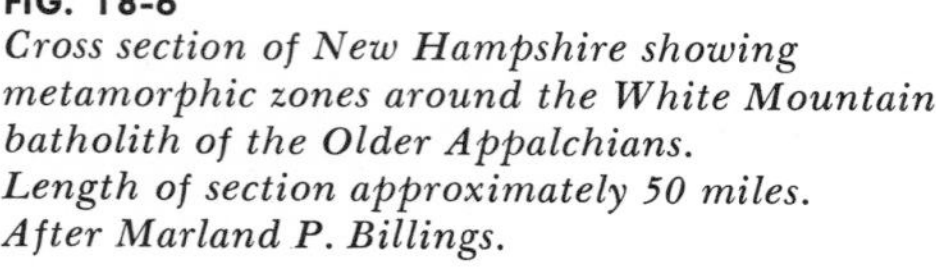

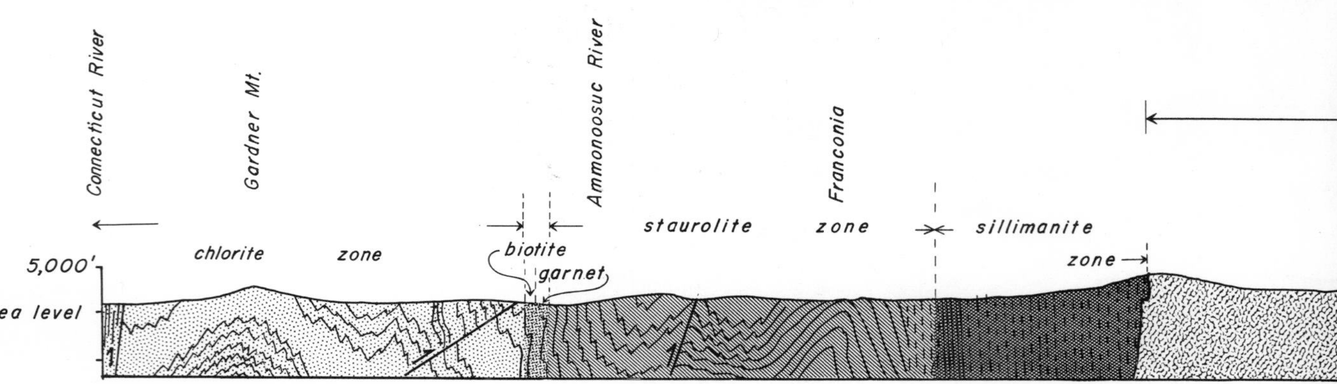

FIG. 18-6
Cross section of New Hampshire showing metamorphic zones around the White Mountain batholith of the Older Appalchians. Length of section approximately 50 miles. After Marland P. Billings.

been formed by changes of a single uniform rock type such as a shale, they are sometimes so drastically changed that they are thought to be unrelated.

These and other characteristics of regionally metamorphosed shale are well illustrated in New Hampshire. Along the Connecticut River west of the White Mountains, rocks that were originally shales are found in a low-grade metamorphic zone as slate, with chlorite, then biotite present. Southeast of these, the original shale is now found as phyllite, grading into schist. New metamorphic minerals appear one after the other toward the southeast: almandite, staurolite, then sillimanite. These metamorphosed shales occur in a belt surrounding the White Mountain batholith (see Fig. 18-6). The closer the area is to the batholith, the higher is its grade of regional metamorphism. This correlation is indicated by the presence of the index minerals found in the metamorphic rock.

Texture of metamorphic rocks

In most rocks that have been subjected to heat and deforming pressures during regional metamorphism, the minerals tend to be arranged in parallel layers of flat or elongated grains. This arrangement gives the rocks a property called *foliation* (from the Latin *foliatus,* "leaved, or leafy," hence consisting of leaves or thin sheets).

The textures most commonly used to classify metamorphic rocks are simply (1) *foliated,* and (2) *unfoliated* (either *dense* or *granular*). Let us look first at the unfoliated textures. In rocks with dense texture, the individual grains cannot be distinguished by the unaided eye, and these rocks do not exhibit rock cleavage. You will remember that we have used the term "cleavage" to describe the relative ease with which a mineral breaks along parallel planes. But notice here that we are using the modifier "rock" to distinguish rock cleavage from mineral cleavage. In rocks with granular texture, the individual grains are clearly visible, but again no rock cleavage is evident.

Rocks with foliated texture, however, invariably exhibit rock cleavage. There are three degrees of rock cleavage:

1. *Slaty* (from the French *esclat,* "fragment or splinter"), in which the cleavage occurs along planes separated by distances of microscopic dimensions.

2. *Phyllitic* (from the Greek *phyllon,* "leaf"), in which the cleavage produces flakes barely visible to the unaided eye. Phyllitic cleavage produces fragments thicker than those of slaty cleavage.

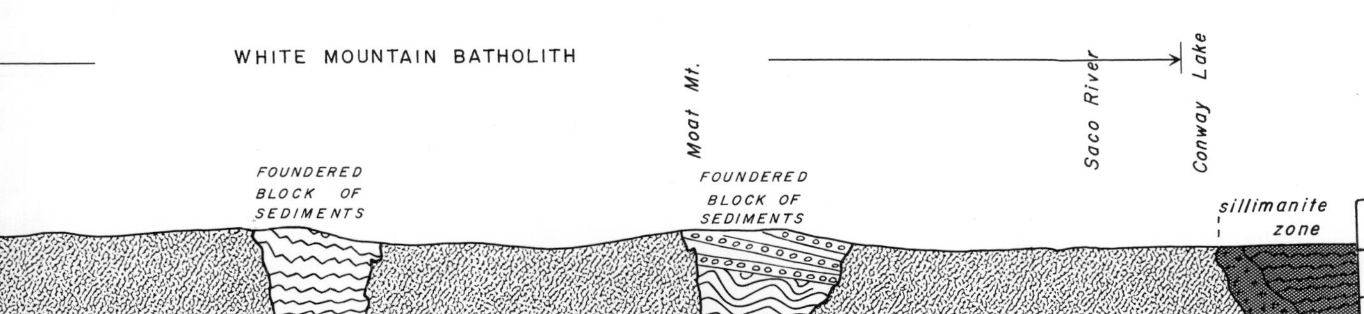

3. *Schistose* (from the Greek *schistos,* "divided, divisible"), in which the cleavage produces flakes that are clearly visible. Here cleavage surfaces are rougher than in slaty or phyllitic cleavage.

The name *gneiss* (a German word, pronounced "nice," originally applied to a granitic rock) is given to a metamorphic or igneous rock characterized by alternating bands, usually a few millimeters or centimeters thick, of differing mineral compostion. These bands are rich in light minerals in many cases; others are rich in dark minerals. The layers may or may not possess foliation or rock cleavage.

Types of metamorphic rocks

The many types of metamorphic rocks stem from the great variety of original rocks and the varying kinds of metamorphism. Metamorphic rocks may be derived from any or all of the sedimentary and igneous rocks.

Metamorphic rocks are usually named on the basis of texture. A few of these rocks may also be further classified by including the name of a mineral present in them, such as chlorite schist, mica schist, and hornblende schist.

SLATE. *Slate* is a metamorphic rock that has been produced from the low-grade metomorphism of shale. It is fine-grained with a slaty cleavage caused by the alignment of platy minerals under the pressures of metamorphism (see Fig. 18-7). Some of the clay minerals in the original shale have been transformed by heat into chlorite and mica. In fact, slate is composed predominantly of small, colorless mica flakes, with smaller quantities of chlorite. It occurs in a wide variety of colors. Dark-colored slate owes its color to the presence of carbonaceous material or iron sulfides.

PHYLLITE. *Phyllite* is a metamorphic rock with much the same composition as slate, but whose minerals exist in larger units. Phyllite is actually slate that has undergone further metamorphism. When slate is subjected to heat greater than 500° or 600°F (250° or 300°C), the chlorite and mica minerals

FIG. 18-7
Vermont slate quarry, showing how rock cleavage controls breaking. Photo from Gardner Collection, Harvard University.

of which it is composed develop large flakes, giving the resulting rock its characteristic phyllitic cleavage and a silky sheen on freshly broken surfaces. The predominant minerals in phyllite are chlorite and muscovite. This rock usually contains the same impurities as slate but sometimes a new metamorphic mineral such as tourmaline or magnesium garnet makes its appearance.

SCHIST. Of the metamorphic rocks formed by regional metamorphism, *schist* is the most abundant. There are many varieties of schist, for it can be derived from many igneous, sedimentary, or lower-grade metamorphic rocks. But all schists are dominated by clearly visible flakes of some platy mineral, such as mica, talc, chlorite, or hematite. Fibrous minerals are commonly present as well. Schist tends to break between the platy or fibrous minerals, giving the rock its characteristic schistose cleavage.

Table 18-1 lists some of the more common varieties of schist, together with the names of the rocks from which they were derived.

TABLE 18-1
Common schists

VARIETY	ROCK FROM WHICH DERIVED
Chlorite schist	Shale
Mica schist	
Hornblende schist	Basalt or gabbro
Biotite schist	
Quartz schist	Impure sandstone
Calc-schist	Impure limestone

Schists often contain large quantities of quartz and feldspar as well as lesser amounts of minerals such as augite, hornblende, garnet, epidote, and magnetite. A green schistose rock produced by low-grade metamorphism, sometimes called a *greenschist,* owes its color to the presence of the minerals chlorite and epidote.

AMPHIBOLITE. *Amphibolite* is composed mainly of hornblende and plagioclase. There is some foliation or lineation due to alignment of hornblende grains, but it is less conspicuous than in schists. Amphibolites may be green, gray, or black and sometimes contain such minerals as epidote, green augite, biotite, and almandite. They are the products of medium-grade to high-grade regional metamorphism of ferromagnesian igneous rocks and of some impure calcareous sediments.

GNEISS. A coarse-grained metamorphic rock, *gneiss* is most commonly formed during high-grade regional metamorphism (see Fig. 18-8). A banded appearance makes it easy to recognize in the field. Although gneiss does exhibit rock cleavage, it is far less pronounced than in the schists.

FIG. 18-8
Metamorphic rock showing alignment of previously unoriented minerals. The light-colored bands are mainly orthoclase and quartz; the dark streaks are biotite and other ferromagnesian minerals. The bulk composition is that of granite; but in contrast to the random mixing in granite, the minerals are here distributed in relatively systematic patterns. Photo by Navias.

In gneiss derived from igneous rocks such as granite, gabbro, or diorite, the component minerals are arranged in parallel layers: the quartz and the feldspars alternate with the ferromagnesians. In gneiss formed from the metamorphism of clayey sedimentary rocks such as graywackes, bands of quartz or feldspar usually alternate with layers of platy or fibrous minerals such as chlorite, mica, graphite, hornblende, kyanite, staurolite, sillimanite, and wollastonite.

MARBLE. This familiar metamorphic rock, composed essentially of calcite or dolomite, is coarse-grained and was derived during the contact or regional metamorphism of limestone or dolomite. It does not exhibit rock cleavage. Marble differs from the original rock in having larger mineral grains. In most marble, the crystallographic direction of its calcite is nearly parallel; this is in response to the metamorphic pres-

FIG. 18-9
Marble quarry showing how blocks are sawed out for dimension stone to be used in buildings. Photo by Benjamin M. Shaub.

sures to which it was subjected. The rock shows no foliation, however, because the grains have the same color, and lineation does not show up.

Although the purest variety of marble is snow-white, many marbles contain small percentages of other minerals that were formed during metamorphism from impurities in the original sedimentary rock. These impurities account for the wide variety of color in marble. *Black marbles* are colored by bituminous matter; *green marbles* by diopside, hornblende, serpentine, or talc; *red marbles* by the iron oxide, hematite; and *brown marbles* by the iron oxide, limonite. Garnets have often been found in marble and, on rare occasions, rubies. The beautiful patterns of some marbles are often produced by the presence of fossilized corals in the original limestone.

Marble occurs most commonly in areas that have undergone regional metamorphism (see Fig. 18-9), where it is often found in layers between mica schists or phyllites.

QUARTZITE. The metamorphism of quartz-rich sandstone forms the rock, quartzite. The grains of quartz in the original sandstone have become firmly bonded together by the entry of silica into the pore spaces.

Quartzite is unfoliated and is distinguishable from sandstone in two ways: there are no pore spaces in the quartzite, and the rock breaks right through the sand grains that make it up, rather than around them.

On rare occasions, limited amounts of quartzite may have been formed by percolating water under the temperatures and pressures of ordinary sedimentary processes working near the surface of the earth. Most quartzites, however, are true metamorphic rocks and may have been formed by metamorphism of any grade.

The structure of quartzite cannot be recognized without a microscope. But when we cut it into thin sections, we can identify both the original rounded sand grains and the silica that has filled the old pore spaces.

Pure quartzite is white, but iron or other impurities sometimes give the rock a reddish or dark color. Among the minor minerals that often occur in quartzite are feldspar, muscovite, chlorite, zircon, tourmaline, garnet, biotite, epidote, hornblende, and sillimanite.

Regional metamorphic facies

In Chapter 8, we defined the term *facies* as it is applied to sedimentary rocks. Actually, though, it has a broader application: in general, *a facies is an assemblage of mineral, rock, or fossil features reflecting the environment in which a rock was formed.*

Previously, we discovered that if at a given time there is an offshore sequence of sedimentation consisting of sands, shales, and limestones, we may speak of the sand facies, the shale facies, and the limestone facies of the rocks formed from those deposits. Similarly, metamorphic rocks that have been subjected to the same general range of temperature and pressure are said to belong to the same facies. A *metamorphic facies* is an assemblage of minerals that reached equilibrium during metamorphism under a specific set of conditions. Each facies is named after a common metamorphic rock that belongs to it, sometimes with a common mineral prefixed (such as epidote-amphibolite). And every metamorphic rock is assigned to a facies according to the conditions that attended its formation, not according to its composition.

It is not always possible to assign a rock to a particular metamorphic facies on the basis of a hand specimen, but it is always possible to do so after examining the other rocks in the region.

Three regional metamorphic facies have been identified.

1. Amphibolite facies—temperature 850°F (450°C) to 1,300°F (700°C); high-grade regional metamorphism.
2. Epidote-amphibolite facies—temperature 500°F (250°C) to 850°F (450°C); middle-grade regional metamorphism.
3. Greenschist facies—temperature 300°F (150°C) to 500°F (250°C); low-grade regional metamorphism.

To illustrate how a parent rock may change from one facies to another, let us assume that we have a mixture of sodium, calcium, iron, magnesium, and silicon in the proportions found in basalt, but actually distributed throughout a shale. If this mixture were subjected to a temperature of around 400°F (200°C), and to low pressures, about 40 per cent of the mixture by volume would form albite, 20 per cent would form chlorite, and 23 per cent would form epidote. This is the assemblage of minerals typical of the greenschist facies formed from the mixture of elements with which we started. If the same original mixture were heated to about 1,100°F (600°C), a different assemblage of minerals would be formed. This time, about 26 per cent would form plagioclase feldspars, 72 per cent would form hornblende, and 2 per cent would form quartz. This assemblage, then, is typical of the amphib-

TABLE 18-2

Products of regional metamorphism •

	METAMORPHIC ZONE				
	Chorite	*Biotite*	*Almandite*	*Staurolite*	*Sillimanite*
ORIGINAL ROCK	METAMORPHIC ROCK				
Shale	Slate	Biotite Phyllite	Biotite-garnet Phyllite	Biotite-garnet-staurolite schist	Sillimanite schist or gneiss
Clayey Sandstone	Micaceous Sandstone	Quartz-mica Schist	Quartz-mica-garnet schist or gneiss		
Quartz Sandstone	Quartzite				
Limestone Dolomite	Limestone Dolomite	Marble			
Basalt	Chlorite-epidote-albite Schist (greenschists)		Albite-epidote Amphibolite	Amphibolite	
Granite	Granite	Granite gneiss			
Rhyolite	Rhyolite	Biotites, schists, or gneisses			

• After Marland P. Billings, *The Geology of New Hampshire. Part II: Bedrock Geology* (Manchester: Granite State Press, Inc., 1956), p. 139.

olite facies formed from the original mixture of elements. Table 18-3 shows the general relationships among zones, facies, and mineral assemblages in the progressive metamorphism of rocks with certain compositions.

TABLE 18-3 *Regional metamorphic facies and related zones*

METAMORPHIC TEMPERATURE F	C	MINERAL ASSEMBLAGE DERIVED FROM METAMORPHISM OF BASALT OR SIMILARLY COMPOSED ROCK	METAMORPHIC FACIES	CORRESPONDING METAMORPHIC ZONES RECOGNIZED IN ROCKS DERIVED FROM SHALES
1,300°	700°	Plagioclase-hornblende(-diopside)* (-garnet) (-epidote)	Amphibolite facies	Sillimanite Kyanite Staurolite
850°	450°	Albite-hornblende-epidote(-chlorite)	Epidote-amphibolite facies	Almandite
500°	250°	Albite-actinolite-epidote-chlorite	Greenschist facies	Biotite
300°	150°	Albite-epidote-chlorite(-calcite)		Chlorite

After Eskola and others. See Francis J. Turner, *Mineralogical and Structural Evolution of the Metamorphic Rocks*, Geol. Soc. Am. Memoir 30, 1948.

* Minerals in parentheses may or may not be present.

ORIGIN OF GRANITE

The eighteenth-century geologist James Hutton once stated that granite was produced by the crystallization of minerals from a molten mass. Ever since, most geologists have accepted the magmatic origin of granite. But several investigators have questioned this conclusion, suggesting instead that granite is a metamorphic rock produced from pre-existing rocks by a process called *granitization*.

In discussing batholiths, we mentioned that one of the reasons for questioning the magmatic origin of granite was the mystery of what happened to the great mass of rock that must have been displaced by the instrusion of the granite batholiths. This so-called "space problems" has led some geologists to conclude that batholiths actually represent pre-existing rocks transformed into granite by metasomatic processes.

Certain rock formations support this theory: these sedimentary rocks were originally formed in a continuous layer, but now grade into schists and then into migmatites ("mixed rocks"), apparently formed when magma squeezed in between the layers of schist. The migmatites in turn grade into rocks containing the large, abundant feldspars characteristic of granite, but that also seem to show shadowy remnants of schistose structure. Finally, these rocks grade into pure granite. The proponents of the granitization theory say that the granite is the result of extreme metasomatism, and that the schists, migmatites, and granite-like rocks with schistose structure are intermediate steps in the transforming of sedimentary rocks into granite.

What mechanism could have brought about granitization? Perhaps ions migrated through the original solid rock, building up the elements characteristic of granite, such as sodium and potassium, and removing superfluous elements, such as calcium, iron, and magnesium. The limit to which the migrating ions are supposed to have carried the calcium, iron, and magnesium is called the *simatic front*. The limit to which the migrating ions are supposed to have deposited the sodium and potassium is called the *granitic front*.

At the middle of the twentieth century, geologists were carrying on an enthusiastic debate over the origin of granite. But they had reached agreement on one fundamental point—namely, that various rocks with the composition and structure of granite may have different histories. In other words, some may be igneous (see Fig. 18-10) and others metasomatic. So the debate between "magmatists" and "granitizationists" has been reduced to the question of what percentage of the world's granite is metasomatic and what percentage is magmatic. Those who favor magmatic origin admit that perhaps 15 per cent of the granite exposed at the earth's surface is metasomatic. But the granitizationists reverse the percentages and insist that about 85 per cent is metasomatic, and only 15 per cent of magmatic origin.

The magmatists are still seeking an adequate explanation for the origin of magma, particularly magma of sialic composition. And the granitizationists are trying to unravel an equally knotty problem—the mechanism by which pre-existing rocks have been converted to granite.

FIG. 18-10
Xenolith in Mt. Airy granite, North Carolina, is evidence in support of magmatic origin of this granite, because the inclusion could not have retained its sharp edges and separate identity during granitization. Photo by T. M. Gathright, II.

SUMMARY OUTLINE

Metamorphic rocks
- Products of metamorphism
- Changed igneous or sedimentary rocks

Metamorphism
- Process by which rocks are changed
- Takes place in solid rock

Agents of metamorphism
- Heat, deforming pressure, chemically active fluids

Metasomatism
- Chemical reactions produced by ionic transfers

Types of metamorphism
- Contact and regional

Contact metamorphism
- Occurs in zones called aureoles, at or near a body of magma

Regional metamorphism
- Involves thousands of square miles of rock thousands of feet thick
- Produced by increases in temperature and pressure
- Develops many new minerals and rocks

Regional metamorphic minerals
- Silicates: sillimanite, kyanite, andalusite, staurolite, garnets, epidote, chlorite

Regional metamorphic zones
- Indicate degree of regional metamorphism
- High-grade, middle-grade, low-grade
  - Identified by index metamorphic minerals

Regional metamorphic rocks
- Vary in appearance, texture, and composition
- Named according to texture

Texture of metamorphic rocks
- Foliated, unfoliated
- Cleavages of foliated: slaty, phyllitic, schistose

Types of metamorphic rocks
- Foliated: slate, phyllite, schist
- Slightly foliated: amphibolite
- Banded: gneiss
- Unfoliated: marble, quartzite

Regional metamorphic facies
- Reflect environment in which metamorphic rock was formed
- Assemblage of minerals that reached equilibrium during metamorphism
- Greenschist, epidote-amphibolite, amphibolite

Origin of granite
- Still under debate
- Granitization vs. magmatic origin

SELECTED REFERENCES

Billings, Marland P., *The Geology of New Hampshire*. Manchester, N.H.: Granite State Press, Inc., 1956.

Hurlbut, Cornelius, Jr., *Dana's Manual of Mineralogy* (17th ed.). New York: John Wiley & Sons, Inc., 1961.

Turner, Francis J., *Mineralogical and Structural Evolution of the Metamorphic Rocks*. New York: Geol. Soc. Am. Memoir 28, 1948.

——— and J. Verhoogen, *Igneous and Metamorphic Petrology* (2nd ed.). New York: McGraw-Hill Book Company, 1960.

Williams, H., Francis J. Turner, and Charles M. Gilbert, *Petrography*. San Francisco: W. H. Freeman & Co., Publishers, 1954.

19 Earthquakes

Again and again in earlier chapters we have seen that the rocks of the earth show evidence of ceaseless change—of oceans flooding over the continents and the receding, of materials being stripped from the land and transported to accumulate in geosynclines, and of the elevation of these sediments into high mountain ranges. All these processes are still going on today in the world around us. They take place very slowly, of course—too slowly for us to be able to observe them firsthand. But certain clues make it clear that they are still operating. Among the most important of these clues are the 150,000 earthquakes that occur around the world every year.

Earthquakes are the shocks caused when rocks that have been distorted beyond their strength finally break. They are evidence of rock deformation, and they reveal the regions where changes in the earth's crust are occurring.

EFFECTS OF EARTHQUAKES

Most people seem to be interested in earthquakes because of their effect on the earth's crust, on human beings, and on structures. Of all the earthquakes that occur every year, only one or two are likely to produce spectacular effects such as landslides or the elevation or depression of large land masses, and a hundred or so may be strong enough near their sources to destroy human life and property. But the rest are too small to have any serious effects.

Fire

When an earthquake occurs near a modern city, fire is a greater hazard than the actual shaking of the ground. In fact, fire has caused an estimated 95 per cent of the total loss caused by some earthquakes. The following account describes a dramatic example of the devastation created by fire after a great earthquake.

JAPAN, 1923. One minute and 28 seconds before noon on Saturday, September 1, 1923, the earth's crust ruptured under Sagami Bay, 50 miles from Yokohama and 70 miles from Tokyo. The rupture produced vibrations that spread outward with such energy that they caused serious damage through an area 90 miles long and 60 miles wide along the coast. In Tokyo, at the Imperial University, Professor Akitsune Imamura was sitting in his office at the Seismological Institute when the earthquake occurred. His account is one of the few accurately documented eyewitness reports of an earthquake from within a zone of heavy damage carefully recorded by an observer who understood what was happening.

At first, the movement was rather slow and feeble, so I did not take it to be the forerunner of so big a shock. As usual, I began to estimate the duration of the preliminary tremors, and determined, if possible to ascertain the direction of the principal movements. Soon the vibration became large, and after 3 or 4 seconds from the commencement, I felt the shock to be very strong indeed. Seven or 8 seconds passed and the building was shaking to an extraordinary extent, but I considered these movements not yet to be the principal portion. At the 12th second from the start, according to my calculation, came a very big vibration, which I took at once to be the beginning of the principal portion. Now the motion, instead of becoming less and less as usual, went on increasing in intensity very quickly, and after 4 or 5 seconds I felt it to have reached its strongest. During this epoch the tiles were showering down from the roof making a loud noise, and I wondered whether the building could stand or not. I was able accurately to ascertain the directions of the principal movements and found them to have been about NW or SE. During the following 10 seconds the motion, though still violent, became somewhat less severe, and its character gradually changed, the vibrations becoming slower but bigger. For the next few minutes we felt an undulatory movement like that which we experience on a boat in windy weather, and we were now and then threatened by severe aftershocks. After 5 minutes from the beginning, I stood up and went over to see the instruments. . . . Soon after the first shock, fire broke out at two places in the University, and within one and a half hours our Institute was enveloped in raging smoke and heat; the shingles now exposed to the open air as the tiles had fallen down due to the shock, began to smoke and eventually took fire three times. . . . It was 10 o'clock at night before I found our Institute and Observatory quite safe. . . . We all, 10 in number, did our best, partly in continuing earthquake observations and partly in extinguishing the fire, taking no food or drink till midnight, while four of us who were residing in the lower part of the town lost our houses and property by fire.

Within 30 minutes after the beginning of the earthquake, fire had broken out in 136 places in Tokyo. In all, 252 started and only 40 were extinguished. Authorities estimated that at least 44 were started by chemicals. A 12-mile-an-hour wind from the south spread the flames rapidly. The wind shifted to the west in the evening and increased to 25 miles an hour, then shifted to the north. These changes in wind direction added greatly to the extent of the area burned. Within 18 hours, 64 per cent of the houses in Tokyo had burned. The fires died away after 56 hours, with 71 per cent of the houses consumed—a total of 366,262. The spread of fire in Yokohama, a city of a half-million population, was even more rapid. Within 12 hours, 65 per cent of the structures in the city had burned, and eventually the city was completely destroyed (see Fig. 19-1).

Fire was also a great killer in this Japanese earthquake. A spectacular example in Tokyo occurred in an area of 250 acres of open ground on the eastern bank of the Sumida

River. People gathered there with their belongings, seeking refuge from the circling fires. By four o'clock on the afternoon of September 1, men, women, and children were so closely packed that movement was almost impossible. Meanwhile, fire had closed in from three sides, pinning them against the river and blanketing them with sparks and suffocating fumes. Suddenly, a fire-whirlwind approached, the result of the rapid heating of the air by the fires, superposed on unstable meteorological conditions. It had the characteristics of a true tornado. The central tube, with winds of incredible violence whirling around and upward, drawing smoke, flames, and debris from the surrounding fires, swept over the area. When it had passed, 38,000 were left dead. Only about 2,000 persons, who had been close to the river on the southern part of the ground, survived. One report states that the majority of the dead were terribly burned, but that many showed no effects of the heat on their skin or clothing. They were apparently suffocated as the tornado sucked up the breathable air and replaced it with smoke and fumes.

Final government statistics for the entire section of Japan devastated by this earthquake reported 99,333 killed, 43,476 missing, and 103,733 injured, with a total of 576,262 houses completely destroyed.

One reason for rapid spread of fire after an earthquake is that the vibrations often disrupt the water system in the area. In San Francisco, for example, some 23,000 service pipes were broken by the great earthquake of 1906. Water pressure throughout the city fell so sharply that when the hoses were attached to fire hydrants only a small stream of water trickled out. Since that time, a system of valves has been installed to isolate any affected area and keep water pressure high in unbroken pipes in the rest of the city.

Damage to structures

Modern, well-designed buildings of steel-frame construction can withstand the shaking of even the most severe earthquakes. In the Tokyo earthquake of 1923, the Mitsubishi Bank building was surrounded by many badly damaged structures of older construction, but it escaped completely unharmed. In

FIG. 19-1
Yokohama, Japan, showing devastation caused by earthquake and fire of September 1, 1923. Photo by L. Don Leet.

the July 28, 1957 earthquake, the 43-story Latino-Americano tower in Mexico City rode the shock waves undamaged, while surrounding buildings suffered greatly.

Chimneys are particularly sensitive to earthquake vibrations, because they tend to shake in one direction while the building on which they stand shakes in another. Consequently, chimneys often break off at the roof line. Two small earthquakes in New Hampshire in 1940 severed dozens of chimneys, but caused no other damage. In contrast, tunnels and other underground structures are little affected by even the largest earthquakes, because they move as a unit with the surrounding rock.

The extent to which a building is affected by the waves of an earthquake depends in part on the type of ground under it. In the 1906 San Francisco earthquake, buildings on water-soaked sand, gravel, or clay suffered up to 12 times as much damage as similar structures standing on solid rock nearby. This factor accounts for some of the seemingly erratic patterns of damage caused by certain earthquakes.

Seismic sea waves

If you are fortunate enough some day to be basking in the sun on Waikiki Beach and the water is suddenly sucked away from the shore to disappear over the horizon, don't start picking up sea shells or digging clams—a seismic sea wave is coming, and the withdrawal of the water is the first warning of its approach.

Some submarine earthquakes abruptly elevate or lower portions of the sea bottom, setting up great sea waves in the water. The same effect may also be produced by submarine landslides at the time of a quake. These giant waves are called *seismic sea waves,* or *tsunami* (tsu-nah'-mē), the Japanese word with the same form in both singular and plural.

Seismic sea waves have devastated oceanic islands and continental coastlines from time to time throughout history. The Hawaiian Islands have been hit thirty times since their discovery by Captain Cook in 1778.

On April 1, 1946, a severe earthquake occured at 53.5°N., 163°W., 80 miles southwest of Unimak island, Alaska, in the Aleutian Trench, where the ocean is 12,000 feet deep. Four hours and 34 minutes later, the first seismic sea wave from this quake reached Oahu, Hawaii, having traveled 2,240 miles at 490 miles per hour. At the time, marine geologist Francis P. Shepard and his wife were living in a seashore cottage on northern Oahu and were wakened by a loud hissing noise. They dashed to the window just in time to see waters of the ocean boiling up over a high ridge and heading toward their house. Shepard grabbed his camera, but when he got to the door, much to his disappointment he saw the water retreating rapidly oceanward. The sea's level quickly dropped 30 feet. It was then that he realized he had seen a seismic sea wave. Several more times after this, the water surged up over high tide levels and then was sucked back into its basin.

Starting in the Alaskan waters where the earthquake occurred, these seismic sea waves had spread out much as waves do when a rock is thrown into a pond. But these waves were tremendous in length: their crests were about a hundred miles apart—not inches or feet—but miles apart. They swept out into the Pacific Ocean, moving at terrific speeds of nearly 500 miles per hour. As they passed ships, these waves went unnoticed; for on 10,000 feet or more of water, 3-foot-high waves with 100 miles between crests go undetected. Their effect is similar to the ground levels rising three feet as you walk 100 miles; you just don't notice it. But upon reaching Oahu and the other Pacific shores, the effect was dramatic. The energy that moved thousands of feet of water in the open ocean became concentrated on moving a few feet of water at a shallow shore. There the water curled into giant crests that increased in height until they washed up over shores tens of feet above ordinary high tide: 35 feet on Oahu, 54 feet on Hawaii (see Fig. 19-2).

These same seismic sea waves swept on down the Pacific. Eighteen hours after being launched, the waves reached Valparaiso, Chile, where they still had enough energy to cause 5-foot rises of the water after traveling 8,000 miles. Some even returned to hit the other side of Hawaii 18 hours later. In fact, tide gauges showed that seismic sea waves sloshed around the Pacific basin for days after the earthquake was over.

A system for predicting the arrival time of seismic sea waves in Hawaii had been wanted for some time. After the 1946 waves, it was put into operation, using seismographic records to determine the time and place of a submarine earthquake (see Chapter 20) within an hour or less of its occurrence. Once the epicenter is located, if it has occurred within the Pacific basin, the seismic sea waves' expected time of arrival at endangered coasts can be predicted. But a missing ingredient was the knowledge of which earthquakes started seismic sea waves and which did not. Commander C.K. Green of the U.S. Coast and Geodetic Survey came up with a gauge capable of detecting the special rise and fall of the ocean's surface associated with seismic sea waves. The gauge recognizes the differences in wave periods and ignores both wind-

FIG. 19-2
Seismic sea wave at Hilo, Hawaii, April 1, 1946. The wave is smashing a warehouse. Seconds later it will sweep the man to his death. Photo taken from a ship's deck by Corps of Engineers, U.S. Army.

caused waves and the daily tides. It rings an alarm when there are waves from 10 to 40 minutes apart, the interval between crests typical of seismic sea waves.

The warning system proved very effective on November 4, 1962, when there was a quake under the sea off Kamchatka Peninsula at 17:07 Greenwich time. Within about an hour, with the help of reports from seismograph stations in Alaska, Arizona, and California, Honolulu located the quake at 51°N., 158°E. Reports from Attu and Dutch Harbor of the warning net indicated that seismic sea waves had been started by the quake. Honolulu thereupon computed the time that the first seismic sea wave would reach Oahu and Hawaii as well as others of the Hawaiian Islands (see Fig. 19-3). It was due at Honolulu at 23:30 Greenwich time, 6 hours and 23 minutes after the quake off Kamchatka. In a little over 3 hours, Midway reported that it was covered by 9 feet of water as the first wave raced over it. At Honolulu and Hilo, the waves were not as lage as those of 1946. Damage was estimated at $800,000, but not a single life was lost, thanks in great measure to the warning system.

Commander Green's seismic sea wave gauges had not been installed along the South American coast in 1960, when a series of heavy shocks culminated in one at 19:10 Greenwich time on May 22, 1960. But the existence of seismic sea waves was soon clearly established along 250 miles of devastated seacoast in the vicinity of Valdivia in southern Chile. As usual, Honolulu had computed the location and time of the submarine earthquake; so when word was flashed that seismic sea waves were racing out over the Pacific, they issued warnings of the dangers, urging evacuation of coastal areas, and correctly predicting the arrival time of the first waves. These arrived on schedule 6 hours after the warnings were broadcast, 15 hours after they started off South America. Through failure of many people to heed the warnings, however, 61 lives were lost in Hilo, mostly by crushing or drowning; 282 were injured enough to require hospitalization and medical care. Two hundred and twenty-nine dwellings were destroyed or severely dam-

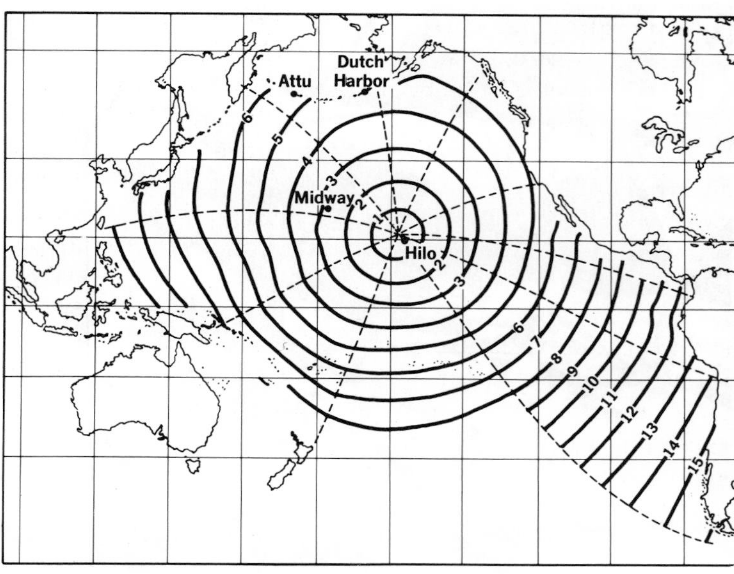

FIG. 19-3
Estimated number of hours for a seismic sea wave to reach the Hawaiian Islands from earthquakes in different parts of the Pacific. After Joseph Bernstein in Scientific American, August, 1954.

FIG. 19-4
A mail truck lies half-buried in the shambles of a residential area in Hilo, Hawaii. Seismic sea waves from the Chilean earthquake of May 22, 1960 devastated the community. Wide World Photos.

aged (see Fig. 19-4) and total damage was estimated at $20 million. About 8 hours after hitting Hawaii, more than 22 hours after the earthquake that started them, these seismic sea waves roared up onto the coasts of Honshu and Hokkaido, Japan. There, more than 10,600 miles from where they started, they brought death to 180 people, significantly affected the homes and livelihood of 150,000, and caused damage estimated close to half a billion dollars.

Fortunately, only an extremely small fraction of all submarine earthquakes cause seismic sea waves.

Landslides

In regions where there are many hills with steep slopes, earthquakes are often accompanied by landslides. These slides occur within a zone seldom exceeding 20 to 30 miles in radius, though the very largest earthquakes have affected areas with as much as a 75-mile radius (Anchorage, Alaska, from earthquake on Prince William Sound, March 28, 1964).

One of the worst earthquake-caused landslides on record occurred on June 7, 1962. More than 20,000 lives were lost and much property destroyed in a large section of the then-bustling town of Port Royal, Jamaica. The whole waterfront was launched into the sea, together with several streets of two- and four-story brick homes. The brick homes and other buildings had been built on loose sands, gravel, and filled land. Shaken loose by the quake, the underlying gravel and sand gave way and slid into the sea; two-thirds of the town, consisting of the government buildings, wharf, streets, homes, and people went with it.

In the province of Kansu, China, in deposits of loess, an earthquake on December 16, 1920, caused some of the most spectacular landslides on record. The death toll was 100,000. Great masses of surface material moved for more than a mile, and some of the blocks carried along undamaged roads, trees, and houses.

In the vicinity of the Japanese earthquake of 1923, one large slide moved down a valley as if it were a wall of water at a

FIG. 19-5
Rock Creek landslide. One of several that occurred in Montana on August 17, 1959. Photo by Gordon Oakeshott.

FIG. 19-6
Cracks in pavement caused by an earthquake in Tokyo, Japan, 1923. Photo by L. Don Leet.

speed of about a mile a minute, destroying a village and a railroad bridge at the mouth of the valley.

Several landslides occurred in the vicinity of Hebgen Reservoir, Montana, when the area was severely shaken by an earthquake just before midnight on August 17, 1959 (see Fig. 19-5). Many sections of U.S. Highway 287 slumped into the Madison River. One gigantic slide consisted of rock broken from the face of a mountain bordering the river. This huge block of rock a half-mile wide, 1300 feet high, and up to 400 feet thick roared into the river, hurling water 430 feet up the opposite slope. The mass contained 43 million cubic yards of material. It dammed the river, and water backed up to form Earthquake Lake, over 6 miles long and 180 feet deep. During the months that followed, engineers constructed spillways and protected slopes to convert this into a permanent dam.

The rock layers that fell were schists and gneiss that were weathered, cracked, and relatively soft; there was also a great deal of mica and clay in many joints. Dipping steeply toward the river, the bedding planes of these rocks rested on a mass of marble-like dolomite that, in effect, held up the side of the mountain. This dolomite was probably split by the first quake; then the schists and gneiss, with their support removed and clay and mica "greasing the skids," shot down the slope into the river.

Cracks in the ground

One of man's most persistent fears about earthquakes is that the earth is likely to open up and swallow everyone and everything in the vicinity. Such fears have been nourished by a good many tall tales, as well as pictures like Fig. 19-6, which shows shallow cracks in a pavement left unsupported by the slumping of a canal bank. One account of the Lisbon earthquake of November 1, 1755 claimed that about 25 miles from Lisbon the earth opened up and swallowed a village's 10,000 inhabitants with all their cattle and belongings, and then closed again. The story probably got its start when a landslide buried some village in the area.

In Japan widespread ideas about the earth's ability to swallow people may have sprung from an allusion in one of the Buddhist scriptures. There it is stated that when Devadatta, one of Sakya Muni's disciples, turned against his Master and even made attempts on his life, Heaven punished him by consigning him to Hades, whereupon the ground opened and immediately swallowed him up.

It is true that landslides and slumps do bury people and buildings, and under special conditions they may even open small, shallow cracks. In California, in 1906, a cow did fall into such a crack and was buried with only her tail protruding. But there is no authenticated case in which solid rock has yawned open and swallowed anything.

Changes in land level

Some earthquakes have been accompanied by changes in the level of the land over broad areas. The land surface has sunk in some places, risen in others, and often tilted.

In Missouri and Tennessee during the 1811 quakes, 20-

square-mile Reelfoot Lake, formed by subsidence of the land, was only part of thousands of square miles that subsided. Many other lakes were formed at the same time, and 200 square miles of forests were drowned.

Elevation and depression occurred in the vicinity of Yakutat Bay, Alaska, in 1899. Three major earthquakes were recorded between September 3 and 29 on the relatively insensitive instruments then in operation around the world. Investigators who journeyed to that remote region 6 years later found deceased barnacles in great profusion still clinging to elevated sections of former shoreline. Not far away, whole forests had been drowned beneath the sea. Geologists found changes in the level of the land over an area of 30 square miles, ranging from depressions of 5 feet to elevations of 50 feet.

The 400 miles of south-central Chilean coast that were devastated by a series of quakes in 1960 were found to have undergone marked changes of level in places. The western side of the Arauco Peninsula was raised about 4 feet and new beaches were formed. Isla Mocha was raised 7 feet. But most of the changes in level were subsidence. Valdivia has been a river port, but the river channel subsided enough to allow sea water to move in and flood lands upriver from the city. Forty-thousand acres of productive meadow and farmland were lost as a result of subsidence and flooding (see Fig. 19-7).

FIG. 19-7
Fields of a productive farm near Valdivia, Chile, flooded when the land sank during earthquakes in 1960. Photo by John H. Hodgson.

Sound

When an earthquake occurs, the vibrations in the ground often disturb the air and produce sound waves that are within the range of the human ear. These are known as *earthquake sounds.* They have been variously described, usually as low, booming noises. Very near the source of an earthquake, sharp snaps are sometimes audible, suggesting the tearing apart of great blocks of rock. Farther away, the sounds have been likened to heavy vehicles passing rapidly over hard ground, the dragging of heavy boxes or furniture over the floor, a loud, distinct clap of thunder, an explosion, the boom of a distant cannon, or the fall of heavy bodies or great loads of stone. The true earthquake sound, of course, is quite distinct from the rumble and roar of shaking buildings, but in some cases the sounds are probably confused.

CAUSE OF EARTHQUAKES

Centuries ago, people believed that mysterious shakings of the earth were caused by the restlessness of a monster that was supposed to be supporting the globe. In Japan, it was first a great spider, then a giant catfish; in some parts of South America, it was a whale; and some of the North American Indians decided that the earth rested on the back of a giant tortoise.

The lamas of Mongolia had another idea. They assured their devout followers that after God made the earth, He had placed it on the back of an immense frog; and every time the frog shook his head or stretched one of his feet, an earthquake occurred immediately above the moving part (see Fig. 19-8). This was a major advance in earthquake theory, for at least it tried to explain the local character of earthquakes.

FIG. 19-8
Cause of earthquakes, according to the lamas of Mongolia. It was believed that when the frog lifted a foot, there was an earthquake immediately above the part that moved.

FIG. 19-9
Sequence of deformation leading to fracture along the San Andreas fault, which caused the California earthquake of 1906.

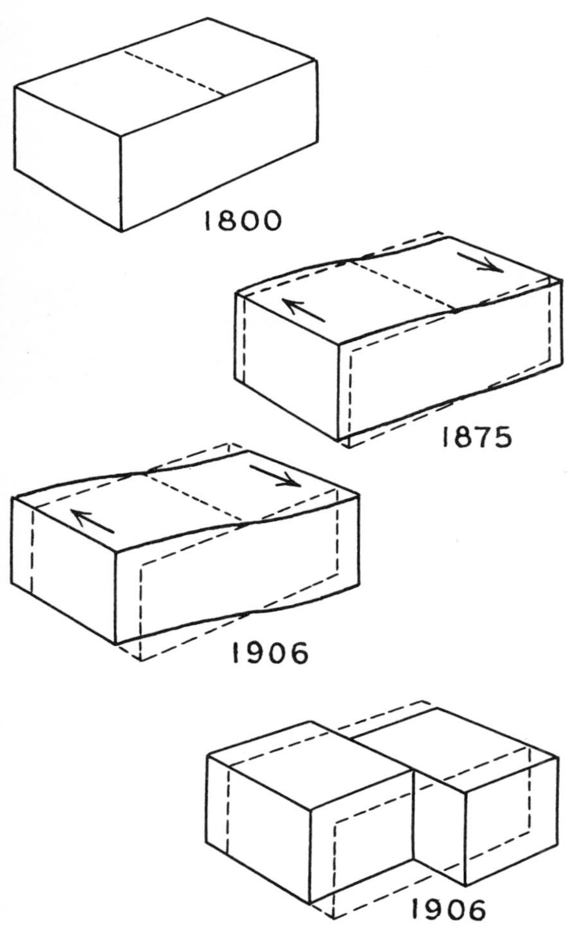

The Greek philosopher Aristotle (384-322 B.C.) held that all earthquakes were caused by air or gases struggling to escape from subterranean cavities. Since the wind must first have been forced into the cavities, he explained that just before an earthquake the atmosphere became close and stifling. As time passed, people began to refer to "earthquake weather," and to this day some people insist that the air turns humid and stuffy when an earthquake is about to occur. A Japanese scientist, Omori, checked on this belief by investigating the conditions that preceded 18 catastrophic earthquakes in Japan between 1361 and 1891. He found that the weather was fair or clear on 12 occasions, cloudy on 2, rainy or snowy on 3, and rainy and windy once, but that humid and sultry "earthquake weather" had never announced the imminent arrival of an earthquake.

Aristotle's idea of imprisoned gases was gradually modified into a theory that earthquakes were caused by gases trying to escape from volcanoes. But by the middle of the eighteenth century observers realized that many of the greatest earthquakes occurred at places quite remote from volcanoes.

Gas explosions at an erupting volcanic vent sometimes do cause vibrations in the ground, which are defined as *volcanic earthquakes.* But these vibrations represent only an extremely small percentage of the earth's least important earthquakes.

What, then, *does* cause earthquakes? Most of them are caused by deforming forces in the earth. *The immediate cause of an earthquake is the sudden break in rocks that have been distorted beyond the limit of their strength, in a process called faulting.*

Elastic rebound

Our assurance that earthquakes are caused by faulting is based on actual observations of effects that can be seen directly on the surface. It is also based on our knowledge of how rocks behave when they are subjected to distorting forces. In the laboratory, rocks have been subjected to pressures that are equivalent to the pressures at various depths in the earth's crust down to 100 miles. Under these pressures, the rocks gradually change shape. But they resist more and more as the pressure builds up, until finally they reach the breaking point. Then they tear apart and snap back into unstrained positions. This snapping-back is called *elastic rebound.*

The mechanism of faulting appears to be fundamentally the same for earthquakes at all depths, judging by the wave patterns they produce. It was once thought that earthquakes occurring at depths where rocks yield plastically presented a special problem, because the elastic strains necessary for earthquakes could not accumulate there. This difficulty has been explained, however, by a property called *viscosity,* the ratio of the deforming force to the *rate* at which a substance changes shape in response to the force. It is possible for material to have such high viscosity that although it flows in an attempt to adjust itself to a deforming force, it flows so slowly that enough force builds up to rupture the material before it completes its adjustment through flow. The viscosity of deeply buried rocks, for example, is so great that forces large enough to cause rupture (and earthquakes) can build up in a century or two, at the very time that steady flow is producing geosynclines, mountain structures, and adjustments toward isostasy over millions of years.

Just before the rocks rupture to cause a major quake, small shocks sometimes announce that the stress has become critical. These often are felt as *foreshocks*. Minor adjustments after the break are called *aftershocks*.

SAN ANDREAS FAULT. Events along the San Andreas fault in California provided an unusual opportunity to study elastic rebound. Surveys of part of the fault had been made by the U.S. Coast and Geodetic Survey at various intervals during the years preceding the great quake of 1906. H. F. Reid of Johns Hopkins University later analyzed the events in three groups: 1851-1865, 1874-1892, and 1906-1907. From the displacements revealed by those surveys, and from the displacements that occurred at the time of the actual earthquake, Reid reconstructed a history of the movement.

Though there was no direct evidence, he assumed that the elastic energy had been stored at a uniform rate over the entire interval, and that the region had started from an unstrained condition approximately a century before the earthquake. As the years passed, a line which in 1800 had cut straight across the fault at right angles became progressively more and more warped. When the relative movement of the blocks on either side of the fault became as great as 20 feet in places, the strength of the rock was exceeded and fracture occurred. The blocks snapped back toward an unstrained position, driven by the stored elastic energy (see Fig. 19-9).

The fault zone runs roughly from northwest to southeast. Land on the western or Pacific Ocean side of the fault moved northwest relative to land on the eastern side. The strains and adjustments were greatest within a zone extending 6 miles each side of the fault. Imagine a straight line 12 miles long crossing this zone at right angles to the fault, which, of course, was in the center of the zone. After the earthquake, this line was broken at the fault and was shifted into two curves. The broken ends were separated by 20 feet at the break, but the other ends were unmoved. Actually, fences, roads, and rows of vegetation, provided short sections of lines by which the displacement at the fault could be gauged (see Fig. 19-10).

The quantity of energy released by an earthquake such as this depends on the kind of rock and the size of the rock mass in which the energy was stored. As a result, some earthquakes are small and others are large. For example, the California earthquake of 1906 released energy equivalent to that of a million A-bombs. In contrast, an A-bomb has 100,000 times the energy of the smallest earthquake.

Surveys in 1922 and 1946 indicated that the region around the San Andreas fault was still warping and storing up energy that may be released in future earthquakes.

DEPTH OF FOCUS

In seismology, the scientific study of earthquakes, the term *focus* is used to designate the source of a given set of earth-

FIG. 19-10
Looking along a fence that crossed the San Andreas fault at approximately right angles. Before the earthquake of April 18, 1906, this fence was a continuous straight line. It is shown here as it appeared after the earthquake. Photo by J. C. Branner.

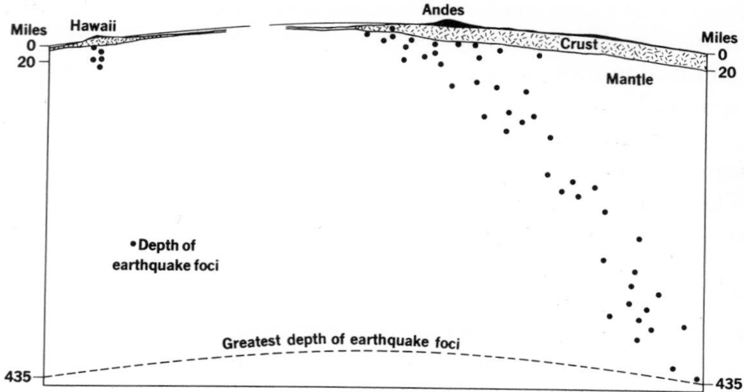

FIG. 19-11
Earthquake foci under Hawaii and South America.

quake waves. Just what is this source? As we know, the waves that constitute an earthquake are generated by the rupture of rock masses. When these waves are recorded by an instrument at some distant point, the pattern indicates that they originated in a single simple source. Of course, this source cannot be just a pinpoint; it must have dimensions. Most sources are probably closer to 30 miles in length and breadth than to 3 miles or 300 miles. But trying to fix these dimensions more accurately offers a real problem that has not yet been solved.

In any event, the focus of an earthquake is usually at some depth below the surface of the earth. An area on the surface vertically above the focus is called the *epicentral area,* or *epicenter,* from the Greek *epi,* "above," and *center.*

Foci have been located at all depths down to 435 miles, a little more than a tenth of the earth's radius (see Fig. 19-11). They are classed as shallow, intermediate, and deep. Shallow foci are those within 40 miles of the surface; intermediate foci are from 40 to 200 miles down; deep foci are at depths greater than 200 miles.

Between 1904 and 1946, 85 per cent of the earthquake energy released was from shallow foci; 12 per cent from intermediate foci; and 3 per cent from deep foci.

EARTHQUAKE INTENSITY

How to specify the size of an earthquake has always posed a problem. Before the modern development of instrumental seismology, some of the early investigations of earthquakes led to various attempts to describe the intensity of the shaking. A missionary in some remote region would keep a diary of earthquakes rated as weak, strong, or very strong. This was at best a personal scale. Then, in Italy in 1874 and Switzerland in 1878, arbitrary scales were developed which culminated soon afterward in the Rossi-Forel scale, combining the efforts of M. S. de Rossi, director of the geodynamic observatory at Rocca di Papa, near Rome, and F. A. Forel of Lausanne, a member of a committee appointed by the Helvetic Society of Natural Sciences to study earthquakes in Switzerland in the last quarter of the nineteenth century. For half a century, the Rossi-Forel scale of earthquake intensity (see Table 19-1) was widely used throughout the world.

According to this scale, earthquake effects were classified in terms of ten degrees of intensity. The scale had definite limita-

TABLE 19-1 *Rossi-Forel scale of earthquake intensity*

I. Recorded by instruments; felt only by experienced observers at rest.
II. Felt by small number of persons at rest.
III. Felt by several persons at rest; strong enough for the duration or direction to be appreciable.
IV. Felt by several persons in motion; disturbance of movable objects, door, windows; creaking of floors.
V. Felt generally by everyone; disturbance of furniture and beds; ringing of some bells.
VI. General awakening of those asleep; general ringing of bells; oscillation of chandeliers; stopping of clocks; visible disturbance of trees and shrubs; some startled persons leave their dwellings.
VII. Overthrow of movable objects, fall of plaster, ringing of church bells, general panic, without damage to buildings.
VIII. Fall of chimneys, cracks in the walls of buildings.
IX. Partial or total destruction of some buildings.
X. Great disaster, ruins, disturbance of strata, fissures in the earth's crust, rock-falls from mountains.

tions, however, from a scientific standpoint. For example, the definition of the sixth degree of intensity included "general awakening of those asleep; general ringing of bells; oscillation of chandeliers; stopping of clocks; some startled persons leave their dwellings." But an earthquake that produced those effects in Italy or Switzerland might not even wake the baby in Japan, or it might cause a stampede in Boston.

By means of postcards, letters, and interviews, investigators made surveys of the number of awakened persons, creaking floors, and ringing bells caused by each earthquake. Then they decided what places had been shaken by about equal amounts

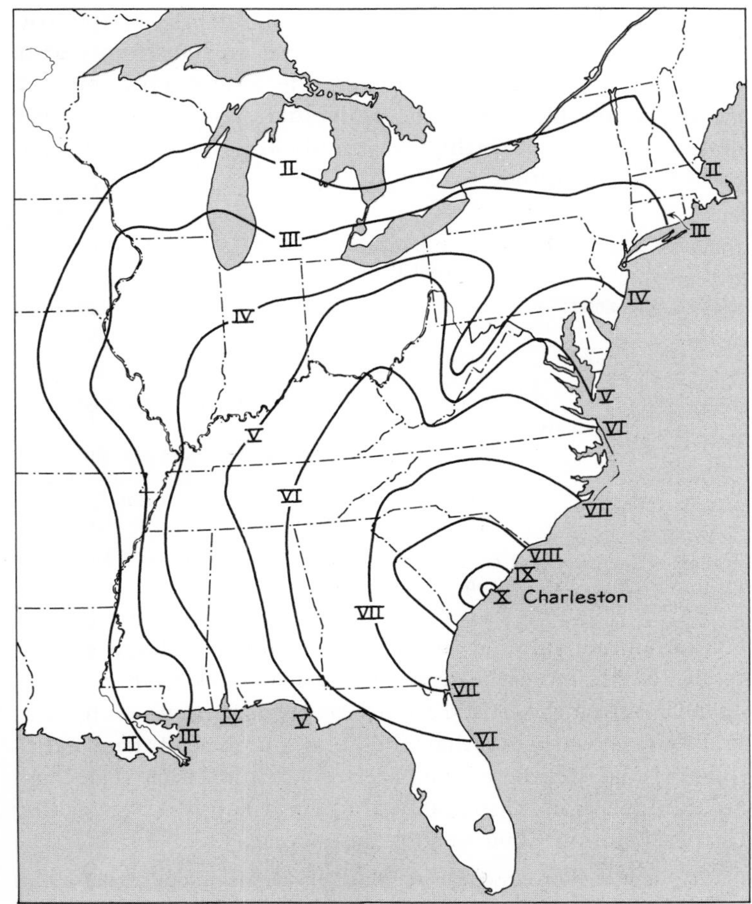

FIG. 19-12
Isoseismic map for the earthquake at Charleston, South Carolina, August 31, 1886.

and connected them on a map with *isoseismic lines,* or lines of equal shaking (see Fig. 19-12).

EARTHQUAKE MAGNITUDE AND ENERGY

Having to rely on the impressions of many people is a very unsatisfactory way of compiling accurate information, so finally a scale was devised in 1935,[1] based on instrumental records. It ascribed to each earthquake a number called the earthquake's *magnitude,* an index of the quake's energy at its source.

According to this scale, an earthquake of magnitude 2.5 is just large enough to be felt nearby; one of magnitude 4.5 or over is capable of causing some very local damage; one of 6 or over is potentially destructive. A magnitude of 7 or over represents a major earthquake. The largest magnitude observed in the first half of the twentieth century was 8.6.

An earthquake of magnitude 5 releases approximately the same amount of energy as the first atomic bomb did when it was tested on the New Mexico desert, July 16, 1945. Of course, the energy is applied in quite different ways—highly concentrated in the bomb, widely dispersed in the earthquake—and the results are correspondingly different. The energy released by an earthquake of magnitude 8.6 is three million times as great as that of an earthquake of magnitude 5, or of the first atomic bomb.

Distribution of earthquakes

The first extensive statistical study of earthquakes to take into account both the energy released and the depths of foci covered the years 1904 through 1946. It revealed that from year to year there were wide variations in the total energy released, as well as in the number of individual shocks. The average annual number of earthquakes of shallow focus is listed according to magnitude in Table 19-2.

TABLE 19-2 *Average annual number of shallow-focus earthquakes* (1904-1946)

EARTHQUAKES	MAGNITUDE	AVG. ANNUAL NUMBER	
Great	7.7–8.6	2	Actually observed
Major	7.0–7.7	12	
Potentially destructive	6.0–7.0	108	
	5.0–6.0	800	Estimates for the whole earth, based on sampling special regions
	4.0–5.0	6,200	
	3.0–4.0	49,000	
	2.5–3.0	100,000	

From B. Gutenberg and C. F. Richter, *Seismicity of the Earth* (Princeton: Princeton Univ. Press, 1949).

The annual number of shallow earthquakes large enough to be felt by someone nearby is estimated to have exceeded 150,000 during the period from 1904 through 1946. Gutenberg and Richter estimate that the total number of true earthquakes "may well be of the order of a million each year," and recording stations throughout the world supply data leading to the location of 600 earthquakes a year.

[1] C. F. Richter, "An Instrumental Earthquake Magnitude Scale," *Bull. Seis. Soc. Am.,* XXV (1935), 1-32.

Earthquakes tend to occur in belts or zones surrounding stable, relatively inactive areas. *The earthquakes that occur in the most active zone, around the borders of the Pacific Ocean, account for a little over 80 per cent of the total energy released throughout the world.* The greatest earthquake activity is in Japan, western Mexico, Melanesia, and the Philippines. The loop of islands bordering the Pacific has a high proportion of great shocks at all focal depths.

Fifteen per cent of the total energy released by all earthquakes is released in a zone that extends from Burma through the Himalaya Range, into Baluchistan, across Iran, and westerly through the Alpine structures of Mediterranean Europe. This is sometimes called the Mediterranean and trans-Asiatic zone. Earthquakes in this zone are of shallow and intermediate depth, with foci aligned along mountain chains.

With 80 per cent of the total earthquake energy released around the Pacific, and 15 per cent along the Mediterranean and trans-Asiatic zone, 5 per cent must be released throughout the rest of the world. Narrow belts of shallow-focus activity follow the mid-Atlantic Ridge and ridges in the Indian and Arctic oceans (see Fig. 19-13).

The total energy released by the world's earthquakes fluctuates greatly from year to year. For example, 1906 showed 6 times the average recorded between 1904 and 1952, and 40 times the minimum; 1950 was another very large year, second only to 1906.

From time to time, observers have tried to correlate the occurrence of earthquakes with sun spots, the tides, the position of heavenly bodies, and other phenomena. But they have all ignored the facts in one way or another. Occasionally, someone steps forward to predict earthquakes on the basis of some correlation that he fancies he has made. Usually, however, he keeps his supporting data secret. One such prophet stated that on each of certain days during three months of one year there would be "an earthquake in the southwest Pacific." Since he did not specify magnitude, time,

FIG. 19-13
Locations of 3,737 earthquakes that occurred in 30 years (1899–1910; 1913–1930, inclusive) on Aitoff's equal area projection. This map stresses the importance of regions of relatively little earthquake activity, since it does not show the number of repetitions at active centers such as Japan. Prepared by L. Don Leet.

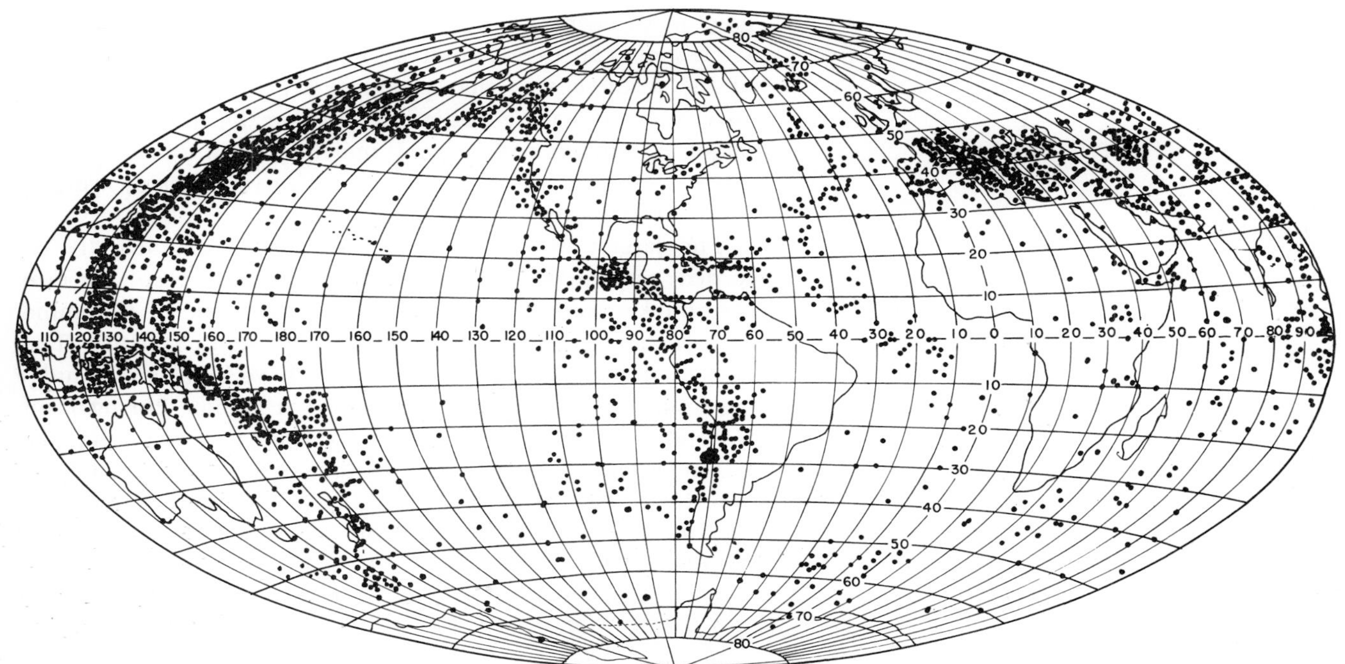

or place in this highly active zone, statistically he couldn't miss.

But the statistics of earthquake occurrence make one fact very clear: *most of the energy released is concentrated in a relatively small number of very large earthquakes.* A single earthquake of magnitude 8.4 releases just about as much energy as was released, on the average, each year during the first half of the twentieth century. It is not unusual for the energy of one great earthquake to exceed that of all the others in a given year, or of several years put together. Seven great shallow-focus earthquakes represented nearly 25 per cent of the total energy released from 1906 to 1964 (Table 19-3).

TABLE 19-3 *Great shallow-focus earthquakes* (1906-1964)

Date	Location	Coordinates	*Magnitude*
Jan. 31, 1906	Colombia	1°N., 82°W.	8.6
Aug. 17, 1906	Chile	33°S., 72°W.	8.4
Jan. 3, 1911	Tien Shan	44°N., 78°E.	8.4
Dec. 16, 1920	Kansu	36°N., 105°E.	8.5
Mar. 2, 1933	Japan	39°N., 145°E.	8.5
Aug. 15, 1950	Asia	29°N., 97°E.	8.6
Mar. 28, 1964	Alaska	61°N., 147°W.	8.5

The maximum energy released by earthquakes becomes progressively less as depth of focus increases. The 7 largest shallow-focus earthquakes listed in Table 19-3 had magnitudes of 8.6, 8.4, 8.4, 8.5, 8.5, 8.5, and 8.6. The five largest intermediate-depth shocks over the same interval had magnitudes of 8.1, 8.2, 8.1, 7.9, and 8.0; and the three largest deep-focus shocks had magnitudes of only 8.0, 7.75, and 7.75. This trend suggests that the force required to rupture rocks decreases as depth increases.

For many years it was believed that a large number of small earthquakes in a region reduced the hazard of a major shock. This belief was based on the "safety-valve" principle that small earthquakes periodically relieved accumulated strains. Improved statistical data do not support that view, however, since shocks in a limited area seldom, if ever, release a total amount of energy that even begins to approximate that of a large shock. So they cannot be relieving any significant part of the strain energy that produces a great earthquake, and they probably have a negligible effect on the time at which a major earthquake will occur. It may be true in some instances, however, that small earthquakes provide warnings of a major shock by signaling a condition of strain.

The largest magnitude assigned to an instrumentally recorded earthquake between 1904 and 1964 was 8.6. Two earthquakes were rated at that magnitude: one in Colombia on January 31, 1906 and one in Asia on August 15, 1950. The only earthquake in history that might have been larger, judging from the reported effects, occurred at Lisbon, Portugal, on November 1, 1755. Possibly, the magnitude of that earthquake was between 8.7 and 9.0. An earthquake with a magnitude of over 10 should theoretically be perceptible in scattered areas over the entire earth, but such an occurrence has never been recorded.

SUMMARY OUTLINE

Effects of earthquakes
Fire, damage to structures, seismic sea waves, landslides, cracks in ground, changes in land level, sound

Fire
Greater hazard to life and property than shaking of ground
Spreads because of broken water pipes

Damage to structures
Depends in part on the type of ground under buildings; also on type of construction

Seismic sea waves
Generated by submarine earthquakes or landslides
Travel approximately 500 miles per hour

Landslides
Caused by vibrations shaking loose sand, gravel, or rock

Cracks in the ground
Produced in loose soil and pavement by slumps and landslides
Never produced in solid rock

Changes in land level
Occur over broad areas; may be elevation, depression, or tilting

Sound
Vibrations in the ground often disturb the air and produce audible sound waves

Cause of earthquakes
Break in rocks, called faulting

Mechanism of faulting
Elastic rebound

Focus
Source of earthquake
Shallow, intermediate, deep

Intensity
Description of effects at various places on the surface

Magnitude
Size of earthquake at the focus
Measure of energy released

Distribution of earthquakes
Amount of energy released

SELECTED REFERENCES

Byerly, Perry, *Seismology*. Englewood Cliffs, N.J.: Prentice-Hall, Inc., 1942.

Gutenberg, B. and C. F. Richter, *Seismicity of the Earth* (2nd ed.) Princeton: Princeton Univ. Press, 1954.

Hodgson, John H., *Earthquakes and Earth Structure*. Englewood Cliffs, N.J.: Prentice-Hall, Inc., 1964 (paperback).

Leet, L. Don, *Earth Waves*. Cambridge: Harvard Univ. Press, 1950.

——— and Florence J. Leet, *The World of Geology*. New York: McGraw-Hill Book Company, 1961.

———, *Earthquake—Discoveries in Seismology*. New York: Dell Publishing Co., 1964 (paperback).

Roberts, Elliott, *Our Quaking Earth*. Boston: Little, Brown & Co., 1963.

20 The earth's interior

By studying the manner in which earth waves travel out from earthquakes, geologists have assembled a wealth of information about the structure of the globe from surface to center. But before we look at the results of these studies, let us review the methods of obtaining information.

INSTRUMENTAL OBSERVATION

One of the first devices used to detect earthquake waves is credited to a Chinese named Choko who lived around A.D. 136. It consisted of a hollow sphere, with a handle-like projection above. Suspended from the handle was a pendulum, with its bob in the sphere. Eight channels permitted the pendulum to swing in the principal directions of the compass. Protruding from the sphere at the end of each channel was a dragon's head with an open mouth containing a small ball. Below each head was a frog, also with an open mouth, and with its head tipped back to catch the ball when the dragon dropped it (see Fig. 20-1). When ground vibrations disturbed the pendulum, it swung into one or more of the channels and kicked the corresponding balls into the mouths of the waiting frogs. In this way, the direction of an earthquake's movement was supposedly indicated. But we know today that the ground moves in different directions as earthquake waves pass a given point. So, although Choko's gimmick was an artistic triumph, it was based on a scientific misconception.

In 1703, the same general idea was rediscovered by a French scientist, de Hautefeuille, who placed a bowl of mercury in the top of a truncated hemisphere with eight channels leading down to cups. The direction from which the mercury slopped over into the cups during an earthquake was supposed to show the direction of earthquake's source.

In the late nineteenth century, inventors came up with several devices designed to stop a clock at the instant of a shock. A modification of this idea, worked out in 1900, consisted of a pendulum that, when displaced by a vibration, released mercury from a funnel-shaped reservoir. The mercury fell into a cup balanced on one end of a lever. When the lever moved, it lighted electric bulbs that, in turn, illuminated a clock face. The clock was photographed to give a record of the time, and the lever depressed a second arm that closed another switch and rang a gong to summon the seismologist.

The first real records of earthquake waves seem to have come about by accident. Toward the end of the nineteenth century, German scientists were using a pendulum to register the slight tilting of the ground from the changing weight of water as tides in the North Sea rose and fell. Often, however, they found that their records became fuzzy (see Fig. 20-2) and that the fuzziness sometimes lasted for two or more hours. Eventually they discovered that these distortions were caused by waves from distant earthquakes. With this discovery, modern seismology was born.

The seismograph

The waves that constitute an earthquake travel into and through the earth, as well as around its surface. They are now recorded by instruments called seismographs (from *seismos*, "a shaking," and *graphein* "to write"). The record itself is called a seismogram.

A seismograph is designed to measure and record displacements of the ground. It does so by means of a mass that is either suspended on a spring to record vertical movements, or attached to the end of a rod to record horizontal ones. A stylus or other device attached to the mass will record the motion of the earth relative to the virtually unmoving mass. A special device marks off minutes and hours on the recording sheet. Most earthquake recording stations have seismo-

FIG. 20-1
Choko seismometer, A.D. *136, supposedly furnished seismic data from the dragon's mouth. Drawn by Congdon for History of the Seismograph, a picture series published by Texas Instruments, Inc.*

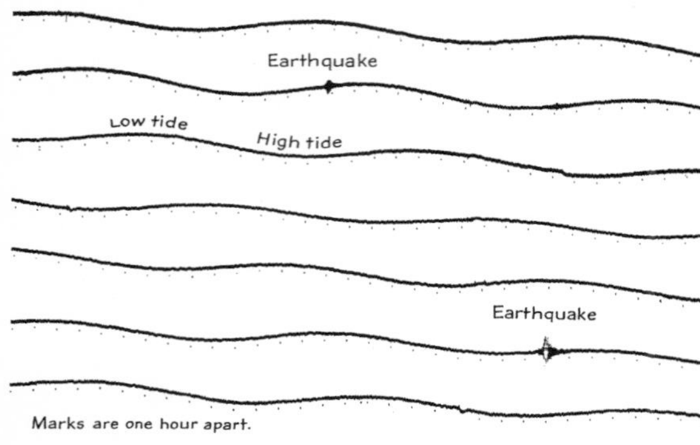

FIG. 20-2
Record showing tilting of the ground from tides in the Gulf of Maine. Taken at the Harvard Seismograph Station, 35 miles inland.

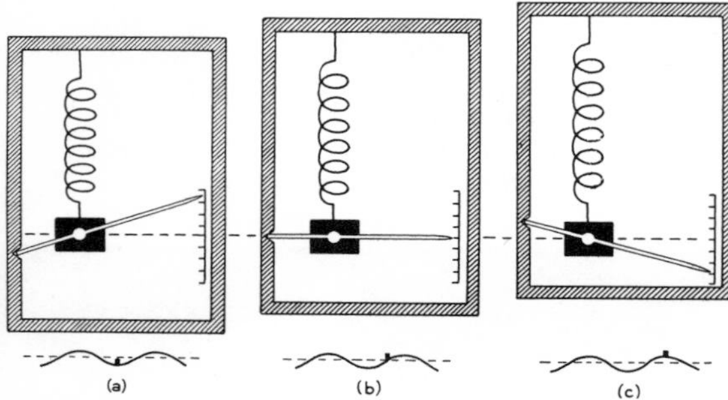

FIG. 20-3
The principle of a seismograph.
The weight on its spring can bounce up and down, requiring a certain length of time (called the period) to complete each oscillation. But as long as the ground under the instrument moves up and down with a shorter period (taking less time for each oscillation than the weight does if it is bouncing freely), the weight hangs still in space, or nearly so. It can then become the fulcrum of a simple lever.
Sketch B *shows the seismograph in its neutral position. Sketch* A *shows that as the seismograph's case dips into the trough of an earth wave and the weight remains at the original level, the short arm of the lever goes down while the long arm goes up a greater amount.*
A record is obtained at the long arm of the lever (it is usually magnified optically or electronically, to make it large enough to be seen). Sketch C *shows the opposite happening, when the case rides up onto the crest of an earth wave.*
The seismograph in the example records vertical movements, but the same general principle can be applied to the design of a seismograph that records horizontal movements.

graphs designed to respond to both horizontal (east-west and north-south) motion and vertical motion.

Seismographs are so designed that if the earth moves quickly their mass remains at rest. For instance, a mass suspended on a spring so that it moves freely up and down, but not sideways, requires a certain length of time to complete one up-and-down cycle. This time is called the *period.* If the ground under the mass moves up and down with a shorter period (taking less time for each oscillation than the weight does if bouncing freely), the weight hangs still in space, or nearly so, as the ground moves up and down (see Fig. 20-3). It then serves as a point of reference from which to measure the earth's motion—so small that it must be magnified in order to be recorded.

One way we can make a record of the earth's motion is to have a beam of light bounced off the steady mass to a recorder that moves with the earth and records the relative motion between the mass and the light. The farther the light is bounced, the greater the magnification.

To obtain recordings of most earth waves generated by earthquakes, we need seismographs capable of responding to short- and long-period waves. Short-period waves have periods of 1 to 5 seconds; long-period waves have periods of 5 to 60 seconds or more.

There are many kinds of seismographs. Some weigh hundreds of pounds, or even several tons, and are set up in underground vaults. They can record anything from the vibrations of railroad trains miles away, to the tremors of an earthquake any place in the world (if the earthquake is large enough). Other seismographs are small enough to be slipped into a vest pocket, or carried several in a hand, and are used to record waves generated by small dynamite charges in prospecting for minerals.

EARTH WAVES

When rocks break and cause an earthquake, the energy released travels away by means of earth waves. The manner in which earth waves transmit energy can be illustrated by the behavior of waves on the surface of water.

A pebble dropped into a quiet pool creates ripples that travel outward over the water's surface in concentric circles. These ripples carry away part of the energy that the pebble possessed as it struck the water. A listening device at some distant point beneath the surface can detect the noise of impact. The noise is transmitted through the body of the water by sound waves, far different from surface waves and not visible by ordinary means.

Just as with water-borne waves, there are two general classes of earth waves: (1) *body waves* travel through the interior of the mass in which they are generated, and (2) *surface waves* travel only along the surface.

Body waves

Body waves are of two general types: push-pull and shake. Each is defined by its manner of moving particles as it travels along.

Push-pull waves, more commonly known as sound waves, *can travel through any material—solid, liquid, or gas.* They move the particles forward and backward; consequently, the materials in the path of these waves are alternately compressed and rarefied. For example, when we strike a tuning fork sharply, the prongs vibrate back and forth, first pushing then pulling the molecules of air with which they come in contact. Each molecule bumps the next one, and a wave of pressure is set in motion through the air. If the molecules next to your ear drum are compressed at the rate of 440 times per second, you hear a tone that is called middle A (see Fig. 20-4).

Shake waves can travel only through solids. These waves shake the particles in their path at right angles to the direction of their advance. Imagine that you are holding one end of a rope fastened to a wall. If you move your hand up and down regularly, a series of waves will travel along the rope to the wall. As each wave moves along, the particles in the rope move up and down, just as the particles in your hand did. In other words, the particles move at *right angles* to the direction of the wave's advance. The same is true when you move your hand from side to side instead of up and down (see Fig. 20-5).

Surface waves

Surface waves can travel along any material. Let us look again at the manner in which waves transmit energy along the surface of water. If you stand on the shore and throw a pebble into a quiet pool, setting up surface waves, some of the water seems to be moving toward you. Actually, though, what is coming toward you is *energy* in the form of waves. The particles of water move in a definite pattern as each wave advances: up, forward, down, and back, in a small circle. We can observe this pattern by dropping a small cork into the path of the waves (see Fig. 20-6).

When surface waves are generated in rock, one common type of particle motion is just the reverse of the water-particle motion—that is, forward, up, back, and down.

RECORDS OF EARTHQUAKE WAVES

The first records of earthquake motion registered on a tilt instrument were too fuzzy to be analyzed accurately because the events of an hour were compressed into the space of a quarter of an inch. But when the speed of the recording drum was increased to spread the events of one hour over a space of

FIG. 20-4
Push-pull wave, sometimes called compressional wave. In the top row, the balls connected by springs are all at rest. The second row shows conditions after the ball on the left-hand end has been pushed against its neighbor and the compression has started down the line. As each ball responds to this push, it compresses the next spring and pushes against the next ball. A wave of compression moves down the line, followed by a wave of pulling or rarefaction. In this type of wave, each particle in the path of the wave moves back and forth about its starting position, along the line of the wave's advance.

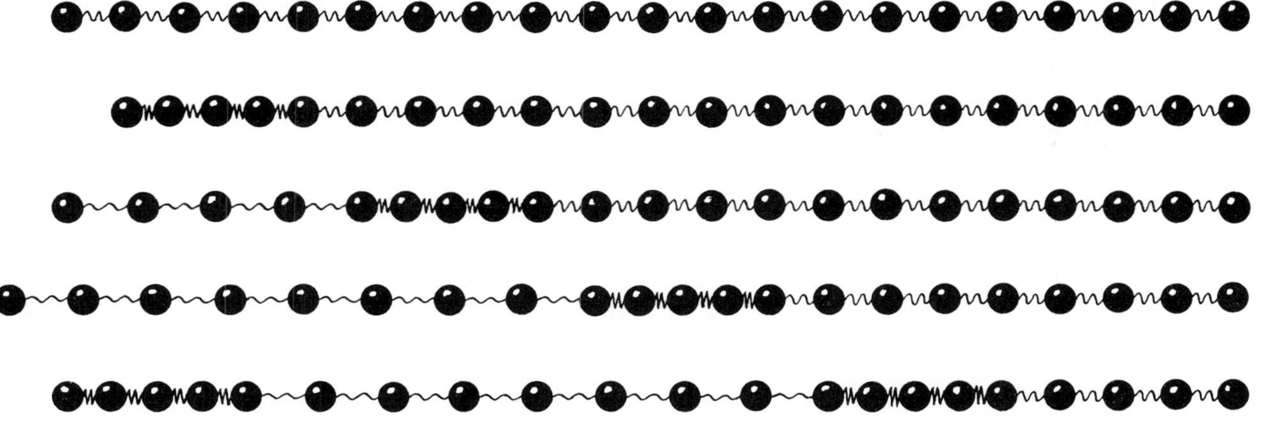

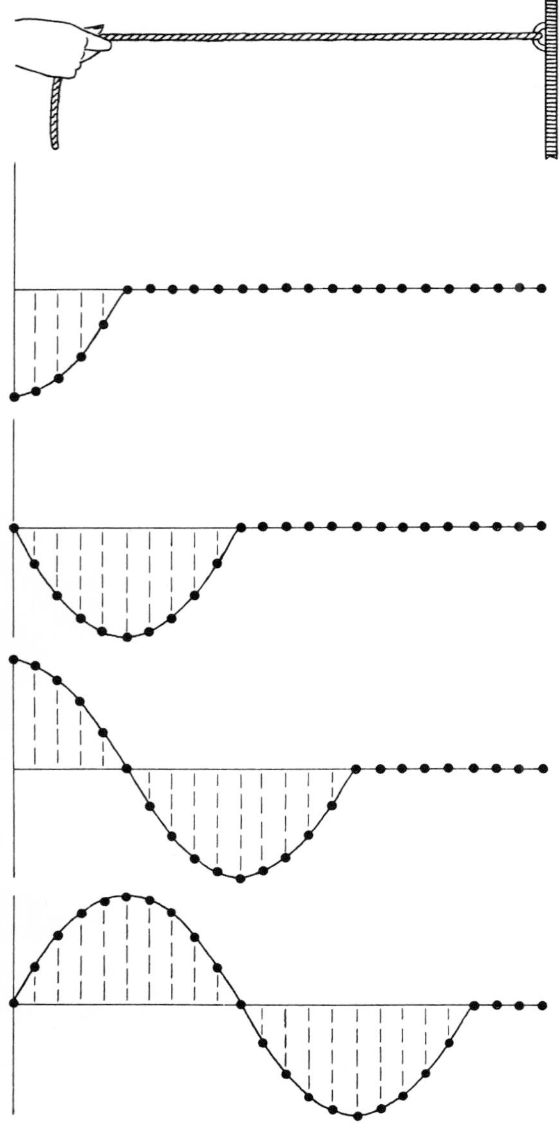

FIG. 20-5
Shake wave, sometimes called shear wave. If the hand is moved up and down rhythmically, adjacent particles are displaced, as shown in the sequence of diagrams, and a wave form moves along the rope. As the wave form moves forward, particles in its path move up and down. A similar result could be obtained by moving the hand from side to side or in any intermediate direction.

two or three feet or more, it was found that the fuzziness cleared up and a sharp pattern emerged.

This pattern consisted of three sets of earth waves. The first waves to arrive at the recording station were named Primary; the second to arrive were named Secondary; and the last to arrive were named Large waves. The abbreviations, P, S, and L are commonly used for these three types. Closer study revealed that the P waves are push-pull waves and travel with a speed determined by the bulk modulus, the rigidity, and the density of rocks.[1] It also revealed that the S waves are shake waves and travel with a speed determined by the rigidity and the density of rocks.[2]

The Primary and Secondary waves travel from the focus of an earthquake through the interior of the earth to the recording station. The L waves are surface waves that travel from the area directly above the focus, where they are generated by P and S waves, along the crust's surface, and finally to the station.

Remember that the P waves arrive at the station before the S waves. For, although these two sets of waves follow the same general path, they travel at different speeds. The push-pull mechanism by which the P waves travel generates more rapid speed than does the shake mechanism of the S waves.[3] The L waves are the last to arrive, because they travel at a slower speed and over a longer route (see Fig. 20-8).

Travel times

If we know where a major earthquake has taken place, we can measure the distance from the point of origin to the various seismograph stations that have recorded its waves. The records at these stations indicate the exact time the various waves arrived.

LESS THAN 7,000 MILES. From thousands of measurements the world over, we have learned that P, S, and L waves have regular travel schedules for distances up to 7,000 miles. From an earthquake in San Francisco, for example, we can predict that:

P will reach El Paso, 1,000 mi away, in 3 min 22 sec; S in 6 min 3 sec.

P will reach Indianapolis, 2,000 mi away, in 5 min 56 sec; S in 10 min 48 sec.

P will reach Costa Rica, 3,000 mi away, in 8 min 1 sec; S in 14 min 28 sec.

The travel schedules move along systematically out to a distance of 7,000 miles, as shown in Table 20-1.

BEYOND 7,000 MILES. Beyond 7,000 miles, however, something happens to the schedule, and the P waves are delayed. By 10,000 miles, they are 3 minutes late. When we consider

[1] When V = velocity of P waves, B = bulk modulus, G = rigidity, and d = density, then

$$V^2 = \frac{B + \frac{4}{3}G}{d}.$$

[2] When V = velocity of S waves, G = rigidity, and d = density, then

$$V^2 = \frac{G}{d}.$$

[3] S waves travel at about 3/5 the speed of P waves in any given earth material.

TABLE 20-1 *Sample timetable for P and S*

MILES FROM SOURCE	TRAVEL TIME FOR P (Min)	TRAVEL TIME FOR P (Sec)	TRAVEL TIME FOR S (Min)	TRAVEL TIME FOR S (Sec)	INTERVAL BETWEEN P AND S (S–P) (Min)	INTERVAL BETWEEN P AND S (S–P) (Sec)
1,000	3	22	6	03	2	41
2,000	5	56	10	48	4	52
3,000	8	01	14	28	6	27
4,000	9	50	17	50	8	00
5,000	11	26	20	51	9	25
6,000	12	43	23	27	10	44
7,000	13	50	25	39	11	49

that up to 7,000 miles we could predict their arrival time within seconds, a 3-minute delay becomes significant.

The fate of the S waves is even more spectacular: they disappear altogether, never to be heard from again (see Fig. 20-9).

When the strange case of the late P and the missing S was first recognized, seismologists became excited. For now they realized that they were not just recording earthquakes, but were developing a picture of the interior of the globe.

Locating earthquakes

We now have timetables for P, S, and L for all possible distances from an earthquake. These are represented in the graph of Fig. 20-10. Data of this sort are the essential tools of the seismologist.

When the records of a station give clear evidence of the P, S, and L waves from an earthquake, the observer first determines the intervals between them. By using an interval table (see Table 20-1), he can immediately translate the intervals into actual distances. For example, if he observes that S arrived 8 minutes after P, he knows that the earthquake must have been 4,000 miles away. He then notes that P arrived at 4 hr 12 min 22 sec that morning. From the timetable, he then finds that P requires 9 min 50 sec to travel 4,000 miles. The earthquake therefore occurred at 4 hr 02 min 32 sec.[4]

This process is carried out at all the seismograph stations that have recorded the quake. Then an arc is drawn on a globe to represent the computed distance from each station. The point where all the arcs intersect indicates the center of the disturbance.

Although this whole procedure is essentially very simple, some have found its accuracy hard to believe. On Thursday, December 16, 1920, seismologists all over the world found the record of an exceptionally severe earthquake on their seismographs. Each of them computed the distance of the quake and sent the information along to the central bureaus where the various reports were assembled. The next day, the location of the earthquake was announced to the press, unlike many lesser shocks that fail to make the news. The announcement stated that a very severe earthquake had occurred at 5 min 43 sec after 12:00, Greenwich time, December 16, 1920, in the vicinity of 35.6°N., 105.7°E. That placed it in the province of Kansu, China, about 1,000 miles inland from Shanghai, on the border of Tibet. This area is densely populated, but quite

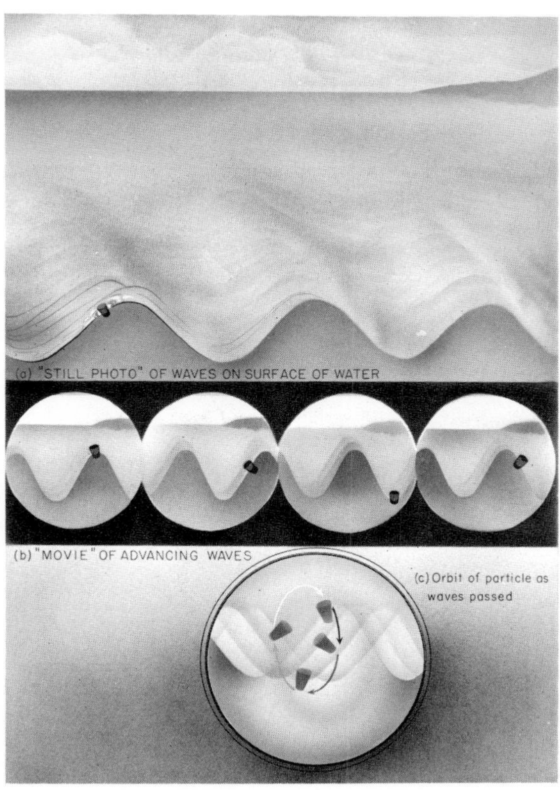

FIG. 20-6
Methods of illustrating or describing surface wave motion.

[4] 4 hr 12 min 22 sec *minus* 9 min 50 sec = 4 hr 02 min 32 sec.

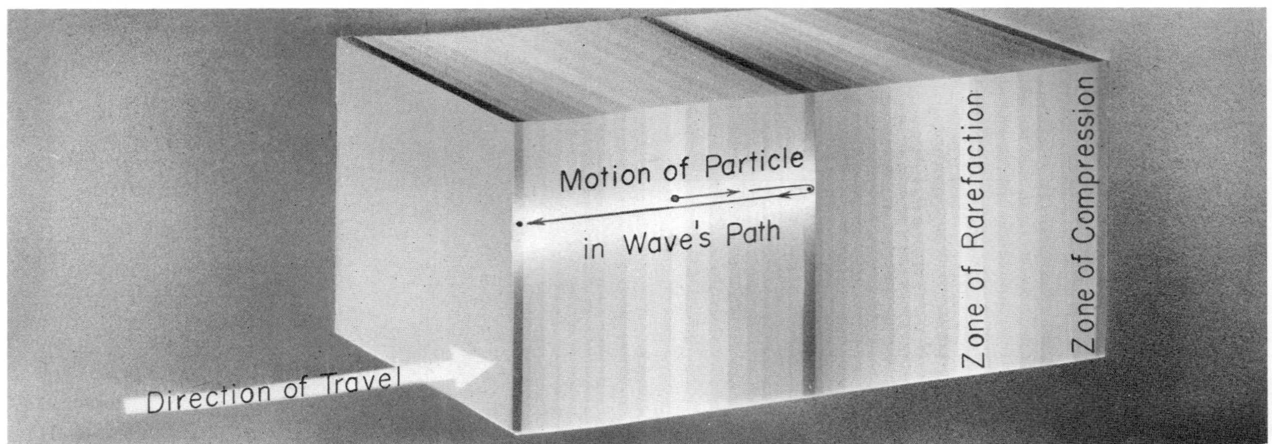

PUSH-PULL (Compressional) WAVE

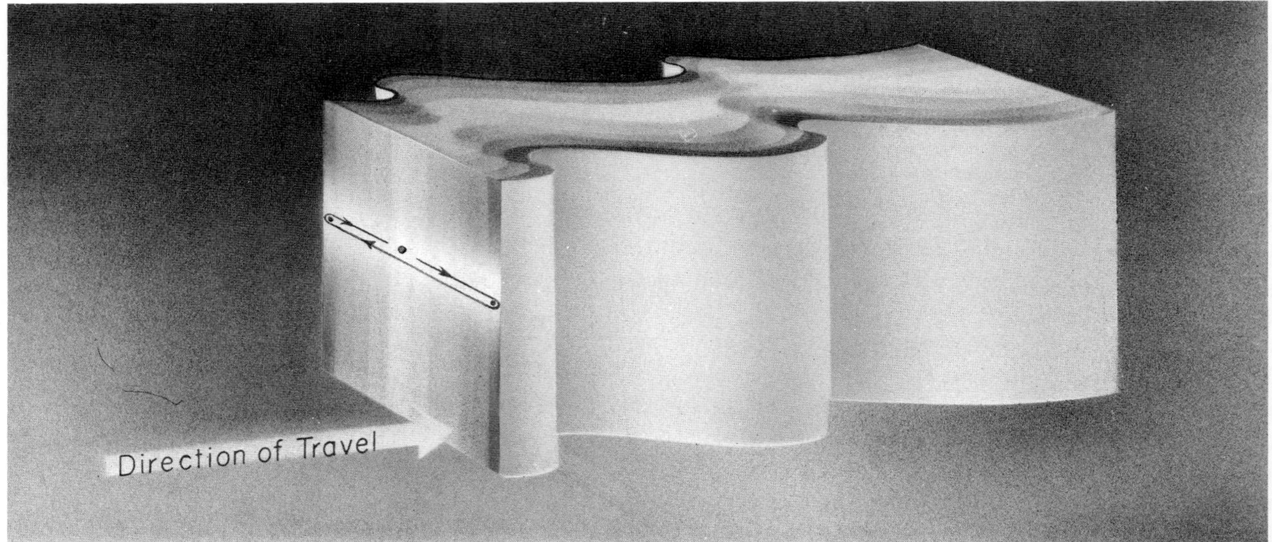

SHAKE (Shear) WAVE

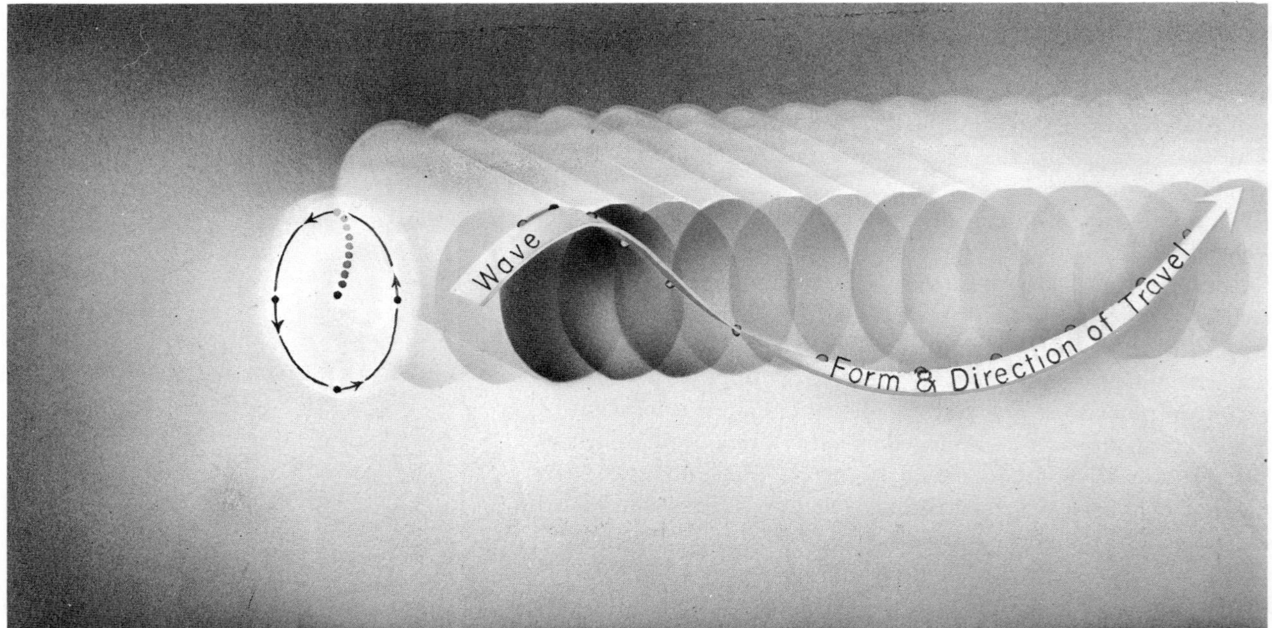

SURFACE WAVE

FIG. 20-7
Motion produced by three important earthquake wave types.

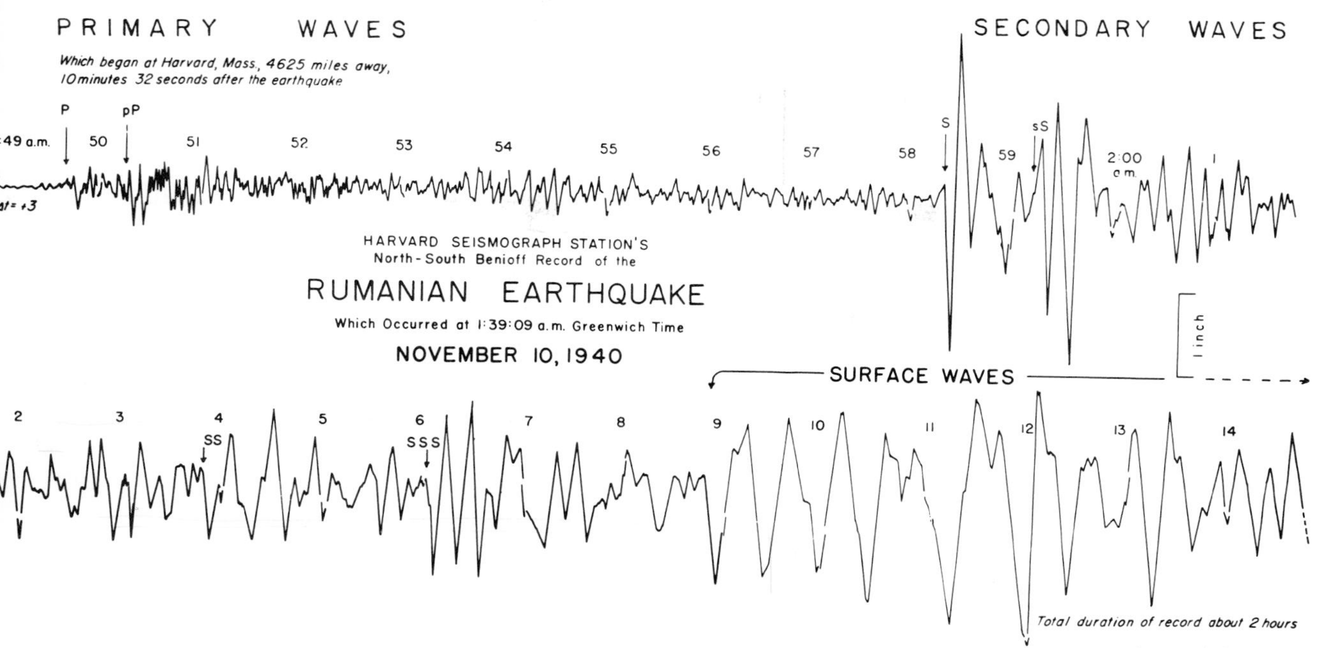

isolated. No reports of damage came in, however, and the matter was soon forgotten by the general public. But it was not forgotten by the members of the press, who were sure they had been misinformed. Then, three months later, a survivor staggered into the range of modern communications with a story of a catastrophe in Kansu on the day and at the time announced, a catastrophe that had killed an estimated 100,000 persons and had created untold havoc by causing the great landslides described in Chapter 19.

In contrast, however, on another occasion the news of an earthquake traveled faster than the waves themselves. On August 20, 1937, at 6:59 P.M., an earthquake occurred at Manila, in the Philippines, and the news story was transmitted with unusual promptness. It was flashed to North America and found its way to the Boston office of a news agency. An opera-

FIG. 20-8
A modern seismogram on which 1 minute is spread over more space than was given to 3 hours in Fig. 20-2. All waves started in Rumania at the same instant. They arrived as indicated above because of different speeds and paths. Experience has shown that when the Secondary waves begin 8 min 41 sec after the start of the Primary waves, as here, and each group includes a special wave (marked pP and sS), they are 4,625 miles from their places of origin at a depth of 80 miles below the earth's surface.

FIG. 20-9
Successive positions of the advancing front of push-pull waves in the earth's interior. Also shown are the paths of P, S, and surface waves to three different distances, with the seismograms for those distances. The effect of the core in delaying P and eliminating S is illustrated at the greatest distance.

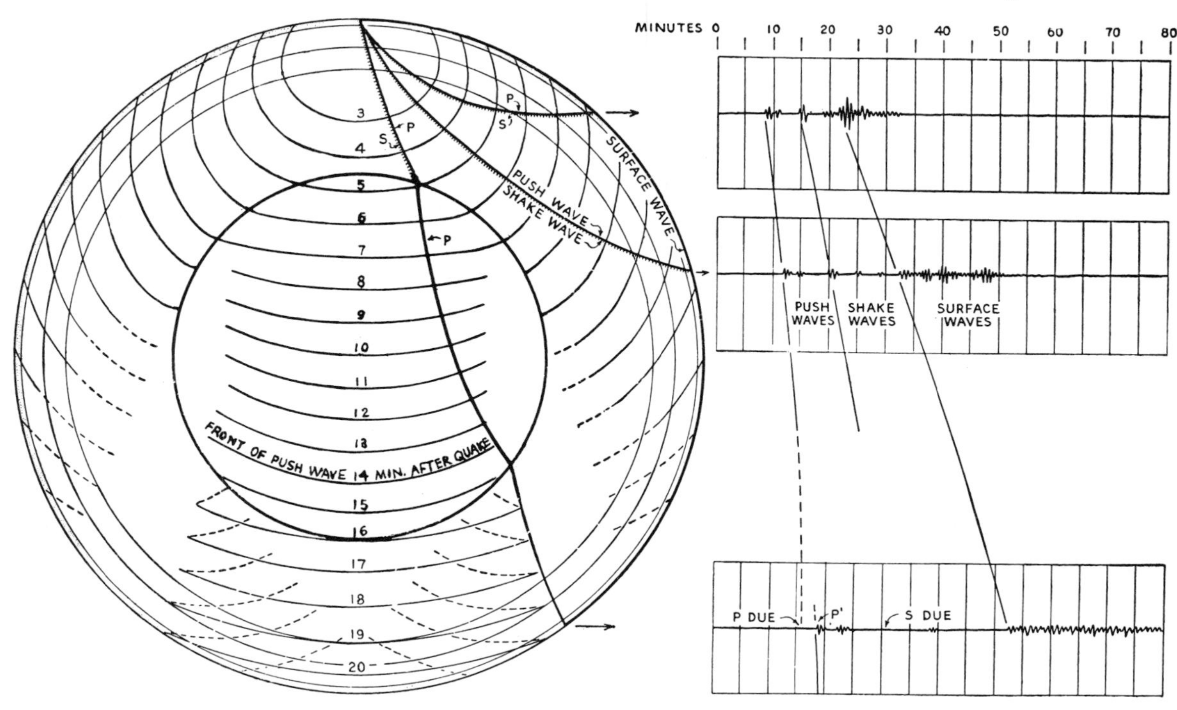

tor there picked up a phone and called the Harvard Seismograph Station at Harvard, Massachusetts, 8,400 miles from Manila, an hour after the earthquake happened, to inquire whether the disturbance had been recorded. The conversation took place ten minutes before the earthquake's surface waves reached the station.

STRUCTURE OF THE EARTH'S INTERIOR

Studies of the travel habits of waves through the earth, and of surface waves around the earth, have given us information about the structure of the globe from its surface to its center. These studies have been made possible by our knowledge of the speed of these earth waves and of their behavior in different materials. For example, waves travel at greater speeds through simatic materials than through sialic materials.

When earth waves move from one kind of material to another, they are deflected, as light waves are deflected by a lens. Part of the energy of the waves is bounced back to the surface, where it can be recorded. The rest of the energy travels on into the new material. Seismic data have revealed several places within the earth's interior where the waves indicate a change in the physical properties of the material. The boundary between two such different materials is called a *discontinuity*.

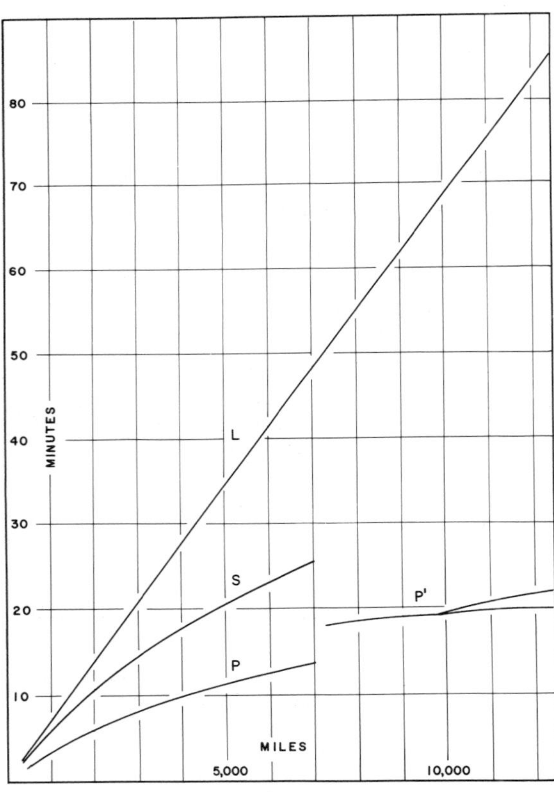

FIG. 20-10
Time-distance graph for earthquake waves. P′ is a push-pull wave that has traversed the core. The line for P′ is split beyond 10,000 miles by the effect of the solid inner core.

For body waves to reach greater and greater distances on the surface, they must penetrate deeper and deeper into the earth's interior. Thus, in traveling from an earthquake in San Francisco to a station at Dallas, a surface distance of 1,500 miles, the body waves penetrate to 300 miles below the surface. This holds true for any other 1,500-mile surface distance. To reach a station 7,000 miles away, the body waves dip into the interior to a maximum depth of 1,800 miles and bring us information from that depth.

On the basis of data assembled from studies of the travel habits of earth waves, the earth has been divided into three zones: *crust, mantle,* and *core.*

The earth's crust

Information on the earth's crust comes primarily from seismological observations. These include P and S waves from local earthquakes (within 700 miles), dynamite, and nuclear blasts. One of the first things revealed is that the earth's crust is solid rock. Early in the history of crustal studies a seismologist in Yugoslavia, A. Mohorovičić (Mō-hō-rō-vee′-cheech), made a special study of records of the earth waves from an earthquake on October 8, 1909, in the Kulpa Valley, Croatia. He concluded that velocities of P and S increased abruptly below a depth of about 30 miles. This abrupt change in the speed of P and S indicated a change in material and became known as the *Mohorovicic discontinuity*. For convenience, it is now referred to as the *Moho*. The Moho marks the bottom of the earth's crust and separates it from the mantle.

THE CRUST OF CONTINENTS. The depth to the Moho varies in different parts of the continents. In the United States, data collected up to the present time show the shallowest portion is approximately 22 miles; the thickest 35 miles.

It has been difficult to get precise data on the earth's crust from the waves of earthquakes. Waves from dynamite blasts, however, with precisely known locations on the surface, and times of detonation, have filled in some of the details. In 1941, the Harvard Seismograph Station determined the structure of the continental crust in New England, which has turned out to be fairly representative of other sections of continents. Analysis of many blast records revealed that in New England the continental crust has three layers, each one with different elastic properties, indicating different rock types. Table 20-2 summarizes the data.

TABLE 20-2
Earth's crust under New England

THICKNESS (miles)		VELOCITY (mi/sec) P	S	ROCK TYPE
10	Layer 1	3.8	2.1	Sialic
8	Layer 2	4.2	2.4	Intermediate
4	Layer 3	4.5	2.7	Simatic
		MOHO		
Top of Mantle		5.2	2.9	

L. D. Leet, "Trial Travel Times for Northeastern America," *Bull. Seis. Soc. Am.* XXXI (1941), 325-34.

The first layer is sialic in composition and has been called the *granitic layer.* The second and third layers are more and more simatic in composition. The third is believed to be basalt.

The crust under the United States is thickest—more than 35 miles—under the eastern front of the Rocky Mountain ranges and the adjacent plateau. It thins from there toward each ocean, with the exception of a local thicker pocket under the part of Nevada popularly known as the Great Basin.

THE CRUST UNDER OCEANS. Our knowledge of the structure of the crust beneath the oceans is based on observations of rocks exposed on volcanic islands and on studies of the velocities of L waves from earthquakes. These are now being supplemented in a few places by dynamite-wave profiles.

The rock types found on islands help to determine the edges of the Pacific Basin. The *andesite line* (see Fig. 20-11) has on its ocean side younger, extrusive rocks composed of basalt, while on the other side they are principally andesite. This has been viewed as the dividing line between oceanic and continental crusts.

On the basis of seismic wave velocities, it appears that the crust under the Pacific is not layered and is appreciably thinner than the crust of continents. Thicknesses as little as 3 miles have been measured in the northeast Pacific.

The crust under the Pacific Ocean is made up of simatic rocks. The composition of the crust under the Atlantic and Indian oceans is still a subject of debate, mainly because we lack reliable information on the speeds of waves traveling through it. Some investigators think that simatic rocks underlie at least parts of the Indian and Atlantic oceans and that the sialic layer is missing. On the other hand, the shape of these oceans' submarine ridges resembles continental-type fold mountains made up of sedimentary or sialic rocks.

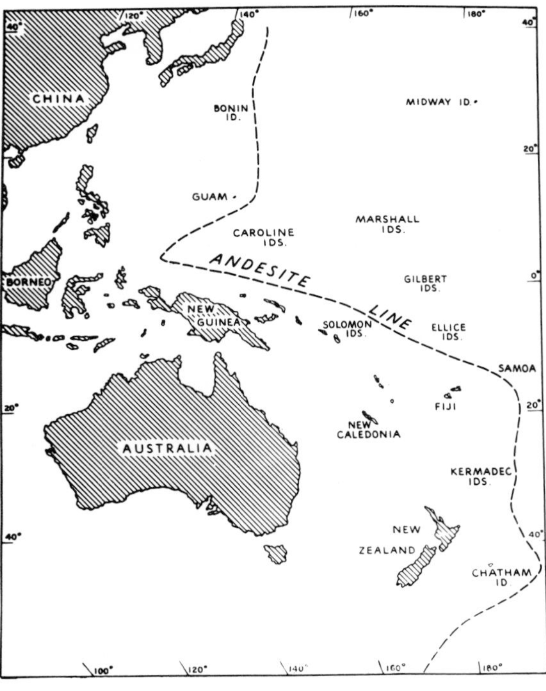

FIG. 20-11
Position of the andesite line in the southwestern Pacific Ocean. This line marks the border of the true Pacific basin in a geological sense. On the Pacific side of the line, young eruptive rocks are basaltic; on the other side, they are principally andesitic. Islands east of the line are isolated or grouped volcanic peaks; west of the line they have the characteristic structure of folded continental mountain ranges. After R. A. Daly.

The mantle

Below the earth's crust is a second major zone, the *mantle*, which extends to a depth of approximately 1,800 miles into the interior of the earth. Our knowledge of the mantle is based in part on evidence supplied by the behavior of P and S waves recorded between 700 and 7,000 miles.

At the Moho, the speeds of P and S increase sharply, an indication that the composition of the material suddenly changes. We have no direct evidence of the new material's nature, but the change in speed suggests that it may contain more ferromagnesian minerals than the crust. A project is now under way for drilling a Mohole to find out.

We know that the mantle is solid, because it is capable of transmitting S waves. In an attempt to explain mountain-building processes and the tendency of the earth's crust toward isostasy, some observers have emphasized that the mantle material may undergo slow flow as it adapts to changing conditions on the surface. Some have suggested that at least the upper portion of the mantle may consist of elements arranged in a random pattern. They feel that a disorderly atomic arrangement might permit the material of the mantle to flow more readily than it would if it were crystalline.

The S waves travel through the outer part of the mantle with a velocity of 2.9 miles per second, and the speed increases with depth. As a result of these observations, geophysicists have concluded that the rigidity of the mantle increases with depth.

There is a worldwide discontinuity in the mantle at a depth of about 300 miles. The velocities of P and S waves increase sharply to create the *20° Discontinuity,* so called because it becomes apparent on earth wave records at stations 20° (1,400 miles) from an earthquake focus. What produces this change in the mantle? It may be a rearrangement of atoms under pressure or a change in the kinds of atoms present. We do not know exactly; yet, whatever the new material is that produces the change, it seems to be substantially uniform down to 1,800 miles, the inner limit of the mantle.

The core

We come now to the core, a zone that extends from the 1,800-mile inner limit of the mantle to the center of the earth, at a depth of 3,950 miles. An analysis of seismographic records from earthquakes 7,000 miles or more distant reveals that the core has two parts: an outer zone 1,360 miles thick, and an inner core with a radius of 790 miles (see Fig. 20-12).

In traveling between two points 7,000 surface miles apart, we know that P and S waves pentrate 1,800 miles into the interior. But once they go deeper than that, they enter a material that delays P and eliminates S altogether. Since S waves are capable of traveling through only solids, we can conclude that the outer zone of the core is not solid. It is generally believed to be liquid rather than gas, for it is unlikely that any gas could support the terrific pressures existing at that depth.

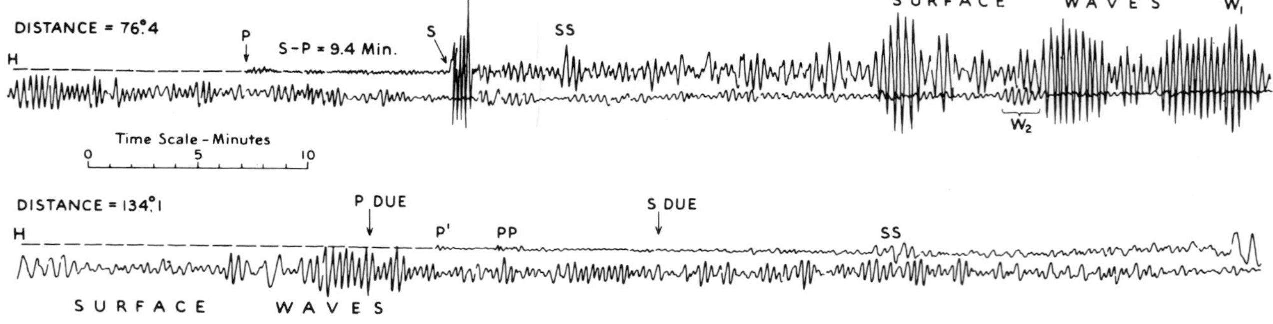

FIG. 20-12
Two earthquake records showing the effect of the earth's core on wave propagation. H on each record is the time of the earthquake's occurrence. The first P-wave reached 76.4° (5,276 miles) about 11.5 minutes after leaving the source. On the travel schedule that this represents, this P-wave was due to arrive at 134.1° (9,315 miles) about 3 minutes before the first waves were actually recorded there. No S-waves reached 9,315 miles. P-waves and S-waves reaching 5,275 miles do not travel deeply enough into the earth to reach the core. But those that enter the earth at an angle that would return them to the surface 9,315 miles from their source do encounter the core en route. If travel schedules out to 7,000 miles are extended to 9,315 miles, they show that P and S are due at the times indicated by arrows on the more distant record. But P is delayed and arrives as P', and no S or delayed equivalent of S ever arrives.

The P waves travel on through the outer zone of the core, though at a lower speed. Then, at a depth of 3,160 miles, they suddenly speed up again, an indication that the inner core is solid.

As the earth swings around the sun, it behaves like a sphere with a specific gravity of 5.5. But geologists have found the average specific gravity of rocks exposed at the surface is less than 3.0. And even if rocks with this same specific gravity were squeezed under 1,800 miles of similar rocks, their specific gravity would increase to only 5.7. Geophysicists have computed that the specific gravity of the core must be about 15.0 in order to give the whole globe an average of 5.5. To meet this requirement, it has been suggested that the core may be composed primarily of iron, possibly mixed with about 8 per cent of nickel and some cobalt, in the same proportions that exist in metallic meteorites.

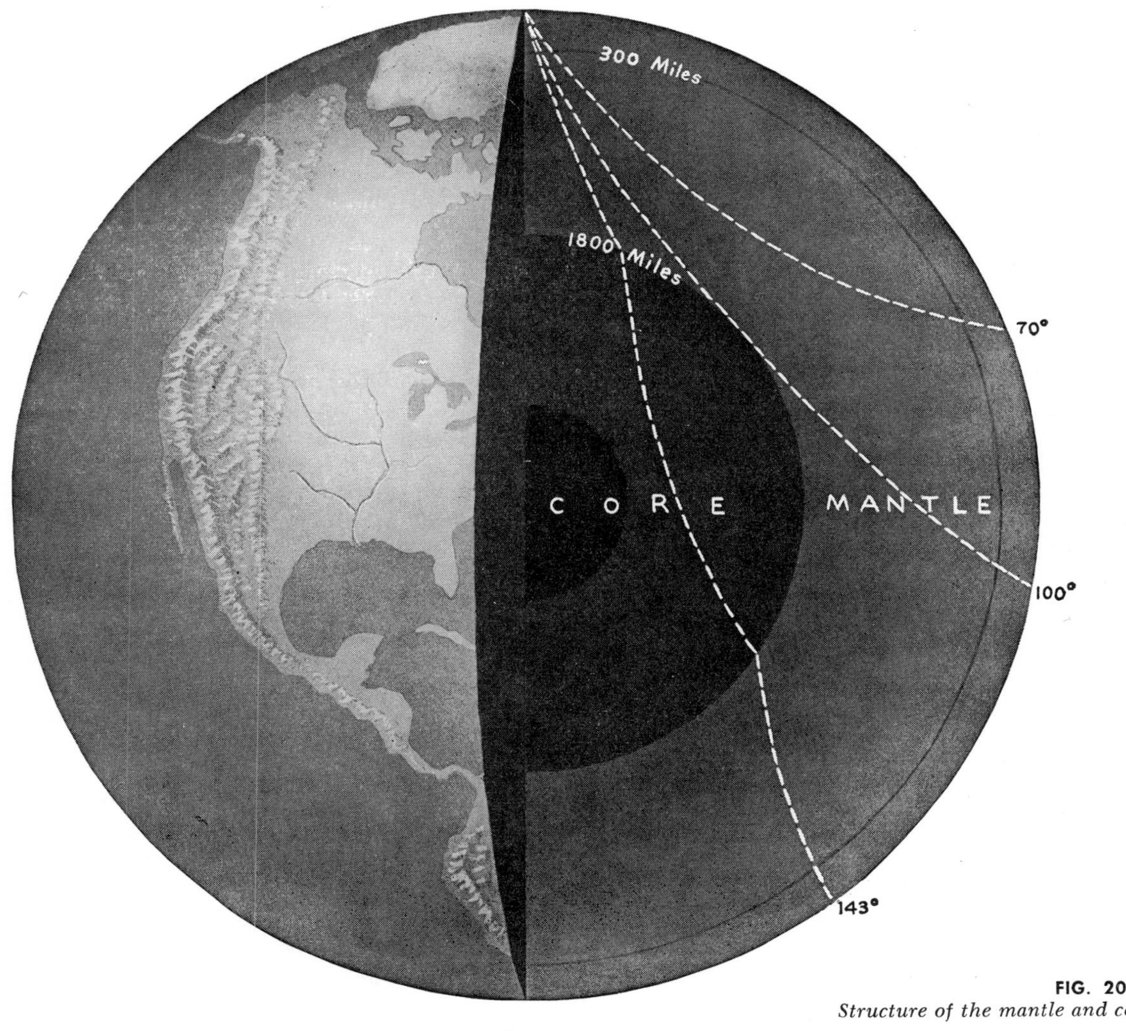

FIG. 20-13
Structure of the mantle and core.

SUMMARY OUTLINE

Seismograph
- Instrument for recording earth waves

Earth waves
- Carry energy away from earthquakes
- Two classes: body waves, surface waves

Body waves
- Push-pull waves, or P waves, travel through any material—solid, liquid, or gas
- Shake waves, or S waves, travel through only solids

Surface waves
- L waves travel along the earth's surface

Records of earthquake waves
- P and S waves travel from the focus of an earthquake through the interior of the earth to the recording station
  - P waves: faster than S waves
- L waves travel from the epicenter along the earth's surface to the recording station
  - L waves: the last to arrive because they travel at a slower speed and over a longer route

Travel schedules of earthquake waves
- Used to determine location and time of occurrence of earthquakes
- Reveal interior structure of the earth

The earth's crust
- That portion of the earth above the Moho
- Composed of solid rock
- Continental crust, oceanic crust

Continental crust
- Thickness: 22 to 35 miles
- Layered: sialic, intermediate, and simatic rock

Oceanic crust
- Unlayered, as thin as 3 miles in some sections of the Pacific Basin
- Composed of simatic rock
- Atlantic and Indian oceanic crust under debate

Mantle
- Extends from the base of the earth's crust to a depth of 1,800 miles
- Composition unknown
- Worldwide discontinuity at a depth of about 300 miles

Core
- Two layers: liquid exterior, solid interior
- Average specific gravity about 15.0; mixture of iron, nickel, and cobalt

SELECTED REFERENCES

Byerly, Perry, *Seismology*. Englewood Cliffs, N.J.: Prentice-Hall, Inc., 1942.

Gutenberg, B., and C. F. Richter, *Seismicity of the Earth* (2nd ed.). Princeton: Princeton Univ. Press, 1954.

Hodgson, John H., *Earthquakes and Earth Structure*. Englewood Cliffs, N.J.: Prentice-Hall, Inc., 1964 (paperback).

Leet, L. Don, *Earth Waves*. Cambridge: Harvard Univ. Press, 1950.

——— and Florence J. Leet, *The World of Geology*. New York: McGraw-Hill Book Company, 1961.

———, *Earthquake—Discoveries in Seismology*. New York: Dell Publishing Company, 1964 (paperback).

Roberts, Elliott, *Our Quaking Earth*. Boston: Little, Brown & Co., 1963.

Magnetism and continental drift

THE EARTH AS A MAGNET

CAUSE OF THE EARTH'S MAGNETISM

PALEOMAGNETISM

CONTINENTAL DRIFT

Erosion of continents, creation of mountains, and shifting outlines of the seas are changes of the earth that can be documented and visualized without overtaxing our credulity. But now we must consider change on a different scale, challenging not only our sense of direction, but our concept of geographic permanency as well. Here we wish to investigate whether the north and south poles have shifted position through time—and if so, why? We shall examine the question of continental drift—whether or not our land masses have been rent from their moorings and have gone skidding round the globe's surface. Although we will look at some evidence in each of these areas, we cannot expect to arrive at a definitive conclusion. We are dealing here with problems on the growing fringe of knowledge, and their solution lies somewhere in man's future.

THE EARTH AS A MAGNET

All of us are familiar with the fact that the earth behaves as if it were a magnet and for that reason the compass needle seeks the north magnetic pole. It will pay us to review the earth's magnetism before examining its geologic implications.

We can picture the earth's magnetic field as a series of lines of force. A magnet, free to move in space, will lie parallel to one of these lines. At a point north of the Prince of Wales Island at about 75°N. and 100°W., the north-seeking end of the magnetic needle will dip vertically downward. This is the *north magnetic* or *dip pole*. Near the coast of Antarctica, at about 67°S. and 143°E., the same end of our needle points directly skyward at the *south magnetic* or *dip pole*. Between these dip poles, the magnetic needle assumes positions of intermediate tilt. Halfway between the dip poles, the magnetic needle is horizontal and lies on the *magnetic equator*. Here the intensity of the earth's field is least, and it increases toward the dip poles, where the field is approximately twice as strong as it is at the magnetic equator (see Fig. 21-1).

The angle that the magnetic needle makes with the surface of the earth is called the *magnetic inclination* or *dip*.

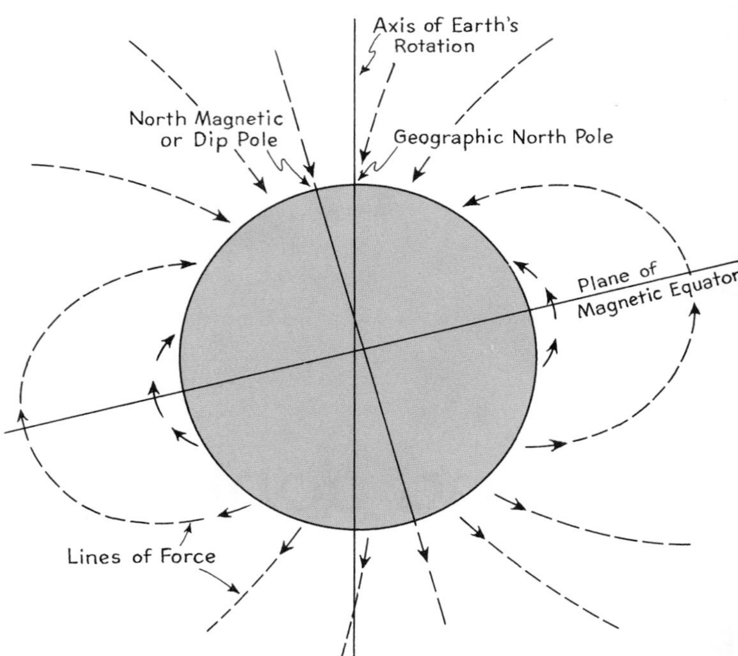

FIG. 21-1
The earth's magnetic field can be pictured as a series of lines of force. The small arrows indicate positions that would be taken by a magnetic needle free to move in space, located at various positions in the earth's field. The magnetic or dip poles do not coincide with the geographic poles, nor are the north and south magnetic poles directly opposite each other.

The north and south dip poles do not correspond to true north and south geographic poles, defined by the earth's rotation. Because of this the direction of the magnetized needle will in most instances diverge from the true geographic poles. The angle of this divergence between a geographic meridian and the magnetic meridian is called the *magnetic declination* and is measured in degrees east and west of geographic north (see Fig. 21-2).

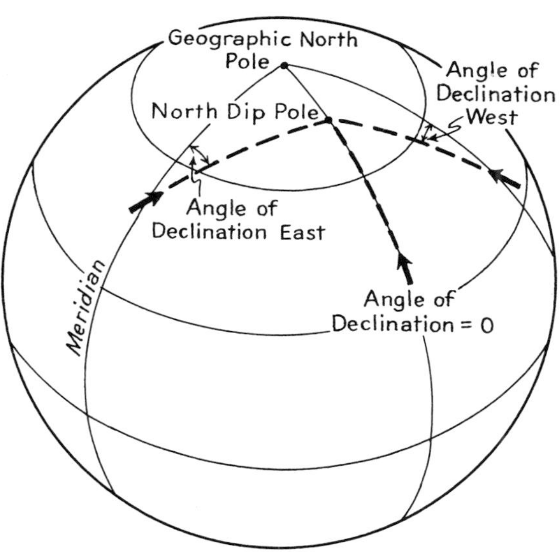

FIG. 21-2
Because the dip poles and geographic poles do not coincide, the compass needle does not point to true north. The angle of divergence of the compass from the geographic pole is the declination and is measured east and west of true north.

Secular variation of the magnetic field

As long ago as the mid-seventeenth century it was known that the magnetic declination changed with time. Since then we have been able to demonstrate not only slow changes in declination but also changes in inclination and intensity. These changes in magnetism take place over periods measured in hundreds of years. Because they are detectable only with long historical records, these changes are called *secular changes* from the Latin *saeculum,* meaning "age" or "generation," implying a long period of time.

Figure 21-3 shows changes in the declination and inclination records at Paris during Gallo-Roman times and from 1540 to 1950. Another long-range record, from 1573 to the present, is available from London and shows a pattern very similar to that of Paris from the sixteenth century on. Such records tempt us to suspect that these might represent worldwide, periodic variations in the earth's magnetic field. In truth, when records are compiled for the entire earth, it becomes apparent that the changes in the magnetic field are regional rather than global. The centers of greatest change wax and wane and also move generally westward at a rate averaging approximately one-fifth of a degree per year.

The geomagnetic pole

The magnetic field at the earth's surface can be considered as composed of three separate components. There is, first, a small component that seems to result from activity above the earth's surface and is sometimes referred to as the external field. Secondly, there is a quantitatively more important component, best described as if it were caused by a dipole—such as a simple bar magnet—passing through the center of the earth and inclined to the earth's axis of rotation. Finally, there is what we refer to as the nondipole field, that portion of the earth's field remaining after the dipole field and the external field are removed.

The dipole best approximating the earth's observed field is one inclined 11½° from the axis of rotation. The points at which the ends of this imaginary magnetic axis intersect the earth's surface are known as the *geomagnetic poles* and should not be confused with the magnetic or dip poles. The north geomagentic pole is about 78½°N., 69°W., and the south geomagnetic pole is exactly antipodal to it at 78½°S. and 111°E. (see Fig. 21-4).

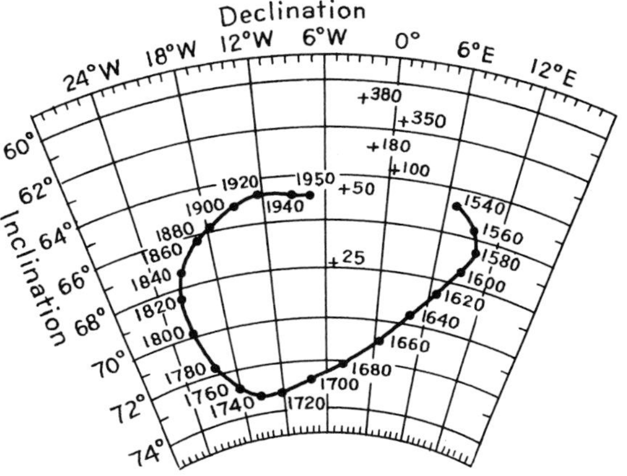

FIG. 21-3
Magnetic inclination and declination vary with time. At Paris we have a continuous record of these changes since 1540. The data for inclination and declination for Gallo-Roman times are based on magnetic measurements of archaeological materials. Adapted from Emile Thellier, "Recherches sur le champ magnétique terrestre," l'Astronomie (May 1957), p. 182, Fig. 64.

CAUSE OF THE EARTH'S MAGNETISM

The cause of the earth's magnetism has remained one of the most vexing problems of earth study. A completely satisfactory answer to the question is still forthcoming.

We have already indicated that the earth's magnetic field is composed both of internal and external components. The external portion of the field is due largely to the activity of the sun. This activity affects the ionosphere and appears to explain magnetic storms and the northern lights. The changes and effects of the external field may be rapid and dramatic, but they have little effect on the internal field of the earth, which is of greatest concern to us.

William Gilbert, who first showed that the earth behaves as if it were a magnet, suggested that the earth's magnetic field results from a large mass of permanently magnetized material beneath the surface. The idea is attractive not only because large quantities of magnetic minerals have been found in the earth's crust, but also because geologists think that the earth's core is made largely of iron (Chapter 20).

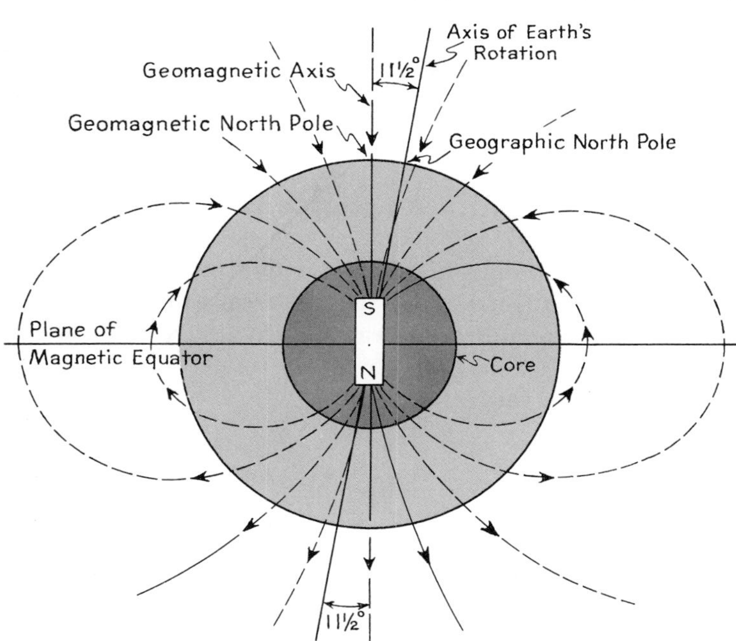

FIG. 21-4
The geomagnetic poles are defined by an imaginary magnetic axis passing through the earth's center and inclined 11½° from the axis of rotation. This magnetic axis is determined by a hypothetical, earth-centered bar magnet positioned to best approximate the earth's known magnetic field.

Close examination reveals the average intensity of the earth's magnetization is greater than that of the observable crustal rocks. We must therefore look deeper for the source of magnetism.

In looking deeper, the first difficulty we face is that materials normally magnetic at the earth's surface lose their magnetism above a certain temperature. This temperature is called the *Curie temperature* and varies with each material. The Curie temperature for iron is about 1400°F (760°C), for nickel, 660°F (350°C), for magnetite, 1080°F (580°C), and 1260°F (680°C) for hematite. The temperature gradient for the earth's crust is estimated to average about 150°F per mile (30°C per kilometer). At this rate of increase, the temperature should approximate the Curie temperature of iron about 16 miles (25 kilometers) below the surface and exceed the Curie temperatures for most normally magnetic materials. Therefore, below 16 miles we would not expect earth materials to be magnetic, and permanent magnetism can exist only above this level.

On the other hand, if all of the earth's magnetism were concentrated in the crustal rocks, then the intensity of magnetism of these rocks would have to be some 80 times that of the earth as a whole. And yet we know that the magnetic intensity of the surface rocks is less than that of the earth's average intensity.

From this observation we must conclude that the earth's magnetic field is not due to permanently magnetized masses either at depth or near the surface.

Some physicists have suggested that the rotation of the earth accounts for the earth's magnetic field. This explanation, like that of permanent magnetization, has met with insuperable difficulties.

The theory of earth magnetism most widely entertained at present is that the earth's core acts as a self-exciting dynamo. The model of the earth's core developed in Chapter 20 pictures its outer portion as a fluid composed largely of iron. This core therefore not only is an excellent conductor of electrical currents but also exists in a physical state in which motions can easily occur. Electromagnetic currents are pictured as generated and then amplified by motions within the current-conducting liquid. The energy to drive the fluid is thought to come from convection, which in turn results from temperature differences.

The dynamo theory further requires that the random convective motions and their accompanying electromagnetic fields be ordered to produce a single united magnetic field. It is thought that the rotation of the earth can impose such an order. The dynamo theory of earth magnetism still remains a theory, but so far it has proved the most satisfactory explanation of the earth's magnetism.

PALEOMAGNETISM

Some rocks, such as iron ores of hematite or magnetite, are strongly magnetic. Most rocks, however, are only weakly so. Actually, the magnetism of a rock is located in its individual minerals, and we would be more correct to speak of the magnetism of minerals rather than of the rock. By convention, however, we refer to rock magnetism. This magnetism is referred to as the rock's *natural remanent magnetism,* or *NRM*. This remanent magnetism may or may not agree with the present orientation of the earth's field and may have been acquired by the rock in many different ways. Identifying, measuring, and interpreting the different components of a rock's NRM forms the basis of paleomagnetism, the study of the earth's magnetic field in the geologic past.

Let us examine some of the ways an igneous rock acquires its magnetism. As a melt cools, minerals begin to crystallize. Those which are magnetically susceptible acquire a permanent magnetism as they cool below their Curie temperatures. This magnetism has the orientation of the earth's field at the time of crystallization. It is called *thermo remanent magnetism* (abbreviated *TRM*). This remanent magnetism remains with the minerals—and hence with the rock—unless the rock is reheated past the Curie temperatures of the minerals involved. This new heating destroys the original magnetism; and when the temperature again drops below the Curie temperatures of the magnetic minerals, the rock acquires a new TRM.

The NRM of our igneous rock may include other components. One of these is an *induced magnetism* arising from the present magnetic field of the earth. This induced magnetism is parallel to the earth's present field, but it is weak when compared with the TRM of the rock.

Sedimentary rocks acquire remanent magnetism in a different way than do igneous rocks. Magnetic particles such as magnetite tend to orient themselves in the earth's magnetic field as they are deposited. This orientation is retained as the soft sediments are lithified. This magnetism, known as *depositional remanent magnetism* or *DRM,* records the earth's field at the time the rock particles were deposited. Of course, the sedimentary rock, like the igneous rock, may also acquire an induced magnetism reflecting the current magnetic field.

VIRTUAL GEOMAGNETIC POLES. Paleomagnetic studies define the earth's magnetic field at various localities at different moments in geologic time. Instead of expressing the data on declination and inclination for a given locality, we usually express them in terms of equivalent pole positions. We refer to these poles as *virtual geomagnetic poles*. These are different from the dip poles and the geomagnetic poles we have already discussed. The pole consistent with the magnetic field as measured at any one locality is the virtual geomagnetic pole of that locality. It differs from the geomagnetic pole because it refers to the field direction of a single observational station, whereas the geomagnetic pole is the best fit of a geocentric dipole for the entire earth's field. Inasmuch as it is impossible to describe the entire earth's field at various times in the past, the virtual geomagnetic pole is commonly used in expressing paleogeomagnetic data.

Results of paleomagnetic studies

Clearly, if we can measure the TRM or the DRM of a rock and relate it to the earth's present field, we can determine

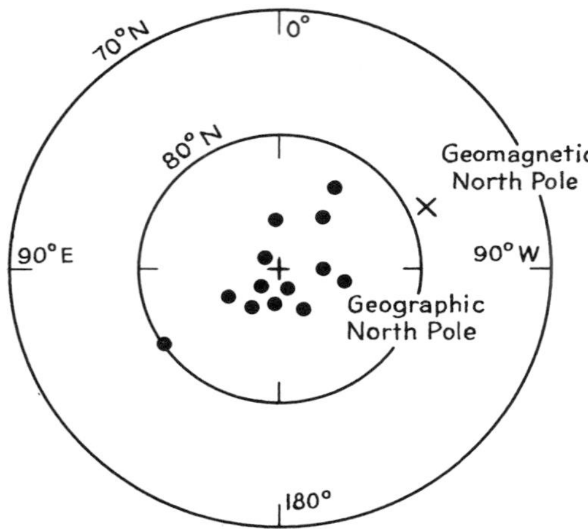

FIG. 21-5
The virtual geomagnetic poles determined by magnetic measurements of earth materials of Pleistocene and Recent age cluster around the modern geographic pole rather than around the present geomagnetic pole. (See text for discussion of virtual geomagnetic poles and geomagnetic poles.) Redrawn from Allan Cox and R. R. Doell, "Review of Paleomagnetism," Geol. Soc. Am. Bull., LXXI (1960), 734, Fig. 17.

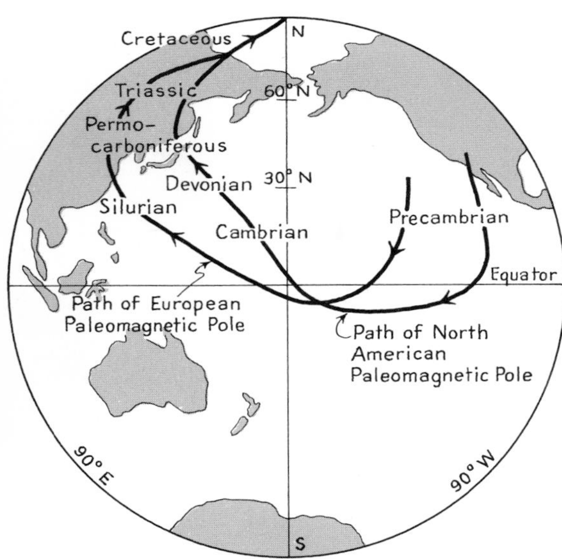

FIG. 21-6
Paleomagnetic measurements of rocks from North America and Europe show the paths followed by the magnetic poles of these two continents from Precambrian times to the present. Redrawn from Cox and Doell, ibid., p. 758, Fig. 33.

to what extent the orientation of the earth's magnetic field has varied at that spot through time.

Studies of ancient pole positions assume that the earth's field has been dipolar and, further, that this dipole has approximated the earth's axis of rotation. A consequence of these assumptions is that the earth's geographic poles must have coincided in the past with the earth's geomagnetic poles. Clearly this is not so at present. Why should we think that it was true in the past?

A partial answer to the question lies in the dynamo theory of earth magnetism. If the dynamo theory is correct, then theoretical considerations suggest that the rotation of the earth should orient the axis of the magnetic field parallel to the axis of rotation.

Observational data support the theoretical considerations. When we plot the virtual geomagnetic poles of changing fields recorded over long periods at magnetic observatories around the world, we find a tendency for these pole positions to group around the geographic poles. More convincing are the paleomagnetic poles calculated on the basis of magnetic measurements of rocks of Pleistocene and recent age. These materials, including lava flows and varves, reveal pole positions clustered around the present geographic pole rather than the present geomagnetic pole (see Fig. 21-5).

As a result of theoretical and observational data, therefore, most authorities feel that the apparent, present-day discrepancy between magnetic and rotational poles would disappear if measurements were averaged out over a span of approximately 2,000 years. The same principle would apply for any 2,000 year period throughout geologic time. Thus when we speak of a paleomagnetic pole, we have some confidence that it had essentially the same location as the true geographic pole of the time.

Paleomagnetic data derived from rocks of Tertiary age indicate, fairly conclusively, no significant shift of the geomagnetic poles from the Oligocene to the present. The farther backward we go in time beyond the Oligocene, however, the more convincing becomes the case for a changing magnetic pole and, on the basis of the above discussion, for a changing geographic pole. The magnitude of this change is suggested in Fig. 21-6.

Figure 21-6 shows that the paleomagnetic poles for Europe and North America were in the eastern Pacific during Precambrian time. Thereafter they moved southwestward and crossed the equator into the Southern Hemisphere before moving northwestward toward Asia and eventually to the position of the present globe.

The extensive migration of the magnetic poles (and by extension the geographic poles), combined with the observation that the paths of polar migration of different continents fail to coincide, raise tantilizing questions. We find ourselves, in fact, faced with the entire concept of continental drift.

CONTINENTAL DRIFT

In considering the theory of continental drift we should bear in mind that two general types of movements may be involved: movement of individual continents in relation to one another, and movement of the earth's poles. Actually, if this latter movement did take place, most students feel that a slippage of the earth's crust over the substratum of the mantle has produced an apparent motion of the poles. In other words, the magnetic and rotational poles remain fixed within the earth, but different points on the earth's crust would at different times be located at the polar positions as the crust moved. Such motion might involve the crust as a single unit or fragments of it.

The first coherent theory that our continents have moved as individual blocks was presented a few years before World War I by Alfred Wegener (1880-1930), a German meteorologist and a student of the earth. Wegener, as many before and after him, was intrigued with the apparent relationship in form between the opposing coasts of South America and Africa. Was it possible that these two land masses were once part of the same general continent but have since drifted apart? Wegener's emphatic "yes" and his extensive documentation of the lateral motion of continents started a spirited discussion that has continued to the present and is still unsettled.

The case for continental drift

WEGENER'S THEORY. In 1912, Wegener published in detail his theory of continental drift. He pictured the dry land of the earth as included in a single, vast continent that he named *Pangaea* (from the Greek for *"all"* and *"earth"*). This primeval continent, he argued, began to split asunder toward the end of the Mesozoic. These fragments began a slow drift across the earth's face; and by the Pleistocene, they had taken up their positions as our modern continents.

The idea of continental drift has been argued now for more than 50 years. The early evidence for the theory was drawn almost entirely from the geologic record. In the mid-twentieth century, the development of geophysical techniques brought new data into the discussion of continental drift. Let us look at some of the evidence.

THE SHAPE OF CONTINENTS. Anyone observing the map of Africa and South America is struck by the jig-saw puzzle match of the two continents. If we fit the eastern nose of South America into the large western bight of Africa, the two continents have a near perfect match. This match becomes even more impressive if we match the two continents at a level 2,000 meters below the present sea level as shown in Fig. 21-7. One distinguished geologist, while admitting to scepticism of continental drift, found this fit so credible that he opined, "if the fit between South America and Africa is not genetic, surely it is a device of Satan for our frustration."[1]

If one examines the outlines of the other continents, one can perhaps persuade himself that these landmasses, too, can be reassembled into a single large landmass as suggested

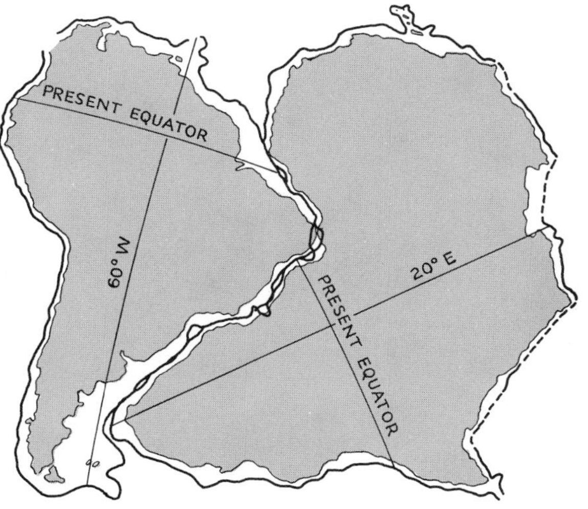

FIG. 21-7
South America and Africa fit very closely together, particularly if the match is made at a level 2,000 meters (6,500 feet) below sea level. Redrawn from S. Warren Carey, "The Tectonic Approach to Continental Drift," in Continental Drift, a Symposium, op. cit., p. 223, Fig. 21.

[1] Chester Longwell, "My Estimate of the Continental Drift Concept," in *Continental Drift, a Symposium* (Hobart, Australia: Tasmania Univ., 1958), p. 10.

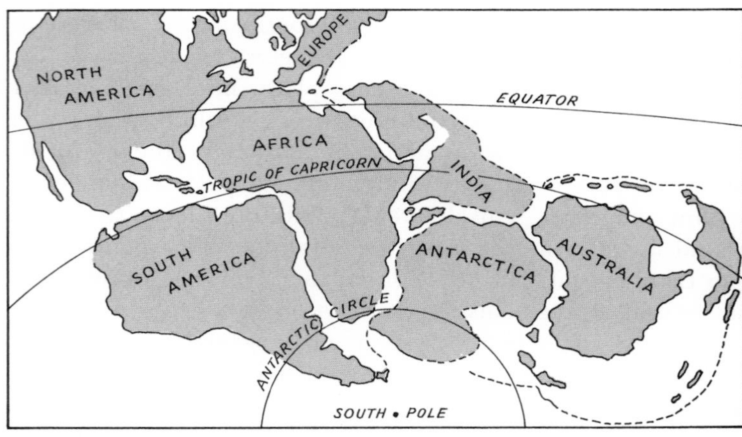

FIG. 21-8
A suggested reassembly of a portion of Pangaea, the postulated original continent. Redrawn from Carey, op. cit., p. 280, Fig. 39.

by Wegener. A more recent attempt at the reassemblage of some of the continents is shown in Fig. 21-8.

EVIDENCE FROM PALEOMAGNETISM. We pointedly began this chapter with a consideration of the earth's magnetism, for it has been the increasing body of information on rock magnetism and paleomagnetism that has kindled new interest in the old theory of continental drift. Figure 21-6 shows how the paleomagnetic poles have shifted during the last half-billion years. For the two continents represented, North America and Europe, there is a divergence between the ancient poles—that is, the virtual paleomagnetic poles—of these two landmasses as we go back in time. The case of North America and Europe is not unique. The pattern of polar migration, as sketched from paleomagnetic information, is different for each continent.

The divergence of the paths of polar migration among continents can be explained by the shifting of the landmasses in relation to each other. The course of polar migration suggests that the continental movement consists of a general drift of continents away from each other, and in some instances there is an additional rotation of continents.

EVIDENCE FROM ANCIENT CLIMATES. Much geologic evidence cited in support of continental drift and polar wandering is based on the reconstruction of climates of the past. Their use is justified by the fact that modern climatic belts are arranged in roughly parallel zones whose boundaries are east-west and which range from the tropical equatorial climates to the polar ice climates, as suggested in Fig. 21-9. Although climates at various times in earth history have been both colder and warmer than the present, we assume that basic climatic controls have remained the same and, therefore, the

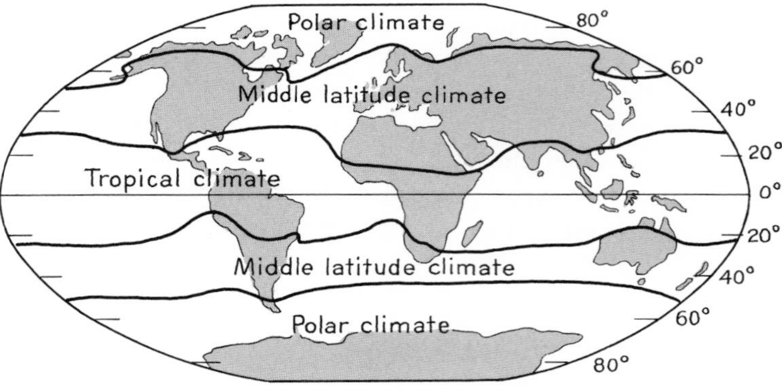

FIG. 21-9
Present-day climatic boundaries are arranged concentrically around the poles and thus are approximately parallel to lines of latitude.

climatic belts of the past have always paralleled the equator and been concentric outward from the poles.

Evidence from the geologic record allows us to map in a very general way the distribution of ancient climates. The pattern of some ancient climatic zones suggests that they were related to poles and an equator with locations different from those of today and that, therefore, the landmasses and the poles have varied relative to each other since those climates existed.

Late Paleozoic glaciation. On the Indian peninsula lies a sequence of rocks known as the Gondwana system, reaching in age from the late Paleozoic to early Cretaceous. Beds of similar nature and age are recorded in South Africa, Malagasy, South America, the Falkland Islands, Australia, and Antarctica. In these other localities they are known by other names, but we can still refer to them as belonging to the Gondwana system.

Geologists who have worked on the Gondwana formations have discovered many similarities among the rocks of the various continents, despite their wide geographic separation. Some of these similarities are so striking, many accept only one interpretation: the various southern lands must once have been part of a single landmass, a great southern continent, early called *Gondwanaland* by these geologists.

The distribution of ancient glacial deposits is one of the most convincing lines of evidence for continental drift in these southern lands. During late Paleozoic time, continental ice sheets covered sections of what are now South America, Africa, the Falkland Islands, India, and Australia. In southwestern Africa, deposits related to these ancient glaciers are as much as 2,000 feet thick. In many places, the now-lithified deposits (tillites) rest on older rocks striated and polished by these vanished glaciers (see Fig. 21-10).

Plot the distribution of these deposits and the direction of ice flow on a map (see Fig 21-11), and two observations can be made immediately. First, these traces of Paleozoic ice sheets occur in areas where no ice sheets exist now or have

FIG. 21-10
The Dwyka tillite of South Africa is the deposit of a continental ice sheet of late Paleozoic age. Here the bedrock floor striated by the Paleozoic glacier passes beneath the tillite. Photo by R. B. Young.

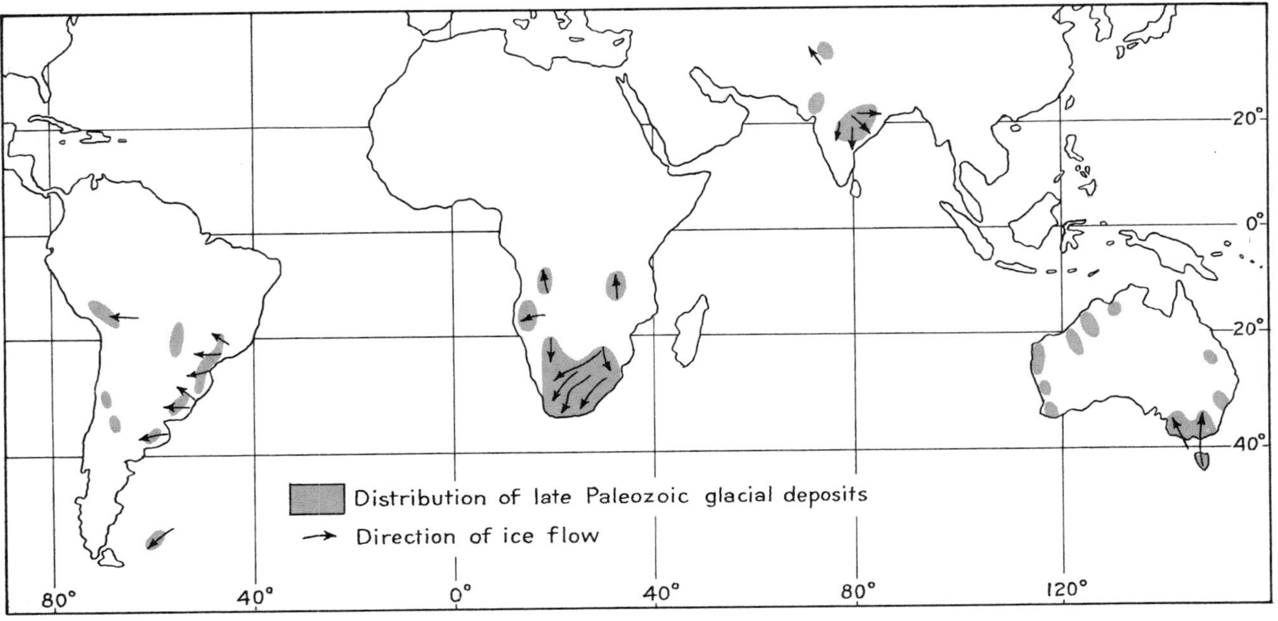

FIG. 21-11
Direction of movement of late Paleozoic ice sheet and distribution of known late Paleozoic tillites.

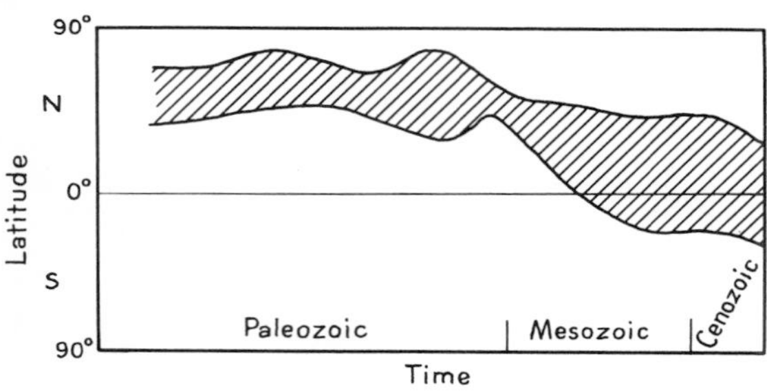

FIG. 21-12
The growth of coral reefs today is restricted to warm, equatorial waters between 30° N. and 30° S. During the Paleozoic and early Mesozoic, the reef belt was displaced far northward, as suggested by this displacement of the reef belt northward along 40° E. longitude. Adapted from Martin Schwarzbach (Princeton: D. Van Nostrand Co., Inc., 1963), p. 214, Fig. 123.

existed during the glacial epochs of the Pleistocene ice age. Only an occasional towering peak may bear the scars of modern or Pleistocene ice. Continental ice sheets cannot exist in these latitudes today. Second, the direction of glacier flow is such that we can imagine the ice of Africa and South America to have been part of the same ice sheet when the two continents were one.

These observations have lead some students of the earth to two conclusions. First, to account for glaciers in present tropical and subtropical areas, they locate the South Pole at this time somewhere in or near southern Africa. Second, to account for, among other things, the apparent continuity of glacier flow, these same students have postulated a single southern continent. This continent later split into several sections that drifted apart to form the modern landmasses.

Ancient evaporite deposits and coral reefs. Evaporites, sedimentary rocks composed of minerals that have been precipitated from solutions concentrated by the evaporation of the solvents, are generally accepted as evidence of an arid climate (see Chapter 8). The ancient evaporite deposits represent the great arid belts of the past. The present "hot arid" belts are located in the zones of subtropical high pressure centered at about 30° north and south of the equator. In the Northern Hemisphere, an "evaporite belt" has shifted through time from a near polar location in the Ordovician and Silurian to its present position in the modern desert belts. This again suggests a relative motion of pole and landmasses of the past as compared with present-day conditions.

Turning to another line of evidence, we find that corals depict a climate shifting geographically through time. Today, true coral reefs are restricted to warm, clear, marine waters between 30° north and south of the equator. If we assume ancient reef-forming corals had similar restrictions, then plotting their distribution in the past will show the distribution of tropical waters of the past and the location of the past equator. Doing this, we find that reef-forming corals did not approximate their present distribution until halfway through the Mesozoic. Prior to that time they lay well north of the present equator, as shown in Fig. 21-12.

PLANTS, REPTILES, AND CONTINENTAL DRIFT. Shortly after the disappearance of the Southern Hemisphere's late Paleozoic ice sheets, an assemblage of primitive land plants became widespread. This group of plants, known as *Glossopteris* flora, named for the tonguelike leaves of the seed fern *Glossopteris* (see Fig. 21-13), has been found in South America, South Africa, Australia, India, and within 300 miles of the South Pole in Antarctica. The *Glossopteris* flora is very uniform in its composition and differs markedly from the more varied contemporary flora of the Northern Hemisphere. Some geologists have argued that the uniformity of the *Glossopteris* flora could not have been achieved across the wide expanses of water now separating the different collecting localities. In other words, in one way or another, there must have been continuous or near-continuous land connections between now separate continents. To some, this suggests that a single continent with a single uniform flora has been split apart into smaller continents that have since migrated to their present position. As we shall see, this conclusion has not gone unchallenged.

Among the vertebrate fossils of the late Paleozoic and earliest Mesozoic, we find a great number of different reptile types in the southern continents. None of these argues one way or the other for continental drift, except perhaps the fish-eating reptile *Mesosaurus*. This toothed, early reptile lived in the water and thus far is known only from Brazil and South Africa. Although he was aquatic, most paleontologists do not believe that he could have made the trip across the South Atlantic. If this be so, then *Mesosaurus* may offer evidence for a closer proximity of South America and Africa and thus for continental drift.

OTHER EVIDENCE. Some anciently formed mountain chains now terminate abruptly at the continental margins. Join the continents together, and some of these geologic structures match up between the two landmasses. Thus the Cape Mountains of South Africa are thought to be the broken extension of the Sierra de la Ventana of Argentina in one direction, and of the Great Dividing Range in eastern Australia in the other direction. The entire stretch is cited by some adherents of continental drift as a once continuous chain of mountains now segmented and separated. Similarly, the Appalachian Mountains system ends in the sea on the northern shore of Newfoundland. Is its extension to be found in the orogenic belts of the British Isles and western Europe? Some geologists think so.

Planetary winds (Fig. 14-2 repeated at right) probably always existed. It would be interesting to see if ancient aeolian deposits might give some indication of such major wind belts as the northeast and southeast trades of the past. Sand beds accumulated on the face of a sand dune dip in the direction

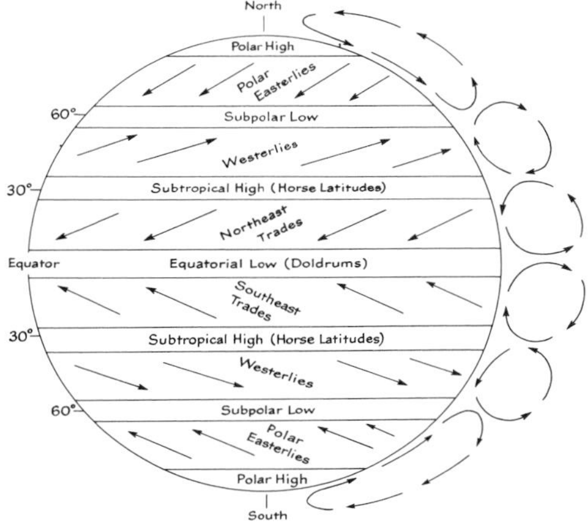

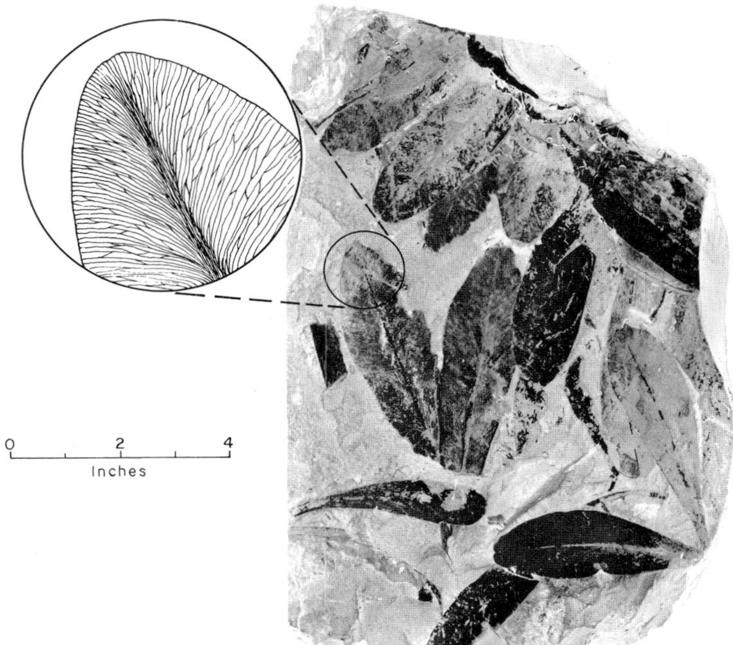

FIG. 21-13
These leaves of the fossil plant, Glossopteris, come from strata of Permian age in Australia. The Glossopteris flora is found also in South America, Africa, India and Antarctica. The widespread occurrence of this very uniform flora has been used as evidence both by opponents and proponents of continental drift. Specimen from Paleobotanical Gardens, Princton University. Photo by Willard Starks.

that the wind blows (Fig. 14-19 repeated left). We can measure such dip in ancient wind-deposited sediments. If enough of these directions are available, the direction of the dune-forming wind can be determined statistically. Preliminary studies on presumed aeolian deposits of late Paleozoic age in Wyoming, Utah, Arizona, and England indicate that these areas fell within the northeast trade wind belt when the earth's pole (as suggested by the paleomagnetic evidence) was located on the East China coast.

The case against continental drift

So far, we have considered only the case in support of the theory of continental drift and wandering poles, and nothing of the case against the hypothesis. Let us now look at some of the evidence on the other side.

GONDWANALAND. We have already referred to Gondwanaland as a great southern continent. Supporters of the concept of drifting continents believe that this continent broke into pieces, and these pieces moved to the present positions of the southern continents. But those who first proposed the concept of Gondwanaland had no idea of suggesting such a radical explanation for the present geography as that demanded by continental drift.

The initial concept of Gondwanaland to explain the similarity of geologic events in now widely separated areas pictured the southern continent as a continuous landmass stretching from South America through Africa and India to Australia. Sometime after the late Paleozoic, large portions of this vast east-west landmass foundered, leaving only fragments of Gondwanaland to form the present continents and the subcontinent of India. One of the best-known of these reconstructions is reproduced in Fig. 21-14.

The difficulty of explaining how great masses of the earth's crust could sink to create ocean basins has been as difficult for some geologists to accept as has been the idea of shifting continents. To avoid problems of both explanations, some

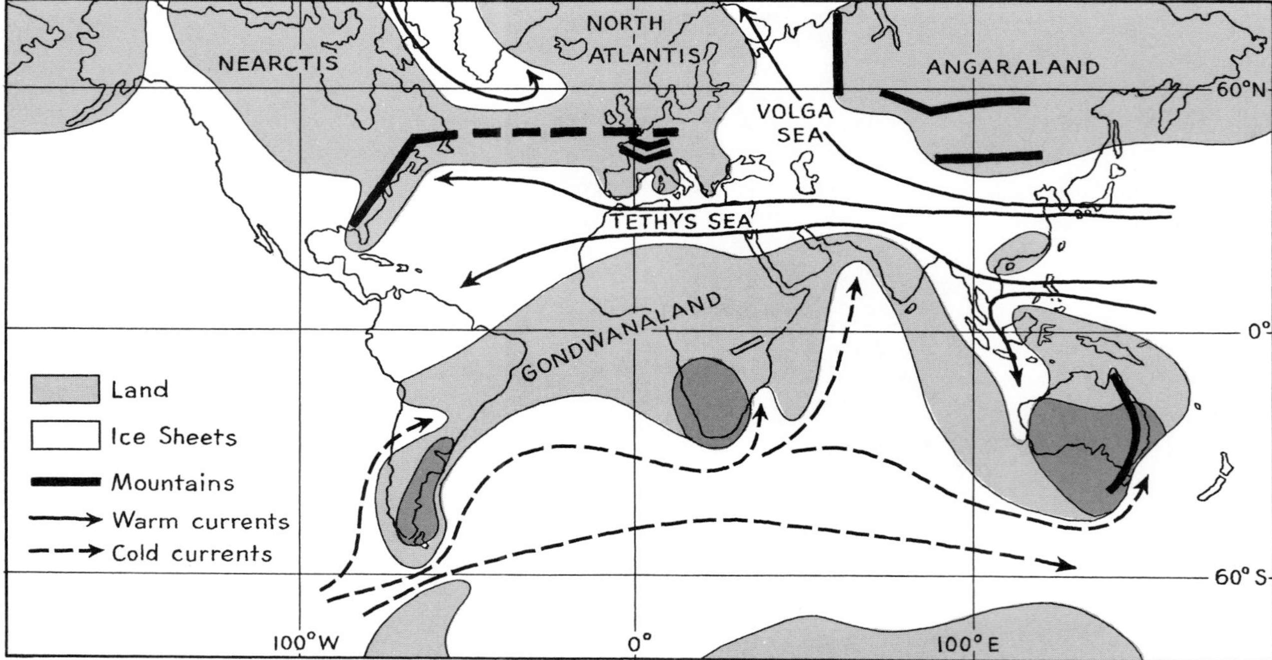

FIG. 21-14
Some scientists reject the idea of drifting continents. They have pictured Gondwanaland as a once-continuous southern continent, portions of which foundered into the deep oceans, leaving fragments to stand as South America, Africa, Australia, and India. This point of view is reflected in a reconstruction of late Paleozoic geography. Redrawn from C. E. P. Brooks, Climate Through the Ages (New York: McGraw-Hill Book Company, 1949), p. 248, Fig. 29.

have proposed that the southern lands were connected by narrow land bridges and that Gondwanaland was thus made up of what is now South America, Africa, India, Australia, and Antarctica, hooked together with narrow bridges of land. Such a theory allows for the permanency of the continents and requires only that narrow (although hypothetical) land bridges need to be postulated and then drowned. Supporters of this theory are faced with the dilemma that thus far there is no geophysical evidence from the southern oceans suggesting the presence of drowned "light-weight" land bridges.

THE FOSSIL EVIDENCE. Some paleontologists have questioned whether there is any evidence of climatic belts having changed their position in time and hence of poles having moved or continents having shifted. They cite the evidence of fossil plants and animals.

One reconstruction of past climate based on the distribution of fossil plants suggests the climatic zones of the Eocene were arranged with boundaries parallel to the modern equator. If so, then there is no need to postulate a shift in poles since the early Cenozoic. But proponents of a polar shift find this not unreasonable. Other evidence indicates to them that the greatest part of polar movement had already taken place by the Eocene.

In a recent attempt to refine the analysis of fossils as climatic indicators, the use of the diversity within fossil groups has been used. This technique is based on the fact that not only is the distribution of an individual species controlled by climate and hence by latitude, but so are the numbers of different forms within any taxonomic group. For instance, the numbers of species in a given genera decreases with decreasing temperature, and the latter, in turn, is related to latitude (see Fig. 21-15). Statistical analysis demonstrated that the diversity gradient slopes downward toward the lower temperatures of the poles.

The technique of diversity gradients has been applied to some bivalved marine animals of Permian age. These particular animals, known as brachiopods, have a diversity suggesting that the North Pole was in essentially the same location during the Permian as it is today (see Fig. 21-16).

RELIABILITY OF EVIDENCE. The reliability of evidence cited in support of continental drift has been questioned by many workers. The paleowind directions discussed above, for example, are thought by some to be not only inconclusive but actually based on deposits not aeolian.

Some of the evidence from the fossil record is attacked as too fragmentary and open to too many interpretations to be diagnostic. The use of *Mesosaurus* as representing evidence for continental drift is one such example.

Paleomagnetic evidence is currently regarded as one of the most conclusive arguments in favor of continental drift. But some argue that the evidence may not be as strong as it first appears, and they point out that this evidence may be overextrapolated. For instance, we said earlier that discussions of paleomagnetism assume a dipolar magnetic field for the earth. Yet, the more ancient fields could have had another

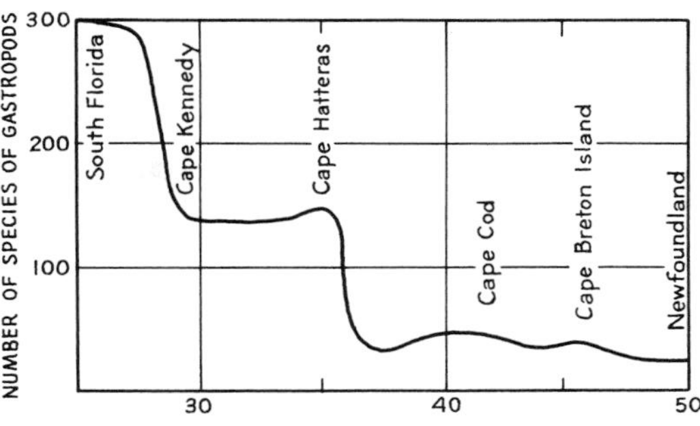

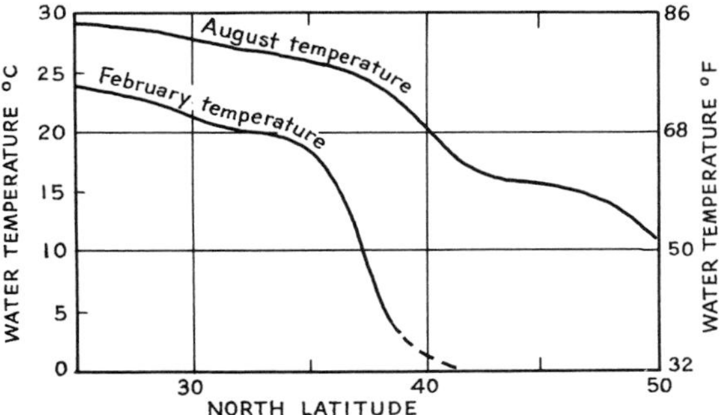

FIG. 21-15
The number of different species of living things decreases with decreasing temperature. This change is called a diversity gradient. It is illustrated here in the relation between number of species of gastropods, temperature of water, and latitude along the eastern coast of North America. Adapted from A. G. Fischer, "Latitudinal Variations in Organic Diversity," Evolution, XIV, No. 1 (1960), 69, Fig. 10.

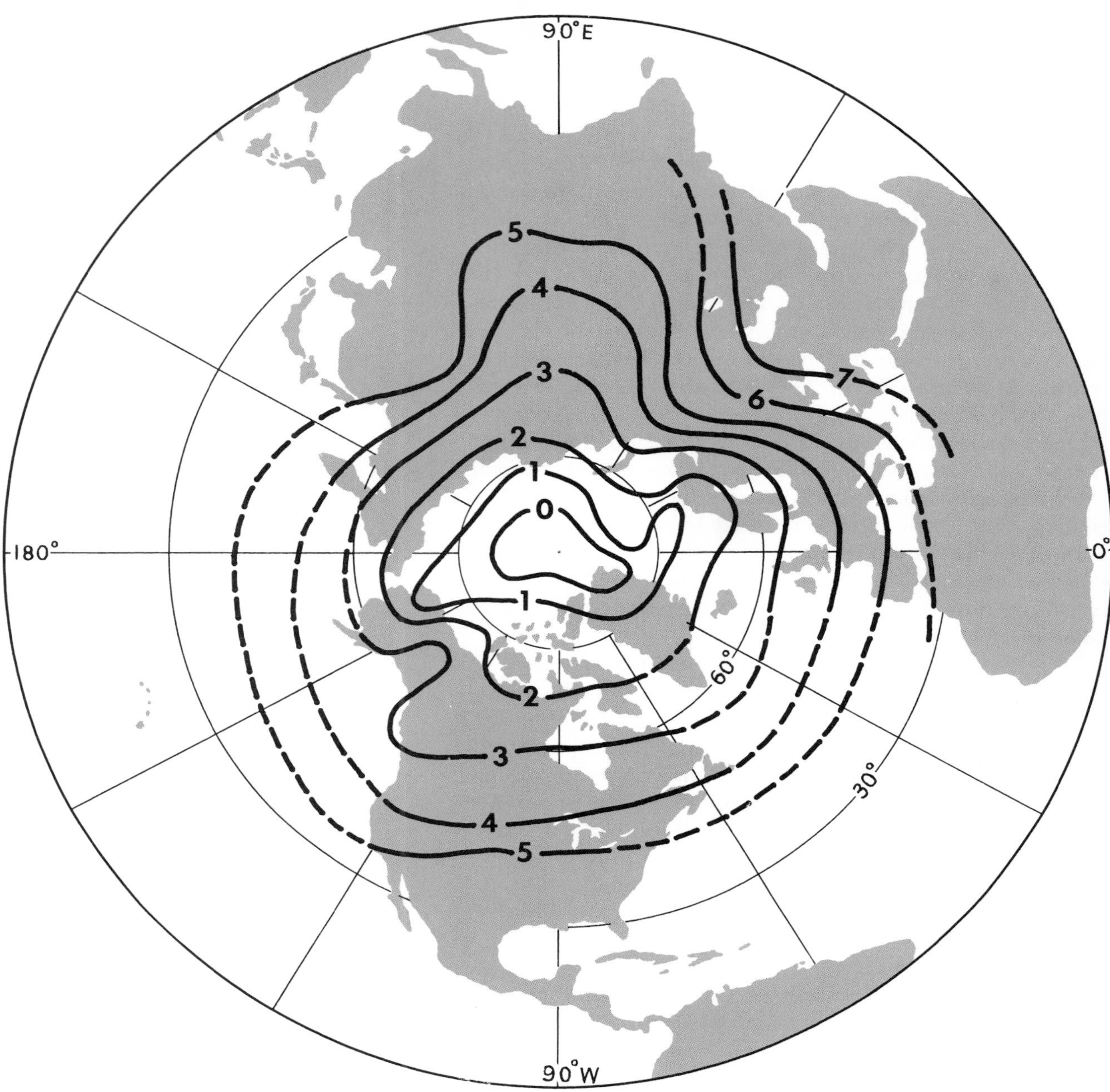

FIG. 21-16
The number of genera of Permian Brachipods decreases toward the position of modern geographic pole in the Northern Hemisphere. This pattern suggests to some that there has not been a motion of pole since the late Paleozoic. Redrawn from F. G. Stehli and C. E. Helsley, "Paleontologic Technique for Defining Ancient Pole Positions," Science, CXLII (1963), 1058, Fig. 3.

form—four poles instead of two, perhaps. If so, the entire paleomagnetic argument in support of continental drift would have to be re-evaluated.

Status of the problem

Prior to World War II, most of the supporters of the theory of continental drift lived in the Southern Hemisphere, particularly in South Africa. Geologists and geophysicists of the Northern Hemisphere, particularly in the United States and western Europe, felt that there was little or no support for the motion of continents or the wandering of the poles. In fact, it was hardly respectable to entertain the possibility of such movement.

Subsequent to World War II, the techniques of geophysics, and particularly those of paleomagnetic measurement, began to bring new data into the discussion. This new evidence reopened the entire question of continental drift for American and European geologists. Although the subject is now a respectable one in scientific circles of the Northern Hemisphere, the question is still far from settled. And if it is settled in favor of the drifting continents and wandering poles, we then face the question, "What caused the motion?"

SUMMARY OUTLINE

Earth magnetism

- Earth's behavior as if it were a magnet
- Dip poles diverge from geographic poles and are not antipodal
- Geomagnetic poles defined by an imaginary, simple bar magnet (dipole) inclined $11\frac{1}{2}°$ from rotational axis. This dipole passes through earth's center and is dipole best fitted to earth's field.
- Declination and inclination measure divergence of a magnetic pole from geographic pole
- Intensity and orientation of magnetic field changes with time

Cause of magnetism

- Small portion of magnetic field is external and caused by sun
- Bulk of field originates inside earth
- Most satisfactory current theory is the dynamo theory

Paleomagnetism

- Thermal remanent magnetism (TRM) formed in igneous rock-forming minerals as they cool below Curie temperature
- Depositional remanent magnetism (DRM) formed as magnetic particles align at time of deposition
- DRM and TRM oriented to magetic field existing at time of rock formation
- Virtual geomagnetic pole, the equivalent pole position representing the field at one observation point
- Discrepancy between geomagnetic poles and geographic poles thought to average out in time
- Ancient poles thought to be dipolar and thus similar to modern poles
- Ancient poles have shifted thousands of miles since Precambrian
- Paths of polar migration differ for each continent

Continental drift

- Theory supported by paleomagnetism, shape of continents, and ancient climatic patterns
- Alternative explanations involve land bridges and differing interpretation of the climatic evidences

SELECTED REFERENCES

Cox, Allan and R. R. Doell, "Review of Paleomagnetism," *Geol. Soc. Am., Bull.,* LXXI (1960), 645–768.

Jacobs, J. A., *The Earth's Core and Geomagnetism.* London: Pergamon Press Ltd., 1963.

Kummell, B., *History of the Earth.* San Francisco: W. H. Freeman & Co., Publishers, 1961.

Martin, H., "The hypothesis of continental drift in the light of recent advances of geological knowledge in Brazil and in South West Africa," *Geol. Soc. South Africa,* Annex to LXIV, 1961.

Schwarzbach, M., *Climates of the Past.* Princeton: D. Van Nostrand Co., Inc., 1963.

22 Our earth's resources

ORE DEPOSITS

CONCENTRATION BY IGNEOUS ACTIVITY

CONCENTRATION BY WEATHERING

CONCENTRATION BY SEDIMENTARY PROCESSES

CONCENTRATION DURING ROCK FORMATION

SOURCES OF ENERGY AVAILABLE TODAY

CHEMICAL ENERGY

COAL

OIL AND GAS

TOMORROW'S ENERGY

ATOMIC ENERGY

URANIUM ORES

All through this book, we have been talking about minerals and rocks, about geological processes and the landforms they produce. By this time you have a wealth of detailed information about the materials and processes on which the science of geology rests. But what practical use can you make of this information? How is it related to your everyday life?

Our modern civilization demands a great range of materials and tremendous amounts of energy. We use more of these than others have at any other time in the history of the human race. And our demands are increasing. We depend on materials for our buildings, transportation, communication, work, and security. We depend on energy to make these materials available. Where do these materials and energy come from? Most come from deposits in the earth's crust. These deposits have been formed by nature working through the very geological processes we have been discussing. They constitute our earth's resources.

For victory in war and wealth in peace, nations make fantastic demands on our earth's bounty. And once removed, most resources cannot be replaced. No nation has within its boundaries or under its control all the natural resources it needs to maintain its way of life. The United States, though most richly endowed, is still dependent on others for some of its needs. Its supply of energy from the fossil fuels oil, gas, and coal, as well as water power, is excellent, but it is still dependent on free trade with other nations to maintain its industrial life and security. Of the 30 most critical minerals, we are significantly deficient in 14 and have no supply at all of 4.[1] Also, our increasingly complex machines are often completely dependent on small quantities of rare minerals, such as exceptionally heat-resistant ones. So a lack of a few ounces of one mineral may bring to a halt the use of tons of another. We are in a situation similar to that in which the loss of a nail caused the loss of a shoe, a horse, and a kingdom.

[1] Alan M. Bateman, *The Formation of Mineral Deposits* (New York: John Wiley & Sons, Inc., 1951).

ORE DEPOSITS

The materials in use today are mostly minerals. They can be grouped into two broad categories: (1) *metals,* such as aluminum, copper, gold, silver, iron, tin, platinum, chromium, nickel, lead, and zinc, and (2) *non-metals,* such as diamond, salt, limestone, cement, sulfur, and asbestos. Most of these can be found in some quantity, in some form, almost anywhere. But all deposits cannot be used, because methods of separating the desired mineral from associated minerals are not available, or because the deposit is too small, or inaccessible. When minerals occur so that they can be worked at a profit, they are called *ore deposits.*

Although a mineral is more concentrated by nature in an ore deposit than in another place, it still is mixed with unwanted material from which it must be separated. Gold, for instance, in sugar-sized grains spread through a gravel deposit has to be separated from the other minerals in the gravel. Separation is done by amalgamation, which uses the strong tendency for gold to combine with mercury. Gold-bearing gravel is poured onto a tilted table with closely spaced ridges across it and a surface coated with mercury. The table is shaken rapidly. Grains of gold work down through the gravel; and when they come into contact with the mercury, they cling to it while the gravel slides on.

Some sulfide minerals are desired for the metal they contain. But most sulfides are not found alone; they are often associated with valueless minerals. In order to retrieve the sulfides from the other minerals, they are all ground, then separated by a process called *flotation.* Finely ground sulfides have an affinity for air, whereas other minerals such as quartz have an affinity for water. In a thoroughly stirred mixture of water and finely ground minerals, with air bubbling up through it, sulfides cling to the air bubbles and rise while other minerals sink. The sulfide-coated air bubbles form a froth on top of the liquid. This is allowed to overflow the tank; then it is gathered and strained to drain the water and to collect the sulfides. These are heated to burn off the sulfur and melt the metal in a process called smelting.

A convenient way of discussing mineral deposits is to classify them on the basis of the geologic processes that have created them: igneous activity, weathering, sedimentation, and the formation of the original rock masses.

Concentration by igneous activity

You will remember that in Chapter 6 we discussed the formation of igneous rocks from a mixture of elements in a solution called a magma. Some magmas, however, also contain elements that, because of the size of their ions, do not combine readily with the common rock-forming minerals. Sometimes these elements crystallize early in the cooling of the magma and settle out of the solution. Sometimes they form late and are trapped in the crystallized magma. But more often they become mixed with hot volatiles, including water, and are injected into the surrounding rocks.

FIG. 22-1
Abandoned pit of Kimberley diamond mine in the rock of a volcanic neck near Kimberley, South Africa. Water now stands in the pit to within 600 feet of ground level. Before it was abandoned, the mine was developed to a depth of 3,500 feet. Photo by Cornelius S. Hurlbut, Jr.

Diamond is most familiar to us as a precious gem. But it is also widely used in industry as an abrasive, for it is the hardest mineral known. Diamond is found only where carbon has been trapped in magma under terrific pressure. Consequently, we cannot expect to find diamond deposits where these conditions have not prevailed. Most diamonds have been discovered in old volcanic necks, where the cooling magma formed the rock peridotite at depths of several miles beneath the surface (see Fig. 22-1). Diamonds may be crystallizing out of magma at this very moment, deep below Mauna Loa or in other places in the world where igneous activity persists. But these diamonds will not be found until the volcano has become dormant, and until erosion has stripped away both the volcano itself and miles of the earth materials on which it stands.

Deposits of *chromium, nickel,* and *platinum* occur in formations of simatic rock all around the world. At Sudbury, Ontario, for example, there are valuable deposits of nickel in rock of this sort. Apparently these minerals somehow became concentrated in the cooling magma; and since they were heavier than the rock-forming minerals, they settled out during crystallization.

Although the chromium and nickel that make up the deposits have combined with other elements to form compounds, the platinum occurs in an uncombined state. The chief source of chromium is *chromite,* $FeCr_2O_4$. Most of the chromium produced in the United States comes from Shasta County, California, but much greater quantities are imported from Cuba, Oceania, Southern Rhodesia, and Turkey. Chromium is used chiefly to form an alloy with steel that has extreme hardness, toughness, and resistance to chemical attack. It is also used for plating hardware, plumbing fixtures, and automobile accessories.

About half of the chromite consumed in the United States goes into metallurgical uses of this sort. The other half is used in the construction of furnaces and other equipment where heat resistance is required, and in various chemical processes.

Although nickel is a relatively rare element in the earth's crust, it is extremely important in modern industry. It is used in the manufacture of a strong, tough alloy known as *nickel steel* (2.5 to 3.5 per cent nickel) and in the preparation of *monel metal* (68 per cent nickel) and *nichrome* (35-85 per cent nickel). It is also used in various plating processes, and it forms 25 per cent of the United States five-cent coin. Finally, its low expansion makes it an ideal metal for watch springs and other delicate instruments.

An important ore of nickel is pentlandite $(Fe,Ni)_9S_8$. Large deposits of this mineral at Sudbury, Ontario, and elsewhere make it the world's most valuable source of nickel.

Platinum also occurs in association with the nickel deposits at Sudbury. The value of platinum in industry results from its high melting point, 1,755°C, and its resistance to chemical attack. These properties make it especially useful in laboratory equipment such as crucibles, dishes, and spoons, and for the contact points of bells, magnetos, and induction coils. Platinum also finds special uses in the manufacture of jewelry, in dentistry, and in photography.

Gold, copper, tin, and *silver* are deposited from the hydrothermal solutions that penetrate into the rock surrounding a magma during igneous activity. Deposition is a result of a drop in temperature and pressure as well as reaction with the wall rock.

Gold is a rare element used principally in coinage and jewelry. It occurs normally in the uncombined state in sialic igneous rocks, particularly those that are rich in quartz (see Fig. 22-2). About half of the gold that is mined in California, the leading gold-producing state, comes from the Mother Lode, a series of hydrothermal veins lying along the western slope of the Sierra Nevada. The rest comes from placer deposits (see below, "Concentration by sedimentary processes").

Copper occurs both in the uncombined state and in combination with other elements in minerals such as *chalcopyrite* ($CuFeS_2$), *bornite* (Cu_5FeS_4), *chalcocite* (Cu_2S), and *enargite* (Cu_3AsS_4). Most copper deposits consist of concentrations created by hydrothermal solutions. Chalcocite deposits, however, are usually the result of secondary enrichment (see below, "Concentration by weathering processes").

Copper is second only to iron among the important metals used in modern technology. It is used extensively for electrical equipment, mostly as wire, and also in the manufacture of sheets and nails. In combination with other metals, it forms several useful alloys: brass is an alloy of copper and zinc; bronze is an alloy of copper, tin, and zinc; and German silver is an alloy of copper, zinc, and nickel.

The only important ore of tin is *cassiterite,* SnO_2. Tin is used principally as a coating on steel to form *tin plate* for food containers. A good bit of tin occurs in original hydrothermal deposits, but 75 per cent of the world's supply comes from placers.

Native *silver* (see Fig. 22-3) has been deposited from hydrothermal solutions, as has another ore of silver, argentite, Ag_2S, silver sulfide. Argentite as an ore may also be of secondary origin when it has been concentrated by weathering processes.

For centuries, silver was used in jewelry and coins. In 1940, however, it became an important industrial metal. It is extensively used in photography, in laboratory and electrical goods, for medical and dental work, as an alloy in bearings, solders, and brazing compounds. During World War II, Clinton Engineer Works, near Knoxville, Tennessee, used 27,680,000 lbs in the manufacture of the atomic bomb.

Lead and zinc deposits have been created mainly by the process of metasomatism (see Chapter 18), in which hydrothermal solutions and magmatic gases have replaced some of the original components of the rock surrounding a magma. Limestone exposed to igneous activity is particularly susceptible to metasomatism. In the Tristate District of Missouri, Oklahoma, and Kansas, for example, the magmatic solutions have replaced whole layers in a nearly horizontal series of limestone and chert beds.

FIG. 22-2
Underground gold mine in gold-bearing quartz vein 4 feet wide. Bralorne, British Columbia.

FIG. 22-3
Native silver. The specimen, approximately 3 inches long, came from Kongsberg, Norway. Harvard Mineralogical Collection. Photo by Harry Groom.

The principal ore of lead is *galena,* PbS; the principal ore of zinc is *sphalerite,* ZnS. Lead is used in the manufacture of bullets, cable coverings, foil, pipes, storage batteries, weights, and a gasoline additive. It forms an alloy with tin to make solder, with antimony to make type-metal, and with bismuth and tin to make metals that melt at low temperatures. Large quantities of lead are used every year in the preparation of paint pigment. Zinc is used chiefly for galvanizing iron, as an alloy with copper in making brass, and in the manufacture of batteries.

Concentration by weathering

So far, we have been discussing deposits that were originally created by igneous activity in about the same form in which they now appear. But other important deposits have been built up by the action of weathering on pre-existing rocks. There are three important weathering processes in the formation of ore deposits:

(1) *The chemical alteration of compounds from which desired elements cannot otherwise be extracted economically.*

Aluminum, although it is one of the most common elements in the earth's crust, almost always occurs in feldspars and other silicates from which it cannot be extracted economically by any process now known. Fortunately, however, under tropical conditions, weathering breaks the feldspars down into clay minerals; they in turn become hydrous oxides of aluminum and iron. The soils produced by this activity are sometimes known as "laterites" (see Chapter 7), and the aluminum ore is called *bauxite.* The principal deposits of bauxite in the United States occur in Arkansas.

Aluminum is a very light, strong metal used extensively in the manufacture of cooking utensils, furniture, household appliances, automobiles, airplanes, railway cars, and machinery. It is becoming increasingly popular as an insulating material in buildings.

(2) *The removal of undesired components, leaving the desired compounds more concentrated than they were originally.*

Iron, the most widely used metal in our industrial civilization, has been concentrated by this weathering process in many areas of the world—in the extremely important deposits around Lake Superior, for example. In Minnesota and Michigan, iron-bearing formations underlie thousands of square miles; but for years, only where percolating ground water had removed enough silica from the parent rock was the iron (in the form of Fe_2O_3) sufficiently concentrated to make mining practicable.

(3) *The solution and redeposition of desired elements in useful concentrations, a process sometimes called secondary (or supergene) enrichment.*

In some regions, igneous activity has built up original deposits of copper, but not in great enough concentrations to be worked. Here ground water has dissolved the copper and has carried it down to be deposited in an enriched zone. At Bingham Canyon, Utah (see Fig. 22-4), is a spectacular open-pit mining operation that recovers at a profit an ore containing as little as four-tenths of 1 per cent of copper, and averaging about 1 per cent. The ore is sialic porphyry that contains finely disseminated sulfides concentrated by secondary enrichment. The benches of the mine are from 50 to 70 ft high and not less than 65 ft wide. The operation covers 878 acres and contains about 160 miles of standard-gauge railroad track, most of which is moved continually to meet operating needs. In 1952, this mine was producing more than one-half billion pounds of copper a year, about 30 per cent of all the copper mined in the United States. At Morenci, Arizona, the impoverished zone is as deep as 220 feet, but beneath it the enriched zone extends about 1,000 feet farther down. Underlying the enriched zone is the unaltered bedrock, often too low grade to mine.

Concentration by sedimentary processes

Some of the sedimentary processes described in Chapters 7 and 8 pick up the products of weathering and ultimately deposit them below base level. Both mechanical and chemical processes are involved in the transportation and deposition of the weathered rock.

Flowing water moves great quantities of mineral material along the channels of streams, particularly in mountainous

FIG. 22-4
Copper mine at Bingham Canyon, Utah. The benches are 50 to 70 feet high, and not less than 65 feet wide. Photo by Rotkin, P.F.I.

FIG. 22-5
Panning for gold. The prospector partly fills the pan with water and throws in a shovelful of dirt. He picks out the pebbles and stirs the mass until clay-sized particles are dislodged and can be sloughed away in the muddied water. He then partly fills the pan with water again and gives it a slightly eccentric circular motion to build up a wave to slop over the edge each time, carrying with it a little sand. He continues this process until only the specks of gold, which have greater specific gravity, remain in the pan. On the Anderson River, tributary to the Fraser River, British Columbia's Sierra Cascade Mts. Photo by Elliott A. Riggs.

regions. The heavier minerals—harder for the water to transport, yet resistant to chemical decay—tend to accumulate in the channel basins, in a deposit called a *placer* (rhymes with "passer"). Gold is exceptionally well adapted to placer deposition. Weathering breaks it from the rocks and veins where it originally crystallized from hydrothermal solutions, but its malleability prevents it from being finely pulverized. Moreover, its high specific gravity (ranging from 15 to 19, depending on the percentage of impurities present) causes it to settle readily from agitated mixtures of water, sand, and lighter materials. The gold discovered in 1848 on the western slopes of the Sierra Nevada in California was concentrated in placers so rich that great fortunes were made simply by panning it out by hand (see Fig. 22-5). Less concentrated placer deposits can now be worked by modern hydraulic giants, which wash away the barren material that overlies the pay dirt, and sluice the gold-bearing gravels into boxes where the gold is trapped.

Even deposits of gold in gravel below groundwater or ocean level can be worked by specially designed dredges that recover at a profit gold so thinly dispersed that there are only a few cents' worth in each cubic yard. The world's greatest gold deposits are in the Witwatersrand District of South Africa, on a plateau standing 6,000 feet above sea level about 800 miles northeast of Cape Town. ("Witwatersrand" means white divide, so called because of a prominent white quartzite that resists erosion and stands forth as a "water ridge" or "divide.") The deposits in this rich area occur in conglomerates, themselves formed from ancient placer deposits, according to some geologists. Others think that permeable channels in the original rock were invaded by gold-bearing hydrothermal solutions. Approximately 40 per cent of the world's gold is produced by the Union of South Africa.

Nearly 75 per cent of the world's *tin* production comes from placer deposits. Most of the ore is in the form of *cassiterite,* or tin dioxide (SnO_2), which has a specific gravity of 7 (see Fig. 22-6).

FIG. 22-6
Cassiterite from Cornwall, England. Waterworn pebbles from a placer deposit. Photo by Benjamin M. Shaub.

Initially, the world's greatest deposits of *iron* ores were built up by chemical precipitation in sediments. But most of the deposits could not be worked commercially until weathering processes had increased the concentration by secondary enrichment.

About nine-tenths of the iron ore in the United States occurs as hematite (Fe_2O_3). In the Lake Superior District, the zone that has still not been leached by weathering consists of a mineral called *taconite,* containing chert with *hematite, magnetite* (Fe_3O_4) (see Fig. 22-7), *siderite* ($FeCO_3$), and *hydrous iron silicates.* The iron content of taconite averages about only 25 per cent. But in the zone that has been leached, most of the iron has been oxidized to hematite, which produces ores of from 50 to 60 per cent iron. Recently, however, commercial methods have been developed for recovering iron even from the taconite of this district.[1] So great stretches of original unleached rock have been added to our iron reserve (see Figs. 22-8 and 22-9).

The newest reserves of iron ore on the North American continent, near 55°N., 67°W., on the Labrador-Quebec border, also consist of deposits enriched by weathering. Other deposits are being worked in sedimentary formations of Silurian age, known as the Clinton beds, which outcrop across Wisconsin and New York, and along the southern Appalachians. These beds are being mined extensively in Alabama, in the Birmingham District. The primary unleached ores from the Clinton beds are often high in $CaCO_3$ and contain 35 to 40 per cent iron. But after the $CaCO_3$ has been leached out by weathering, they may contain as much as 50 per cent iron (see Figs. 22-10 and 22-11).

FIG. 22-7
Magnetite from Magnet Cove, Arkansas. This magnetic mineral is the component of taconite that is removed by the processed outlined in Fig. 22-9, then converted to hematite, from which iron is recovered. Photo by Benjamin M. Shaub.

Concentration during rock formation

Many rock materials are valuable in their original condition, produced by rock-forming processes, without undergoing any additional enrichment or concentration. Stone, of course, has been used for several thousand years as a building material. But its importance has grown tremendously during the last half-century, with the discovery of new techniques for removing it from the ground by blasting (see Fig. 22-12), and for crushing it into usable sizes. Every mode of transportation in the modern world depends in some degree on crushed or broken stone: it provides the basis for countless miles of modern highways, ballast for railways, bases for landing fields, and jetty stone for harbor facilities.

Other rocks have commercial value because of their chemical properties. *Limestone,* for example, is used to neutralize acids in the processing of sugar, to correct the acidity of soil, and to supply calcium to plants. Limestone that contains limited amounts of impurities serves as the raw material in the manufacture of cement; the impurities give cement its characteristic hardness. The type known as Portland cement consists of 75 per cent calcium carbonate (limestone), 13 per

FIG. 22-8
Mining magnetic taconite in an open pit at Babbitt, Minnesota. The ore, containing 25 per cent iron, is one of the hardest rocks in the world—almost as hard as diamond. The operation is like that of a rock quarry producing crushed stone. Photo by Hercules Powder Co., courtesy Reserve Mining Co.

[1] Lewis Nordyke, "Taconite," *The Explosives Engineer,* Jan.-Feb., 1957, pp. 7-25.

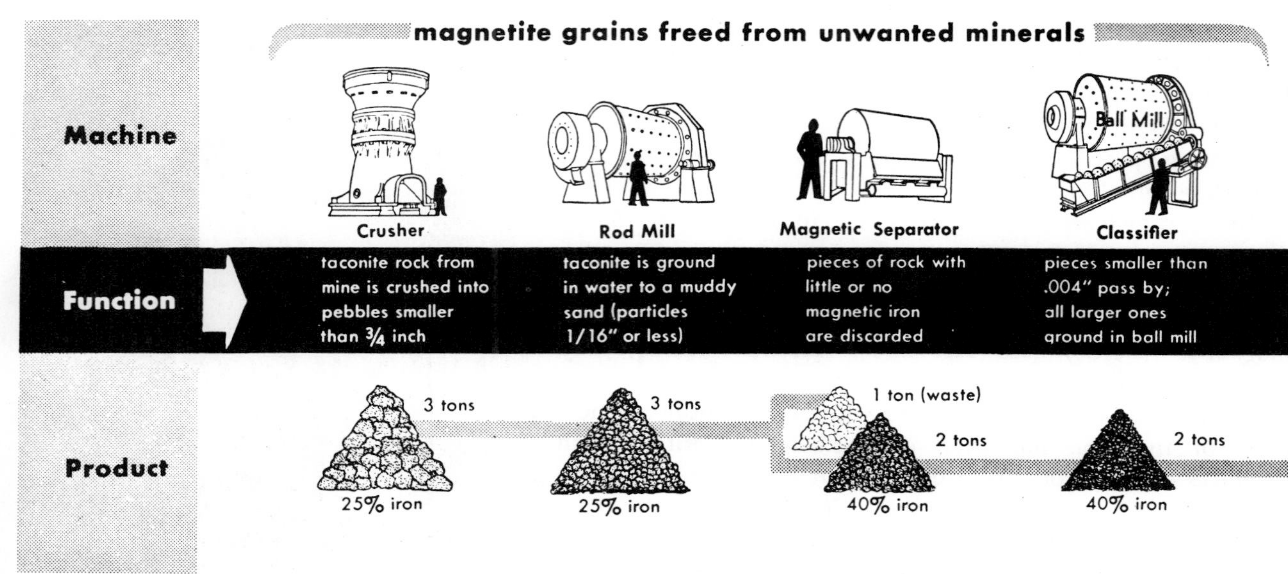

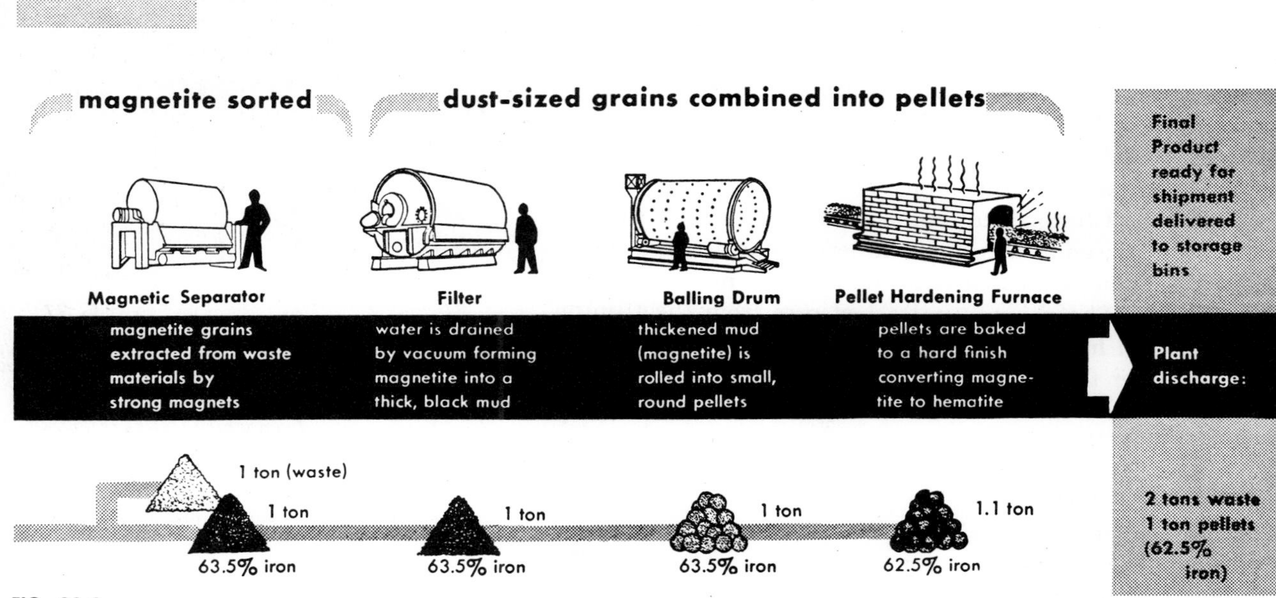

FIG. 22-9
Graphic presentation of Reserve Mining Company's methods of processing crushed taconite ore into pellets containing 62.5 per cent iron. Babbit, Minnesota. Courtesy Reserve Mining Company.

cent silica, and 5 per cent aluminum oxide, along with the silica and alumina that are normally present in clays or shales. Some manufacturers add the right percentages of impurities to the limestone; others use deposits called *cement rock,* in which the impurities occur naturally.

Phosphate rock is a popular term used for sedimentary rocks that contain high percentages of phosphate, usually in the form of the mineral *apatite,* calcium fluophosphate. This rock is extremely important as a source of agricultural fertilizer. The Rocky Mountain states have phosphate reserves estimated at 6 billion tons, enough to last for many centuries, and reserves in Idaho run close to 5 billion tons. Other deposits are being mined in Florida and Tennessee.

Asbestos is a general term applied to certain minerals that form soft, silky, flexible fibers in metamorphic rocks (see Fig. 22-13). The most common asbestos is *chrysotile,* a variety of the mineral *serpentine,* a magnesium silicate. The longer fibers are woven into yarn for use in brake linings and heat-resistant tapes and cloth. Asbestos materials are extremely versatile, for they withstand fire, insulate against heat and sound, are light in weight, can be made into pliable fabrics, and resist soil, corrosion, and vermin. The United States, the greatest user of asbestos, imports up to 90 per cent of its needs from Canada where there is an important belt of serpentine in Quebec around Thetford.

Salt, NaCl, essential to life, and fortunately one of the most abundant substances in the world, is derived commercially both from sea water and from rocks that were formed by the natural evaporation of sea water. Rock salt is produced by about half the states of the United States.

The primary use of salt is in the chemical industries, but it is also valuable in the preparation and transportation of foods, in various manufacturing processes, and in treating icy highways.

Under the pressure of a few thousand feet of sediments, rock salt flows plastically. In some regions it has been pushed up into overlying sediments in great plugs known as *salt domes.* Although the details of shape and history vary a good bit from one dome to another, they all tend to have a cylindrical shape with a top diameter of about a mile. They may rise to within a few hundred feet of the surface, or they may get no nearer than a few thousand feet. Some of them have forced their way upward from the original salt bed through 20,000 feet of overlying sediments. Reservoirs of oil and gas are often trapped by salt domes as they form (see Fig. 22-14).

PROSPECTING FOR ORE DEPOSITS. A search for ore deposits is always guided by a theory of some kind. The theory may be based on dreams or phases of the moon. It may be an assumption that because a certain species of spoofberry bush once grew on the surface above a copper mine, anybody who finds a spoofberry bush can expect to find a copper deposit below it. Or it may be based on the latest ideas in geophysics. But the theory is there.

On the other hand, luck has often played a large role in even the most carefully planned prospecting. It did so in Nevada, where a painstaking program laid out to pan for gold was rendered ineffective by a soft, sticky, bluish mineral. When somebody recovered from the disappointment of not

FIG. 22-10
Outcrop of Clinton iron ore near Birmingham, Alabama. The ore is the thick bottom layer. Photo by Aloia Studio. Courtesy Republic Steel Corp.

FIG. 22-11
Underground mine in Clinton iron ore near Birmingham, Alabama (see Fig. 22-10). Courtesy Tennessee Coal and Iron Division, United States Steel Corporation.

FIG. 22-12
Modern methods break over 200,000 tons of rock from a quarry face with 53,377 pounds of explosive. Courtesy New York Trap Rock Corporation.

finding gold and had the bluish "clay" assayed, it turned out to be an important silver ore, argentite, a silver sulfide. This discovery led to the development of the fabulous Comstock Lode. Many mining camps have a story of a prospector who threw a hammer at a fox and had it bounce off an outcrop of rock. When he went to retrieve the hammer, he found ore in the outcrop. Another popular account of accidental finding tells of a prospector tracking down his stray mule and finding the mule grazing near an outcrop of ore. And rich deposits of gold and copper were discovered in rock cuts made for westward-driving railroad lines in the early days.

Known occurrences are the best guide to conditions under which to look for a particular ore. Even the most highly instrumented methods of modern geophysics or geology are best adapted to extending old ore deposit outlines, or looking for new deposits under geological conditions similar to those where old ones were formed.

Geophysical methods of prospecting for ore deposits are indirect, for the most part: they determine geological structures favorable for the presence of desired minerals. By making magnetic measurements, however, the mineral magnetite can be located directly because of its magnetism. But even this method is more often used indirectly, to locate minerals that commonly have magnetite associated with them. Iron ores, such as hematite and limonite, though themselves nonmagnetic, have enough magnetite associated with them to permit detection and mapping. Magnetic measurements aided in finding gold-bearing veins in the Witwatersrand, "the Rand," near Johannesburg, South Africa. In this section of South Africa, gold is scattered through steeply dipping beds of Precambrian quartz conglomerate that extend for a hundred miles from east to west. Parallel to these conglomerates are some shales rich in magnetite. When the Witwatersrand ran into barren ground some years ago, a geologist and geophysicist worked together to see if the gold-bearing vein could be found again. They measured the vertical intensity of the magnetic field over extensive areas, tracing what they believed to be the magnetite-bearing shales associated with the gold-bearing conglomerates. From their measurements, they were able to map the area containing the magnetite. Drilling confirmed their location of the magnetite and then the gold-bearing formation. These were both found under a cover of 2,000 feet of other rock.

Seismic methods have been used successfully in mapping bedrock under glacial deposits. This method has paid off in some areas where low places in the bedrock were sought as possible locations for placer accumulations of heavy minerals. But seismic methods have not worked well in most ore-finding problems because they cannot distinguish one mineral from another.

SOURCES OF ENERGY AVAILABLE TODAY

In our present state of knowledge, we can draw on only a few sources of energy, principally coal, oil, and gas—the very sources that have been known to man for centuries. And

FIG. 22-13
Chrysotile asbestos, a fibrous variety of serpentine from Thetford, Quebec. Photo by Benjamin M. Shaub.

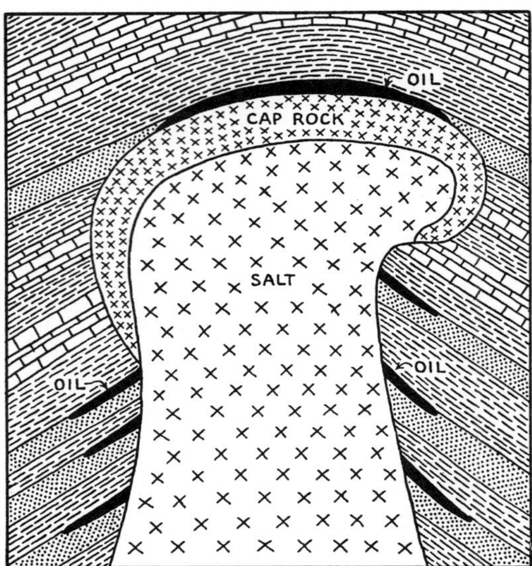

FIG. 22-14
Schematic diagram of a salt dome.

FIG. 22-15
Coal seams form part of a series of sedimentary rocks. The darkest layers are coal and shale; the lightest are limestone. Near Cokedale, Colorado. Photo by Tozier.

even these can be employed only if they have been concentrated by geological processes.

Chemical energy

The discovery of fire and its uses was one of man's first steps along the road to civilization, and even today fire still serves as the basis of civilization. Fire is a type of combustion in which oxygen combines chemically with the carbon and other elements of organic substances to produce heat and light. Of the various substances that can be used as fuels, wood is the least efficient. Coal, oil, and gas are far more efficient, for they represent energy that has been concentrated by the decay of organic material. These three fuels are often referred to as *fossil* fuels, for obvious reasons. During the decay process, the less combustible components are driven off, leaving behind the highly combustible elements carbon, hydrogen, and oxygen.

When organic fuels are burned, great quantities of stored chemical energy are released in the form of heat energy. This heat may either be used directly or converted into other forms, such as electrical energy.

COAL. Coal is the end product of vegetable matter that accumulated in the swamplands of the earth millions of years ago. The size of a coal bed depends on the extent of the original swamp and the amount of vegetable matter that collected in it.

We distinguish among varieties of coal on the basis of their carbon content, which increases the longer the material has undergone decay. The plant matter from which coal has developed contains about 50 per cent carbon. Peat, the first stage in the decay process, contains about 60 per cent; anthracite, the final stage, contains 95 to 98 per cent. Although carbon is by all odds the most important element in coal, as many as 72 elements have been found in some deposits. Over 1 per cent of the ash formed by the bituminous coals of West Virginia consists of sodium, potassium, calcium, aluminum, silicon, iron, and titanium. And there are 26 metals present in concentrations ranging down to .01 per cent, including lithium, rubidium, chromium, cobalt, copper, gallium, germanium, lanthanum, nickel, tungsten, and zirconium.

Coal is also important as the source of coke used in the steel industry. In fact, one-fourth of the coal produced every year is used for this purpose. The coke is burned in blast furnaces, where it supplies carbon, which combines with the oxygen of iron ores to free the metallic iron. In the future, coal may become even more valuable as a source of coke than as a direct source of heat.

Methods of finding coal. Although most of the coal reserves of the United States have been charted, the maps do not tell whether the seams are thick enough, or whether the quality of the coal is high enough, to make mining operations profitable. The best way of obtaining this information is to drill out samples that show the thickness of the beds and the types of rock in which they lie. The seams must be at least a foot thick if they are to be mined economically.

Coal reserves. Recent estimates indicate that about half the world's coal reserves occur in North America. But these estimates are based on generalized geologic maps, and actual drilling may reveal that even in what seems to be a promising area, the coal is missing because of faulting or the pinching out of beds. Or the beds may be too thin for them to be mined economically. Not many years ago, beds as thick as a maximum of 100 feet were being mined. Today the average thickness is around 5 feet.

Coal-mining operations are being carried on throughout the world, and deposits have been discovered even in Antarctica. In the United States, coal is produced in many states, but the quality and quantity are extremely variable (see Figs. 22-15 and 22-16). Pennsylvania and West Virginia are the largest producers.

According to some estimates, known world coal reserves represent roughly a 2,000-year supply at the present rate of use, but other estimates are in sharp disagreement. Here is one evaluation: "We cannot say yet whether the present United States coal reserve is equivalent to 1,700 times the present total annual United States energy requirements, or one-tenth this amount." [2]

OIL AND GAS. Coal is rapidly being replaced as a fuel by more efficient, easier-to-handle oil and gas. Fortunately, there are also large supplies of these fuels in the United States, and it is to them that we owe much of our industrial progress and high standard of living. Great Britain, on the other hand, although her coal and iron ore enabled her to pioneer the industrial revolution, now has to buy large quantities of oil and gas reserves in other countries. Her own resources do not include the large sedimentary basins where oil and gas accumulate.

What are oil and gas? Oil and gas are the remains of living matter that has been reduced by decay to a state in which carbon and hydrogen are the principal elements. These elements are combined in a great variety of ways to form molecules of substances called *hydrocarbons.* The distinguishing feature of the molecule of each hydrocarbon is the number of carbon atoms it contains. One carbon atom combined with four hydrogen atoms, for example, forms a molecule of a gas called methane, CH_4. Two carbon atoms combined with six hydrogen atoms form a molecule of a gas called ethane, C_2H_6. Various hydrocarbons are listed in Table 22-1.

Natural deposits of oil contain many kinds of hydrocarbons mixed together. They are separated by an industrial process called *fractional distillation,* based on the principle that light molecules are volatilized more readily than heavy molecules. As early as 600 B.C., Nebuchadnezzar, king of Babylon, was building roads that consisted of stones set in asphalt. The asphalt was nothing more than the hydrocarbons left behind where natural oil had seeped to the surface and lost its lighter components by evaporation.

FIG. 22-16
Underground coal mine. Coal seams alternate with bands of other rock. The miner is loading a charge of dynamite to break up the material for removal. Photo courtesy Hercules Powder Co.

[2] Eugene Ayres and Charles A. Scarlott, *Energy Sources: The Wealth of the World* (New York: McGraw-Hill Book Company, 1952), p. 55.

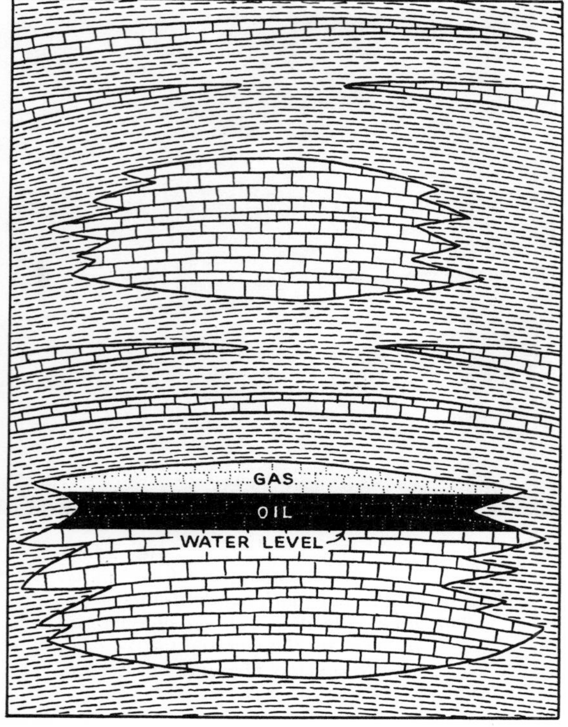

FIG. 22-17
Oil and gas trapped in an ancient coral reef, surrounded by impermeable shales. Some reefs are believed to have contributed animal remains as a source material for petroleum as well as reservoir rocks for storing the naturally distilled hydrocarbons.

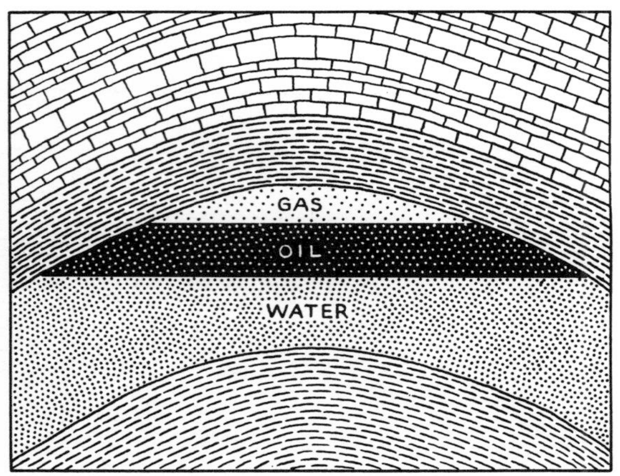

FIG. 22-18
Symmetrical anticlinal trap for oil and gas separated from water by differences in specific gravity. The oil and gas move upward above the water associated with them in a permeable reservoir rock (shown here as a sandstone) until they encounter an impermeable shale folded into an anticline and can rise no further. There they accumulate, with gas above the oil.

TABLE 22-1 *Petroleum products*

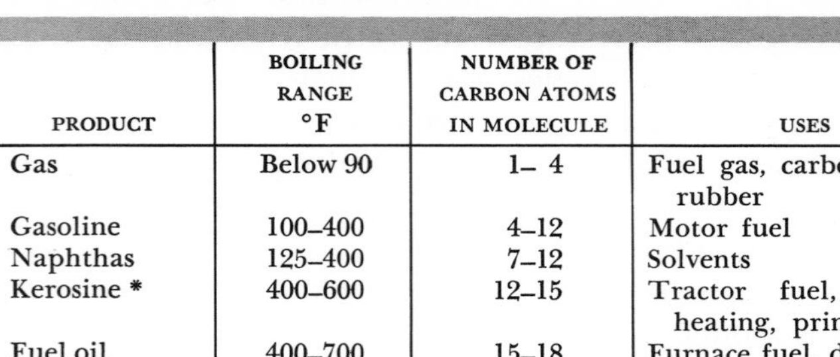

PRODUCT	BOILING RANGE °F	NUMBER OF CARBON ATOMS IN MOLECULE	USES
Gas	Below 90	1– 4	Fuel gas, carbon black, rubber
Gasoline	100–400	4–12	Motor fuel
Naphthas	125–400	7–12	Solvents
Kerosine *	400–600	12–15	Tractor fuel, diesels, heating, printing ink
Fuel oil	400–700	15–18	Furnace fuel, diesels
Lubricating oil	above 650	16–20	Lubrication
Petrolatum	above 650	18–22	Lubrication, salves
Wax	melts 125–130	20–34	Waterproofing, candles
Asphalt	residue		Road-making, roofing

* Spelling adopted by American Society for Testing Materials.

Source beds. Most petroleum (from the Latin *petra,* "rock," and *oleum,* "oil"; hence, "rock oil") and natural gas have developed from organic remains originally deposited in a marine sedimentary environment. A modern example of such an environment is the Black Sea. Here the water circulates very slowly, and the bottom sediments contain as much as 35 per cent organic matter, in contrast to the 2.5 per cent that is normal for marine sediments. When the putrefaction of organic remains takes place in an environment of this sort, the product is a slimy black mud known as *sapropel* (from Greek *sapros,* "rotten," and *pelagos,* "sea"). Petroleum and natural gas are believed to develop from the sapropel through a series of transformations not unlike the stages in coal's development from peat.

Three conditions are required for the development of a deposit of petroleum or natural gas: (1) source beds where the hydrocarbons can form, (2) a relatively porous and permeable reservoir bed into which they can migrate, and (3) a trap at some point in the reservoir bed where they can become imprisoned.

The most important source beds are generally believed to be marine shales, although certain limestones, particularly if they form a reef, may also serve the purpose (see Fig. 22-17). There are also extensive beds of shales formed from fresh-water deposits, such as the Eocene lake deposits in Utah, Colorado, and Wyoming. These *oil shales* have yielded from 5 to 10 gallons of oil per ton and constitute important fuel reserves.

LOCATION OF RESERVOIR BEDS. Just where we will find a reservoir of petroleum or natural gas depends on the laws that govern the migration of these substances to reservoir rocks. Unfortunately, we do not yet understand just what these laws are, although several empirical relationships have been established.

Simple gravity seems to explain the location of many occurrences. According to the *gravitational theory,* if oil, gas, and water are present in a reservoir bed, the oil and gas, being lighter than water, will rise to the top, with the gas uppermost. If the reservoir is trapped in a dome or an anticline capped by an impermeable formation, the oil and gas will accumulate along the crest of the anticline or dome (see

Figs. 22-18 and 22-19). This *anticlinal theory* of accumulation, one aspect of the gravitational theory, has proved to be a valuable guide to prospectors and has led to a substantial volume of production.

A corollary of the gravitational theory is that if no water is present, the oil will gather in the trough of a syncline with the gas above it. Some reservoirs of this type have led careless critics of geological methods to point with scorn to the demonstrably successful anticlinal theory.

Another structure that is important in the gravitational theory is the *stratigraphic trap,* formed when oil and gas in the presence of water are impeded by a zone of reduced permeability as they migrate upward (see Fig. 22-20). This situation may develop, for example, along old shorelines or in ancient sandbars, where facies change horizontally from sand to clay. Or the upward progress of the oil and gas through a permeable reservoir bed may be blocked by an impermeable bed at an unconformity, or at a fault.

Significant oil deposits throughout the world, excluding those under Russian control, are indicated on Fig. 22-21.

METHODS OF FINDING OIL AND GAS. Since concentrations of oil and gas seem to develop only in thick masses of marine sediments, prospectors limits their search to sedimentary rock formations. They have mapped and tested most of the anticlines that crop out at the surface in the United States and Canada and are now concentrating on rock structures beneath the surface. They use several methods in their search, including (1) core drilling, (2) seismic prospecting, and (3) gravity prospecting. These methods reveal whether or not there is a structure that is likely to trap oil and gas, but they do not give direct evidence of the presence of an actual reservoir.

In core drilling, several closely spaced holes are drilled into the surface to reveal the structure of the underlying sedimentary beds. On the basis of the core samples (see Fig. 22-22), the beds are matched from hole to hole, and the height of each above sea level is determined. Then each of the beds is carefully plotted, and a map of the entire structure is built up.

Seismic prospecting is based on our knowledge of earthquake waves. Small dynamite blasts are set off in shallow holes about 50 feet deep, and the waves generated are tracked as they travel into the interior (see Fig. 22-23 and 22-24). If they originate in a zone of shale, for example, and encounter a bed of sandstone, some of them bounce back to the surface where instruments pick them up and register the time of their arrival. The depth to which they have traveled can then be computed, and through a series of such measurements an entire structure can be plotted.

Gravity prospecting makes use of variations in the specific gravity of sedimentary rock formations (see Fig. 22-25). If a sedimentary bed lies in a horizontal position beneath the surface, sensitive instruments known as gravity meters will give a constant reading for the force of gravity all along the surface above the bed. But if the bed dips or rises, the gravity-meter readings reflect the changing structure. When

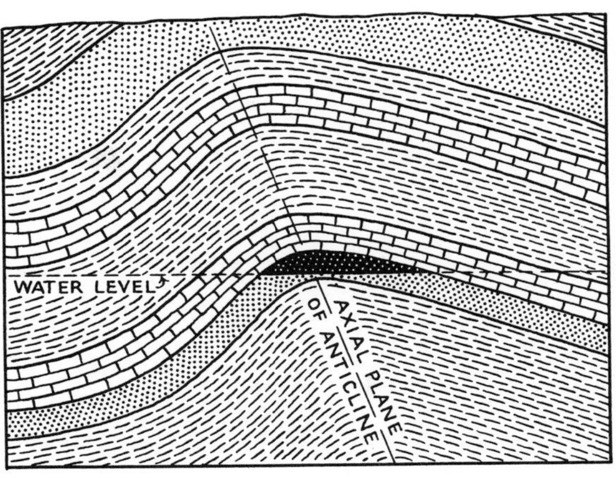

FIG. 22-19
Distorted anticlinal trap for oil. If the anticlinal fold is slightly steeper on one side than on the other, its crest at the surface (outcrop of the axial plane) will not be vertically above its crest at the depth where oil and gas have accumulated.

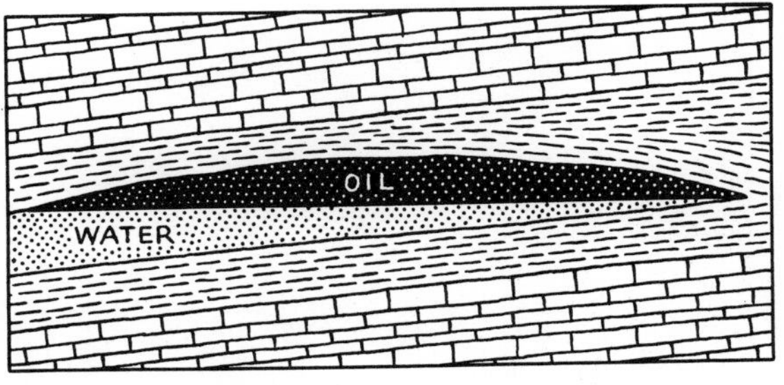

FIG. 22-20
Stratigraphic trap for oil. If old shorelines or sandbars developed conditions in which sand graded into clay, the rock equivalents of these deposits will show permeability for the sand and none for the clay. If oil migrating upward in the sand is trapped by a sudden change to impermeable shale, without structural deformation, a stratigraphic trap develops.

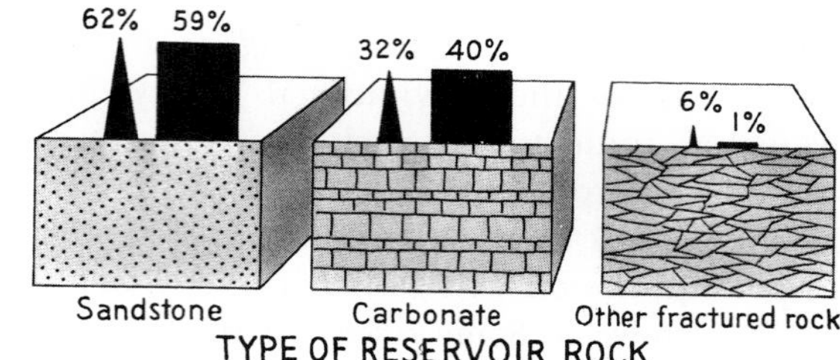

FIG. 22-21
Where the world's oil (excluding Russian controlled areas) has been found. The analysis was based on 236 oil fields with ultimate yields exceeding 100 million barrels each (past production plus proved reserves). From data prepared by G. M. Knebel (Standard Oil Company of New Jersey) and Guillermo Rodriguez-Eraso (Creole Petroleum Corporation). After drawing by W. Holloway.

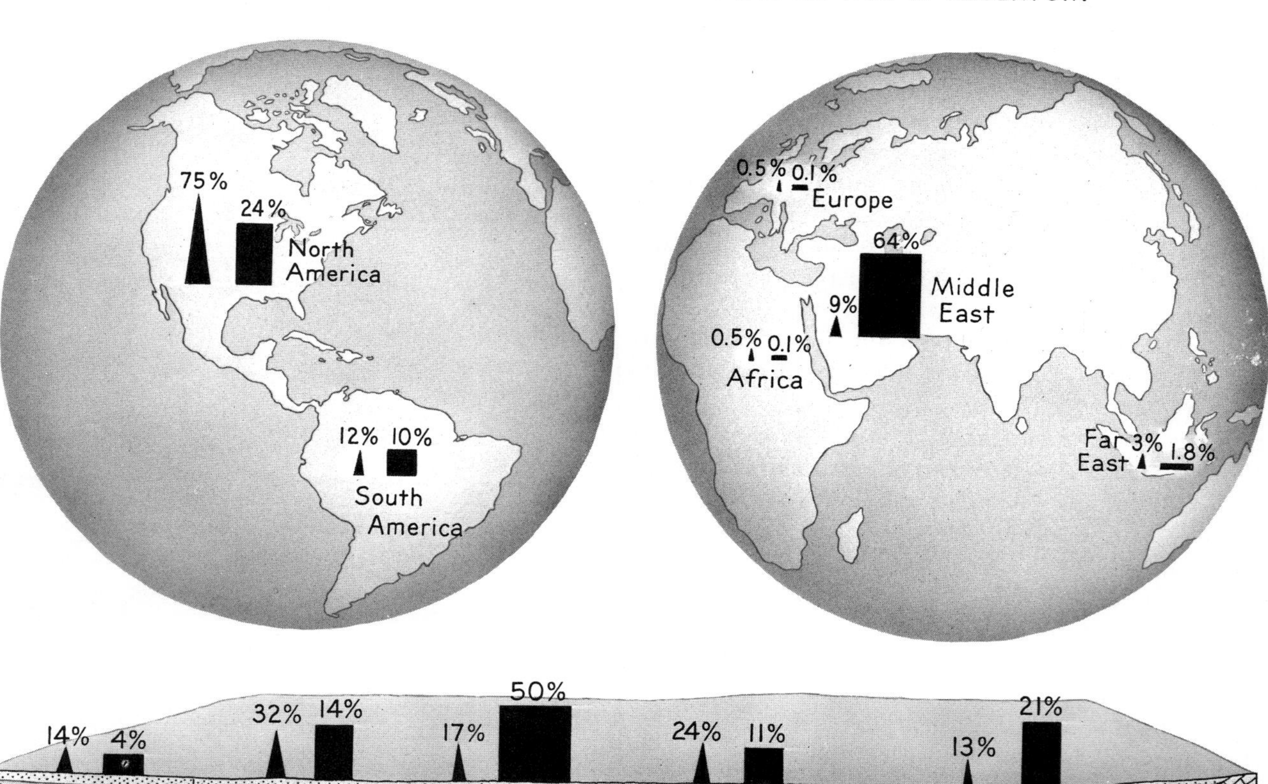

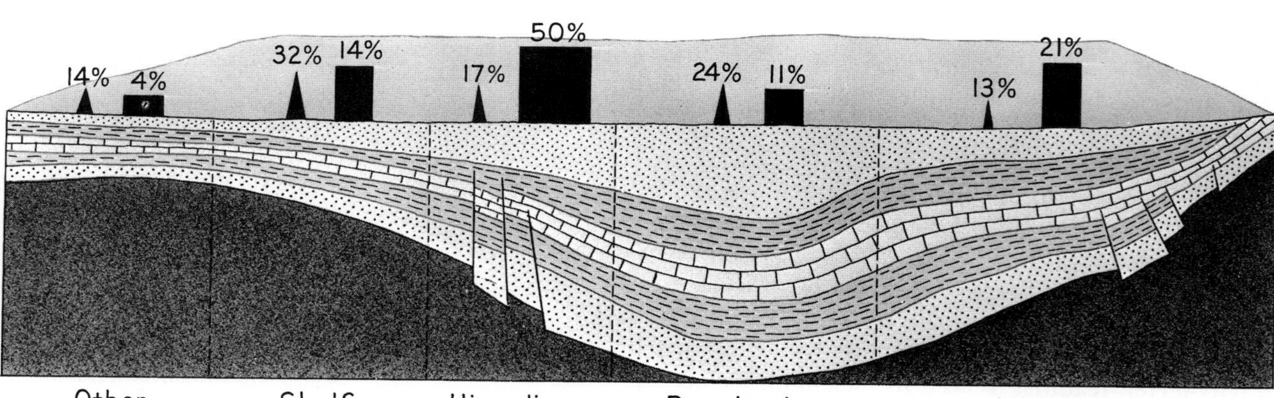

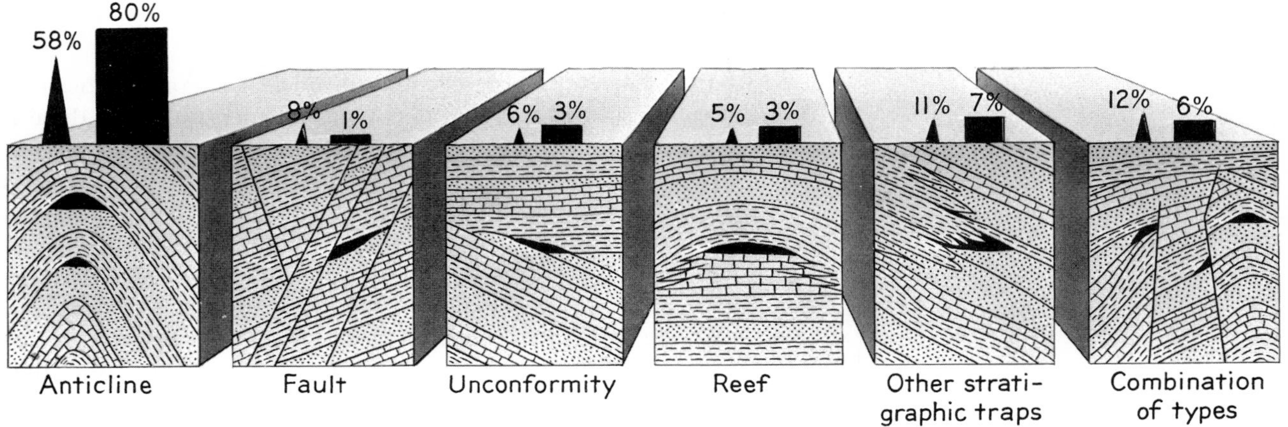

the readings suggest the presence of anticlines, faults, or other structures in which oil might accumulate, test wells are drilled to determine whether reservoirs actually exist beneath the surface.

USES OF OIL AND GAS. By 1953, oil supplied 40 per cent of the energy requirements of the United States, and natural gas supplied over 20 per cent. Natural gas, once an unwanted by-product of oil production, has been rapidly increasing in importance as a source of energy. Over 320,000 miles of great pipe lines now carry it from gas fields to most parts of the country. Composed for the most part of the hydrocarbon methane, natural gas is light, clean, and highly efficient. Oil and gas are also the basic materials for making many chemicals and plastics.

OIL AND GAS RESERVES. The known reserves of natural gas in the United States amount to about 185 trillion cubic feet, the equivalent in heat units of 30 billion barrels of oil. Of the known oil reserves—about 25 billion barrels—85 per cent are in or adjacent to Texas. The world's total potential production of oil has been estimated at 610 billion barrels. About 10 per cent of it has been produced to date.

The search for additional reserves is still going on, and the methods of locating and extracting the oil and gas are constantly being improved. Wells have been drilled far offshore beneath the ocean, and some wells now reach 4 miles into the crust. Promising new regions are being explored in such remote areas as northern Alaska. As a result, although demand has increased steadily, so have the estimated reserves.

TOMORROW'S ENERGY

Atomic energy will undoubtedly be our greatest source of energy in the future. Coal, oil, and gas supply only the chemical energy stored in the electrons of atoms; atomic fuels release the much greater energy that is locked in atomic nuclei. Since mass and energy are interchangeable, the nucleus of an atom, which contains 99.95 per cent of its mass, contains almost all of its total energy. In fact, if atomic nuclei could interact with one another in a way that would release their inner sources of energy, the reaction would produce a million times more energy than is released by ordinary energy-producing chemical reactions.

FIG. 22-22
Core samples lined up for examination. Photo by Ohio Oil Co., Inc.

FIG. 22-23
Seismic prospecting for oil-bearing structures. Dynamite is shot in a shallow hole from one of the trucks on the left. After the vibrations are reflected from buried rocks, they are recorded on seismographs operated from the other truck. The rig on the right drills the shot-holes. Bar-S Ranch, West Texas. Photo by Humble Oil and Refining Co.

FIG. 22-24
A reflection seismograph record being inspected by operator after shot, in Oklahoma. Final interpretation of this record is made in the computing offices of the Carter Oil Co. Photo by Standard Oil Company of New Jersey.

Atomic energy

So far, however, this great store of nuclear energy has been released from the atoms of only a few elements. One of these is uranium, a naturally unstable element. In 1938, it was discovered that when the istope uranium-235 captures a neutron to form uranium-236, its nucleus becomes unstable and splits apart. Two other elements are produced whose protons total the 92 of uranium, but whose mass numbers do not total 236 (see Fig. 2-12). Clearly, some of the neutrons have escaped, carrying with them tremendous amounts of energy. When this process is initiated in a pile of uranium, the neutrons that have escaped from one atom hit the nuclei of other atoms and set up a chain reaction. It was a large-scale reaction of this sort that produced the first atomic bomb explosion on July 16, 1945. Since then, scientists have been developing methods of controlling the reaction so that the energy released can be used for constructive purposes. In fact, nuclear energy is now driving submarines and producing electric power, and in the near future it will be used to propel airplanes.

Uranium ores

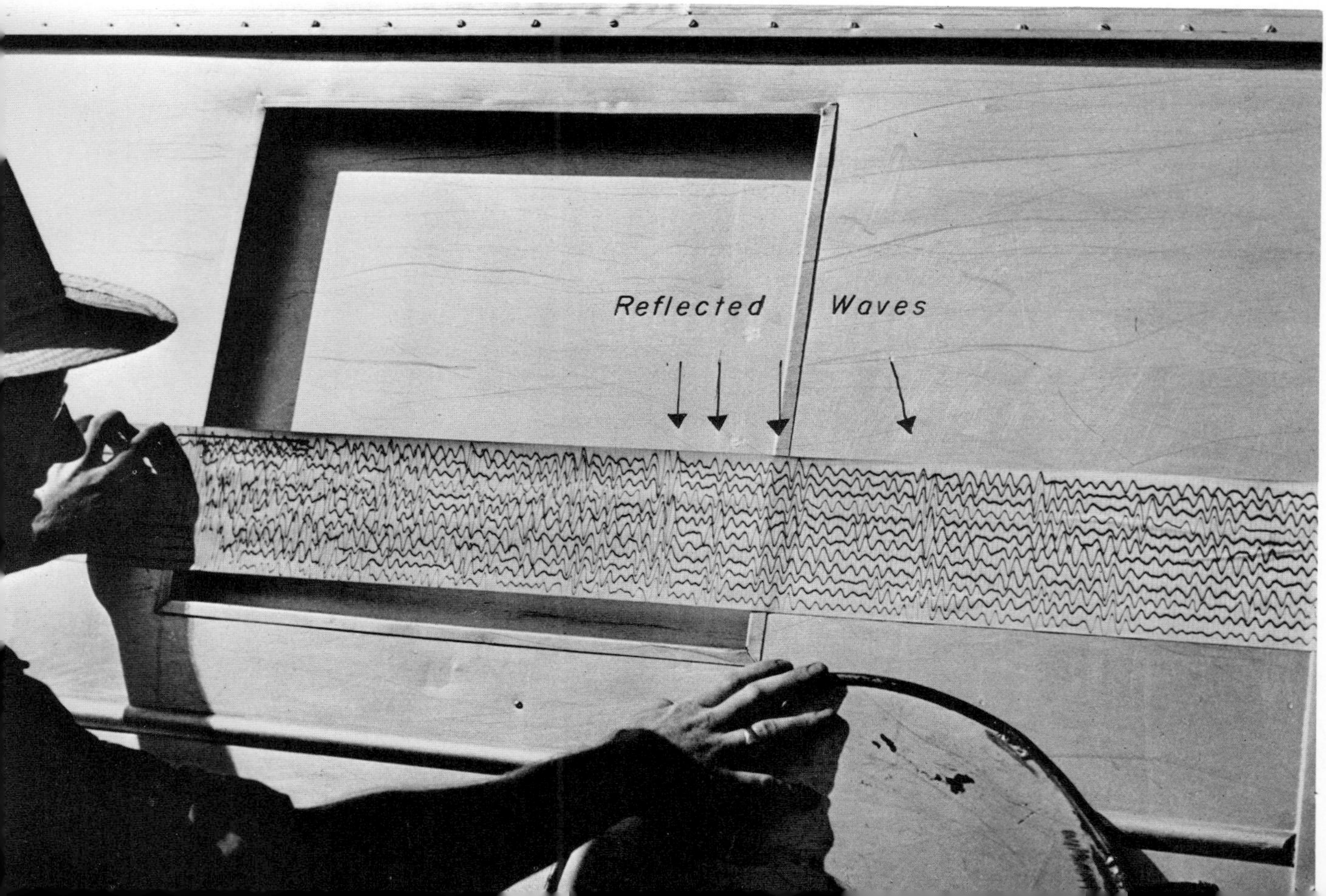

Uranium deposits were built up by igneous activity, and they occur in igneous rocks, pegmatite dikes, and vein deposits. The primary ore of uranium is the mineral *uraninite,* a complex oxide sometimes called *pitchblende.* Another complex oxide, containing smaller amounts of uranium, is the soft, yellow mineral *carnotite,* found in the sandstones of the Colorado Plateau. It constitutes the principal source of uranium in the United States. Uranium in this form has gone through several steps, including solution from igneous rocks, transportation to the sea, and redeposition.

METHODS OF FINDING URANIUM ORES. Most of the world's supply of uranium comes from primary deposits at Great Bear Lake, Canada, in the Belgian Congo, and in Czechoslovakia. But important quantities are found in sedimentary rocks such as those of the Colorado Plateau, the Blind River, Canada, and Witwatersrand conglomerates in Africa.

Uranium prospectors use a Geiger counter, an instrument that makes an audible click every time it is hit by a particle released by the spontaneous decay of uranium (see Fig. 22-26). Since this is a simple, inexpensive device, much of the prospecting for this mineral is being done by ordinary laymen with a little spare cash and time. In fact, Geiger counters can actually be purchased in some California supermarkets.

URANIUM RESERVES. The supply of uranium-235 is fairly limited. It has been estimated that uranium-238 is 140 times as abundant, but it cannot be used directly as an atomic fuel. Processes for utilizing uranium in any form are being developed, however, and a scheme for "breeding" an atomic fuel from uranium-238 has been announced. Consequently, any estimate of usable reserves should include uranium in all its forms.

Measured in terms of tons, the uranium reserves now known are not great. But measured in terms of their potential energy, they probably equal the reserves of coal, oil, and gas combined.

FIG. 22-25
Gravity prospecting for oil-bearing structures. Party chief and assistant make gravity-meter reading near Shiprock, an eroded volcanic neck at Farmington, New Mexico. Radiating from the volcanic neck are basaltic dikes that formerly fed the volcano. Photo by Humble Oil and Refining Co.

SUMMARY OUTLINE

Materials and energy in useful form
- Concentrated by geological processes

Materials
- Metals and nonmetals

Concentration by igneous activity
- Diamond, tin, lead, zinc, gold, copper, silver, nickel, platinum, chromium

Concentration by weathering
- Aluminum, iron, copper

Concentration by sedimentary processes
- Placers (gold, tin), iron

Concentration during rock formation
- Crushed stone, limestone, phosphate rock, asbestos, salt

Sources of energy available today
- Chemical energy: coal, oil, gas

Tomorrow's energy
- Atomic
- Uranium ores
  - Reserves probably equal coal, oil, and gas combined

FIG. 22-26
Checking a suspected uranium deposit with a Geiger counter and a drill. Photo by Ohio Oil Co., Inc.

SELECTED REFERENCES

Ayres, Eugene, and Charles A. Scarlott, *Energy Sources—The Wealth of the World.* New York: McGraw-Hill Book Company, 1952.

Bateman, Alan M., *The Formation of Mineral Deposits.* New York: John Wiley & Sons, Inc., 1951.

McKinstry, Hugh E., *Mining Geology.* Englewood Cliffs, N.J.: Prentice-Hall, Inc., 1948.

Van Royen, William, and Oliver Bowles, *Atlas of the World's Resources:* Vol. II, *The Mineral Resources of the World.* Englewood Cliffs, N.J.: Prentice-Hall, Inc., 1952.

Appendix A

ELECTRONIC CONFIGURATION OF THE FIRST THIRTY ELEMENTS
(These elements constitute 99.6 per cent of the earth's crust)

ATOMIC NUMBER (PROTONS)	NAME OF ELEMENT	SYMBOL	NUMBER OF ELECTRONS IN 1-shell *s*	2-shell *s*	*p*	3-shell *s*	*p*	*d*	4-shell *s*	*p*	*d*	*f*	MASS NUMBER (PROTONS + NEUTRONS) OF STABLE ISOTOPES IN ORDER OF ABUNDANCE	PARTS PER MILLION IN EARTH'S CRUST
1	HYDROGEN	H	1										1, 2	1,400.
2	Helium	He	2 INERT GAS										4, 3	.003
3	Lithium	Li	2	1									7, 6	65.
4	Beryllium	Be	2	2									9	<.001
5	Boron	B	2	2	1								11, 10	3.
6	CARBON	C	2	2	2								12, 13	320.
7	Nitrogen	N	2	2	3								14, 15	46.
8	*OXYGEN*	O	2	2	4								16, 18	466,000.
9	Fluorine	F	2	2	5								19	300.
10	Neon	Ne	2	2	6 INERT GAS								20, 22, 21	<.001
11	*Sodium*	Na	2	2	6	1							23	28,300.
12	*Magnesium*	Mg	2	2	6	2							24, 25, 26	20,900.
13	*Aluminum*	Al	2	2	6	2	1						27	81,300.
14	*SILICON*	Si	2	2	6	2	2						28, 29, 30	277,200.
15	Phosphorus	P	2	2	6	2	3						31	1,180.
16	Sulfur	S	2	2	6	2	4						32, 34, 33, 36	520.
17	Chlorine	Cl	2	2	6	2	5						35, 37	314.
18	Argon	A	2	2	6	2	6 INERT GAS						40, 36, 38	.04
19	*Potassium*	K	2	2	6	2	6		1				39, 41	25,900.
20	*Calcium*	Ca	2	2	6	2	6		2				40, 42, 43, 44, 46, 48	36,300.
21	Scandium	Sc	2	2	6	2	6	1	2	Transition Elements (21–29)			45	5.
22	Titanium	Ti	2	2	6	2	6	2	2				48, 46, 47, 49, 50	4,400.
23	Vanadium	V	2	2	6	2	6	3	2				51	150.
24	Chromium	Cr	2	2	6	2	6	5	1				52, 53, 50, 54	200.
25	Manganese	Mn	2	2	6	2	6	5	2				55	1,000.
26	*Iron*	Fe	2	2	6	2	6	6	2				56, 54, 57, 58	50,000.
27	Cobalt	Co	2	2	6	2	6	7	2				59	23.
28	Nickel	Ni	2	2	6	2	6	8	2				58, 60, 62, 61, 64	80.
29	Copper	Cu	2	2	6	2	6	10	1				63, 65	70.
30	Zinc	Zn	2	2	6	2	6	10	2				64, 66, 68, 67, 70	132.
														996,108. (99.61 per cent)

NUMBER OF ELECTRONS IN

ATOMIC NUMBER (PROTONS)	NAME OF ELEMENT	SYMBOL	1-shell	2-shell		3-shell			4-shell				5-shell				6-shell				7-shell				
			s	*s*	*p*	*s*	*p*	*d*	*s*	*p*	*d*	*f*	*s*	*p*	*d*	*f*	*s*	*p*	*d*	*f*	*s*	*p*	*d*	*f*	
31	Gallium	Ga	2	2	6	2	6	10	2	1															
32	Germanium	Ge	2	2	6	2	6	10	2	2															
33	Arsenic	As	2	2	6	2	6	10	2	3															
34	Selenium	Se	2	2	6	2	6	10	2	4															
35	Bromine	Br	2	2	6	2	6	10	2	5															
36	Krypton	Kr	2	2	6	2	6	10	2	6															INERT GAS
37	Rubidium	Rb	2	2	6	2	6	10	2	6			1												
38	Strontium	Sr	2	2	6	2	6	10	2	6			2												
39	Yttrium	Y	2	2	6	2	6	10	2	6	1		2												Transition Elements
40	Zirconium	Zr	2	2	6	2	6	10	2	6	2		2												Transition Elements
41	Niobium (Columbium	Nb Cb)	2	2	6	2	6	10	2	6	4		1												Transition Elements
42	Molybdenum	Mo	2	2	6	2	6	10	2	6	5		1												Transition Elements
43	Technetium	Tc	2	2	6	2	6	10	2	6	6		1												Transition Elements
44	Ruthenium	Ru	2	2	6	2	6	10	2	6	7		1												Transition Elements
45	Rhodium	Rh	2	2	6	2	6	10	2	6	8		1												Transition Elements
46	Palladium	Pd	2	2	6	2	6	10	2	6	10														Transition Elements
47	Silver	Ag	2	2	6	2	6	10	2	6	10		1												Transition Elements
48	Cadmium	Cd	2	2	6	2	6	10	2	6	10		2												
49	Indium	In	2	2	6	2	6	10	2	6	10		2	1											
50	Tin	Sn	2	2	6	2	6	10	2	6	10		2	2											
51	Antimony	Sb	2	2	6	2	6	10	2	6	10		2	3											
52	Tellurium	Te	2	2	6	2	6	10	2	6	10		2	4											
53	Iodine	I	2	2	6	2	6	10	2	6	10		2	5											
54	Xenon	Xe	2	2	6	2	6	10	2	6	10		2	6											INERT GAS
55	Cesium	Cs	2	2	6	2	6	10	2	6	10		2	6			1								
56	Barium	Ba	2	2	6	2	6	10	2	6	10		2	6			2								
57	Lanthanum	La	2	2	6	2	6	10	2	6	10		2	6	1		2								"Rare Earths"; Transition Elements
58	Cerium	Ce	2	2	6	2	6	10	2	6	10	1	2	6	1		2								"Rare Earths"; Transition Elements
59	Praseodymium	Pr	2	2	6	2	6	10	2	6	10	2	2	6	1		2								"Rare Earths"; Transition Elements
60	Neodymium	Nd	2	2	6	2	6	10	2	6	10	3	2	6	1		2								"Rare Earths"; Transition Elements
61	Promethium	Pm	2	2	6	2	6	10	2	6	10	4	2	6	1		2								"Rare Earths"; Transition Elements
62	Samarium	Sm	2	2	6	2	6	10	2	6	10	5	2	6	1		2								"Rare Earths"; Transition Elements
63	Europium	Eu	2	2	6	2	6	10	2	6	10	6	2	6	1		2								"Rare Earths"; Transition Elements
64	Gadolinium	Gd	2	2	6	2	6	10	2	6	10	7	2	6	1		2								"Rare Earths"; Transition Elements
65	Terbium	Tb	2	2	6	2	6	10	2	6	10	8	2	6	1		2								"Rare Earths"; Transition Elements
66	Dysprosium	Dy	2	2	6	2	6	10	2	6	10	9	2	6	1		2								"Rare Earths"; Transition Elements
67	Holmium	Ho	2	2	6	2	6	10	2	6	10	10	2	6	1		2								"Rare Earths"; Transition Elements
68	Erbium	Er	2	2	6	2	6	10	2	6	10	11	2	6	1		2								"Rare Earths"; Transition Elements
69	Thulium	Tm	2	2	6	2	6	10	2	6	10	12	2	6	1		2								"Rare Earths"; Transition Elements
70	Ytterbium	Yb	2	2	6	2	6	10	2	6	10	13	2	6	1		2								"Rare Earths"; Transition Elements
71	Lutetium	Lu	2	2	6	2	6	10	2	6	10	14	2	6	1		2								"Rare Earths"; Transition Elements
72	Hafnium	Hf	2	2	6	2	6	10	2	6	10	14	2	6	2		2								Transition Elements
73	Tantalum	Ta	2	2	6	2	6	10	2	6	10	14	2	6	3		2								Transition Elements
74	Wolfram (Tungsten)	W	2	2	6	2	6	10	2	6	10	14	2	6	4		2								Transition Elements
75	Rhenium	Re	2	2	6	2	6	10	2	6	10	14	2	6	5		2								Transition Elements
76	Osmium	Os	2	2	6	2	6	10	2	6	10	14	2	6	6		2								Transition Elements
77	Iridium	Ir	2	2	6	2	6	10	2	6	10	14	2	6	7		2								Transition Elements
78	Platinum	Pt	2	2	6	2	6	10	2	6	10	14	2	6	8		2								Transition Elements
79	Gold	Au	2	2	6	2	6	10	2	6	10	14	2	6	10		1								Transition Elements
80	Mercury	Hg	2	2	6	2	6	10	2	6	10	14	2	6	10		2								
81	Thallium	Tl	2	2	6	2	6	10	2	6	10	14	2	6	10		2	1							
82	Lead	Pb	2	2	6	2	6	10	2	6	10	14	2	6	10		2	2							
83	Bismuth	Bi	2	2	6	2	6	10	2	6	10	14	2	6	10		2	3							

ELECTRONIC CONFIGURATION OF ELEMENTS 31-102 (Cont.)

ATOMIC NUMBER (PROTONS)	NAME OF ELEMENT	SYMBOL	1-shell s	2-shell s	2-shell p	3-shell s	3-shell p	3-shell d	4-shell s	4-shell p	4-shell d	4-shell f	5-shell s	5-shell p	5-shell d	5-shell f	6-shell s	6-shell p	6-shell d	6-shell f	7-shell s	7-shell p	7-shell d	7-shell f
84	Polonium	Po	2	2	6	2	6	10	2	6	10	14	2	6	10		2	4						
85	Astatine	At	2	2	6	2	6	10	2	6	10	14	2	6	10		2	5						
86	Radon	Rn	2	2	6	2	6	10	2	6	10	14	2	6	10		2	6	INERT GAS					
87	Francium	Fr	2	2	6	2	6	10	2	6	10	14	2	6	10		2	6			1			
88	Radium	Ra	2	2	6	2	6	10	2	6	10	14	2	6	10		2	6			2			
89	Actinium	Ac	2	2	6	2	6	10	2	6	10	14	2	6	10		2	6	1		2	Transition Elements		
90	Thorium	Th	2	2	6	2	6	10	2	6	10	14	2	6	10	1	2	6	1		2			
91	Protactinium	Pa	2	2	6	2	6	10	2	6	10	14	2	6	10	2	2	6	1		2			
92	Uranium	U	2	2	6	2	6	10	2	6	10	14	2	6	10	3	2	6	1		2			
93	Neptunium	Np	2	2	6	2	6	10	2	6	10	14	2	6	10	4	2	6	1		2			
94	Plutonium	Pu	2	2	6	2	6	10	2	6	10	14	2	6	10	5	2	6	1		2			
95	Americium	Am	2	2	6	2	6	10	2	6	10	14	2	6	10	6	2	6	1		2			
96	Curium	Cm	2	2	6	2	6	10	2	6	10	14	2	6	10	7	2	6	1		2			
97	Berkelium	Bk	2	2	6	2	6	10	2	6	10	14	2	6	10	8	2	6	1		2			
98	Californium	Cf	2	2	6	2	6	10	2	6	10	14	2	6	10	9	2	6	1		2			
99	Einsteinium	En	2	2	6	2	6	10	2	6	10	14	2	6	10	10	2	6	1		2			
100	Fermium	Fm	2	2	6	2	6	10	2	6	10	14	2	6	10	11	2	6	1		2			
101	Mendelevium	Me	2	2	6	2	6	10	2	6	10	14	2	6	10	12	2	6	1		2			
102	Nobelium	No	2	2	6	2	6	10	2	6	10	14	2	6	10	13	2	6	1		2			

ALPHABETICAL LIST OF THE ELEMENTS

ELEMENT	SYMBOL	ATOMIC NUMBER
Actinium	Ac	89
Aluminum	Al	13
Americium	Am	95
Antimony	Sb	51
Argon	A	18
Arsenic	As	33
Astatine	At	85
Barium	Ba	56
Berkelium	Bk	97
Beryllium	Be	4
Bismuth	Bi	83
Boron	B	5
Bromine	Br	35
Cadmium	Cd	48
Calcium	Ca	20
Californium	Cf	98
Carbon	C	6
Cerium	Ce	58
Cesium	Cs	55
Chlorine	Cl	17
Chromium	Cr	24
Cobalt	Co	27
Columbium (or Niobium	Cb Nb)	41
Copper	Cu	29
Curium	Cm	96
Dysprosium	Dy	66
Einsteinium	En	99
Erbium	Er	68
Europium	Eu	63
Fermium	Fm	100
Fluorine	F	9
Francium	Fr	87
Gadolinium	Gd	64
Gallium	Ga	31
Germanium	Ge	32
Gold	Au	79
Hafnium	Hf	72
Helium	He	2
Holmium	Ho	67
Hydrogen	H	1
Indium	In	49
Iodine	I	53
Iridium	Ir	77
Iron	Fe	26
Krypton	Kr	36
Lanthanum	La	57
Lead	Pb	82
Lithium	Li	3
Lutetium	Lu	71
Magnesium	Mg	12
Manganese	Mn	25
Mendelevium	Me	101
Mercury	Hg	80
Molybdenum	Mo	42
Neodymium	Nd	60
Neon	Ne	10
Neptunium	Np	93
Nickel	Ni	28
Niobium (or Columbium	Nb Cb)	41
Nitrogen	N	7
Nobelium	No	102
Osmium	Os	76
Oxygen	O	8
Palladium	Pd	46
Phosphorus	P	15
Platinum	Pt	78
Plutonium	Pu	94
Polonium	Po	84
Potassium	K	19
Praseodymium	Pr	59
Promethium	Pm	61
Protactinium	Pa	91
Radium	Ra	88
Radon	Rn	86
Rhenium	Re	75
Rhodium	Rh	45
Rubidium	Rb	37
Ruthenium	Ru	44
Samarium	Sm	62
Scandium	Sc	21
Selenium	Se	34
Silicon	Si	14
Silver	Ag	47
Sodium	Na	11
Strontium	Sr	38
Sulfur	S	16
Tantalum	Ta	73
Technetium	Tc	43
Tellurium	Te	52
Terbium	Tb	65
Thallium	Tl	81
Thorium	Th	90
Thulium	Tm	69
Tin	Sn	50
Titanium	Ti	22
Tungsten (or Wolfram)	W	74
Uranium	U	92
Vanadium	V	23
Wolfram (or Tungsten)	W	74
Xenon	Xe	54
Ytterbium	Yb	70
Yttrium	Y	39
Zinc	Zn	30
Zirconium	Zr	40

MASS AND ENERGY

It has been found that the mass of an atomic nucleus is less than the total mass of its components as separate particles. This is explained by the fact that when a nucleus forms, a small amount of mass disappears by changing into energy, which is radiated away. The energy represented by this mass defect is called the *binding energy*. It is the amount of energy that must be supplied in order to break the nucleus into its component particles again.

The discovery of the equivalence of mass and energy is one of the most fundamental and significant events in the history of mankind.

Consider, for example, a helium nucleus of 2 protons and 2 neutrons:

1 proton	1.00758 mass units
1 proton	1.00758 mass units
1 neutron	1.00893 mass units
1 neutron	1.00893 mass units
Total 4 particles	4.03302 mass units
Helium nucleus	4.00280 mass units
	.03022 mass units deficiency converted to energy when nucleus was formed

In 1905, Albert Einstein expressed the equivalence of mass and energy by the now-famous equation

$$E = mc^2$$

where E is the energy in ergs, m is the mass in grams, and c is the velocity of light in centimeters per second.

It was not until 1932 that experimental proof of this relationship was obtained. When ${}_3Li^7$ was bombarded with high-speed protons (${}_1H^1$), alpha particles (${}_2He^4$) were ejected from the lithium:

	Lithium + Hydrogen	yielded	Alpha Particles
	${}_3Li^7 + {}_1H^1$	$\longrightarrow$	${}_2He^4 + {}_2He^4$
Mass:	8.0241		8.0056

FIG. A-1
Equivalence of mass and energy. Two protons plus 2 neutrons as separate particles (left-hand scale pan) total 4.03302 mass units. When they are combined to form an alpha particle, mass disappears in the form of energy, so the alpha particle has only 4.00280 mass units (right-hand scale pan). This lost energy (or mass) is called the binding energy and must be applied to the alpha particle to break it up into separate particles again.

The lost mass was 8.0241 — 8.0056 = .0185, which the two alpha particles were found to possess in the form of velocity of motion.

The quantities of energy released in reactions of this kind are almost inconceivably greater than those released by any other type of reaction involving similar quantities of material. For example, 1 kilogram (2.2 pounds) of matter, if converted entirely into energy, would give 25 billion kilowatt hours of energy. This is equal to the energy that was generated during approximately a two-month period by the total electric power industry existing in the United States in 1939. In contrast, the burning of an equal amount of coal gives 8.5 kilowatt hours of heat energy.

It is now generally believed that a series of nuclear changes maintains the energy of the sun. If the conversion of mass into energy can be accomplished under controlled conditions by man, an almost limitless source of energy in vast quantities will be provided.

Appendix B

POWERS OF TEN

We need a special vocabulary to describe the size of things ranging from invisible atoms to the vast reaches of space around us. Such a vocabulary is supplied by the *powers of ten.*

$10^0 = 1$	1 with decimal point moved zero places
$10^1 = 10$	1 with decimal point moved 1 place to right
$10^2 = 100$	1 with decimal point moved 2 places to right
$10^3 = 1{,}000$	1 with decimal point moved 3 places to right
$10^4 = 10{,}000$	1 with decimal point moved 4 places to right
$10^5 = 100{,}000$	1 with decimal point moved 5 places to right
$10^6 = 1{,}000{,}000$ (1 million) etc.	1 with decimal point moved 6 places to right

In other words, the exponent of 10 indicates the number of places the decimal point is moved to the right (or the number of zeros following 1).

For numbers smaller than 1, a negative exponent is used.

$10^{-1} = .1$	1 with decimal point moved 1 place to left
$10^{-2} = .01$	1 with decimal point moved 2 places to left
$10^{-3} = .001$	1 with decimal point moved 3 places to left
	etc.

In other words, the negative exponent of 10 indicates the number of places the decimal point is moved to the left of the number 1.

In comparing the sizes of things expressed in powers of 10, we need to recall certain laws of exponents taught in school algebra:

Multplication. Add exponents. Examples:

$$10^3 \cdot 10^3 = 10^{3+3} = 10^6$$

or

$$1{,}000 \cdot 1{,}000 = 1{,}000{,}000 \text{ (1 million)}$$

$$10^{21} \cdot 10^6 = 10^{27}$$

(That is, 10^{27} is 10^6 or one million times as large as 10^{21}.)

Division. Subtract exponents. Examples:

$$10^6/10^3 = 10^{6-3} = 10^3$$

$$10^{27}/10^{21} = 10^{27-21} = 10^6$$

SOME DISTANCES AND SIZES EXPRESSED IN POWERS OF TEN

	Centimeters
1 light-year	10^{18}
	10^{17}
	10^{16}
	10^{15}
	10^{14}
Distance earth to sun ($1.5 \cdot 10^{13}$ cm)	10^{13}
	10^{12}
	10^{11}
	10^{10}
Diameter of earth ($1.3 \cdot 10^{9}$ cm)	10^{9}
	10^{8}
	10^{7}
Distant view	10^{6}
	10^{5}
Lengths of radio waves	10^{4}
	10^{3}
Meter stick (approximately 1 yard)	10^{2}
Width of hand	10^{1}
Width of pencil 1(cm = .39 in.)	10^{0}
	10^{-1}
Thickness of sheet of paper	10^{-2}
	10^{-3}
	10^{-4}
Wave length of visible light	10^{-5}
Diameter of some molecules	10^{-6}
X-rays	10^{-7}
Diameter of atom (1 angstrom)	10^{-8}
	10^{-9}
	10^{-10}
	10^{-11}
Diameter of atomic nucleus	10^{-12}
	10^{-13}
	10^{-14}

Appendix C

MINERALS

Many of the most common minerals may be identified in hand specimens by their physical properties. Among the characteristics useful for this purpose are (1) hardness, (2) specific gravity, (3) streak (sometimes color), (4) shape (that is, crystal form, cleavage, and fracture), and (5) response to light as indicated by luster and transparency.

Hardness

The hardness of a mineral is determined by scratching the smooth surface of one mineral with the edge of another. In making a hardness test, be sure that the mineral being tested is actually scratched. Sometimes particles simply rub off the specimen, suggesting that it has been scratched, even though it has not been.

Ten common minerals have been arranged in the Mohs scale of relative hardness.

MOHS SCALE OF HARDNESS

Softest	1	Talc	
	2	Gypsum	
	3	Calcite	2½ Fingernail 3 Copper coin
	4	Fluorite	
	5	Apatite	
	6	Orthoclase	5½–6 Knife blade or plate glass 6½–7 Steel file
	7	Quartz	
	8	Topaz	
	9	Corundum	
Hardest	10	Diamond	

Each of these minerals will scratch all those lower in number on the scale and will be scratched by all those higher. In other words, this is a *relative scale.* In terms of absolute hardness, the steps are nearly, though not quite, uniform up to 9. Number 7 is 7 times as hard as 1, and number 9 is 9 times as hard as 1. But number 10 is about 40 times as hard as 1.

Luster

Luster is the way a mineral looks in reflected light. There are several kinds of luster.

Metallic, the luster of metals.
Adamantine, the luster of diamonds.
Vitreous, the luster of a broken edge of glass.
Resinous, the luster of yellow resin.
Pearly, the luster of pearl.
Silky, the luster of silk.

Fracture

Many minerals that do not exhibit cleavage (see Chapter 4) do break, or fracture, in a distinctive manner. Some of the types of fracture are:

Conchoidal: along smooth, curved surfaces like the surface of a shell (*conch*). Commonly observed in glass and quartz.

Fibrous or *splintery:* along surfaces roughened by splinters or fibers.

Uneven or *irregular:* along rough, irregular surfaces.

Hackly: along a jagged, irregular surface with sharp edges.

MINERAL	CHEMICAL COMPOSITION AND NAME	SPECIFIC GRAVITY	STREAK	HARDNESS	CLEAVAGE OR FRACTURE	LUSTER
ACTINOLITE (An asbestos; an amphibole)	$Ca_2(Mg,Fe)_5Si_8O_2(OH)_2$ Calcium iron silicate	3.0–3.3	Colorless	5–6	*See* Amphibole	Vitreous
ALBITE	(*See* Feldspars)					
AMPHIBOLE	(*See* Hornblende)				Perfect prismatic at 56° and 124°, often yielding a splintery surface	
ANDALUSITE	Al_2SiO_5 Aluminum silicate	3.16	Colorless	7½	Not prominent	Vitreous
ANHYDRITE	$CaSO_4$ Anhydrous calcium sulfate	2.89–2.98	Colorless	3–3½	3 directions at right angles to form rectangular blocks	Vitreous; pearly
ANORTHITE	(*See* Feldspars)					
APATITE	$Ca_5(F,Cl)(PO_4)_3$ Calcium fluophosphate	3.15–3.2	White	5	Poor cleavage, one direction; conchoidal fracture	Glassy
ASBESTOS	(*See* Actinolite, Chrysotile, Serpentine)					
AUGITE (A pyroxene)	$Ca(Mg,Fe,Al)(Al,Si_2O_6)$ Ferromagnesian silicate	3.2–3.4	Greenish gray	5–6	Perfect prismatic along two planes at nearly right angles to each other, often yielding a splintery surface	Vitreous
AZURITE	$Cu_3(CO_3)_2(OH)_2$ Blue copper carbonate	3.77	Pale blue	4	Fibrous	Vitreous to dull, earthy
BAUXITE	Hydrous aluminum oxides of indefinite composition; not a mineral	2–3	Colorless	1–3	Uneven fracture	Dull to earthy
BIOTITE (Black mica)	$K(Mg,Fe)_3AlSi_3O_{10}(OH)_2$ Ferromagnesian silicate	2.8–3.2	Colorless	2½–3	Perfect in one direction into thin, elastic, transparent, smoky sheets	Pearly, glassy
BORNITE (Peacock ore; purple copper ore)	Cu_5FeS_4 Copper iron sulfide	5.06–5.08	Grayish black	3	Uneven fracture	Metallic
CALCITE	$CaCO_3$ Calcium carbonate	2.72	Colorless	3	Perfect in 3 directions at 75° to form unique rhombohedral fragments	Vitreous
CARNOTITE	$K_2(UO_2)_2(VO_4)_2$ Potassium uranyl vanadate	4		Very soft	Uneven fracture	Earthy
CASSITERITE (Tin stone)	SnO_2 Tin oxide	6.8–7.1	White to light brown	6–7	Conchoidal fracture	Adamantine to submetallic and dull
CHALCEDONY	(*See* Quartz)					
CHALCOCITE (Copper glance)	Cu_2S Copper sulfide	5.5–5.8	Grayish black	2½–3	Conchoidal fracture	Metallic

COLOR	TRANSPARENCY	FORM	OTHER PROPERTIES
White to light green	Transparent to translucent	Slender crystals, usually fibrous	A common ferromagnesian metamorphic mineral.
			A group of silicates with tetrahedra in double chains; hornblende is the most important; contrast with pyroxene.
Flesh-red, reddish brown, olive-green	Transparent to translucent	Usually in coarse, nearly square prisms; cross section may show black cross	Found in schists formed by the middle-grade metamorphism of aluminous shales and slates. The variety *chiastolite* has carbonaceous inclusions in the pattern of a cross.
White; may have faint gray, blue, or red tinge	Transparent to translucent	Commonly in massive fine aggregates not showing cleavage; crystals rare	Found in limestones and in beds associated with salt deposits; heavier than calcite, harder than gypsum.
Green, brown, red	Translucent to transparent	Massive, granular	Widely disseminated as an accessory mineral in all types of rocks; unimportant source of fertilizer; a transparent variety is a gem, but too soft for general use.
		A general term applied to certain fibrous minerals that display similar physical characteristics although they differ in composition. The most common asbestos mineral is *chrysotile,* a variety of serpentine.	
Dark green to black	Translucent only on thin edges	Short, stubby crystals with 4- or 8-sided cross section; often in granular crystalline masses	An important igneous rock-forming mineral found chiefly in simatic rocks.
Intense azure blue	Opaque	Crystals complex in habit and distorted; sometimes in radiating spherical groups	An ore of copper; a gem mineral; effervesces with HCl.
Yellow, brown, gray, white	Opaque	In rounded grains; or earthy, clay-like masses	An ore of aluminum; produced under subtropical to tropical climatic conditions by prolonged weathering of aluminum-bearing rocks; a component of *laterites;* clay odor when wet.
Black, brown, dark green	Transparent, translucent	Usually in irregular foliated masses; crystals rare	Constructed around tetrahedral sheets; a common and important rock-forming mineral in both igneous and metamorphic rocks.
Brownish bronze on fresh fracture; quickly tarnishes to variegated purple and blue, and finally black	Opaque	Usually massive; rarely in rough cubic crystals	An important ore of copper.
Usually white or colorless; may be tinted gray, red, green, blue, yellow	Transparent to opaque	Usually in crystals or coarse to fine granular aggregates; also compact, earthy; crystals extremely varied—over 300 different forms	A very common rock mineral, occurring in masses as limestone and marble; effervesces freely in cold dilute hydrochloric acid.
Brilliant canary yellow	Opaque	Earthy powder	An ore of vanadium and uranium.
Brown or black; rarely yellow or white	Translucent; rarely transparent	Commonly massive granular	The principal ore of tin.
Shiny lead-gray; tarnishes to dull black	Opaque	Commonly fine-grained and massive; crystals rare; small, tabular with hexagonal outline	One of the most important ore minerals of copper; occurs principally as a result of secondary sulfide enrichment.

MINERAL	CHEMICAL COMPOSITION AND NAME	SPECIFIC GRAVITY	STREAK	HARDNESS	CLEAVAGE OR FRACTURE	LUSTER
CHALCOPYRITE (Copper pyrites; yellow copper ore; fool's gold)	$CuFeS_2$ Copper iron sulfide	4.1–4.3	Greenish black; also greenish powder in groove when scratched	3½–4	Uneven fracture	Metallic
CHLORITE	$(Mg,Fe)_5(Al,Fe'')_2$ $Si_3O_{10}(OH)_8$ Hydrous ferromagnesian aluminum silicate	2.6–2.9	Colorless	2–2½	Perfect in 1 direction like micas, but into inelastic flakes	Vitreous to pearly
CHROMITE	$FeCr_2O_4$ Iron chromium oxide	4.6	Dark brown	5½	Uneven fracture	Metallic to submetallic or pitchy
CHRYSOTILE (Serpentine asbestos)	(*See* Serpentine)					
CLAY	(*See* Kaolinite)					
CORUNDUM (Ruby, sapphire)	Al_2O_3 Aluminum oxide	4.02	Colorless	9	Basal or rhombohedral parting	Adamantine to vitreous
DIAMOND	C	3.5	Colorless	10	Octahedral cleavage	Adamantine; greasy
DOLOMITE	$CaMg(CO_3)_2$ Calcium magnesium carbonate	2.85	Colorless	3½–4	Perfect in 3 directions at 73°45′	Vitreous or pearly
EMERY	(*See* Corundum)					
EPIDOTE	$Ca_2(Al,Fe)_3(SiO_4)_3(OH)$ Hydrous calcium aluminum iron silicate	3.35–3.45	Colorless	6–7	Good in 1 direction	Vitreous
FELDSPARS	Alumino silicates	2.55–2.75		6	Good in 2 directions at or near 90°	
ORTHOCLASE	$K(AlSi_3O_8)$ Potassic feldspar	2.57	White	6	"	Vitreous
PLAGIOCLASE	Soda-lime feldspars, a continuous series varying in composition from pure albite to pure anorthite					
ALBITE	$Na(AlSi_3O_8)$ Sodic feldspar	2.62	Colorless	6	Good in 2 directions at 93°34′	Vitreous to pearly
ANORTHITE	$Ca(Al_2Si_2O_8)$	2.76	Colorless	6	Good in 2 directions at 94°12′	Vitreous to pearly
FLUORITE	CaF_2 Calcium fluoride	3.18	Colorless	4	Good in 4 directions parallel to the faces of an octahedron	Vitreous
GALENA	PbS Lead sulfide	7.4–7.6	Lead-gray	2½	Good in 3 directions parallel to the faces of a cube	Metallic

to blow
will melt at very low temp.

COLOR	TRANSPARENCY	FORM	OTHER PROPERTIES
Brass-yellow; tarnishes to bronze or iridescence, but more slowly than bornite or chalcocite	Opaque	Usually massive	An ore of copper; distinguished from pyrite by being softer than steel while pyrite is harder than steel; distinguished from gold by being brittle while gold is not; known as "fool's gold," a term also applied to pyrite.
Green of various shades	Transparent to translucent	Foliated massive, or in aggregates of minute scales	A common metamorphic mineral characteristic of low-grade metamorphism.
Iron-black to brownish black	Subtranslucent	Massive, granular to compact	The only ore of chromium; a common constituent of peridotites and serpentines derived from them; one of the first minerals to crystallize from a cooling magma.
Brown, pink, or blue; may be white, gray, green, ruby-red, sapphire-blue	Transparent to translucent	Barrel-shaped crystals; sometimes deep horizontal striations; coarse or fine granular	Common as an accessory mineral in metamorphic rocks such as marble, mica schist, gneiss; occurs in gem form as *ruby* and *sapphire;* the abrasive emery is black granular corundum mixed with magnetite, hematite, or the magnesian aluminum oxide *spinel.*
Colorless or pale yellow; may be red, orange, green, blue, black	Transparent	Octahedral crystals, flattened, elongated, with curved faces	Gem and abrasive; 95 per cent of natural diamond production is from South Africa; abrasive diamonds have been made in commercial quantities in the laboratory in the United States.
Pink, flesh; may be white, gray, green, brown, black	Transparent to opaque	Rhombohedral crystals with curved faces; coarse-grained cleavable masses, or fine-grained compact	Occurs chiefly in rock masses of dolomitic limestone and marble, or as the principal constituent of the rock named for it; distinguished from limestone by its less vigorous action with cold hydrochloric acid (the powder dissolves with effervescence, large pieces only if the acid is hot).
Pistachio-green, yellowish to blackish green	Transparent to translucent	Prismatic crystals striated parallel to length; usually coarse to fine granular; also fibrous	A metamorphic mineral often associated with chlorite; derived from metamorphism of impure limestone; characteristic of contact metamorphic zones in limestone.
			The most common igneous rock-forming group of minerals; weather to clay minerals.
White, gray, flesh pink	Translucent to opaque	Prismatic crystals; most abundantly in rocks as formless grains	Characteristic of sialic rocks.
			Important rock-forming minerals; characteristic of simatic rocks.
Colorless, white, gray	Transparent to translucent	Tabular crystals; striations caused by twinning	Opalescent variety, *moonstone.*
Colorless, white, gray, green, yellow, red	Transparent to translucent	Lath-like or platy grains tabular crystals; striations caused by twinning; lath-like or platy grains	A unique and beautiful play of colors is common on plagioclase feldspars intermediate between albite and anorthite in composition, as with *andesine* (70 to 50 per cent albite) and *labradorite* (50 to 30 per cent albite).
Variable; light green, yellow, bluish green, purple, etc.	Transparent to translucent	Well-formed interlocking cubes; also massive, coarse or fine grains	Some varieties fluoresce; a common, widely distributed mineral in dolomites and limestone; an accessory mineral in igneous rocks; used as a flux in making steel.
Lead-gray	Opaque	Cube-shaped crystals; also in granular masses	The principal ore of lead; so commonly associated with silver that it is also an ore of silver.

MINERAL	CHEMICAL COMPOSITION AND NAME	SPECIFIC GRAVITY	STREAK	HARDNESS	CLEAVAGE OR FRACTURE	LUSTER
GARNET	$R''_3R''{}'_2(SiO_4)_3$ R″ may be Calcium, Magnesium, Iron, or Manganese. R″′ may be Aluminum, Iron, Titanium, or Chromium. Ferromagnesian silicates	3.5–4.3	Colorless	6½–7½	Uneven fracture	Vitreous to resinous
GRAPHITE (Plumbago; black lead)	C Carbon	2.3	Black	1–2	Good in one direction; folia flexible but not elastic	Metallic or earthy
GYPSUM	$CaSO_4 \cdot 2H_2O$ Hydrous calcium sulfate	2.32	Colorless	2	Good cleavage in one direction yielding flexible but inelastic flakes; fibrous fracture in another direction; conchoidal fracture in a third direction	Vitreous, pearly, silky
HALITE (Rock salt; common salt)	NaCl Sodium chloride	2.16	Colorless	2½	Perfect cubic cleavage	Glassy to dull
HEMATITE	Fe_2O_3 Iron oxide	5.26	Light to dark Indian-red; becomes black on heating	5½–6½	Uneven fracture	Metallic
HORNBLENDE (An amphibole)	Complex ferromagnesian silicate of Ca, Na, Mg, Ti, and Al	3.2	Colorless	5–6	Perfect prismatic at 56° and 124°	Vitreous; fibrous variety often silky
KAOLINITE (Clay)	$Al_2Si_2O_5(OH)_4$ Hydrous aluminum silicate	2.6	Colorless	2–2½	None	Dull earthy
KYANITE	Al_2SiO_5 Aluminum silicate	3.56–3.66	Colorless	5 along, 7 across crystals	Good in one direction	Vitreous to pearly
LIMONITE (Brown hematite; bog iron ore; rust)	Hydrous iron oxides; not a mineral	3.6–4	Yellow-brown	5–5½ (Finely divided, apparent H as low as 1)	None	Vitreous
MAGNETITE	Fe_3O_4 Iron oxide	5.18	Black	6	Some octahedral parting	Metallic
MICA	(*See* Biotite and Muscovite)					
MUSCOVITE (White mica; potassic mica; common mica)	$KAl_3Si_3O_{10}(OH)_2$ Nonferromagnesian silicate	2.76–3.1	Colorless	2–2½	Good cleavage in one direction, giving thin, very flexible and elastic folia	Vitreous, silky, pearly
OLIVINE (Peridot)	$(Mg,Fe)_2SiO_4$ Ferromagnesian silicate	3.27–3.37	Pale green, white	6½–7	Conchoidal fracture	Vitreous

COLOR	TRANSPARENCY	FORM	OTHER PROPERTIES
Red, brown, yellow, white, green, black	Transparent to translucent	Usually in 12- or 24-sided crystals; also massive granular, coarse or fine	Common and widely distributed, particularly in metamorphic rocks; brownish red variety *almandite,* $Fe_3Al_2(SiO_4)_3$, used to define one of the zones of middle-grade metamorphism; striking in schists.
Black to steel-gray	Opaque	Foliated or scaly masses common; may be radiated or granular	Feels greasy; common in metamorphic rocks such as marble, schists, and gneisses.
Colorless, white, gray; with impurities, yellow, red, brown	Transparent to translucent	Crystals prismatic, tabular, diamond-shaped; also in granular, fibrous, or earthy masses	A common mineral widely distributed in sedimentary rocks, often as thick beds; *satin spar* is a fibrous gypsum with silky luster; *selenite* is a variety which yields broad, colorless, transparent folia; *alabaster* is a fine-grained massive variety.
Colorless or white; impure: yellow, red, blue, purple	Transparent to translucent	Cubic crystals; massive granular	Salty taste; permits ready passage of heat rays (i.e., diathermanous); a very common mineral in sedimentary rocks; interstratified in rocks of all ages to form a true rock mass.
Reddish brown to black	Opaque	Crystals tabular; botryoidal; micaceous and foliated; massive	The most important ore of iron; red earthy variety known as *red ocher;* botryoidal form known as *kidney ore,* micaceous form *specular;* widely distributed in rocks of all types and ages.
Dark green to black	Translucent on thin edges	Long, prismatic crystals; fibrous; coarse- to fine-grained masses	Distinguished from augite by cleavage; a common, rock-forming mineral which occurs in both igneous and metamorphic rocks.
White	Opaque	Claylike masses	Usually unctuous and plastic; other clay minerals similar in composition and physical properties, but different in atomic structure, are *illite* and *montmorillonite;* derived from the weathering of the feldspars.
Blue; may be white, gray, green, streaked	Transparent to translucent	In bladed aggregates	Characteristic of middle-grade metamorphism; compare with andalusite, which has the same composition and is formed under similar conditions, but has a different crystal habit; contrast with sillimanite, which has the same composition but different crystal habit and forms at highest metamorphic temperatures.
Dark brown to black	Opaque	Amorphous; mammillary to stalactitic masses; concretionary, nodular, earthy	Always of secondary origin from alteration or solution of iron minerals; mixed with fine clay, it is a pigment, *yellow ocher.*
Iron-black	Opaque	Usually massive granular, coarse or fine in grain	Strongly magnetic; may act as a natural magnet, known as *lodestone;* an important ore of iron; found in black sands on the seashore; mixed with corundum, it is a component of *emery.*
Thin: colorless; thick: light yellow, brown, green, red	Thin: transparent; thick: translucent	Mostly in thin flakes	Widespread and very common rock-forming mineral; characteristic of sialic rocks; also very common in metamorphic rocks such as gneiss and schist; the principal component of some mica schists; sometimes used for stove doors, lanterns, etc., as transparent *isinglass;* used chiefly as an insulating material.
Olive to grayish green, brown	Transparent to translucent	Usually in imbedded grains or granular masses	A common rock-forming mineral found primarily in simatic rocks; the principal component of peridotite; actually, a series grading from *forsterite,* Mg_2SiO_4, to *fayalite,* Fe_2SiO_4; the most common olivines are richer in magnesium than in iron; the clear green variety *peridot* is sometimes used as a gem.

MINERAL	CHEMICAL COMPOSITION AND NAME	SPECIFIC GRAVITY	STREAK	HARDNESS	CLEAVAGE OR FRACTURE	LUSTER
OPAL	(*See* Quartz)					
ORTHOCLASE	(*See* Feldspars)					
PERIDOT	(*See* Olivine)					
PITCHBLENDE	(*See* Uraninite)					
PLAGIOCLASE	(*See* Feldspars)					
PYRITE (Iron pyrites; fool's gold)	FeS_2 Iron sulfide	5.02	Greenish or brownish black	6–6½	Uneven fracture	Metallic
PYROXENE	(*See* Augite)					
QUARTZ (Silica)	SiO_2 Silicon oxide but structurally a silicate, with tetrahedra sharing oxygens in 3 dimensions	2.65	Colorless	7	Conchoidal fracture	Vitreous, greasy, splendent
ROCK SALT	(*See* Halite)					
RUBY	(*See* Corundum)					
SALT	(*See* Halite)					
SAPPHIRE	(*See* Corundum)					
SERPENTINE	$Mg_3Si_2O_5(OH)_4$ Hydrous magnesium silicate	2.2–2.65	Colorless	2–5	Conchoidal fracture	Greasy, waxy, or silky
SIDERITE (Spathic iron; chalybite)	$FeCO_3$ Iron carbonate	3.85	Colorless	3½–4	Perfect rhombohedral cleavage	Vitreous
SILICA	(*See* Quartz)					
SILLIMANITE (Fibrolite)	Al_2SiO_5 Aluminum silicate	3.23	Colorless	6–7	Good cleavage in 1 direction	Vitreous
SPHALERITE (Zinc blende; black jack)	ZnS Zinc sulfide	3.9–4.1	White to yellow and brown	3½–4	Perfect cleavage in 6 directions at 120°	Resinous
STAUROLITE	$Fe''Al_5Si_2O_{12}(OH)$ Iron aluminum silicate	3.65–3.75	Colorless	7–7½	Not prominent	Fresh: resinous, vitreous; altered: dull to earthy
TACONITE	Not a mineral					

COLOR	TRANSPARENCY	FORM	OTHER PROPERTIES
Brass-yellow	Opaque	Cubic crystals with striated faces; also massive	The most common of the sulfides; used as a source of sulfur in the manufacture of sulfuric acid; distinguished from chalcopyrite by its paler color and greater hardness; from gold by its brittleness and hardness.
			A group of silicates with tetrahedra in single chains; augite is the most important; contrast with amphibole.
Colorless or white when pure; any color from impurities	Transparent to translucent	Prismatic crystals with faces striated at right angles to long dimension; also massive forms of great variety	An important constituent of sialic rocks; coarsely crystalline varieties: *rock crystal, amethyst* (purple), *rose quartz, smoky quartz, citrine* (yellow), *milky quartz, cat's eye;* cryptocrystalline varieties: *chalcedony, carnelian* (red chalcedony), *chrysoprase* (apple-green chalcedony), *heliotrope* or *bloodstone* (green chalcedony with small red spots), *agate* (alternating layers of chalcedony and opal); granular varieties: *flint* (dull to dark brown), *chert* (like flint but lighter in color), *jasper* (red from hematite inclusions), *prase* (like jasper, but dull green).
Variegated shades of green	Translucent	Platy or fibrous	Platy variety, *antigorite;* fibrous variety, *chrysotile,* an asbestos; an alteration product of magnesium silicates such as olivine, augite, and hornblende; common and widely distributed.
Light to dark brown	Transparent to translucent	Granular, compact, earthy	An ore of iron; an accessory mineral in taconite.
Brown, pale green, white	Transparent to translucent	Long, slender crystals without distinct terminations; often in parallel groups; frequently fibrous	Relatively rare, but important as a mineral characteristic of high-grade metamorphism; contrast with andalusite and kyanite, which have the same composition but form under conditions of middle-grade metamorphism.
Pure: white, green; with iron: yellow to brown and black; red	Transparent to translucent	Usually massive; crystals many-sided, distorted	A common mineral; the most important ore of zinc; the red variety is called *ruby zinc;* streak lighter than corresponding mineral color.
Red-brown to brownish black	Translucent	Usually in crystals, prismatic, twinned to form a cross; rarely massive	A common accessory mineral in schists and slates; characteristic of middle-grade metamorphism; associated with garnet, kyanite, sillimanite, tourmaline.
			Unleached iron formation in the Lake Superior District, consists of chert (*see* Quartz) with hematite, magnetite, siderite, and hydrous iron silicates; an ore of iron.

MINERAL	CHEMICAL COMPOSITION AND NAME	SPECIFIC GRAVITY	STREAK	HARDNESS	CLEAVAGE OR FRACTURE	LUSTER
TALC (Soapstone; steatite)	$Mg_3Si_4O_{10}(OH)_2$ Hydrous magnesium silicate	2.7–2.8	White	1	Good cleavage in 1 direction, gives thin folia, flexible but not elastic	Pearly to greasy
many uses; most common face powder, marking chalk						
TOPAZ	$Al_2SiO_4\,(F,OH)_2$ Aluminum fluosilicate	3.4–3.6	Colorless	8	Good in 1 direction	Vitreous
TOURMALINE	Complex silicate of boron and aluminum, with sodium, calcium, fluorine, iron, lithium, or magnesium	3–3.25	Colorless	7–7½	Not prominent; black variety fractures like coal	Vitreous to resinous
URANINITE (Pitchblende)	Complex oxide of uranium with small amounts of lead, radium, thorium, yttrium, nitrogen, helium, and argon	9–9.7	Brownish black	5½	Not prominent	Submetallic, pitchy
WOLLASTONITE	$CaSiO_3$ Calcium silicate	2.8–2.9	Colorless	5–5½	Good cleavage in 2 directions at 84° and 96°	Vitreous or pearly on cleavage surfaces

Reference: Cornelius Hurlbut, Jr., *Dana's Manual of Mineralogy,* 16th ed. New York: John Wiley and Sons, Inc., 1952.

MINERALS ARRANGED ACCORDING TO SPECIFIC GRAVITY

SPECIFIC GRAVITY	MINERAL	SPECIFIC GRAVITY	MINERAL	SPECIFIC GRAVITY	MINERAL
2.00–3.00	Bauxite	3.00–3.25	Tourmaline	3.90–4.10	Sphalerite
2.16	Halite	3.00–3.30	Actinolite		
2.20–2.65	Serpentine	3.15–3.20	Apatite	4.00	Carnotite
2.30	Graphite	3.16	Andalusite	4.02	Corundum
2.32	Gypsum	3.18	Fluorite	4.10–4.30	Chalcopyrite
2.57	Orthoclase	3.20	Hornblende	4.60	Chromite
2.60	Kaolinite	3.20–3.40	Augite		
2.60–2.90	Chlorite	3.23	Sillimanite	5.02	Pyrite
2.62	Albite	3.27–3.37	Olivine	5.06–5.08	Bornite
2.65	Quartz	3.35–3.45	Epidote	5.18	Magnetite
2.70–2.80	Talc	3.40–3.60	Topaz	5.26	Hematite
2.72	Calcite	3.50	Diamond	5.50–5.80	Chalcocite
2.76	Anorthite	3.50–4.30	Garnet		
2.76–3.10	Muscovite	3.56–3.66	Kyanite	6.80–7.10	Cassiterite
2.80–2.90	Wollastonite	3.60–4.00	Limonite		
2.80–3.20	Biotite	3.65–3.75	Staurolite	7.40–7.60	Galena
2.85	Dolomite	3.77	Azurite		
2.89–2.98	Anhydrite	3.85	Siderite	9.00–9.70	Uraninite

COLOR	TRANSPARENCY	FORM	OTHER PROPERTIES
Gray, white, silver-white, apple-green	Translucent	Foliated, massive	Of secondary origin, formed by the alteration of magnesium silicates such as olivine, augite, and hornblende; most characteristically found in metamorphic rocks.
Straw-yellow, wine-yellow, pink, bluish, greenish	Transparent to translucent	Usually in prismatic crystals, often with striations in direction of greatest length	Represents 8 on Mohs scale of hardness; a gem stone.
Varied: black, brown; red, pink, green, blue, yellow	Translucent	Usually in crystals; common: with cross section of spherical triangle	Gem stone; an accessory mineral in pegmatites, also in metamorphic rocks such as gneisses, schists, marbles.
Black	Opaque	Usually massive and botryoidal (i.e. like a bunch of grapes)	An ore of uranium and radium; the mineral in which helium and radium were first discovered.
Colorless, white or gray	Translucent	Commonly massive, fibrous, or compact	A common contact metamorphic mineral in limestones.

MINERALS ARRANGED ACCORDING TO HARDNESS

HARDNESS	MINERAL	HARDNESS	MINERAL	HARDNESS	MINERAL
1	Talc	3½–4	Siderite	6	Magnetite
1–2	Graphite	3½–4	Sphalerite	6	Orthoclase
1–3	Bauxite			6–6½	Pyrite
		4	Azurite	6–7	Cassiterite
2	Gypsum	4	Fluorite	6–7	Epidote
2–2½	Chlorite			6–7	Sillimanite
2–2½	Kaolinite	5	Apatite	6½–7	Olivine
2–2½	Muscovite	5	Kyanite (along crystal)	6½–7½	Garnet
2–5	Serpentine	5–5½	Limonite		
2½	Galena	5–5½	Wollastonite	7	Kyanite (across crystal)
2½	Halite	5–6	Actinolite	7	Quartz
2½–3	Biotite	5–6	Augite	7–7½	Staurolite
2½–3	Chalcocite	5–6	Hornblende	7–7½	Tourmaline
		5½	Chromite	7½	Andalusite
3	Bornite	5½	Uraninite		
3	Calcite	5½–6½	Hematite	8	Topaz
3–3½	Anhydrite				
3½–4	Chalcopyrite	6	Albite	9	Corundum
3½–4	Dolomite	6	Anorthite	10	Diamond

ROCK-FORMING MINERALS

IGNEOUS		METAMORPHIC		SEDIMENTARY		ORE MINERALS	
Essential	*Accessory*	*Regional*	*Contact*	*Essential*	*Cements*		
Quartz	Apatite	Actinolite	*Thermal*	Quartz	Silica	Azurite	Galena
Feldspars	Corundum	Andalusite	Corundum	Feldspars	Calcite	Bauxite	Hematite
Micas	Garnet	Asbestos	Garnet	Kaolinite	Hematite	Bornite	Magnetite
Augite	Hematite	Chlorite	Graphite	Calcite	Limonite	Carnotite	Siderite
Hornblende	Magnetite	Garnet		Dolomite		Cassiterite	Sphalerite
Olivine	Pyrite	Graphite	*Hydrothermal*	Gypsum		Chalcocite	Uraninite
		Kyanite	Epidote	Anhydrite		Chalcopyrite	
		Serpentine	Garnet	Halite		Chromite	
		Sillimanite	Olivine				
		Staurolite	Ore minerals				
		Talc	Quartz				
			Tourmaline				
			Wollastonite				

Appendix D

TOPOGRAPHIC AND GEOLOGIC MAPS

TOPOGRAPHIC MAPS *

The term *topography* refers to the shape of the physical features of the land. A *topographic map* is the representation of the position, relation, size, and shape of the physical features of an area. In addition to hills, valleys, rivers, and mountains, most topographic maps also show the culture of a region—that is, roads, towns, houses, political boundaries, and similar features.

Topographic maps are used in the laboratory for the observation and analysis of the effects of the several geologic processes that are constantly changing the face of the earth.

Definitions

Relief of an area is the difference in elevation between the tops of hills and the bottoms of valleys.

Height is the vertical difference in elevation between an object and its immediate surroundings.

Elevation or *altitude* is the vertical distance between a given point and the datum plane.

Datum plane is the reference surface from which all altitudes on a map are measured. This is usually mean sea level.

Bench mark is a point of known elevation and position, which is usually indicated on a map by the letters B.M., with the altitude given to the nearest foot.

Contour line is a map line connecting points representing places on the earth's surface that have the same elevation. It thus locates the intersection with the earth's surface of a plane at any arbitrary elevation parallel to the datum plane. Contours represent the vertical or third dimension on a map, which has only two dimensions. They show the size and shape of physical features such as hills and valleys. A hachured contour line indicates a depression. It resembles an ordinary contour line except for the hachures or short dashes on one side pointing toward the center of the depression.

Contour interval is the difference in elevation represented by adjacent contour lines.

Scale of a map is the ratio of the distance between two points on the ground and the same two points on the map. It may be expressed in three ways:

(1) *Fractional scale.* If two points are exactly one mile apart, they may be represented on the map as being separated by some fraction of that distance, say one inch. In this instance, the scale is one inch to the mile. There are 63,360 inches in a mile, so this scale can be expressed as the fraction or ratio 1:63,360. Actually, many topographic maps of the United States Geological Survey have a scale of 1:62,500.

(2) *Graphic scale.* This scale is a line printed on the map and divided into units that are equivalent to some distance, such as one mile.

(3) *Verbal scale.* This is an expression in common speech, such as "an inch to a mile," or "two miles to the inch."

* Adapted by permission from Sheldon Judson and Margaret Skillman Woyski, *Laboratory Manual for Physical Geology*. Dubuque: Wm. C. Brown Co., 1950.

Conventional symbols

An explanation of the symbols used on topographic maps is printed on the back of each topographic sheet, along the margin or, for newer maps, on a separate legend sheet. In general, culture (works of man) is shown in black. All water features, such as streams, swamps, and glaciers, are shown in blue. Relief is shown by contours in brown. Red may be used to indicate main highways, and green overprints may be used to designate areas of woods, orchards, vineyards, or scrub.

The United States Geological Survey distributes free of charge (apply to The Director, Geological Survey, Washington 25, D.C.) a single sheet entitled "Topographic Maps" that includes an illustrated summary of topographic map symbols.

Locating points

Any particular point or area may be located in several ways on a topographic map. The three most commonly used are:

(1) *In relation to prominent features.* A point may be referred to as being so many miles in a given direction from a city, mountain, river mouth, lake, or other easily located feature on the map.

(2) *By latitude and longitude.* Topographic maps of the United States Geological Survey are bounded on the north and south by parallels of latitude, and on the east and west by meridians of longitude. These intersecting lines form the grid into which the earth has been divided. Latitude is measured north and south from the equator, and longitude is measured east and west from the prime meridian that passes through Greenwich, England. Thus, maps in the United States are within north latitude and west longitude.

(3) *By township and range.* The greater part of the United States has been subdivided by a system of land survey in which a square six miles on a side forms the basic unit, called a township. Not included in this system are all the states along the eastern seaboard (with the exception of Florida), West Virginia, Kentucky, Tennessee, Texas, and parts of Ohio. Townships are laid off north and south from a base line, and east and west from a principal meridian. Each township is divided into 36 sections, usually a mile on a side. Each section may be further subdivided into half-sections, quarter-sections, or sixteenth-sections. Thus, in Fig. D-1 the point "X" can be located as in the northeast quarter of the northwest quarter of section 3, township 9 north, range 5 west. This is abbreviated as NE¼ NW¼ Sec 3, T9N, R5W, or NW NE Sec 3–9N–5W.

Contour sketching

Many contour maps are now made from aerial photographs. Before this can be done, however, the position and location of a number of reference points, or bench marks, must be determined in the field. If the topographic map is surveyed

FIG. D-1 *Subdivision by township and range. See text for discussion.*

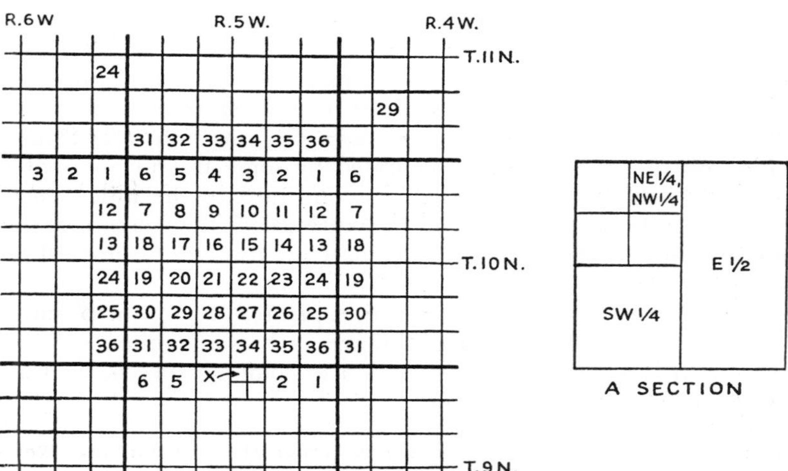

in the field rather than from aerial photographs, the topographer first determines the location and elevation of bench marks and a large number of other points that are selected for their critical position. Such points may be along streams, on hilltops, on the lowest point in a saddle between hills, or at places where there is a significant change in slope. On the basis of these points, contours may be sketched through points of equal elevation. Preferably, the contours are sketched in the field, in order to include minor irregularities that are visible to the topographer.

Because contours are not ordinary lines, certain requirements must be met in drawing them to satisfy the definition of contour lines. These are listed below.

(1) All points on one contour line have the same elevation.

(2) Contours separate all points of higher elevation than the contour from all points of lower elevation.

(3) The elevation represented by a contour line is always a simple multiple of the contour interval. Every contour line that is a multiple of 5 times the contour interval is heavier than the others. (Exception: 25-foot contours, in which every multiple of 4 times the interval is heavier.)

(4) Contours never cross or intersect one another.

(5) A vertical cliff is represented by coincident contours.

(6) Every contour closes on itself either within or beyond the limits of the map. In the latter case, the contours will end at the edge of the map.

(7) Contour lines never split.

(8) Uniformly spaced contour lines represent a uniform slope.

(9) Closely spaced contour lines represent a steep slope.

(10) Contour lines spaced far apart represent a gentle slope.

(11) A contour line that closes within the limits of the map indicates a hill.

(12) A hachured contour line represents a depression. The short dashes or hachures point into the depression.

(13) Contour lines curve up a valley but cross a stream at right angles to its course.

(14) Maximum ridge and minimum valley contours always go in pairs. That is, no single lower contour can lie between two higher ones, and vice versa.

Topographic profiles

A topographic profile is a cross section of the earth's surface along a given line. The upper line of this section is irregular and shows the shape of the land along the line of profile or section.

Profiles are most easily constructed with graph paper. A horizontal scale, usually the map scale, is chosen. Then a vertical scale sufficient to bring out the features of the surface is chosen. The vertical scale is usually several times larger than the horizontal—that is, it is exaggerated. The steps in the construction of a profile are as follows:

(1) Select a base (one of the horizontal lines on the graph paper). This may be sea level or any other convenient datum level.

(2) On the graph paper, number each fourth or fifth line above the base, according to the vertical scale chosen.

(3) Place the graph paper along the line of profile.

(4) With the vertically ruled lines as guides plot the elevation of each contour line that crosses the line of profile.

(5) If great accuracy is not important, plot only every heavy contour and the tops and bottoms of hills and the bottoms of valleys.

(6) Connect the points.

(7) Label necessary points along the profile.

(8) Give the vertical and horizontal scales.

(9) State the vertical exaggeration.

(10) Title the profile.

VERTICAL EXAGGERATION. The profile represents both vertical and horizontal dimensions. These dimensions are not usually on the same scale, because the vertical needs to be greater than the horizontal to give a clear presentation of changes in level. Thus, if the vertical scale is 500 feet to the inch and the horizontal scale is 5,280 feet to the inch—or say 1:62,500—the vertical exaggeration is about ten times, written 10×. This is obtained by dividing the horizontal scale by the vertical scale. Note that both horizontal and vertical scales must be expressed in the same unit (commonly feet to the inch) before dividing.

GEOLOGIC MAPS

Geologic maps show the distribution of earth materials on the surface. In addition, they indicate the relative age of these materials and suggest their arrangement beneath the surface.

Definitions

FORMATION. The units depicted on a geologic map are usually referred to as formations. We define a formation as a rock unit with upper and lower boundaries that can be recognized easily in the field and that is large enough to be shown on the map. A formation receives a distinctive designation made up of two parts. The first part is geographic and refers to the place or general area where the formation is first described. The second refers to the nature of the rock. Thus, *Trenton limestone* is a formation composed dominantly of limestone and is named after Trenton Falls in central New York State, where it was first formally described. *Wausau granite* designates a body of granite in the Wausau, Wisconsin, area. If the lithology is so variable that no single lithologic distinction is appropriate, the word "formation" may be used. For instance, the *Raritan formation* is named for the area of the Raritan River and Raritan Bay in New Jersey, and its lithology includes both sand and clay.

DIP AND STRIKE. The dip and strike of a rock layer refers to its orientation in relation to a horizontal plane. In Chapter 16 we found that the dip is the acute angle that a tilted rock layer makes with an imaginary plane. We also found that the strike is the compass direction of a line formed by the intersection of the dipping surface with an imaginary horizontal plane. The direction of strike is always at right angles to the direction of dip. The dip-and-strike symbol used on a geologic map is in the form of a topheavy T. The cross bar represents the direction of the strike of the bed. The short upright represents the direction of the dip of the bed. This sometimes, but not always, has an arrow pointing in the direction of dip. Very often the angle of dip is indicated alongside the symbol.

Example:

⊤ 30 Strike E-W; Dip 30° S.
25 Strike N 45° E; Dip 25° SE.

Note: In this example, the top of the page is considered to be north.

CONTACT. A contact is the plane separating two rock units. It is shown on the geologic map as a line that is the intersection of the plane between the rock units and the surface of the ground.

OUTCROP. An outcrop is an exposure of rock material that crops out at the surface through the cover of soil and weathered material. In areas of abundant rainfall, soil and vegetation obscure the underlying rock material and only a small fraction of 1 per cent of the surface may be in outcrop. In dry climates where soils are shallow or absent and the plant cover is discontinuous, bedrock usually crops out much more widely.

LEGEND AND SYMBOLS. A legend is an explanation of the various symbols used on the map. There is no universally accepted set of standard symbols, but some that are more widely used are given in Fig. D-2. In addition to the graphic symbols in Fig. D-2, letter symbols are sometimes used to designate rock units. Such a symbol contains a letter or letters referring to the geologic column, followed by a letter or letters referring to the specific name of the rock unit. Thus in the symbol *Ot* the "O" stands for Ordovician and the "t" for the Trenton limestone of central New York State. The letters or abbreviations generally used for the geologic column are given in Table D-1.

FIG. D-2 *Symbols commonly used on geological maps.*

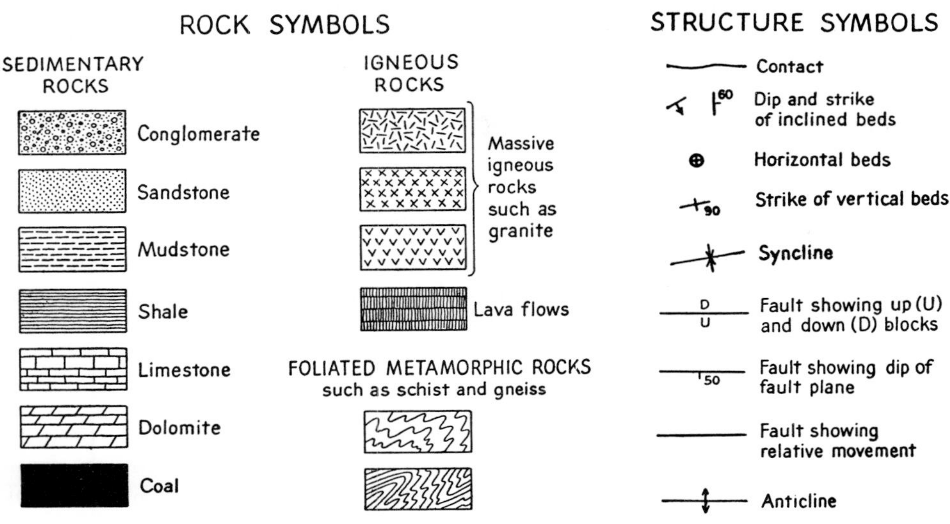

TABLE D-1 *Letter symbols commonly used to designate units in the geologic column*

	SYMBOL		SYMBOL		SYMBOL
Pleistocene	Q	Cretaceous	K	Devonian	D
Pliocene	Tpl	Jurassic	J	Silurian	S
Miocene	Tm	Triassic	TR	Ordovician	O
Oligocene	To	Permian	Cpm	Cambrian	€
Eocene	Te	Pennsylvanian	Cp	Precambrian	P€
Paleocene	Tp	Mississippian	Cm		

Sometimes different colors are used to indicate different rock systems. There is no standardized color scheme, but many of the geologic maps of the United States Geological Survey use the following colors, combined with varying patterns, for systems of sedimentary rocks:

Pleistocene	yellow and gray
Paleocene through Pliocene	yellow ocher
Cretaceous	olive-green
Jurassic	blue-green
Triassic	light peacock-blue or bluish gray-green
Mississippian through Permian	blue
Devonion	gray-purple
Silurian	purple
Ordovician	red-purple
Cambrian	brick-red
Precambrian	terra-cotta and gray-brown

No specific colors are designated for igneous rocks, but when colors are used, they are usually purer and more brilliant than those used for sedimentary rocks.

Construction of a geologic map

The basic idea of geologic mapping is simple. We are interested first in showing the distribution of the rocks at the earth's surface. Theoretically, all we need to do is plot the occurrence of the different rocks on a base map, and then we have a geologic map. Unfortunately, the process is not quite this simple.

In most areas the bedrock is more or less obscured in one way or another, and only a small amount of outcrop is available for observation, study, and sampling. From the few exposures available, the geologist must extrapolate the general distribution of rock types. In this extrapolation, his field data are obviously of prime importance. But he will also be guided by changes in soil, vegetation, and landscape, as well as by patterns that can be detected on aerial photographs. Furthermore, he may be aided by laboratory examination of field samples and by the records of both deep and shallow wells. The geologist may also have available to him geophysical data that help determine the nature of obscured bedrock. Eventually, when he has marshaled as many data as possible, he draws the boundaries delineating the various rock types.

In addition to the distribution of rock types, the geologist is also concerned with depicting, as accurately as he can, the ages of the various rocks and their arrangement beneath the surface. These goals, also, will be realized in part through direct observations in the field and in part through other lines of evidence. The preparation of an accurate, meaningful, geologic map demands experience, patience, and judgment.

Geologic cross sections

A geologic map tells us something of how rocks are arranged in the underground. Often, to show these relations more clearly, we find it convenient to draw geologic cross sections. Such a section is really a diagram showing a side view of a block of the earth's crust as it would look if we could lift it up to view. We have used cross sections in many illustrations throughout this book.

A geologic cross section is drawn, insofar as possible, at right angles to the general strike of the rocks. The general manner in which a geologic cross section is projected from a geologic map is shown in Fig. D-3. If the projection is made onto a topographic profile in which the vertical scale has been exaggerated, then the angle of the dip of the rocks should be exaggerated accordingly.

FIG. D-3 *Construction of a geologic cross section from a geologic map.*

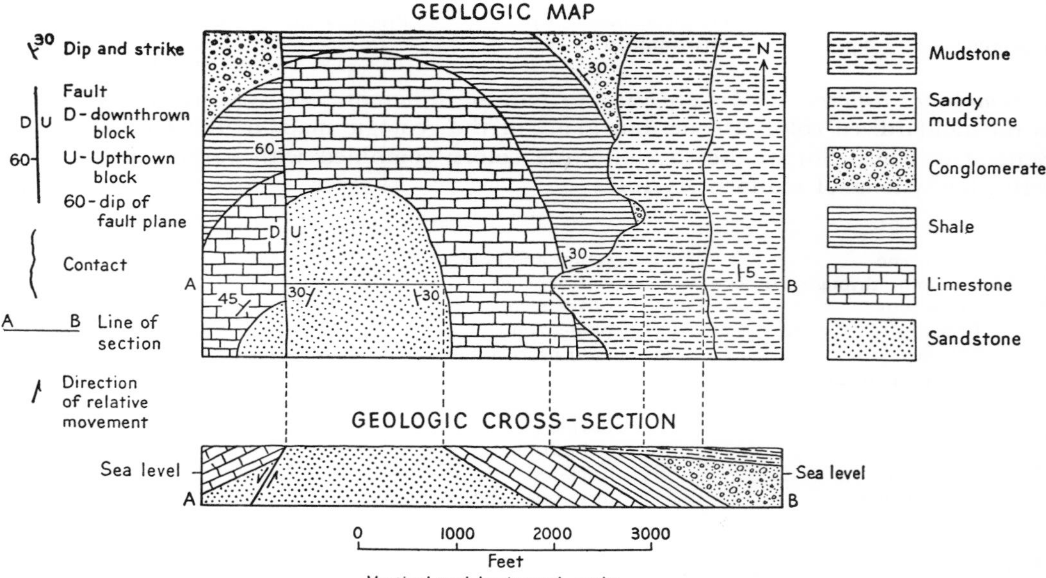

Glossary

The definitions in this glossary have been coordinated with the *Glossary of Geology and Related Sciences,* 2nd edition, published by The American Geological Institute, 2101 Constitution Ave., Washington, D.C.

A Abbreviation for angstrom, a unit of length, 10^{-8} cm.

ABLATION As applied to glacier ice, the process by which ice below the snow line is wasted by evaporation and melting.

ABRASION Erosion of rock material by friction of solid particles moved by water, ice, wind, or gravity.

ABSOLUTE TIME Geologic time measured in terms of years. Compare with *relative time.*

ACTINOLITE A metamorphic ferromagnesian mineral. An asbestos.

AFTERSHOCK An earthquake that follows a larger earthquake and originates at or near the focus of the larger earthquake. Generally, major shallow earthquakes are followed by many aftershocks. These decrease in number as time goes on, but may continue for many days or even months.

AGATE A variety of chalcedony with alternating layers of chalcedony and opal.

A-HORIZON The soil zone immediately below the surface, from which soluble material and fine-grained particles have been moved downward by water seeping into the soil. Varying amounts of organic matter give the A-horizon a gray to black color.

ALBITE The feldspar in which the diagnostic positive ion is Na^+. Sodic feldspar, $Na(AlSi_3O_8)$. One of the plagioclase feldspars.

ALLUVIAL FAN The land counterpart of a delta. An assemblage of sediments marking the place where a stream moves from a steep gradient to a flatter gradient and suddenly loses its transporting power. Typical of arid and semiarid climates, but not confined to them.

ALMANDITE A deep red garnet of iron and aluminum formed during regional metamorphism.

ALPHA PARTICLE A helium atom lacking electrons and therefore having a double positive charge.

ALPINE GLACIER A glacier confined to a stream valley. Usually fed from a cirque. Also called *valley glacier* or *mountain glacier.*

AMORPHOUS A state of matter in which there is no orderly arrangement of atoms.

AMPHIBOLE GROUP Ferromagnesian silicates with a double chain of silicon-oxygen tetrahedra. Common example: hornblende. Contrast with *pyroxene group.*

AMPHIBOLITE A faintly foliated metamorphic rock developed during the regional metamorphism of simatic rocks. Composed mainly of hornblende and plagioclase feldspars.

AMPHIBOLITE FACIES An assemblage of minerals formed at moderate to high pressures between 850°F and 1300°F (450°C and 700°C) during regional metamorphism.

ANDALUSITE A silicate of aluminum built around independent tetrahedra. Al_2SiO_5. Characteristic of middle-grade metamorphism. Compare with *kyanite,* which has the same composition and forms under similar conditions, but has a different crystal habit. Contrast with *sillimanite,* which has the same composition but different crystal habit and forms at highest metamorphic temperatures.

ANDESITE A fine-grained igneous rock with no quartz or orthoclase, composed of about 75 per cent plagioclase feldspars and the balance ferromagnesian silicates. Important as lavas, possibly derived by fractional crystallization from basaltic magma. Widely characteristic of mountain-making processes around the borders of the Pacific Ocean. Confined to continental sectors.

ANDESITE LINE A map line designating the petrographic boundary of the Pacific Ocean. Extrusive rocks on the Pacific side of the line are basaltic and on the other side andesitic.

ANGSTROM A unit of length, equal to one hundred-millionth of a centimeter, 10^{-8} cm. Abbreviation, A.

ANGULAR MOMENTUM A vector quantity, the product of mass times radius of orbit times velocity. The energy of motion of the solar system.

ANGULAR UNCONFORMITY An unconformity in which the older strata dip at a different angle from that of the younger strata.

ANHYDRITE The mineral calcium sulfate, $CaSO_4$, which is gypsum without water.

ANORTHITE The feldspar in which the diagnostic positive element is Ca^{2+}. Calcic feldspar, $Ca(Al_2Si_2O_8)$. One of the plagioclase feldspars.

ANTECEDENT STREAM A stream that maintains after uplift the same course it originally followed prior to uplift.

ANTICLINAL THEORY The theory that water, petroleum, and natural gas accumulate in up-arched strata in the order named (water lowest), provided the structure contains reservoir rocks in proper relation to source beds and capped by an impervious barrier.

ANTICLINE A configuration of folded, stratified rocks in which the rocks dip in two directions away from a crest, as the principal rafters of a common gable roof dip away from the ridgepole. The reverse of a *syncline.* The "ridgepole" or crest is called the axis.

AQUIFER A permeable material through which ground water moves.

ARÊTE A narrow, saw-toothed ridge formed by cirques developing from opposite sides into the ridge.

ARKOSE A detrital sedimentary rock formed by the cementation of individual grains of sand size and predominantly composed of quartz and feldspar. Derived from the disintegration of granite.

ARROYO Flat-floored, vertically walled channel of an intermittent stream typical of semiarid climates. Often applied to such features of southwestern United States. Synonymous with *wadi* and *wash.*

ARTESIAN WATER Water that is under pressure when tapped by a well and is able to rise above the level at which it is first encountered. It may or may not flow out at ground level.

ASBESTOS A general term applied to certain fibrous minerals that display similar physical characteristics although they differ in composition. Some asbestos has fibers long enough to be spun into fabrics with great resistance to heat, such as those used for automobile brake linings. Types with shorter fibers are compressed into insulating boards, shingles, etc. The most common asbestos mineral (95 per cent of U.S. production) is chrysotile, a variety of serpentine, a metamorphic mineral.

ASPHALT A brown to black solid or semisolid bituminous substance. Occurs in nature but is also obtained as a residue from the refining of certain hydrocarbons (then known as "artificial asphalt").

ASYMMETRIC FOLD A fold in which one limb dips more steeply than the other.

ATOLL A ring of low coral islands arranged around a central lagoon.

ATOM A combinations of protons, neutrons, and electrons. Ninety-two kinds are found in nature; 102 kinds are now known.

ATOMIC ENERGY Energy associated with the nucleus of an atom. It is released when the nucleus is split, or is derived from mass that is lost when a nucleus is fused together.

ATOMIC MASS The nucleus of an atom contains 99.95 per cent of its mass. The total number of protons and neutrons in the nucleus is called the *mass number*.

ATOMIC NUMBER The number of positive charges on the nucleus of an atom; the number of protons in the nucleus.

ATOMIC SIZE The radius of an atom (average distance from the center to the outermost electron of the neutral atom). Commonly expressed in angstroms.

AUGITE A rock-forming ferromagnesian silicate mineral built around single chains of silicon-oxygen tetrahedra.

AUREOLE A zone in which contact metamorphism has taken place.

AXIAL PLANE A plane through a rock fold that includes the axis and divides the fold as symmetrically as possible.

AXIS The ridge, or place of sharpest folding, of an anticline or syncline.

B Symbol for bulk modulus.

B-HORIZON The soil zone of accumulation that lies below the A-horizon. Here is deposited some of the material that has moved downward from the A-horizon.

BACKSET BEDS Inclined layers of sand developed on the gentler dune slope to the windward. These beds may constitute a large part of the total volume of a dune, especially if there is enough vegetation to trap most of the sand before it can cross over to the slip face.

BACK SWAMP Marshy area of a flood plain at some distance from and lower than the banks of a river confined by natural levees.

BARCHAN A crescent-shaped dune with wings or horns pointing downwind. Has a gentle windward slope and steep lee slope inside the horns. About 100 feet in height and 1,000 feet wide from horn to horn. Moves with the wind at about 25 to 50 feet per year across a flat, hard surface where a limited supply of sand is available.

BARRIER ISLAND A low, sandy island near the shore and parallel to it, on a gently sloping offshore bottom.

BARRIER REEF A reef that is separated from a landmass by a lagoon of varying width and depth opening to the sea through passes in the reef.

BASALT A fine-grained igneous rock dominated by dark-colored minerals, consisting of over 50 per cent plagioclase feldspars and the balance ferromagnesian silicates. Basalts and andesites represent about 98 per cent of all extrusive rocks.

BASE LEVEL For a *stream,* a level below which it cannot erode. There may be temporary base levels along a stream's course, such as those established by lakes, or resistant layers of rock. Ultimate base level for a stream is sea level.

For a *region,* a plane extending inland from sea level sloping gently upward from the sea. Erosion of the land progresses toward this plane, but seldom, if ever, quite reaches it.

BASEMENT COMPLEX Undifferentiated rocks underlying the oldest identifiable rocks in any region. Usually sialic, crystalline, metamorphosed. Often, but not necessarily, Precambrian.

BATHOLITH A discordant pluton that increases in size downward, has no determinable floor, and shows an area of surface exposure exceeding 40 square miles.

BAUXITE The chief ore of commercial aluminum. A mixture of hydrous aluminum oxides.

BAY BARRIER A sandy beach, built up across the mouth of a bay, so that the bay is no longer connected to the main body of water.

BED LOAD Material in movement along a stream bottom, or, if wind is the moving agency, along the surface. Contrast with material carried in suspension or solution.

BEDDING (1) A collective term used to signify the existence of beds or layers in sedimentary rocks. (2) Sometimes synonymous with *bedding plane.*

BEDDING PLANE Surface separating layers of sedimentary rocks. Each bedding plane marks the termination of one deposit and the beginning of another of different character, such as the surface separating a sand bed from a shale layer. A rock tends to separate or break readily along bedding planes.

BEHEADED STREAM The lower section of a stream that has lost its upper portion through *stream piracy.*

BELT OF SOIL MOISTURE Subdivision of zone of aeration. Belt from which water may be used by plants or withdrawn by soil evaporation. Some of the water passes down into the intermediate belt, where it may be held by molecular attraction against the influence of gravity.

BERGSCHRUND The gap or crevasse between glacier ice and the headwall of a cirque.

BERMS In the terminology of coastlines, berms are storm-built beach features that resemble small terraces; on their seaward edges are low ridges built up by storm waves.

BINDING ENERGY The amount of energy that must be supplied to break an atomic nucleus into its component fundamental particles. It is equivalent to the mass that disappears when fundamental particles combine to form a nucleus.

BIOCHEMICAL ROCK A sedimentary rock made up of deposits resulting directly or indirectly from the life processes of organisms.

BIOTITE "Black mica," ranging in color from dark brown to green. A rock-forming ferromagnesian silicate mineral with its tetrahedra arranged in sheets.

BITUMINOUS COAL Soft coal, containing about 80 per cent carbon and 10 per cent oxygen.

BLOWOUT A basin, scooped out of soft, unconsolidated deposits by the process of deflation. Ranges from a few feet to several miles in diameter.

BODY WAVE Push-pull or shake earthquake wave that travels through the body of a medium, as distinguished from waves that travel along a free surface.

BOND See *covalent bond; ionic bond.*

BORNITE A mineral, CU_5FeS_4. An important ore of copper.

BOTTOMSET BED Layer of fine sediment deposited in a body of standing water beyond the advancing edge of a growing delta. The delta eventually builds up on top of the bottomset beds.

BOULDER SIZE A volume greater than that of a sphere with a diameter of 256 mm, or 10 in.

BOULDER TRAIN A series of glacier erratics from the same bedrock source, usually with some property that permits easy identification. Arranged across the country in the shape of a fan with the apex at the source and widening in the direction of glacier movement.

BOWEN'S REACTION SERIES A series of minerals for which any early-formed phase tends to react with the melt that remains, to yield a new mineral further along in the series. Thus early-formed crystals of olivine react with remaining liquids to form augite crystals; these in turn may further react with the liquid then remaining to form hornblende. See also *continuous reaction series* and *discontinuous reaction series.*

BRAIDED STREAM A complex tangle of converging and diverging stream channels separated by sand bars or islands. Characteristic of flood plains where the amount of debris is large in relation to the discharge.

BRECCIA A clastic sedimentary rock made up of angular fragments of such size that an appreciable percentage of the volume of the rock consists of particles of granule size or larger.

BROWN CLAY An extremely fine-grained deposit characteristic of some deep ocean basins, particularly those of the Pacific.

BULK MODULUS The number that expresses a material's resistance to elastic changes in volume. For example, the number of pounds per square inch necessary to cause a specified change in volume. Represented by the symbol B.

C-HORIZON The soil zone that contains partially disintegrated and decomposed parent material. It lies directly under the B-horizon and grades downward into unweathered material.

CALCIC FELDSPAR Anorthite, $Ca(Al_2Si_2O_8)$.

CALCITE A mineral composed of calcium carbonate, $CaCO_3$.

CALDERA A roughly circular, steep-sided volcanic basin with a diameter at least three or four times its depth. Commonly at the summit of a volcano. Contrast with *crater*.

CALICHE A whitish accumulation of calcium carbonate in the soil profile.

CALVING As applied to glacier ice, the process by which a glacier that terminates in a body of water breaks away in large blocks. Such blocks form the icebergs of polar seas.

CAPACITY The amount of material that a transporting agency such as a stream, a glacier, or the wind can carry under a particular set of conditions.

CAPILLARY FRINGE Belt above zone of saturation in which underground water is lifted against gravity by surface tension in passages of capillary size.

CAPILLARY SIZE "Hairlike," or very small, such as tubes from .001 to .100 in. in diameter.

CARBOHYDRATE A compound of carbon, hydrogen, and oxygen. Carbohydrates are the chief products of the life process in plants.

CARBONATE MINERAL Mineral formed by the combination of the complex ion $(CO_3)^{2-}$ with a positive ion. Common example: calcite, $CaCO_3$.

CARBON CYCLE A cycle of atomic reactions, catalyzed by carbon, in which helium nuclei are formed from hydrogen nuclei. Probable source of the energy radiated by stars.

CARBON-14 Radioactive isotope of carbon, ${}_6C^{14}$, with a half life of 5,720 years. Used to date events back to about 50,000 years ago.

CARBON-RATIO A number obtained by dividing the amount of fixed carbon in a coal by the sum of fixed carbon and volatile matter, and multiplying by 100. This is the same as the percentage of fixed carbon, assuming no moisture or ash.

CASSITERITE A mineral; tin dioxide, SnO_2. Ore of tin with a specific gravity of 7. Nearly 75 per cent of the world's tin production is from placer deposits, mostly in the form of cassiterite.

CAVITATION A process of erosion in a stream channel caused by sudden collapse of vapor bubbles against the channel wall.

CELLULOSE The most abundant carbohydrate, $C_6H_{10}O_5$, with a chain structure like that of the paraffin hydrocarbons. With lignin, an important constituent of plant material, from which coal is formed.

CEMENTATION The process by which a binding agent is precipitated in the spaces between the individual particles of an unconsolidated deposit. The most common cementing agents are calcite, dolomite, and quartz. Others include iron oxide, opal, chalcedony, anhydrite, and pyrite.

CEMENT ROCK A clayey limestone used in the manufacture of hydraulic cement. Contains lime, silica, and alumina in varying proportions.

CENTRAL VENT An opening in the earth's crust, roughly circular, from which magmatic products are extruded. A volcano is an accumulation of material around a central vent.

CHALCEDONY A general name applied to fibrous cryptocrystalline silica, and sometimes specifically to the brown, translucent variety with a waxy luster. Deposited from aqueous solutions and frequently found lining or filling cavities in rocks. *Agate* is a variety with alternating layers of chalcedony and opal.

CHALCOCITE A mineral, copper sulfide, Cu_2S, sometimes called *copper glance*. One of the most important ore minerals of copper.

CHALCOPYRITE A mineral, a sulfide of copper and iron, $CuFeS_2$. Sometimes called copper pyrite or yellow copper ore.

CHALK A variety of limestone made up in part of biochemically derived calcite, in the form of the skeletons or skeletal fragments of microscopic oceanic plants and animals which are mixed with very fine-grained calcite deposits of either biochemical or inorganic chemical origin.

CHEMICAL ENERGY Energy released or absorbed when atoms form compounds. Generally becomes available when atoms have lost or gained electrons, and often appears in the form of heat.

CHEMICAL ROCK In the terminology of sedimentary rocks, a chemical rock is composed chiefly of material deposited by chemical precipitation, either organic or inorganic. Compare with *detrital sedimentary rock*. Chemical sedimentary rocks may have either a clastic or nonclastic (usually crystalline) texture.

CHEMICAL WEATHERING The weathering of rock material by chemical processes that transform the original material into new chemical combinations. Thus chemical weathering of orthoclase produces clay, some silica, and a soluble salt of potassium.

CHERT Granular cryptocrystalline silica similar to flint but usually light in color. Occurs as a compact massive rock, or as nodules.

CHLORITE A family of tetrahedral sheet silicates of iron, magnesium, and aluminum characteristic of low-grade metamorphism. Green color, with cleavage like that of mica, except that small scales of chlorite are not elastic whereas those of mica are.

CHROMITE A mineral. An oxide of iron and chromium, $FeCr_2O_4$, the only ore of commercial chromium. It is one of the first minerals to crystallize from a magma and is concentrated within the magma.

CHRYSOTILE A metamorphic mineral, an asbestos, the fibrous variety of serpentine. A silicate of magnesium, with tetrahedra arranged in sheets.

CHUTE or CHUTE CUTOFF As applied to stream flow, the term "chute" refers to a new route taken by a stream when its main flow is diverted to the inside of a bend, along a trough between low ridges formed by deposition on the inside of the bend where water velocities were reduced. Compare with *neck cutoff*.

CINDER Rough, slag-like fragment from a hundredth of an inch to an inch across, formed from magma blown into the air during an eruption.

CINDER CONE Built exclusively or in large part of pyroclastic ejecta dominated by cinders. Parasitic to a major volcano, it seldom exceeds 1,500 feet in height. Slopes up 30° to 40°. Example: Parícutin.

CIRQUE A steep-walled hollow in a mountainside at high elevation, formed by ice-plucking and frost action, and shaped like a half-bowl or half-amphitheater. Serves as principal gathering ground for the ice of a valley glacier.

CLASTIC TEXTURE Texture shown by sedimentary rocks formed from deposits of mineral and rock fragments.

CLAY MINERALS Finely crystalline, hydrous silicates that form as a result of the weathering of such silicate minerals as feldspar, pyroxene, and amphibole. The most common clay minerals belong to the kaolinite, montmorillonite, and illite groups.

CLAY SIZE A volume less than that of a sphere with a diameter of 1/256 mm (.004 mm, or .00015 in.).

CLEAVAGE (1) *Mineral cleavage.* A property possessed by many minerals of breaking in certain preferred directions along smooth plane surfaces. The planes of cleavage are governed by the atomic pattern, and represent directions in which atomic bonds are relatively weak.

(2) *Rock cleavage.* A property possessed by certain rocks of breaking with relative ease along parallel planes or nearly parallel surfaces. Rock cleavage is designated as *slaty, phyllitic, schistose,* and *gneissic.*

COAL A sedimentary rock composed of combustile matter derived from the partial decomposition and alteration of cellulose and lignin of plant materials.

COBBLE SIZE A volume greater than that of a sphere with a diameter of 64 mm (2.5 in.), and less than that of a sphere with a diameter of 256 mm (10 in.).

COL A pass through a mountain ridge. Created by the enlargement of two cirques on opposite sides of the ridge until their headwalls meet and are broken down.

COLLOIDAL SIZE Between two-tenths of a micron and one micron (.0002 mm to .001 mm, or 8×10^{-6} in. to 4×10^{-5} in.).

COLUMN A column or post of dripstone joining the floor and roof of a cave; the result of joining of a stalactite and a stalagmite.

COLUMNAR JOINTING A pattern of jointing that blocks out columns of rock. Characteristic of tabular basalt flows or sills.

COMPACTION Reduction in pore space between individual grains as a result of pressure of overlying sediments or pressures resulting from earth movement.

COMPETENCE The maximum size of particle that a transporting agency, such as a stream, a glacier, or the wind, can move.

COMPOSITE VOLCANIC CONE Composed of interbedded lava flows and pyroclastic material. Characterized by slopes of close to 30° at the summit, reducing progressively to 5° near the base. Example: Mayon.

COMPOUND A combination of the atoms or ions of different elements. The mechanism by which they are combined is called a *bond.*

CONCHOIDAL FRACTURE A mineral's habit of breaking in which the fracture produces curved surfaces like the interior of a shell (*conch*). Typical of glass and quartz.

CONCORDANT PLUTON An intrusive igneous body with contacts parallel to the layering or foliation surfaces of the rocks into which it was intruded.

CONCRETION An accumulation of mineral matter that forms around a center or axis of deposition after a sedimentary deposit has been laid down. Cementation consolidates the deposit as a whole, but the concretion is a body within the host rock that represents a local concentration of cementing material. The enclosing rock is less firmly cemented than the concretion. Commonly spheroidal or disk-shaped, and composed of such cementing agents as calcite, dolomite, iron oxide, or silica.

CONE OF DEPRESSION A dimple in the water table, which forms as water is pumped from a well.

CONE SHEET A dike that is part of a concentric set that dips inward, like an inverted cone.

CONGLOMERATE A detrital sedimentary rock made up of more or less rounded fragments of such size that an appreciable percentage of the volume of the rock consists of particles of granule size or larger.

CONNATE WATER Water that was trapped in a sedimentary deposit at the time the deposit was laid down.

CONSEQUENT STREAM A stream following a course that is a direct consequence of the original slope of the surface on which it developed.

CONTACT METAMORPHISM Metamorphism at or very near the contact between magma and rock during intrusion.

CONTINENTAL CRUST Portion of the earth's crust composed of two layers: first layer, sialic rock, 10 to 15 miles thick; second layer, simatic rock, 10 to 15 miles thick.

CONTINENTAL DRIFT A theory that an original single continent, sometimes referred to as *Pangaea,* split into several pieces that "drifted" laterally to form the present-day continents.

CONTINENTAL GLACIER An ice sheet that obscures mountains and plains of a large section of a continent. Existing continental glaciers are on Greenland and Antarctica.

CONTINENTAL SHELF Shallow, gradually sloping zone from the sea margin to a depth where there is a marked or rather steep descent into the depths of the ocean down the continental slope. The seaward boundary of the shelf is about 600 feet (100 fathoms) in depth, but may be either more or less than this.

CONTINENTAL SLOPE Portion of the ocean floor extending from about 600 feet (100 fathoms), at the seaward edge of the continental shelves, to the ocean deeps. Continental slopes are steepest in their upper portion, and commonly extend more than 12,000 feet (2,000 fathoms) downward.

CONTINUOUS REACTION SERIES That branch of Bowen's reaction series (*q.v.*) comprising the plagioclase feldspars, in which reaction of early-formed crystals with later liquids takes place continuously—that is, without abrupt phase changes.

CONVECTION A mechanism by which material moves because its density is different from that of surrounding material. The density differences are frequently brought about by heating.

CONVECTION CELL A pair of *convection currents* adjacent to each other.

CONVECTION CURRENT A closed circulation of material sometimes developed during convection. Convection currents normally develop in pairs; each pair is called a *convection cell.*

COQUINA A coarse-grained, porous, friable variety of clastic limestone made up chiefly of fragments of shells.

CORE The innermost zone of the earth. Surrounded by the mantle.

CORE DRILLING Drilling with a hollow bit and barrel, which cut out and recover a solid core of the rock penetrated.

CORIOLIS EFFECT The tendency of any moving body, on or starting from the surface of the earth, to continue in the direction in which the earth's rotation propels it. The direction in which the body moves because of this tendency, combined with the direction in which it is aimed, determines the ultimate course of the body relative to the earth's surface. In the Northern Hemisphere, the coriolis effect causes a moving body to veer or try to veer to the right of its direction of forward motion; in the Southern Hemisphere, to the left. The magnitude of the effect is proportional to the velocity of a body's motion. This effect causes cyclonic stormwind circulation to be counterclockwise in the Northern Hemisphere and clockwise in the Southern, and determines the final course of ocean currents relative to trade winds.

CORRELATION The process of establishing the contemporaneity of rocks or events in one area with other rocks or events in another area.

COVALENT BOND A bond in which atoms combine by the sharing of their electrons.

CRATER A roughly circular, steep-sided volcanic basin with a diameter less than three times its depth. Commonly at the summit of a volcano. Contrast with *caldera.*

CREEP As applied to soils and surficial material, slow downward movement of a plastic type. As applied to elastic solids, slow permanent yielding to stresses which are less than the yield point if applied for a short time only.

CREVASSE (1) A deep crevice or fissure in glacier ice. (2) A breach in a natural levee.

CROSSCUTTING RELATIONSHIPS, LAW OF A rock is younger than any rock across which it cuts.

CRUST The outermost zone of the earth, composed of solid rock between 20 and 30 miles thick. Rests on the mantle, and may be covered by sediments.

CRYPTOCRYSTALLINE A state of matter in which there is actually an orderly arrangement of atoms characteristic of crystals, but in which the units are so small (that is, the material is so fine-grained) that the crystalline nature cannot be determined with the aid of an ordinary microscope.

CRYSTAL A solid with orderly atomic arrangement. May or may not develop external faces that give it crystal form.

CRYSTAL FORM The geometrical form taken by a mineral, giving an external expression to the orderly internal arrangement of atoms.

CRYSTALLINE STRUCTURE The orderly arrangement of atoms in a crystal. Also called crystal structure.

CRYSTALLIZATION The process through which crystals separate from a fluid, viscous, or dispersed state.

CURIE TEMPERATURE The temperature above which ordinarily magnetic material loses its magnetism. On cooling below this temperature it regains its magnetism. Example: iron loses its magnetism above 1400°F (760°C) and regains it as it cools below this temperature. This is its curie temperature.

CURRENT RIPPLE MARKS Ripple marks, asymmetric in form, formed by air or water moving more or less continuously in one direction.

CUTOFF See *chute cutoff; neck cutoff.*

CYCLE OF EROSION A qualitative description of river valleys and regions passing through the stages of youth, maturity, and old age with respect to the amount of erosion that has been effected.

DEBRIS SLIDE A small, rapid movement of largely unconsolidated material that slides or rolls downward to produce an irregular topography.

DECOMPOSITION Synonymous with *chemical weathering.*

DEEP FOCUS Earthquake focus deeper than 200 miles (300 km). The greatest depth of focus known is 435 miles (700 km).

DEEP-SEA TRENCHES See *island arc deeps.*

DEFLATION The erosive process in which the wind carries off unconsolidated material.

DEFORMATION OF ROCKS Any change in the original shape or volume of rock masses. Produced by mountain-building forces. Folding, faulting, and plastic flow are common modes of rock deformation.

DELTA A plain underlain by an assemblage of sediments that accumulate where a stream flows into a body of standing water where its velocity and transporting power are suddenly reduced. Originally so named because many deltas are roughly triangular in plan, lie the Greek letter *delta* (Δ). with the apex pointing upstream.

DENDRITIC PATTERN An arrangement of stream courses that, on a map or viewed from the air, resembles the branching habit of certain trees, such as the oaks or maples.

DENSITY A number that measures the concentration of matter, expressed as the mass per unit volume. (Mass equals weight divided by acceleration of gravity.)

DENSITY CURRENT A current due to differences in the density of sea water from place to place caused by changes in temperature and variations in salinity or the amount of material held in suspension.

DEPOSITIONAL REMANENT MAGNETISM Magnetism resulting from the tendency of magnetic particles such as magnetite to orient themselves in the earth's magnetic field as they are deposited. Their orientation is maintained as the soft sediments are lithified and thus records the earth's field when the particles were laid down. Abbreviation, DRM.

DESICCATION Loss of water from pore spaces of sediments through compaction or through evaporation caused by exposure to air.

DETRITAL SEDIMENTARY ROCKS Rocks formed from accumulations of minerals and rocks derived either from erosion of previously existing rock, or from the weathered products of these rocks.

DIAMOND A mineral composed of the element carbon; the hardest substance known. Used as a gem and industrially in cutting tools.

DIATOMACEOUS OOZE A siliceous deep-sea ooze made up of the cell walls of one-celled marine algae known as diatoms.

DIFFERENTIAL WEATHERING The process by which different sections of a rock mass weather at different rates. Caused chiefly by variations in composition of the rock itself but also by differences in intensity of weathering from one section to another in the same rock.

DIKE A tabular discordant pluton.

DIORITE A coarse-grained igneous rock with the composition of andesite (no quartz or orthoclase), composed of about 75 per cent plagioclase feldspars and the balance ferromagnesian silicates.

DIP (1) The acute angle that a rock surface makes with a horizontal plane. The direction of the dip is always perpendicular to the strike. (2) See *magnetic declination.*

DIPOLE Any object that is oppositely charged at two points. Most commonly refers to a molecule that has concentrations of positive or negative charge at two different points.

DIPOLE MAGNETIC FIELD The portion of the earth's magnetic field that can best be described by a dipole passing through the earth's center and inclined to the earth's axis of rotation. See also *nondipole field* and *external magnetic field.*

DIP POLE See *magnetic pole.*

DISCHARGE With reference to stream flow, the quantity of water that passes a given point in unit time. Usually measured in cubic feet per second, abbreviated cfs.

DISCONFORMITY An unconformity in which the beds on opposite sides are parallel.

DISCONTINUITY (within the earth's interior) Sudden or rapid changes with depth in one or more of the physical properties of the materials constituting the earth, as evidenced by seismic data.

DISCONTINUOUS REACTION SERIES That branch of Bowen's reaction series (*q.v.*) including the minerals olivine, augite, hornblende, and biotite, for which each change in the series represents an abrupt phase change.

DISCORDANT PLUTON An intrusive igneous body with boundaries that cut across surfaces of layering or foliation in the rocks into which it has been intruded.

DISINTEGRATION Synonymous with *mechanical weathering.*

DISTRIBUTARY CHANNEL or STREAM A river branch that flows away from a main stream and does not rejoin it. Characteristic of deltas and alluvial fans.

DIVIDE Line separating two drainage basins.

DOLOMITE A mineral composed of the carbonate of calcium and magnesium, $CaMg(CO_3)_2$. Also used as a rock name for formations composed largely of the mineral dolomite.

DOME An anticlinal fold without a clearly developed linearity of crest, so the beds involved dip in all directions from a central area, like an inverted but usually distorted cup. The reverse of a *basin.*

DRAINAGE BASIN The area from which a given stream and its tributaries receive their water.

DRIFT Any material laid down directly by ice, or deposited in lakes, oceans, or streams as a result of glacial activity. Unstratified glacial drift is called *till* and forms *moraines.* Stratified glacial drift forms *outwash plains, eskers, kames,* and *varves.*

DRIPSTONE Calcium carbonate deposited from solution by underground water entering a cave in the zone of aeration. Sometimes called *travertine.*

DRM See *depositional remanent magnetism.*

DRUMLIN A smooth, streamlined hill composed of till. Its long axis is oriented in the direction of ice movement. The blunt nose points upstream and a gentler slope tails off downstream with reference to the ice movement. In height, drumlins range from 25 feet to 200 feet, with the average somewhat less than 100 feet. Most drumlins are between a quarter and a half mile in length. The length is commonly several times the width. Diagnostic characteristics are the shape and the composition of unstratified glacial drift, in contrast to kames, which are of random shapes and stratified glacial drift.

DUNE A mound or ridge of sand piled by wind.

DUST-CLOUD HYPOTHESES Theories that the solar system was formed from the condensation of interstellar dust clouds.

DUST SIZE A volume less than that of a sphere with a diameter of $\frac{1}{16}$ mm (.06 mm or .0025 in.). Used in reference to particles carried in suspension by wind.

EARTHFLOW A combination of slump and mudflow.

EARTHQUAKE Waves in the earth generated when rocks break after being distorted beyond their strength.

EARTHQUAKE SOUNDS Sounds in air generated by earthquake waves of audible frequencies.

ECLIPTIC The apparent path of the sun in the heavens; the plane of the planets' orbit.

ELASTIC DEFORMATION A nonpermanent deformation after which the body returns to its original shape or volume when the deforming force is removed.

ELASTIC ENERGY The energy stored within a solid during elastic deformation, and released during elastic rebound.

ELASTIC LIMIT The maximum stress that produces only elastic deformation.

ELASTIC REBOUND The recovery of elastic strain when a material breaks or when the deforming force is removed.

ELASTIC SOLID A solid that yields to applied force by changing shape or volume, or both, but returns to its original condition when the force is removed. The amount of yield is proportional to the force.

ELASTICITY A property of materials that defines the extent to which they resist small deformation from which they recover completely when the deforming force is removed. Elasticity = stress/strain.

ELECTRIC CHARGE A property of matter resulting from an imbalance between the number of protons and the number of electrons in a given piece of matter. The electron has a negative charge, the proton a positive charge. Like charges repel each other, unlike attract.

ELECTRICAL ENERGY The energy of moving electrons.

ELECTRON A fundamental particle of matter, the most elementary negative electrical charge. Its mass is .00055 unit.

ELECTRON SHELL An imaginary spherical surface representing all possible paths of electrons with the same average distance from a nucleus and with approximately the same energy.

ELEMENT A unique combination of protons, neutrons, and electrons that cannot be broken down by ordinary chemical methods. The fundamental properties of an element are determined by its number of protons. Each element is assigned a number that corresponds to its number of protons. Combinations containing from 1 through 102 protons are now known.

END MORAINE A ridge or belt of till marking the farthest advance of a glacier. Sometimes called *terminal moraine.*

ENERGY The capacity for producing motion. Energy holds matter together. It can become mass, or can be derived from mass. It takes such forms as kinetic, potential, heat, chemical, electrical, and atomic energy, and can be changed from one of these forms to another.

ENERGY LEVEL The distance from an atomic nucleus at which electrons can have orbits. May be thought of as a shell surrounding the nucleus.

ENTRENCHED MEANDER A meander cut into underlying bedrock when regional uplift allows the originally meandering stream to resume downward cutting.

EPIDOTE A silicate of aluminum, calcium, and iron characteristic of low-grade metamorphism and associated with chlorite and albite in the greenschist facies. Built around independent tetrahedra.

EPIDOTE-AMPHIBOLITE FACIES An assemblage of minerals formed between 500°F and 850°F (250°C and 450°C) during regional metamorphism.

ERG A unit of energy, the capacity for doing work. The energy expended when a force of one dyne acts through a distance of one centimeter.

EROSIONAL FLOOD PLAIN A flood plain that has been created by the lateral erosion and the gradual retreat of the valley walls.

ERRATIC In the terminology of glaciation, an erratic is a stone or boulder carried by ice to a place where it rests on or near bedrock of different composition.

ESKER A widening ridge of stratified glacial drift, steep-sided, 10 to 100 feet in height, and from a fraction of a mile to over a hundred miles in length.

EUSTATIC CHANGE OF SEA LEVEL A change in sea level produced entirely by an increase or a decrease in the amount of water in the oceans, hence worldwide.

EVAPORATION The process by which a liquid becomes a vapor at a temperature below its boiling point.

EVAPORITE A rock composed of minerals that have been precipitated from solutions concentrated by the evaporation of solvents. Examples: rock salt, gypsum, anhydrite.

EXFOLIATION The process by which plates of rock are stripped from a larger rock mass by physical forces.

EXFOLIATION DOME A large, rounded domal feature produced in homogeneous coarse-grained igneous rocks and sometimes in conglomerates by the process of exfoliation.

EXTERNAL MAGNETIC FIELD A component of the earth's field originating from activity above the earth's surface. Small when compared with the dipole and nondipole components of the field, which originate beneath the surface.

EXTRUSIVE ROCK A rock that has solidified from a mass of magma that poured or was blown out upon the earth's surface.

FACIES See *sedimentary facies.*

FAULT A surface of rock rupture along which there has been differential movement.

FAULT-BLOCK MOUNTAIN A mountain bounded by one or more faults.

FELDSPARS Silicate minerals composed of silicon-oxygen and aluminum-oxygen tetrahedra linked together in three-dimensional networks with positive ions fitted into the interstices of the negatively charged framework of tetrahedra. Classed as aluminosilicates. When the positive ion is K^+, the mineral is orthoclase; when it is Na^+, the mineral is albite; when it is Ca^{2+}, the mineral is anorthite.

FELSITE A general term for light-colored, fine-grained igneous rocks.

FERROMAGNESIAN SILICATE A silicate in which the positive ions are dominated by iron, magnesium, or both.

FIBROUS FRACTURE A mineral's habit of breaking into splinters or fibers.

FIORD A glacially deepened valley that is now flooded by the sea to form a long, narrow, steep-walled inlet.

FIRN Granular ice formed by the recrystallization of snow. Intermediate between snow and glacier ice. Sometimes called *névé.*

FISSILITY A property of splitting along closely spaced parallel planes more or less parallel to the bedding. Its presence distinguishes shale from mudstone.

FISSURE ERUPTION Extrusion of lava from a fissure in the earth's crust.

FLINT Granular cryptocrystalline silica, usually dull and dark. Often occurs as lumps or nodules in calcareous rocks, such as the Cretaceous chalk beds of southern England.

FLOOD BASALT Basalt poured out from fissures in floods that tend to form great plateaus. Sometimes called *plateau basalt.*

FLOOD PLAIN Area bordering a stream, over which water spreads in time of flood.

FLOOD PLAIN OF AGGRADATION A flood plain formed by the building up of the valley floor by sedimentation.

FLUID Material that offers little or no resistance to forces tending to change its shape.

FOCUS The source of a given set of earthquake waves.

FOLD A bend, flexure, or wrinkle, in rock produced when the rock was in a plastic state.

FOLIATION A layering in some rocks caused by parallel alignment of minerals. A textural feature of some metamorphic rocks. Produces rock cleavage.

FOOTWALL One of the blocks of rock involved in fault movement. The one that would be under the feet of a person standing in a tunnel along or across the fault. Opposite the hanging wall.

FORE DUNE A dune immediately back of the shoreline of an ocean or large lake.

FORESET BEDS Inclined layers of sediment deposited on the advancing edge of a growing delta or along the lee slope of an advancing sand dune.

FORESHOCK A relatively small earthquake that precedes a larger earthquake by a few days or weeks and originates at or near the focus of the larger earthquake.

FOSSIL Evidence of past life, such as the bones of a dinosaur, the shell of an ancient clam, the footprint of a long-extinct animal, or the impression of a leaf in a rock.

FOSSIL FUELS Organic remains (once living matter) used to produce heat or power by combustion. Include petroleum, natural gas, and coal.

FRACTIONAL DISTILLATION The recovery, one or more at a

time, of fractions of a complex liquid, each of which has a different density.

FRACTIONATION A process whereby crystals that formed early from a magma have time to settle appreciably before the temperature drops much further. They are effectively removed from the environment in which they formed.

FRACTURE As a mineral characteristic, the way in which a mineral breaks when it does not have cleavage. May be conchoidal (shell-shaped), fibrous, hackly, or uneven.

FRACTURE CLEAVAGE A system of joints spaced a fraction of an inch apart.

FRINGING REEF A reef attached directly to a landmass.

FRONT In connection with concepts of granitization, the limit to which diffusing ions of a given type are carried. The *simatic front,* for example, is the limit to which diffusing ions carried the calcium, iron, and magnesium that they removed from the rocks in their paths. The *granitic front* is the limit to which diffusing ions deposited granitic elements.

FROST ACTION Process of mechanical weathering caused by repeated cycles of freezing and thawing. Expansion of water during the freezing cycle provides the energy for the process.

FROST HEAVING The heaving of unconsolidated deposits as lenses of ice grow below the surface by acquiring capillary water from below.

FUNDAMENTAL PARTICLES Protons, neutrons, and electrons. These combine to form atoms. Each particle is defined in terms of its *mass* and its *electric charge.*

G Symbol for rigidity modulus.

GABBRO A coarse-grained igneous rock with the composition of basalt.

GALENA A mineral; lead sulfide, PbS. The principal ore of lead.

GARNET A family of silicates of iron, magnesium, aluminum, calcium, manganese, and chromium, which are built around independent tetrahedra and appear commonly as distinctive twelve-sided fully developed crystals. Characteristic of metamorphic rocks. Generally cannot be distinguished from one another without chemical analysis.

GAS (1) A state of matter that has neither independent shape nor volume, can be compressed readily, and tends to expand indefinitely. (2) In geology, the word "gas" is sometimes used to refer to *natural gas,* the gaseous hydrocarbons that occur in rocks, dominated by methane. Compare with use of the word "oil" to refer to *petroleum.*

GEODE A roughly spherical, hollow or partially hollow accumulation of mineral matter from a few inches to more than a foot in diameter. An outer layer of chalcedony is lined with crystals that project inward toward the hollow center. The crystals, often perfectly formed, are usually quartz, although calcite and dolomite are also found and, more rarely, other minerals. Geodes are most commonly found in limestone, and more rarely in shale.

GEOGRAPHIC POLES The points on the earth's surface marked by the ends of the earth's axis of rotation.

GEOLOGIC COLUMN A chronologic arrangement of rock units in columnar form with the oldest units at the bottom and the youngest at the top.

GEOLOGIC TIME-SCALE A chronologic sequence of units of earth time.

GEOLOGY An organized body of knowledge about the earth. It includes both *physical geology* and *historical geology* (*q.v.*).

GEOMAGNETIC POLES The dipole best approximating the earth's observed field is one inclined 11½° from the axis of rotation. The points at which the ends of this imaginary magnetic axis intersect the earth's surface are known as the geomagnetic poles. They should not be confused with the magnetic, dip poles or the virtual geomagnetic poles.

GEOPHYSICAL PROSPECTING Mapping rock structures by methods of experimental physics. Includes measuring magnetic fields, the force of gravity, electrical properties, seismic wave paths and velocities, radioactivity, and heat flow.

GEOPHYSICS The physics of the earth.

GEOSYNCLINE Literally, an "earth syncline." The term now refers, however, to a basin in which thousands of feet of sediments have accumulated, with accompanying progressive sinking of the basin floor explained only in part by the load of sediments. Common usage of the term includes both the accumulated sediments themselves and the geometrical form of the basin in which they are deposited. All folded mountain ranges were built from geosynclines, but not all geosynclines have become mountain ranges.

GEYSER A special type of thermal spring which intermittently ejects its water with considerable force.

GLACIER A mass of ice, formed by the recrystallization of snow, that flows forward, or has flowed at some time in the past, under the influence of gravity. By convention we exclude icebergs from this definition even though they are large fragments broken from the seaward end of glaciers.

GLACIER ICE A unique form of ice developed by the compression and recrystallization of snow, and consisting of interlocking crystals.

GLASS A form of matter that exhibits the properties of a solid but has the atomic arrangements, or lack of order, of a liquid.

GLOBIGERINA OOZE A deep-sea calcareous ooze in which limy shells of minute one-celled animals called *Globigerina* abound.

GLOSSOPTERIS FLORA A late Paleozoic assemblage of fossil plants named for the seed-fern *Glossopteris,* one of the plants in the flora. Widespread in South America, South Africa, Australia, India, and Antarctica.

GNEISS Metamorphic rock with gneissic cleavage. Commonly formed by the metamorphism of granite.

GNEISSIC CLEAVAGE Rock cleavage in which the surfaces of easy breaking, if developed at all, are from a few hundredths of an inch to half an inch or more apart.

GOETHITE Hydrous iron oxide, FeO(OH).

GONDWANALAND Hypothetical continent thought to have broken up in the Mesozoic. The resulting fragments are postulated to form present-day South America, Africa, Australia, India, and Antarctica.

GRADATION Leveling of the land. This is constantly being brought about by the forces of gravity and such agents of erosion as water at the surface and underground, and wind, glacier ice, and waves.

GRADE A term used to designate the extent to which metamorphism has advanced. Found in such combinations as high-grade or low-grade metamorphism. Compare with *rank.*

GRADED BEDDING The type of bedding shown by a sedimentary deposit when particles become progressively finer from bottom to top.

GRADIENT Slope of a stream bed.

GRANITE A coarse-grained igneous rock dominated by light-colored minerals, consisting of about 50 per cent orthoclase, 25 per cent quartz, and the balance plagioclase feldspars and ferromagnesian silicates. Granites and granodiorites comprise 95 per cent of all intrusive rocks.

GRANITIZATION A special type of metasomatism by which solutions of magmatic origin move through solid rocks, change ions with them, and convert them into rocks which achieve granitic character without having passed through a magmatic stage.

GRANODIORITE A coarse-grained igneous rock intermediate in composition between granite and diorite.

GRAPHIC STRUCTURE An intimate intergrowth of potassic feldspar and quartz with the long axes of quartz crystals lining up parallel to a feldspar axis. The quartz part is dark and the feldspar is light in color, so the pattern suggests Egyptian hieroglyphs. Commonly found in pegmatites.

GRAPHITE A mineral composed entirely of carbon. "Black lead." Very soft because of its crystalline structure, in contrast to diamond, which has the same composition but is the hardest substance known.

GRAVITY ANOMALY Difference between observed value of gravity and computed value.

GRAVITY FAULT A fault in which the hanging wall appears to have moved downward relative to the footwall. Also called *normal fault.*

GRAVITY METER An instrument for measuring the force of gravity. Also called gravimeter.

GRAVITY PROSPECTING Mapping the force of gravity at different places to determine differences in specific gravity of rock masses, and, through this, the distribution of masses of different specific gravity. Done with a gravity meter (gravimeter).

GRAYWACKE A variety of sandstone generally characterized by its hardness, dark color, and angular grains of quartz, feldspar, and small rock fragments set in a matrix of clay-sized particles.

GREENSCHIST A schist characterized by green color. The product of regional metamorphism of simatic rocks. The green color is imparted by the mineral chlorite.

GREENSCHIST FACIES An assemblage of minerals formed between 300°F and 500°F (150°C and 250°C) during regional metamorphism.

GROUNDMASS The finely crystalline or glassy portion of a porphyry.

GROUND MORAINE Till deposited from a glacier as a veneer over the landscape and forming a gently rolling surface.

GROUND WATER Underground water within the zone of saturation.

GROUND-WATER TABLE The upper surface of the zone of saturation for underground water. It is an irregular surface with a slope or shape determined by the quantity of ground water and the permeability of the earth materials. In general, it is highest beneath hills and lowest beneath valleys. Also referred to as *water table*.

GUYOT A flat-topped *seamount* rising from the floor of the ocean like a volcano but planed off on top and covered by appreciable depth of water. Synonymous with *tablemount*.

GYPSUM Hydrous calcium sulphate, $CaSO_4 \cdot 2H_2O$. A soft, common mineral in sedimentary rocks, where it sometimes occurs in thick beds interstratified with limestones and shales. Sometimes occurs as a layer under a bed of rock salt, since it is one of the first minerals to crystallize on the evaporation of sea water. Alabaster is a fine-grained massive variety of gypsum.

H Symbol for mineral hardness.

HACKLY FRACTURE A mineral's habit of breaking along jagged, irregular surfaces with sharp edges.

HALF LIFE Time needed for one half of the nuclei in a sample of a radioactive element to decay.

HALITE A mineral; rock salt, or common salt, NaCl. Occurs widely disseminated, or in extensive beds and irregular masses, precipitated from sea water and interstratified with rocks of other types as a true sedimentary rock.

HANGING VALLEY A valley that has a greater elevation than the valley to which it is tributary, at the point of their junction. Often (but not always) created by a deepening of the main valley by a glacier. The hanging valley may or may not be glaciated.

HANGING WALL One of the blocks involved in fault movement. The one that would be hanging overhead for a person standing in a tunnel along or across the fault. Opposite the footwall.

HARDNESS A mineral's resistance to scratching on a smooth surface. The Mohs scale of relative hardness consists of ten minerals. Each of these will scratch all those below it in the scale and will be scratched by all those above it: (1) talc, (2) gypsum, (3) calcite, (4) fluorite, (5) apatite, (6) orthoclase, (7) quartz, (8) topaz, (9) corundum, (10) diamond.

HEAD Difference in elevation between intake and discharge points for a liquid. In geology, most commonly of interest in connection with the movement of underground water.

HEAT ENERGY A special manifestation of kinetic energy in atoms. The temperature of a substance depends on the average kinetic energy of its component particles. When heat is added to a substance, the average kinetic energy increases.

HEMATITE Iron oxide, Fe_2O_3. The principal ore mineral for about nine-tenths of the commercial iron produced in the United States. Characteristic red color when powdered. The name is derived from the Greek word meaning blood.

HISTORICAL GEOLOGY The branch of geology that deals with the history of the earth, including a record of life on the earth as well as physical changes in the earth itself.

HORN A spire of bedrock left where cirques have eaten into a mountain from more than two sides around a central area. Example: Matterhorn of the Swiss Alps.

HORNBLENDE A rock-forming ferromagnesian silicate mineral with double chains of silicon-oxygen tetrahedra. An amphibole.

HORNFELS Dense, granular metamorphic rock. Since this term is commonly applied to the metamorphic equivalent of any fine-grained rock, its composition is variable.

HORNFELS FACIES An assemblage of minerals formed at temperatures greater than 1300°F (700°C) during contact metamorphism.

HOT SPRING A spring that brings hot water to the surface. A *thermal spring*. Water temperature usually 15°F or more above mean air temperature.

HYDRAULIC GRADIENT Head of underground water divided by the distance of travel between two points. If the head is 10 feet for two points 100 feet apart, the hydraulic gradient is .1 or 10 per cent. When head and distance of flow are the same, the hydraulic gradient is 100 per cent.

HYDROCARBON A compound of hydrogen and carbon that burns in air to form water and oxides of carbon. There are many hydrocarbons. The simplest, methane, is the chief component of natural gas. Petroleum is a complex mixture of hydrocarbons.

HYDROLOGIC CYCLE The general pattern of movement of water from the sea by evaporation to the atmosphere, by precipitation onto the land, and by movement under the influence of gravity back to the sea again.

HYDROTHERMAL SOLUTION A hot, watery solution that usually emanates from a magma in the late stages of cooling. Frequently contains and deposits in economically workable concentrations minor elements that, because of incommensurate ionic radii or electronic charges, have not been able to fit into the atomic structures of the common minerals of igneous rocks.

ICECAP A localized *ice sheet*.

ICE SHEET A broad, mound-like mass of glacier ice of considerable extent with a tendency to spread radially under its own weight. Localized ice sheets are sometimes called *icecaps*.

IGNEOUS ROCK An aggregate of interlocking silicate minerals formed by the cooling and solidification of magma.

ILLITE A clay mineral family of hydrous aluminous silicates. Structure similar to that of montmorillonite, but with aluminum substituted for 10 to 15 per cent of the silicon, which destroys montmorillonite's property of expanding with the addition of water because weak bonds are replaced by strong potassium ion links. Structurally, illite is intermediate between montmorillonite and muscovite. Montmorillonite converts to illite in sediments, while illite converts to muscovite under conditions of low-grade metamorphism. Illite is the commonest clay mineral in clayey rocks and recent marine sediments, and is present in many soils.

INDUCED MAGNETISM In the terminology of rock magnetism one of the components of the rock's natural remanent magnetism. It is parallel to the earth's present field and results from it.

INFILTRATION The soaking into the ground of water on the surface.

INTENSITY (of an earthquake) A number related to the effects of earthquake waves on man, structures, and the earth's surface at a particular place. Contrast with *magnitude*, which is a number related to the total energy released by an earthquake.

INTERMEDIATE BELT Subdivision of zone of aeration. The belt that lies between the belt of soil moisture and the capillary fringe.

INTERMEDIATE FOCUS Earthquake focus between depths of 40 to 200 miles (60 to 300 km).

INTERMITTENT STREAM A stream that carries water only part of the time.

INTRUSIVE ROCK A rock that solidified from a mass of magma that invaded the earth's crust but did not reach the surface.

ION An electrically unbalanced form of an atom, or group of atoms, produced by the gain or loss of electrons.

IONIC BOND A bond in which ions are held together by the electrical attraction of opposite charges.

IONIC RADIUS The average distance from the center to the outermost electron of an ion. Commonly expressed in angstroms.

ISLAND ARC DEEPS Arcuate trenches bordering some of the continents. Some reach depths of 30,000 feet or more below the surface of the sea. Also called deep-sea trenches or trenches.

ISOSEISMIC LINE A line connecting all points on the surface of the earth where the intensity of shaking produced by earthquake waves is the same.

ISOSTASY The ideal condition of balance that would be attained by earth materials of differing densities if gravity were the only force governing their heights relative to each other.

ISOTOPE Alternate form of an element. The fundamental properties of the element, and its place in the table of elements, are determined by the number of protons in its nucleus. Variations in the number of neutrons in the nucleus produce isotopes.

JASPER Granular cryptocrystalline silica usually colored red by hematite inclusions.

JET or SHOOTING FLOW A type of flow, related to turbulent flow, occurring when a stream reaches high velocity along a sharply inclined stretch, or over a waterfall, and the water moves in plunging, jet-like surges.

JOINT A break in a rock mass where there has been no relative movement of rock on opposite sides of the break.

JUVENILE WATER Water brought to the surface or added to underground supplies from magma.

KAME A steep-sided hill of stratified glacial drift. Distinguished from a drumlin by lack of unique shape and by stratification.

KAME TERRACE Stratified glacial drift deposited between a wasting glacier and an adjacent valley wall. When the ice melts, this material stands as a terrace along the valley wall.

KAOLINITE A clay mineral, a hydrous aluminous silicate. $Al_4Si_4O_{10}(OH)_8$. Structure consists of one sheet of silicon-oxygen tetrahedra each sharing three oxygens to give a ratio of Si_4O_{10}, linked with one sheet of aluminum and hydroxyl. The composition of pure kaolinite does not vary as it does for the other clay minerals, montmorillonite and illite, in which ready addition or substitution of ions takes place.

KARST TOPOGRAPHY Irregular topography characterized by sinkholes, streamless valleys, and streams that disappear into the underground, all developed by the action of surface and underground water in soluble rock such as limestone.

KETTLE A depression in the ground surface formed by the melting of a block of ice buried or partially buried by glacial drift, either outwash or till.

KINETIC ENERGY Energy of movement. The amount of kinetic energy possessed by an object or particle depends on its mass and speed.

KYANITE A silicate mineral characteristic of the temperatures of middle-grade metamorphism. Al_2SiO_5 in bladed blue crystals is softer than a knife along the crystal's length, harder across. Its crystalline structure is based on independent tetrahedra. Compare with *andalusite,* which has the same composition and forms under similar conditions, but has a different crystal habit. Contrast with *sillimanite,* which has the same composition but different crystal habit and forms at highest metamorphic temperature.

L Symbol for earthquake surface waves.

LACCOLITH A concordant pluton that has domed up the strata into which it was intruded.

LAMINAR FLOW Mechanism by which a fluid such as water moves slowly along a smooth channel, or through a tube with smooth walls, with fluid particles following straight-line paths parallel to the channel or walls. Contrast with *turbulent flow.*

LANDSLIDE A general term for relatively rapid mass movement, such as slump, rock slide, debris slide, mudflow, and earthflow.

LARGE WAVES Earthquake surface waves.

LATENT HEAT OF FUSION The number of calories per unit volume that must be added to a material at the melting point to complete the process of melting. These calories do not raise the temperature.

LATERAL MORAINE A ridge of till along the edge of a valley glacier. Composed largely of material that fell to the glacier from valley walls.

LATERITE Tropical soil rich in hydroxides of aluminum and iron formed under conditions of good drainage.

LAVA Magma that has poured out onto the surface of the earth, or rock that has solidified from such magma.

LEVEE (natural) Bank of sand and silt built by a river during floods, where suspended load is deposited in greatest quantity close to the river. The process of developing natural levees tends to raise river banks above the level of the surrounding flood plains. A break in a natural levee is sometimes called a crevasse.

LIGNITE A low-grade coal with about 70 per cent carbon and 20 per cent oxygen. Intermediate between peat and bituminous coal.

LIMB One of the two parts of an anticline or syncline on either side of the axis.

LIMESTONE A sedimentary rock composed largely of the mineral calcite, $CaCO_3$, which has been formed by either organic or inorganic processes. Most limestones have a clastic texture, but nonclastic, particularly crystalline, textures are common. The carbonate rocks, limestone and dolomite, constitute about 22 per cent of the sedimentary rocks exposed above sea level.

LIMONITE Iron oxide with no fixed composition or atomic structure. Always of secondary origin and not a true mineral. Is encountered as ordinary rust, or the coloring material of yellow clays and soils.

LITHIFICATION The process by which unconsolidated rock-forming materials are converted into a consolidated or coherent state.

LOAD The amount of material that a transporting agency, such as a stream, a glacier, or the wind, is actually carrying at a given time.

LOESS An unconsolidated, unstratified aggregation of small, angular mineral fragments, usually buff in color. Generally believed to be wind-deposited. Characteristically able to stand on very steep to vertical slopes.

LONGITUDINAL DUNE A long ridge of sand oriented in the general direction of wind movement. A small one is less than 10 feet in height and 200 feet in length. Very large ones are called seif dunes.

MAGMA A naturally occurring silicate melt, which may contain suspended silicate crystals or dissolved gases, or both. These conditions may be met in general by a mixture containing as much as 65 per cent crystals, but no more than 11 per cent of dissolved gases.

MAGNETIC DECLINATION The angle of divergence between a geographic meridian and a magnetic meridian. It is measured in degrees east and west of geographic north.

MAGNETIC INCLINATION The angle that the magnetic needle makes with the surface of the earth. Also called dip of the magnetic needle.

MAGNETIC POLE The north magnetic pole is the point on the earth's surface where the north-seeking end of a magnetic needle free to move in space points directly down. At the south magnetic pole the same needle points directly up. These poles are also known as *dip poles.*

MAGNETITE A mineral; iron oxide, Fe_3O_4. Black, strongly magnetic. An important ore of iron.

MAGNITUDE (of an earthquake) A number related to the total energy released by an earthquake. Contrast with *intensity,* which is a number related to the effects of earthquake waves at a particular place.

MANTLE The intermediate zone of the earth. Surrounded by the crust, rests on the core at a depth of about 1,800 miles.

MARBLE Metamorphic rock of granular texture, no rock cleavage, and composed of calcite or dolomite or both.

MARSH GAS Methane, CH_4, the simplest paraffin hydrocarbon. The dominant component of natural gas.

MASS A number that measures the quantity of matter. It is obtained on the earth's surface by dividing the weight of a body by the acceleration due to gravity.

MASS MOVEMENT Surface movement of earth materials induced by gravity.

MASS NUMBER Number of protons and neutrons in the nucleus of an atom.

MASS UNIT One-sixteenth the mass of the oxygen atom. Approximately the mass of the hydrogen atom.

MASSIVE PLUTON Any pluton that is not tabular in shape.

MATTER Anything that occupies space. Usually defined by describing its states and properties: solid, liquid, or gaseous; possesses mass, inertia, color, density, melting point, hardness, crystal form, mechanical strength, or chemical properties. Composed of atoms.

MEANDER (1) *n.,* A turn or sharp bend in a stream's course. (2) *v.i.,* To turn, or bend sharply. Applied to stream courses in geological usage.

MEANDER BELT The zone along a valley floor that encloses a meandering river.

MECHANICAL WEATHERING The process by which rock is broken down into smaller and smaller fragments as the result of energy developed by physical forces. Also known as *disintegration.*

MEDIAL MORAINE A ridge of till formed by the junction of two lateral moraines when two valley glaciers join to form a single ice stream.

METAL A substance that is fusible and opaque, a good conductor of electricity, and has a characteristic luster. Examples: gold, silver, aluminum. Over three-fourths of the elements are metals.

METAMORPHIC FACIES An assemblage of minerals that reached equilibrium during metamorphism under a specific range of temperature.

METAMORPHIC ROCK "Changed-form rock." Any rock that has been changed in texture or composition by heat, pressure, or chemically active fluids after its original formation.

METAMORPHIC ZONE An area subjected to metamorphism and characterized by a certain metamorphic mineral that formed during the process.

METAMORPHISM A process whereby rocks undergo physical or chemical changes, or both, to achieve equilibrium with conditions other than those under which they were originally formed. Weathering is arbitrarily excluded from the meaning of the term. The agents of metamorphism are heat, pressure, and chemically active fluids.

METASOMATISM A process whereby rocks are altered when volatiles exchange ions with them.

METEORIC WATER Ground water derived primarily from precipitation.

METHANE The simplest paraffin hydrocarbon, CH_4. The principal constituent of natural gas. Sometimes called marsh gas.

MICAS A group of silicate minerals characterized by perfect sheet or scale cleavage resulting from their atomic pattern, in which silicon-oxygen tetrahedra are linked in sheets. Biotite is the ferromagnesian black mica. Muscovite is the potassic white mica.

MICROSEISM A small shaking. Specifically limited in technical usage to earth waves generated by sources other than earthquakes, and most frequently to waves with periods of from a second to about 9 seconds from sources associated with atmospheric storms.

MIGMATITE A mixed rock produced by an intimate interfingering of magma and an invaded rock.

MINERAL A naturally occurring solid element or compound, exclusive of biologically formed carbon components. It has a definite composition, or range of composition, and an orderly internal arrangement of atoms known as crystalline structure, which gives it unique physical and chemical properties, including a tendency to assume certain geometrical forms known as *crystals.*

MINERAL DEPOSIT An occurrence of one or more minerals in such concentration and form as to make possible removal and processing for use at a profit.

MOLECULE The smallest unit of a compound which displays the properties of that compound.

MONADNOCK A hill left as a residual of erosion, standing above the level of a peneplain.

MONEL METAL Steel containing 68 per cent nickel.

MONTMORILLONITE A clay mineral family, a hydrous aluminous silicate with a structural sandwich of one ionic sheet of aluminum and hydroxyl between two (Si_4O_{10}) sheets. These sandwiches are piled on each other with water between them, and with nothing but weak bonds to hold them together. As a result, additional water can enter the lattice readily. This causes the mineral to swell appreciably and further weakens the attraction between structural sandwiches. Consequently, a lump of montmorillonite in a bucket of water slumps rapidly into a loose, incoherent mass. Compare with the other clay minerals, kaolinite and illite.

MORAINE A general term applied to certain landforms composed of till.

MOUNTAIN Any part of a landmass that projects conspicuously above its surroundings.

MOUNTAIN CHAIN A series or group of connected mountains having a well-defined trend or direction.

MOUNTAIN GLACIER Synonymous with *alpine glacier.*

MOUNTAIN RANGE A series of more or less parallel ridges, all of which were formed within a single geosyncline or on its borders.

MOUNTAIN STRUCTURE Structure produced by the deformation of rocks.

MUDCRACKS Cracks caused by the shrinkage of a drying deposit of silt or clay under surface conditions.

MUDFLOW Flow of a well-mixed mass of rock, earth, and water that behaves like a fluid and flows down slopes with a consistency similar to that of newly mixed concrete.

MUDSTONE Fine-grained, detrital sedimentary rock made up of silt and clay-sized particles. Distinguished from shale by lack of fissility.

MUSCOVITE "White mica." A nonferromagnesian rock-forming silicate mineral with its tetrahedra arranged in sheets. Sometimes called potassic mica.

NATIVE STATE State in which an element occurs uncombined in nature. Usually applied to the metals, as in native copper, native gold, etc.

NATURAL GAS Gaseous hydrocarbons that occur in rocks. Dominated by methane.

NATURAL REMANENT MAGNETISM The magnetism of a rock. May or may not coincide with present magnetic field of the earth. Abbreviation, NRM.

NECK CUTOFF The breakthrough of a river across the narrow neck separating two meanders, where downstream migration of one has been slowed and the next meander upstream has overtaken it. Compare with *chute cutoff.*

NEUTRON A proton and an electron combined and behaving like a fundamental particle of matter. Electrically neutral, with a mass of 1.00896 units. If isolated, it decays to form a proton and an electron.

NÉVÉ Granular ice formed by the recrystallization of snow. Intermediate between snow and glacier ice. Sometimes called *firn.*

NICHROME A steel alloy with 35 to 85 per cent nickel.

NICKEL STEEL Steel containing 2.5 to 3.5 per cent nickel.

NIVATION Erosion beneath and around the edges of a snowbank.

NODULE An irregular, knobby-surfaced body of mineral that differs in composition from the rock in which it is formed. Silica in the form of chert or flint is the major component of nodules. They are commonly found in limestone and dolomite.

NONCONFORMITY An unconformity where the older rocks are of intrusive igneous origin.

NONDIPOLE MAGNETIC FIELD That portion of the earth's magnetic field remaining after the dipole field and the external field are removed.

NONFERROMAGNESIANS Silicate minerals that do not contain iron or magnesium.

NORMAL FAULT A fault in which the hanging wall appears to have moved downward relative to the footwall. Opposite of a thrust fault. Also called *gravity fault.*

NRM See *natural remanent magnetism.*

NUCLEUS (atomic) The protons and neutrons constituting the central part of an atom.

NUÉE ARDENTE (*plural,* nuées ardentes) "Hot cloud." A French term applied to a highly heated mass of gas-charged lava ejected more or less horizontally from a vent or pocket at the summit of a volcano, onto an outer slope down which it moves swiftly, however slight the incline, because of its extreme mobility.

OBSIDIAN Glassy equivalent of granite.

OCEANIC CRUST Portion of the earth's crust composed of one layer of simatic rock 20 to 30 miles thick.

OIL In geology, refers to petroleum (*q.v.*).

OIL SHALE Shale containing such a proportion of hydrocarbons as to be capable of yielding petroleum on slow distillation.

OLIVINE A rock-forming ferromagnesian silicate mineral that crystallizes early from a magma and weathers readily at the earth's surface. Its crystal structure is based on isolated SiO_4 ions and positive ions of iron or magnesium, or both. General formula: $(Mg,Fe)_2SiO_4$.

OÖLITES Spheroidal grains of sand size, usually composed of calcium carbonate, $CaCO_3$, and thought to have originated by inorganic precipitation. Some limestones are made up largely of oölites.

OOZE Deep-sea deposit consisting of 30 per cent or more by volume of the hard parts of very small, sometimes microscopic, organisms. If a particular organism is dominant, its name is used as modifier, as in *globigerina* ooze, or *radiolarian* ooze.

OPAL Amorphous silica, with varying amounts of water. A mineral gel.

ORDER OF CRYSTALLIZATION The chronological sequence in which crystallization of the various minerals of an assemblage takes place.

ORE A metalliferous mineral deposit.

OROGENY Process by which mountain structures develop.

ORTHOCLASE The feldspar in which K^+ is the diagnostic positive ion; $K(AlSi_3O_8)$.

OUTWASH Material carried from a glacier by meltwater. Laid down in stratified deposits.

OUTWASH PLAIN Flat or gently sloping surface underlain by outwash.

OVERTURNED FOLD A fold in which at least one limb is overturned—that is, has rotated through more than 90°.

OXBOW An abandoned meander, caused by a neck cutoff.

OXBOW LAKE An abandoned meander isolated from the main stream channel by deposition, and filled with water.

OXIDE MINERAL A mineral formed by the direct union of an element with oxygen. Examples: ice, corundum, hematite, magnetite, cassiterite.

P Symbol for earthquake primary waves.

PAIRED TERRACES Terraces that face each other across a stream at the same elevation.

PALEOMAGNETISM The study of the earth's magnetic field as it has existed during geologic time.

PANGAEA A hypothetical continent from which all others are postulated to have originated through a process of fragmentation and drifting.

PARABOLIC DUNE A dune with a long, scoop-shaped form that, when perfectly developed, exhibits a parabolic shape in plan, with the horns pointing upwind. Contrast *barchan,* in which the horns point downwind. Characteristically covered with sparse vegetation, and often found in coastal belts.

PARTICLES, FUNDAMENTAL See *fundamental particles.*

PATER NOSTER LAKES A chain of lakes resembling a string of beads along a glaciated valley where ice-plucking and gouging have scooped out a series of basins.

PEAT Partially reduced plant or wood material containing approximately 60 per cent carbon and 30 per cent oxygen. An intermediate material in the process of coal formation.

PEBBLE SIZE A volume greater than that of a sphere with a diameter of 4 mm or 5/32 in., and less than a sphere of 64 mm or 2.5 in.

PEDALFER A soil characterized by the accumulation of iron salts or iron and aluminum salts in the B-horizon. Varieties of pedalfers include red and yellow soils of the southeastern United States, and podsols of the northeastern quarter of the United States.

PEDIMENT Broad, smooth erosional surface developed at the expense of a highland mass in an arid climate. Underlain by beveled rock, which is covered by a veneer of gravel and rock debris. The final stage of a cycle of erosion in a dry climate.

PEDOCAL A soil characterized by an accumulation of calcium carbonate in its profile. Characteristic of low rainfall. Varieties include black and chestnut soils of the northern Plains states, and the red and gray desert soils of the drier western states.

PEDOLOGY The science that treats of soils—their origin, character, and utilization.

PEGMATITE A small pluton of exceptionally coarse texture, with crystals up to 40 feet in length, commonly formed at the margin of a batholith and characterized by graphic structure. Nearly 90 per cent of all pegmatites are simple pegmatites of quartz, orthoclase, and unimportant percentages of micas. The others are extremely rare ferromagnesian pegmatites, and complex pegmatites. Complex pegmatites have as their major components the sialic minerals of simple pegmatites, but they also contain a variety of rare minerals.

PELAGIC DEPOSIT Material formed in the deep ocean and deposited there. Example: ooze.

PENEPLAIN An extensive, nearly flat surface developed by subaerial erosion, and close to base level, toward which the streams of the region are reducing it. Originally defined as forming in a humid climate.

PERCHED WATER TABLE The top of a zone of saturation that bottoms on an impermeable horizon above the level of the general water table in the area. Is generally near the surface, and frequently supplies a hillside spring.

PERIDOTITE A coarse-grained igneous rock dominated by dark-colored minerals, consisting of about 75 per cent ferromagnesian silicates and the balance plagioclase feldspars.

PERMEABILITY For a rock or an earth material, the ability to transmit fluids. Permeability for underground water is sometimes expressed numerically as the number of gallons per day that will flow through a cross section of 1 square foot, at 60°F, under a hydraulic gradient of 100 per cent. Permeability is equal to velocity of flow divided by hydraulic gradient.

PETROLEUM A complex mixture of hydrocarbons, accumulated in rocks, and dominated by paraffins and cycloparaffins. Crude petroleums are classified as *paraffin-base* if the residue left after volatile components have been removed consists principally of a mixture of paraffin hydrocarbons; as *asphalt-base* if the residue is primarily cycloparaffins.

PHASE (in physical chemistry) A homogeneous, physically distinct portion of matter in a system that is not homogeneous, as in the three phases ice, water, and aqueous vapor.

PHENOCRYST A crystal significantly larger than the crystals of surrounding minerals.

PHOSPHATE ROCK A sedimentary rock containing calcium phosphate.

PHOTOSYNTHESIS The process by which carbohydrates are compounded from carbon dioxide and water in the presence of sunlight and chlorophyll.

PHYLLITE A clayey metamorphic rock with rock cleavage intermediate between slate and schist. Commonly formed by the regional metamorphism of shale or tuff. Micas characteristically impart a pronounced sheen to rock cleavage surfaces. Has phyllitic cleavage.

PHYLLITIC CLEAVAGE Rock cleavage in which flakes are produced that are barely visible to the unaided eye. Coarser than slaty cleavage, finer than schistose cleavage.

PHYSICAL GEOLOGY The branch of geology that deals with the nature and properties of material composing the earth, distribution of materials throughout the globe, the processes by which they are formed, altered, transported, and distorted, and the nature and development of landscape.

PIEDMONT GLACIER A glacier formed by the coalescence of valley glaciers and spreading over plains at the foot of the mountains from which the valley glaciers came.

PIRATE STREAM One of two streams in adjacent valleys that has been able to deepen its valley more rapidly than the other, has extended its valley headward until it has breached the divide between them, and has captured the upper portion of the neighboring stream.

PLAGIOCLASE FELDSPARS Albite and anorthite.

PLASTIC DEFORMATION Permanent change in shape or volume that does not involve failure by rupture, and that, once started, continues without increase in the deforming force.

PLASTIC SOLID A solid that undergoes change of shape continuously and indefinitely after the stress applied to it passes a critical point.

PLATEAU BASALT Basalt poured out from fissures in floods that tend to form great plateaus. Sometimes called *flood basalt.*

PLAYA The flat-floored center of an undrained desert basin.

PLAYA LAKE A temporary lake formed in a playa.

PLEOCHROIC HALO Minute, concentric spherical zones of darkening or coloring that form around inclusions of radioactive minerals in biotite, chlorite, and a few other minerals. About .003 in. in diameter.

PLUNGE The acute angle that the axis of a folded rock mass makes with a horizontal plane.

PLUTON A body of igneous rock that is formed beneath the surface of the earth by consolidation from magma. Sometimes extended to include bodies formed beneath the surface of the earth by the metasomatic replacement of older rock.

PLUTONIC IGNEOUS ROCK A rock formed by slow crystallization, which yields coarse texture. Once believed to be typical of crystallization at great depth, but that is not a necessary condition.

PLUVIAL LAKE A lake formed during a pluvial period (*q.v.*).

PLUVIAL PERIOD A period of increased rainfall and decreased evaporation, which prevailed in nonglaciated areas during the time of ice advance elsewhere.

PODSOL An ashy gray or gray-brown soil of the pedalfer group. This highly bleached soil, low in iron and lime, is formed under moist and cool conditions.

POLAR COMPOUND A compound, such as water, with a molecule that behaves like a small bar magnet with a positive charge on one end and a negative charge on the other.

POLAR WANDERING or MIGRATION A movement of the position of the magnetic pole during past time in relation to its present position.

POROSITY The percentage of open space or interstices in a rock or other earth material. Compare with *permeability.*

PORPHYRITIC A textural term for igneous rocks in which larger crystals, called phenocrysts, are set in a finer groundmass, which may be crystalline or glassy, or both.

PORPHYRY An igneous rock containing conspicuous phenocrysts in a fine-grained or glassy groundmass.

PORTLAND CEMENT A hydraulic cement consisting of compounds of silica, lime, and alumina.

POTASSIC FELDSPAR Orthoclase, $K(AlSi_3O_8)$.

POTENTIAL ENERGY Stored energy waiting to be used. The energy that a piece of matter possesses because of its position or because of the arrangement of its parts.

POTHOLE A hole ground in the solid rock of a stream channel by sands, gravels, and boulders caught in an eddy of turbulent flow and swirled for a long time over one spot.

PRAIRIE SOILS Transitional soils between pedalfers and pedocals.

PRECIPITATION The discharge of water, in the form of rain, snow, hail, sleet, fog, or dew, on a land or water surface. Also, the process of separating mineral constituents from a solution by evaporation (halite, anhydrite) or from magma to form igneous rocks.

PRESSURE Force per unit area applied to the outside of a body.

PRIMARY WAVE Earthquake body waves that travel fastest and advance by a push-pull mechanism. Also known as longitudinal, compressional, or P-waves.

PROTON A fundamental particle of matter with a positive electrical charge of 1 unit (equal in amount but opposite in effect to the charge of an electron), and with a mass of 1.00758 units.

PROTORE The original rock, too poor in mineral values to constitute an ore, from which desired elements have been leached and redeposited as an ore. The process of leaching and redeposition of desired elements is sometimes called supergene enrichment, or secondary sulfide enrichment.

PTEROPOD OOZE A calcareous deep-sea ooze dominated by the remains of minute molluscs of the group *Pteropoda.*

PUMICE Pyroclastic rock filled with gas-bubble holes. Cellular in texture, with many open compartments sealed from one another, it is usually buoyant enough to float on water.

PUSH-PULL WAVE A wave that advances by alternate compression and rarefaction of a medium, causing a particle in its path to move forward and backward along the direction of the wave's advance. In connection with waves in the earth, also known as *primary wave,* or compressional wave, longitudinal wave, or P-wave.

PYRITE A sulfide mineral. Iron sulfide, FeS_2.

PYROCLASTIC ROCK Fragmental rock blown out by volcanic explosion and deposited from the air. Includes bomb, block, cinder, ash, tuff, and pumice.

PYROXENE GROUP Ferromagnesian silicates with a single chain of silicon-oxygen tetrahedra. Common example: augite. Compare with *amphibole group* (example: hornblende), which has a double chain of tetrahedra.

PYRRHOTITE A mineral; iron sulfide. So commonly associated with nickel minerals that it has been called "the world's greatest nickel ore."

QUARTZ A silicate mineral, SiO_2, composed exclusively of silicon-oxygen tetrahedra with all oxygens joined together in a three-dimensional network. Crystal form is a six-sided prism tapering at the end, with the prism faces striated transversely. An important rock-forming mineral.

QUARTZITE Metamorphic rock commonly formed by the metamorphism of sandstone and composed of quartz. Has no rock cleavage. Breaks through sand grains as contrasted to sandstone, which breaks around the grains.

RADIAL DRAINAGE An arrangement of stream courses in which the streams radiate outward in all directions from a central zone.

RADIOACTIVITY The spontaneous breakdown of an atomic nucleus, with emission of radiant energy.

RADIOLARIAN OOZE A siliceous deep-sea ooze dominated by the delicate and complex hard parts of minute marine protozoa called *Radiolaria.*

RANK A term used to designate the extent to which metamorphism has advanced. Compare with *grade.* Rank is more commonly employed in designating the stage of metamorphism of coal.

REACTION SERIES See *Bowen's reaction series.*

RECESSIONAL MORAINE A ridge or belt of till marking a period of moraine formation, probably in a period of temporary stability or a slight re-advance, during the general wastage of a glacier and recession of its front.

RECTANGULAR PATTERN An arrangement of stream courses in which tributaries flow into larger streams at angles approaching 90°.

RECUMBENT FOLD A fold in which the axial plane is more or less horizontal.

REFRACTORY A mineral or compound that resists the action of heat and of chemical reagents.

REGIONAL METAMORPHISM Metamorphism occurring over tens or scores of miles.

REJUVENATION A change in conditions of erosion that causes a stream to begin more active erosion and a new cycle.

RELATIVE TIME Dating of events by means of their place in a chronologic order of occurrence rather than in terms of years. Compare with *absolute time.*

REVERSE FAULT A fault in which the hanging wall appears to have moved upward relative to the footwall. Also called *thrust fault.* Contrast with *normal* or *gravity fault.*

RHYOLITE A fine-grained igneous rock with the composition of granite.

RIFT ZONE A system of fractures in the earth's crust. Often associated with extrusion of lava.

RIGIDITY Resistance to elastic shear.

RIGIDITY MODULUS The number that expresses a material's rigidity. For example, the number of pounds per square inch necessary to cause a specified change of shape. Represented by the symbol G.

RING DIKE An arcuate, rarely circular, dike with steep dip.

RIPPLE MARKS Small waves produced in unconsolidated material by wind or water. See *ripple marks of oscillation; current ripple marks.*

RIPPLE MARKS OF OSCILLATION Ripple marks formed by oscillating movement of water such as may be found along a sea coast outside the surf zone. They are symmetrical, with sharp or slightly rounded ridges separated by more gently rounded troughs.

ROCHE MOUTONNÉE (*plural,* roches moutonnées) A sheep-shaped knob of rock that has been rounded by the action of glacier ice. Usually only a few feet in height, length, and breadth. A gentle slope faces upstream with reference to the ice movement. A steeper slope attributed to plucking action of the ice represents the downstream side.

ROCK An aggregate of minerals of different kinds in varying proportions.

ROCK CYCLE A concept of the sequences through which earth materials may pass when subjected to geological processes.

ROCK FLOUR Finely divided rock material pulverized by a glacier and carried by streams fed by melting ice.

ROCK FLOW The movement of solid rock when it is in a plastic state.

ROCK-FORMING SILICATE MINERALS Minerals built around a framework of silicon-oxygen tetrahedra. Olivine, augite, hornblende, biotite, muscovite, orthoclase, albite, anorthite, quartz.

ROCK GLACIER A tongue of rock waste found in the valleys of certain mountainous regions. Characteristically lobate and marked by a series of arcuate, rounded ridges that give it the aspect of having flowed as a viscous mass.

ROCK MELT A liquid solution of rock-forming mineral ions.

ROCK SALT Halite, or common salt, NaCl.

ROCK SLIDE Sudden and rapid slide of bedrock along planes of weakness.

ROSSI-FOREL SCALE A scale for rating earthquake intensities. Devised in 1878 by de Rossi of Italy and Forel of Switzerland.

RUNOFF Water that flows off the land.

RUPTURE A breaking apart or state of being broken apart.

S Symbol for secondary wave.

SALT This term in geology usually refers to halite, or rock salt, NaCl, particularly in such combinations as salt water, and salt dome.

SALTATION Mechanism by which a particle moves by jumping from one point to another.

SALT DOME A mass of NaCl generally of roughly cylindrical shape and with a diameter of about a mile near the top. These masses have been pushed through surrounding sediments into their present positions, sometimes as far as 20,000 feet. Reservoir rocks above and alongside salt domes sometimes trap oil and gas.

SAND Clastic particles of sand size, commonly but not always composed of the mineral quartz.

SAND SIZE A volume greater than that of a sphere with a diameter of $\frac{1}{16}$ mm (.0625 mm or .0025 in.), and less than that of a sphere with a diameter of 2 mm or $\frac{5}{64}$ in.

SANDSTONE A detrital sedimentary rock formed by the cementation of individual grains of sand size and commonly composed of the mineral quartz. Sandstones constitute about 32 per cent of sedimentary rocks exposed above sea level.

SAPROPEL An aquatic ooze or sludge that is rich in organic matter. Believed to be the source material for petroleum and natural gas.

SCHIST A metamorphic rock dominated by fibrous or platy minerals. Has schistose cleavage and is a product of regional metamorphism.

SCHISTOSE CLEAVAGE Rock cleavage in which grains and flakes are clearly visible and cleavage surfaces are rougher than in slaty or phyllitic cleavage.

SEA ARCH The roof of a cave cut by the sea through a headland.

SEA CAVE A cave formed by the erosive action of sea waves.

SEAMOUNT An isolated, steep-sloped peak rising from the deep ocean floor but submerged beneath the ocean surface. Most have sharp peaks, but some have flat tops and are called *guyots* or *tablemounts.* Seamounts are probably volcanic in origin.

SECONDARY WAVE An earthquake body wave slower than the primary wave. A *shear, shake,* or *S-wave.*

SECULAR VARIATION OF THE MAGNETIC FIELD A change in inclination, declination, or intensity of the earth's magnetic field. Detectable only from long historical records.

SEDIMENTARY FACIES An accumulation of deposits that exhibits specific characteristics and grades laterally into other sedimentary accumulations formed at the same time but exhibiting different characteristics.

SEDIMENTARY ROCK Rock formed from accumulations of sediment, which may consist of rock fragments of various sizes, the remains or products of animals or plants, the product of chemical action or of evaporation, or mixtures of these. *Stratification* is the single most characteristic feature of sedimentary rocks, which cover about 75 per cent of the land area of the world.

SEDIMENTATION The process by which mineral and organic matter is laid down.

SEIF DUNE A very large longitudinal dune. As high as 300 feet and as long as 60 miles.

SEISMIC PROSPECTING A method of determining the nature and structure of buried rock formations by generating waves in the ground (commonly by small charges of explosive) and measuring the length of time these waves require to travel different paths.

SEISMIC SEAWAVE A large wave in the ocean generated at the time of an earthquake. Popularly, but incorrectly, known as a *tidal wave.* Sometimes called a *tsunami.*

SEISMOGRAM The record obtained on a seismograph.

SEISMOGRAPH An instrument for recording vibrations, most commonly employed for recording earth vibrations.

SEISMOLOGY The scientific study of earthquakes and other earth vibrations.

SERPENTINE A silicate of magnesium common among metamorphic minerals. Occurs in two crystal habits, one platy, known as antigorite, the other fibrous, known as chrysotile. Chrysotile is an asbestos. The name "serpentine" comes from mottled shades of green on massive varieties, suggestive of the markings of a serpent.

S.G. Symbol for specific gravity.

SHAKE WAVE Wave that advances by causing particles in its path to move from side to side or up and down at right angles to the direction of the wave's advance, a shake motion. Also called *shear wave* or *secondary wave.*

SHALE A fine-grained detrital, sedimentary rock made up of silt- and clay-sized particles. Contains clay minerals as well as clay-sized and silt-sized particles of quartz, feldspar, calcite, dolomite, and other minerals. Distinguished from mudstone by presence of fissility.

SHALLOW FOCUS Earthquake focus within 40 miles (60 km) or less of the earth's surface.

SHEAR Change of shape without change of volume.

SHEAR MODULUS See *rigidity modulus.*

SHEAR WAVE Wave that advances by shearing displacements (which change the shape without changing the volume) of a medium. This causes particles in its path to move from side to side or up and down at right angles to the direction of the wave's advance. Also called *shake wave* or *secondary wave.*

SHEETING Joints that are essentially parallel to the ground surface. They are more closely spaced near the surface and become progressively farther apart with depth. Particularly well developed in granitic rocks, but sometimes in other massive rocks as well.

SHIELD VOLCANO A volcano built up almost entirely of lava, with slopes seldom as great as 10° at the summit and 2° at the base. Examples: the five volcanoes on the island of Hawaii.

SIAL A term coined from the symbols for silicon and aluminum. Designates the composite of rocks dominated by granites, granodiorites, and their allies and derivatives, which underlie continental areas of the globe. Specific gravity considered to be about 2.7.

SIALIC ROCK An igneous rock composed predominantly of silicon and aluminum. The term is constructed from "si" for silicon and "al" for aluminum. Average specific gravity about 2.7.

SIDERITE A mineral; iron carbonate, $FeCO_3$. An ore of iron.

SILICATE MINERALS Minerals with crystal structure containing SiO_4 tetrahedra arranged as (1) isolated units, (2) single or double chains, (3) sheets, or (4) three-dimensional networks.

SILICON-OXYGEN TETRAHEDRON A complex ion composed of a silicon ion surrounded by 4 oxygen ions. It has a negative charge of 4 units, is represented by the symbol $(SiO_4)^{4-}$, is the diagnostic unit of silicate minerals, and is the central building unit of nearly 90 per cent of the materials of the earth's crust.

SILLIMANITE A silicate mineral, Al_2SiO_5, characteristic of highest metamorphic temperatures and pressures. Occurs in long slender crystals, brown, green, white. Its crystalline structure is based on independent tetrahedra. Contrast with *kyanite* and *andalusite*, which have the same composition but different crystal habits and form at lower temperatures.

SILT SIZE A volume greater than that of a sphere with a diameter of $1/256$ mm (.0039 mm or .00015 in.), and less than that of a sphere with a diameter of $1/16$ mm (.0625 mm or .0025 in.).

SIMA A term coined from "si" for silicon and "ma" for magnesium. Designates a worldwide shell of dark, heavy rocks. The sima is believed to be the outermost rock layer under deep, permanent ocean basins, such as the mid-Pacific. Originally, the sima was considered basaltic in composition, with a specific gravity of about 3.0. It has been suggested also, however, that it may be peridotitic in composition, with a specific gravity of about 3.3.

SIMATIC ROCK An igneous rock composed predominantly of ferromagnesian minerals. The term is constructed from "si" for silicon and "ma" for magnesium. Average specific gravity 3.0 to 3.3.

SINK A sinkhole.

SINKHOLE Depression in the surface of the ground caused by the collapse of the roof over a solution cavern.

SLATE A fine-grained metamorphic rock with well-developed slaty cleavage. Formed by the low-grade regional metamorphism of shale.

SLATY CLEAVAGE Rock cleavage in which ease of breaking occurs along planes separated by microscopic distances.

SLIP-FACE The steep face on the lee side of a dune.

SLOPE FAILURE See *slump*.

SLUMP The downward and outward movement of rock or unconsolidated material as a unit or as a series of units. Also called *slope failure*.

SNOWFIELD A stretch of perennial snow existing in an area where winter snowfall exceeds the amount of snow that melts away during the summer.

SNOWLINE The lower limit of perennial snow.

SOAPSTONE See *talc*.

SODIC FELDSPAR Albite, $Na(AlSi_3O_8)$.

SOIL The superficial material that forms at the earth's surface as a result of organic and inorganic processes. Soil varies with climate, plant and animal life, time, slope of the land, and parent material.

SOIL HORIZON A layer of soil approximately parallel to the land surface with observable characteristics that have been produced through the operation of soil-building processes.

SOLID Matter with a definite shape and volume and some fundamental strength. May be crystalline, glassy, or amorphous (*q.v.*).

SOLIFLUCTION Mass movement of soil affected by alternate freezing and thawing. Characteristic of saturated soils in high latitudes.

SPACE LATTICE In the crystalline structure of a mineral, a three-dimensional array of points representing the pattern of locations of identical atoms or groups of atoms which constitute a mineral's *unit cell* (*q.v.*). There are 230 pattern types.

SPECIFIC GRAVITY A number that represents the ratio between the weight of a given volume of a material and the weight of an equal volume of water at 4°C (39.2°F).

SPECIFIC HEAT The amount of heat necessary to raise the temperature of one gram of any material through one degree Centigrade.

SPHALERITE A mineral; zinc sulfide, ZnS. Nearly always contains iron, (Zn,Fe)S. The principal ore of zinc. Also known as Zinc Blende or Black Jack.

SPHEROIDAL WEATHERING The spalling off of concentric shells from rock masses of various sizes as a result of pressures built up during chemical weathering.

SPIT A sandy bar built by currents into a bay from a promontory.

SPRING A place where the water table crops out at the surface of the ground and where water flows out more or less continuously.

STACK A small island that stands as an isolated, steep-sided rock mass just off the end of a promontory. Has been isolated from the land by erosion and by weathering concentrated just behind the end of a headland.

STALACTITE Icicle-shaped accumulation of dripstone hanging from a cave roof.

STALAGMITE Post of dripstone growing upward from the floor of a cave.

STAUROLITE A silicate mineral characteristic of middle-grade metamorphism. Its crystalline structure is based on independent tetrahedra with iron and aluminum. It has a unique crystal habit that makes it striking and easy to recognize: six-sided prisms intersecting at 90° to form a cross, or at 60° to form an X.

STOCK A discordant pluton that increases in size downward, has no determinable floor, and shows an area of surface exposure less than 40 square miles. Compare with *batholith*.

STOPING A mechanism by which batholiths have moved into the crust by the breaking off and foundering of blocks of rock surrounding the magma chamber.

STRAIN Change of dimensions of matter in response to stress. Commonly, unit strain, such as change in length per unit length (total lengthening divided by original length), change in width per unit width, change in volume per unit volume. Contrast with *stress*.

STRATIFICATION The structure produced by the deposition of sediments in layers or beds.

STRATIGRAPHIC TRAP A structure that traps petroleum or natural gas because of variation in permeability of the reservoir rock, or the termination of an inclined reservoir formation on the up-dip side.

STREAK The color of the fine powder of a mineral. May be different from the color of a hand specimen. Usually determined by rubbing the mineral on a piece of unglazed porcelain (hardness about 7), known as a streak plate, which is, of course, useless for minerals of greater hardness.

STREAM CAPTURE See *stream piracy*.

STREAM PIRACY The process whereby a stream rapidly eroding headward cuts into the divide separating it from another drainage basin, and provides an outlet for a section of a stream in the adjoining valley. The lower portion of the partially diverted stream is called a *beheaded stream*.

STREAM TERRACE A surface representing remnants of a stream's channel or flood plain when the stream was flowing at a higher level. Subsequent downward cutting by the stream leaves remnants of the old channel or flood plain standing as a terrace above the present level of the stream.

STRENGTH The stress at which rupture occurs or plastic deformation begins.

STRESS Force applied to material that tends to change the material's dimensions. Commonly, unit stress, or total force divided by the area over which it is applied. Contrast with *strain*.

STRIATION A scratch or small channel gouged by glacial action. Bedrock, pebbles, and boulders may show striations produced when rocks trapped by the ice were ground against bedrock or other rocks. Striations along a bedrock surface are oriented in the direction of ice flow across that surface.

STRIATIONS (mineral) Parallel thread-like lines or narrow bands on the face of a mineral; reflect the internal atomic arrangement.

STRIKE The direction of the line formed by intersection of a rock surface with a horizontal plane. The strike is always perpendicular to the direction of the dip.

STRIKE-SLIP FAULT A fault in which movement is almost in the direction of the fault's strike.

SUBLIMATION The process by which solid material passes into the gaseous state without first becoming a liquid.

SUBSEQUENT STREAM A tributary stream flowing along beds of less erosional resistance, parallel to beds of greater resistance. Its course is determined subsequent to the uplift that brought the more resistant beds within its sphere of erosion.

SUBSURFACE WATER Water below the surface of the ground. Also referred to as *underground water,* and *subterranean water.*

SUBTERRANEAN WATER Water below the surface of the ground. Also referred to as *underground water,* and *subsurface water.*

SULFATE MINERAL (sulphate mineral) Mineral formed by the combination of the complex ion $(SO_4)^{2-}$ with a positive ion. Common example: gypsum, $CaSO_4 \cdot 2H_2O$.

SULFIDE MINERAL (sulphide mineral) Mineral formed by the direct union of an element with sulfur. Examples: argentite, chalcocite, galena, sphalerite, pyrite, and cinnabar.

SUPERHEAT Heat added to a substance after melting is complete.

SUPERIMPOSED STREAM A stream whose present course was established on young rocks burying an old surface. With uplift, this course was maintained as the stream cut down through the young rocks to and into the old surface.

SUPERPOSITION, LAW OF If a series of sedimentary rocks has not been overturned, the topmost layer is always the youngest and the lowermost is always the oldest.

SURFACE WAVE Wave that travels along the free surface of a medium. Earthquake surface waves are sometimes represented by the symbol L.

SUSPENDED WATER Underground water held in the zone of aeration by molecular attraction exerted on the water by the rock and earth materials and by the attraction exerted by the water particles on one another.

SYMMETRICAL FOLD A fold in which the axial plane is essentially vertical. The limbs dip at similar angles.

SYNCLINE A configuration of folded stratified rocks in which the rocks dip downward from opposite directions to come together in a trough. The reverse of an *anticline.*

TABLEMOUNT See *guyot.*

TABULAR A shape with large area relative to thickness.

TACONITE Unleached iron formation of the Lake Superior District. Consists of chert with hematite, magnetite, siderite, and hydrous iron silicates. An ore of iron. It averages 25 per cent iron, but natural leaching turns it into an ore with 50 to 60 per cent iron.

TALC A silicate of magnesium common among metamorphic minerals. Its crystalline structure is based on tetrahedra arranged in sheets. Greasy and extremely soft. Sometimes known as *soapstone.*

TALUS A slope established by an accumulation of rock fragments at the foot of a cliff or ridge. The rock fragments that form the talus may be rock waste, sliderock, or pieces broken by frost action. Actually, however, the term "talus" is widely used to mean the rock debris itself.

TARN A lake formed in the bottom of a cirque after glacier ice has disappeared.

TECTONIC CHANGE OF SEA LEVEL A change in sea level produced by land movement.

TEMPERATURE An arbitrary number that represents the activity of atoms. Degree of heat.

TEMPORARY BASE LEVEL A base level that is not permanent, such as that formed by a lake.

TERMINAL MORAINE A ridge or belt of till marking the farthest advance of a glacier. Sometimes called *end moraine.*

TERMINAL VELOCITY The constant rate of fall eventually attained by a grain when the acceleration caused by the influence of gravity is balanced by the resistance of the fluid through which the grain falls.

TERRACE A nearly level surface, relatively narrow, bordering a stream or body of water, and terminating in a steep bank. Commonly the term is modified to indicate origin, as in *stream* terrace and *wave-cut* terrace.

TERRIGENOUS DEPOSIT Material derived from above sea level and deposited in deep ocean. Example: volcanic ash.

TETRAHEDRON (*plural,* tetrahedra) A four-sided solid. Used commonly in describing silicate minerals as a shortened reference to the silicon-oxygen tetrahedron (*q.v.*).

TEXTURE The general physical appearance of a rock, as shown by the size, shape, and arrangement of the particles that make up the rock.

THERMAL GRADIENT In the earth, the rate at which temperature increases with depth below the surface. A general average seems to be around 30°C increase per kilometer of depth, or 150°F per mile.

THERMO REMANENT MAGNETISM Magnetism acquired by an igneous rock as it cools below the curie temperatures of magnetic minerals in the rock. Abbreviation, TRM.

THERMAL SPRING A spring that brings warm or hot water to the surface. Sometimes called *warm spring,* or *hot spring.* Temperature usually 15°F or more above mean air temperature.

THIN SECTION A slice of rock ground so thin as to be translucent.

THRUST FAULT A fault in which the hanging wall appears to have moved upward relative to the footwall. Also called *reverse fault.* Opposite of *gravity* or *normal fault.*

TIDAL CURRENT A water current generated by the tide-producing forces of the sun and the moon.

TIDAL INLET Waterway from open water into a lagoon.

TIDAL WAVE Popular but incorrect designation for *tsunami.*

TIDE Alternate rising and falling of the surface of the ocean, other bodies of water, or the earth itself, in response to forces resulting from motion of the earth, moon, and sun relative to each other.

TILL Unstratified and unsorted glacial drift deposited directly by glacier ice.

TILLITE Rock formed by the lithification of till.

TOMBOLO A sand bar connecting an island to the mainland, or joining two islands.

TOPOGRAPHIC DESERTS Deserts deficient in rainfall either because they are located far from the oceans toward the center of continents, or because they are cut off from rain-bearing winds by high mountains.

TOPSET BED Layer of sediment constituting the surface of a delta. Usually nearly horizontal, and covers the edges of inclined foreset beds.

TOREVA BLOCK A large-scale prehistoric slump characteristic of now arid and semiarid sections, as in New Mexico.

TOURMALINE A silicate mineral of boron and aluminum, with sodium, calcium, fluorine, iron, lithium, or magnesium. Formed at high temperatures and pressures through the agency of fluids carrying boron and fluorine. Particularly associated with pegmatites.

TRACTION The process of carrying material along the bottom of a stream. Traction includes movement by saltation, rolling, or sliding.

TRANSITION ELEMENT An element in a series in which an inner shell is being filled with electrons after an outer shell has been started. All transition elements are metallic in the free state.

TRANSPIRATION The process by which water vapor escapes from a living plant and enters the atmosphere.

TRANSVERSE DUNE A dune formed in areas of scanty vegetation and in which sand has moved in a ridge at right angles to the wind. It exhibits the gentle windward slope and the steep leeward slope characteristic of other dunes.

TRAVERTINE A form of calcium carbonate, $CaCO_3$, formed in stalactites, stalagmites, and other deposits in limestone caves, or as incrustations around the mouths of hot and cold calcareous springs. Sometimes known as *tufa,* or *dripstone.*

TRELLIS PATTERN A roughly rectilinear arrangement of stream courses in a pattern reminiscent of a garden trellis, developed in a region where rocks of differing resistance to erosion have been folded, beveled, and uplifted.

TRM See *thermo remanent magnetism.*

TROPICAL DESERTS Deserts lying between 5° to 30° north and south of the equator.

TRUNCATED SPUR The beveled end of a divide between two tributary valleys where they join a main valley that has been glaciated. The glacier of the main valley has worn off the end of the divide.

TSUNAMI ***(plural,* tsunami)** A large wave in the ocean generated at the time of an earthquake. Popularly, but incorrectly, known as a *tidal wave*. Sometimes called *seismic seawave*.

TUFA Calcium carbonate, $CaCO_3$, formed in stalactites, stalagmites, and other deposits in limestone caves, as incrustations around the mouths of hot and cold calcareous springs, or along streams carrying large amounts of calcium carbonate in solution. Sometimes known as *travertine,* or *dripstone.*

TUFF Rock consolidated from volcanic ash.

TUNDRA A stretch of arctic swampland developed on top of permanently frozen ground. Extensive tundra regions have developed in parts of North America, Europe, and Asia.

TURBIDITY CURRENT A current in which a limited volume of turbid or muddy water moves relative to surrounding water because of its greater density.

TURBULENT FLOW Mechanism by which a fluid such as water moves near a rough surface. Fluid not in contact with the irregular boundary outruns that which is slowed by friction or deflected by the uneven surface. Fluid particles move in a series of eddies or whirls. Most stream flow is turbulent, and turbulent flow is important in both erosion and transportation. Contrast with *laminar flow*.

ULTIMATE BASE LEVEL Sea level, the lowest possible base level for a stream.

UNCONFORMITY A buried erosion surface separating two rock masses, the older of which was exposed to erosion for a long interval of time before deposition of the younger. If, in the process, the older rocks were deformed and were not horizontal at the time of subsequent deposition, the surface of separation is an *angular unconformity*. If the older rocks remained essentially horizontal during erosion, the surface separating them from the younger rocks is called a *disconformity*. An unconformity that develops between massive igneous rocks that are exposed to erosion and then covered by sedimentary rocks is called a *nonconformity*.

UNDERGROUND WATER Water below the surface of the ground. Also referred to as *subsurface water,* and *subterranean water*.

UNEVEN FRACTURE A mineral's habit of breaking along rough, irregular surfaces.

UNIFORMITARIANISM The concept that the present is the key to the past. This means that the processes now operating to modify the earth's surface have also operated in the geologic past, that there is a uniformity of processes past and present.

UNIT CELL In the crystalline structure of a mineral, a parallelepiped enclosing an atom or group of atoms arbitrarily selected so that the mineral's structure is represented by periodic repetition of this unit in a *space lattice* (*q.v.*).

UNPAIRED TERRACE A terrace formed when an eroding stream, swinging back and forth across a valley, encounters resistant rock beneath the unconsolidated alluvium and is deflected, leaving behind a single terrace with no corresponding terrace on the other side of the stream.

VALLEY GLACIER A glacier confined to a stream valley. Usually fed from a cirque. Sometimes called *alpine glacier* or *mountain glacier*.

VALLEY TRAIN Gently sloping plain underlain by glacial outwash and confined by valley walls.

VAN ALLEN BELTS Belts composed mostly of energetic ionized nuclei of hydrogen atoms and electrons, trapped in the outer atmosphere by the earth's magnetic field.

VARVE A pair of thin sedimentary beds, one coarse and one fine. This couplet of beds has been interpreted as representing a cycle of one year, or an interval of thaw followed by an interval of freezing in lakes fringing a glacier.

VENTIFACT A pebble, cobble, or boulder that has had its shape or surface modified by wind-driven sand.

VELOCITY OF A STREAM Rate of motion of a stream measured in terms of the distance its water travels in a unit of time, usually in feet per second.

VIRTUAL GEOMAGNETIC POLE For any one locality the pole consistent with the magnetic field as measured at that locality. The term refers to magnetic-field direction of a single point, in contrast to "geometric pole," which refers to the best fit of a geocentric dipole for the entire earth's field. Most paleomagnetic readings are expressed as virtual geomagnetic poles.

VISCOSITY An internal property of rocks that offers resistance to flow. The ratio of deforming force to rate at which changes in shape are produced.

VOLATILE COMPONENTS Materials in a magma, such as water, carbon dioxide, and certain acids, whose vapor pressures are high enough to cause them to become concentrated in any gaseous phase that forms.

VOLCANIC ASH Dust-sized pyroclastic particle: volume equal to or less than that of a sphere with diameter of .06 mm or .0025 in.

VOLCANIC BLOCK An angular mass of newly congealed magma blown out in an eruption. Contrast with *volcanic bomb*.

VOLCANIC BOMB A rounded mass of newly congealed magma blown out in an eruption. Contrast with *volcanic block*.

VOLCANIC DUST Pyroclastic detritus consisting of particles of dust size.

VOLCANIC EARTHQUAKES Earthquakes caused by movements of magma or explosions of gases during volcanic activity.

VOLCANIC ERUPTION The explosive or quiet emission of lava, pyroclastics, or volcanic gases at the earth's surface, usually from a volcano but rarely from fissures.

VOLCANIC NECK The solidified material filling a vent or pipe of a dead volcano.

VOLCANO A landform developed by the accumulation of magnetic products near a central vent.

WARM SPRING A spring that brings warm water to the surface. A *thermal spring*. Temperature 15°F or more above mean air temperature.

WATER GAP The gap cut through a resistant ridge by a superimposed or antecedent stream.

WATER TABLE The upper surface of the zone of saturation for underground water. It is an irregular surface with a slope or shape determined by the quantity of ground water and the permeability of the earth materials. In general, it is highest beneath hills and lowest beneath valleys.

WEATHERING The response of materials that were once in equilibrium within the earth's crust to new conditions at or near contact with water, air, or living matter.

WIND GAP The general term for an abandoned water gap.

XENOLITH A strange rock broken from the wall surrounding a magma chamber and frozen in the intrusion as it solidified.

YARDANG A sharp-edged ridge between two troughs or furrows excavated by wind action.

YARDANG TROUGH A trough excavated by wind action, between two yardangs.

YAZOO-TYPE RIVER A tributary that is unable to enter its main stream because of natural levees along the main stream. The Yazoo-type river flows along the back-swamp zone parallel to the main stream.

YIELD POINT The maximum stress that a solid can withstand without undergoing permanent deformation either by plastic flow or by rupture.

ZONE OF AERATION A zone immediately below the surface of the ground, in which the openings are partially filled with air, and partially with water trapped by molecular attraction. Subdivided into (a) belt of soil moisture, (b) intermediate belt, and (c) capillary fringe.

ZONE OF SATURATION Underground region within which all openings are filled with water. The top of the zone of saturation is called the *water table*. The water contained within the zone of saturation is called *ground water*.

Index

Major Features of the
ATLANTIC OCEAN FLOOR